PLANT
FORM & FUNCTION

Details of other books by the same authors will gladly be sent on request to the publishers at York House, Portugal Street, London, W.C. 2

PLANT
FORM & FUNCTION

By

F. E. FRITSCH
D.Sc., LL.D., F.R.S.
Late Professor of Botany in the University of London

and

SIR EDWARD SALISBURY
C.B.E., D.Sc., LL.D., V.P.R.S.
Director of the Royal Botanic Gardens, Kew,
formerly Quain Professor of Botany in the University of London,
University College

LONDON
G. BELL AND SONS, LTD
1955

First published 1938
Reprinted 1941, 1943, 1944, 1945, 1946 (*twice*), 1947, 1948

New and revised edition 1953
Reprinted 1955

Printed in Great Britain by
NEILL & CO. LTD., EDINBURGH

PREFACE

WE have in response to many requests combined in the present volume the substance of our two previous works, *An Introduction to the Study of Plants* and *An Introduction to the Structure and Reproduction of Plants*. In so doing we have not only endeavoured to bring the subject-matter completely up to date, but have slightly extended the scope. This has involved so many alterations, whether substantive or verbal, that the whole can almost be regarded as a new work. In particular, we may emphasise that, whilst the fundamental knowledge regarding morphology and anatomy has been fully presented, the physiological and ecological aspects have been materially extended. Economic applications have as before been emphasised. We may also call attention to the additional chapter on the British Flora and the introduction of brief accounts of additional families in the taxonomic section with the object of including all those to members of which frequent reference is made in the text.

The majority of the illustrations are original and are taken from our previous works, but over thirty figures have been added, and these embody more than a hundred new drawings and photographs.

The scope of the present work more than covers the first year University syllabus and should provide an adequate foundation for a non-specialised graduate course. To each of the more important sections there is appended a brief selected bibliography which is intended to serve as a guide to useful reference works (also listed under this heading in the index), where further information can be obtained.

We would stress that considerable care has been expended in the preparation of the Index in the belief that it will be found a real aid to the student.

We are indebted to Dr P. Haas for help in revising the biochemical sections, to Dr F. W. Jane for assistance with the sections dealing with cytology and for the preparation of figures illustrating these. We are also indebted for illustrations to Mr E. M. Cutting, Mrs F. E. Fritsch, Dame Helen Gwynne-Vaughan, Professor F. W. Oliver, Miss Pellew, and Miss E. M. Salisbury.

F. E. F.
E. J. S.

LONDON, *February* 1938

PREFACE TO NEW AND REVISED EDITION

No considerable change in the general plan has been made during the preparation of this new edition, although the subject matter has been revised throughout to bring it into conformity with the present-day viewpoint. Certain branches of botany have, however, advanced so materially that a completely new presentation was necessary. We have consequently in large part re-written the chapters dealing with meristems, cell-division and heredity, whilst the sections on plant physiology have not only been brought up to date but appreciably widened in their scope. Bacteria are dealt with in a separate chapter in which we have also included a general account of plant viruses, while references to the plants of the past have been augmented. This new edition should thus continue to provide the broad general introduction to the subject of Botany and the balanced treatment of its diverse aspects which was aimed at in the original work.

Despite the considerable amount of new matter introduced and the more advanced treatment given in the chapters on plant physiology, the size of the volume has not been unduly increased.

We are much indebted to Professor F. M. Haines for help in the revision of the section on plant chemistry and plant physiology, while Professor F. W. Jane has helped us in the preparation of those dealing with cytology and heredity and has amended the list of timbers on p. 181.

F. E. F.
E. J. S.

May 1953

CONTENTS

CHAPTER I

THE PLANT CONSIDERED AS A WHOLE

THE Vegetable Kingdom includes a great variety of simple and complex types and, in order to obtain a general idea of the living organism termed a Flowering Plant, the Shepherd's-purse (*Capsella bursa-pastoris*), which is exceptionally common on waste ground at all times of the year (Fig. 1), can be examined. It soon appears on exposed soil that is not carefully tended, increasing very rapidly and successfully competing with other plants growing in the same situation, and thus possesses some of the distinguishing characteristics of a weed.

This, like all Flowering Plants, has a body consisting of two distinct parts which live under very different conditions. One part, the overground *shoot*,[1] comprising the stem bearing leaves (Fig. 1, *Sh.*), is surrounded on all sides by air and exposed during the daytime to the light of the sun. The other part, the underground *root* (Fig. 1, *Rt.*) is completely embedded in the soil and lives in darkness. The parts of the shoot (stem and leaves) are green, whereas the root and its branches are white. The branches of the root are all similar in appearance, but the stem bears different kinds of appendages, some of which are round and slender like itself, while others are flattened structures known as leaves.

Closer examination of the root shows that there is a main portion (Fig. 2, *m.a.*) which is a direct downward continuation of the stem, its position being therefore more or less vertical. This, the main axis of the root, bears side-branches (the *lateral roots*, Fig. 2, *l.r.*[1]) which grow outwards and slightly downwards at an acute angle. In older plants the lateral roots bear further branches (Fig. 2, *l.r.*[2], *l.r.*[3]) which spread out in all directions.

A short distance behind the tips of the main root and its branches careful examination with a lens may show a number of very short colourless hairs (the *root-hairs*) which, however, can be much more readily seen if a plant of the Shepherd's-purse, after washing away

---

[1] An important reference-book for plant-morphology is K. Goebel, *Organography of Plants* (translated by I. B. Balfour), 2 vols. Clarendon Press, 1900–1905 (3rd German Edition in 3 vols., 1928–33).

I

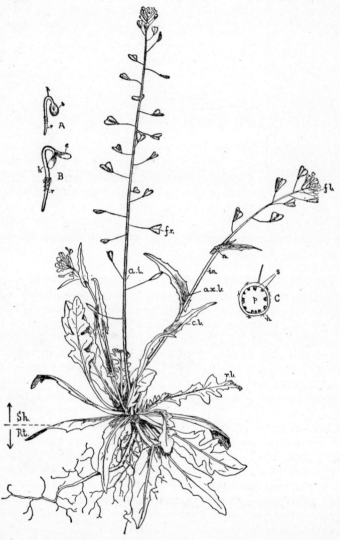

FIG. 1. Complete plant of Shepherd's-purse (*Capsella bursa-pastoris*) (slightly reduced). The surface of the soil is indicated by the dotted line on the left. *a.i.*, axis of inflorescence; *ax.b.*, axillary bud; *c.l.*, cauline leaf (see p. 119); *fl.*, flowers; *fr.*, fruit; *in.*, internode; *n.*, node; *r.l.*, radical leaf (see p. 119); *Rt.*, root; *Sh.*, shoot. A and B, Two stages in germination (somewhat enlarged). *c*, cotyledon; *h*, hypocotyl; *r*, radicle; *s*, testa. C, Cross-section of stem (magnified about 8 diameters). *h*, hair; *p*, pith; *s*, woody strands.

the soil, is placed for a day or two with its roots in water (Fig. 2, C, *r.h.*). In the root-system thus treated the extreme tips are seen to be devoid of root-hairs, each being protected by a darker hood-like covering, the *root-cap* (Fig. 2, C, *r.c.*) which is not readily discernible in a freshly uprooted plant. If the root be scraped with a

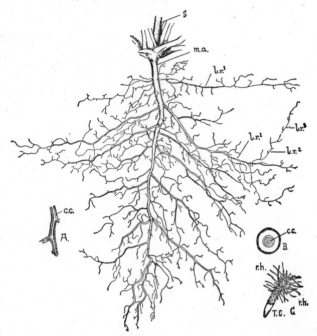

FIG. 2. Root-system of Shepherd's-purse (natural size). *S*, base of stem; *m.a.*, main axis of root; *l.r.*[1], lateral branches of first order; *l.r.*[2], laterals of second order; *l.r.*[3], laterals of third order. A, Longitudinal section through portion of main root (about 3 times natural size). B, Cross-section of same (× 9); *c.c.*, central core. C, Tip of a root grown in water (× 10). *r.h.*, root-hairs; *r.c.*, root-cap.

blunt instrument, the outer part is found to be soft, but, if the scraping be continued, a harder central core (Fig. 2, A and B, *c.c.*), which runs the whole length of the root, is revealed.

In the shoot, as in the root, we can distinguish a vertical main axis (Fig. 1, *a.i.*) bearing lateral branches which, however, grow outwards and upwards. All the lateral branches will be found to arise immediately above a leaf and, since the angle between a leaf and the stem upon which it is borne is termed the *axil* of the leaf (Fig. 3, E, *axil*), the branches are described as axillary (Fig. 1, *ax.b.*; Fig. 3, E, *a.b.*). That part of the stem from which a leaf arises is called a *node* (Fig. 1, *n.*), whilst the portion between two nodes is spoken of as an *internode* (Fig. 1, *in.*). At the base of the stem a considerable number of leaves generally arise close together without perceptible internodes, forming on the surface of the ground a rosette (Fig. 1), which tends to die away as the plant grows older.

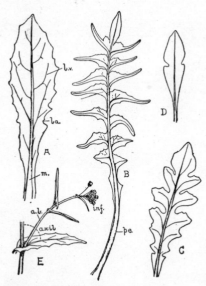

FIG. 3. A–D, Forms of radical leaves of Shepherd's-purse (about half natural size). *m*, midrib; *la*, blade; *l.v.*, lateral vein; *pe.*, petiole. E, Node with leaf and axillary branch bearing inflorescence (*inf.*) (about half natural size). *a.b.*, axillary branch.

By scraping away the surface of the stem, the soft outer part (*cortex*) is found to be quite a thin layer, and almost immediately we come to a number of narrow light-coloured strands consisting of harder substance and running lengthwise. On cutting across the stem these strands appear as a variable number of pale-green dots (Fig. 1, C, *s*) situated around the edge of the cross-section, whilst the central region is occupied by soft tissue (*pith*, *p*), a marked point of contrast to the root in this plant.

In the leaf two parts can usually be distinguished, the leaf-stalk or *petiole* (Fig. 3, B, *pe.*) and the flat *blade* or *lamina* (Fig. 3, A, *la.*). The margin of the latter is not regular, but, if we examine a number of plants, all types outline to those in which it from leaves with an almost smooth outline to those in which it is deeply indented can be found (Figs. 1 and 3). In general the upper leaves are less deeply cut and have a shorter leaf-stalk than those forming the rosette—in fact, most of the upper leaves have no petiole at all (such leaves being described as *sessile*) and the base of their lamina forms two projections enclasping the stem (Fig. 1; Fig. 3, E). The lamina has an upper and a lower surface, of which the former is the darker green. Extending from the base to the tip of the leaf and forming a direct continuation of the petiole is a prominent strand, which projects markedly on the under side and is known as the *midrib* or principal vein (Fig. 3, A, *m*). Arising from the latter are a number of finer strands (the *lateral veins*, *l.v.*) which branch still further to form an inconspicuous network upon which the delicate substance of the blade is spread out.

The surfaces of stem and leaves bear numerous scattered *hairs* (Fig. 1, C, *h*). These outgrowths are of a white colour, and whilst some, especially prominent on the edges of the leaves, are simple and almost straight, others are branched in a star-shaped manner (Fig. 4, C).

Terminating the main stem and some of its larger branches are flowering shoots (*inflorescences*) consisting of small flowers borne on slender stalks (Fig. 1, *a.i.*; Fig. 3, E, *inf.*). Each flower is composed of the following parts (Fig. 4, A): On the outside there

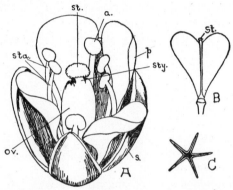

FIG. 4. A, Single flower of Shepherd's-purse (much enlarged); *s*, sepal; *p*, petal; *sta.*, stamens; *a.*, anther; *sty.*, style; *st.*, stigma; *ov.*, ovary. B, Single fruit (much enlarged); *st.*, stigma. C, Single star-shaped hair from leaf (much enlarged).

are four small greenish protective leaves, the *sepals* (*s*), collectively termed the *calyx*; next within, and alternating with the sepals, are four larger white *petals* (*p*), together known as the *corolla*; these are followed by six stamens (*sta.*), each of which consists of a short stalk or *filament* bearing at its tip a yellowish swelling or *anther* (*a*) containing a yellow powder, the *pollen*. In the centre of the flower is situated a small, green, flattened structure, the *ovary* (*ov.*), surmounted by a short peg-like projection, the *style* (*sty.*), which ends in a little sticky knob, the *stigma* (*st.*).

The pollen of the stamens is received by the stigma and, as a result of further growth, the ovary gradually develops into the ripe fruit (Fig. 4, B), during which the stalk of the flower elongates, calyx, corolla, and stamens wither away, and the internodes between the flowers lengthen (see Fig. 1). On older plants the ripe fruits are seen, in the lower part of the inflorescence, as flat green triangular structures with an apical notch in which the remains of style and stigma can be distinguished (Fig. 4, B). Inside a ripe fruit we find a number of small brown bodies attached by short stalks, the seeds; these have developed from minute structures (the *ovules*), present in the ovary of the young flower, as a result of changes following upon the reception of the pollen by the stigma.

Older plants will show the ripe fruits opening of themselves and shedding the seeds, after which the parent sooner or later dies away. The seeds get washed into the soil by rain and after a brief period give rise to new plants. In this way the Shepherd's-purse not only reproduces its kind, but also multiplies.

Like most plants, the Shepherd's-purse is built up of innumerable small units called *cells*, the detailed structure of which can only be studied with a microscope. These cells are of various kinds, and have different functions. At the tips of the branches of root and stem are situated groups of very small cells, which during the growing period are constantly multiplying by division into two and thus providing the new units by means of which an increase in length takes place. These groups of cells are termed the *meristems*.

The purposes or functions of the different parts or organs may now be considered. It is obvious that the root primarily performs the function of fixing the plant in the soil, as shown by the effort which is often required to uproot it. The root-system offers considerable resistance to pulling strains, which is due to the central core of hard substance (p. 3). In the stem, on the other hand, the hard strands situated round the edge (cf. Fig. 1, C with 2, B) render it more suited to meet bending strains under the influence of the wind. The leaves which offer a relatively large surface to the wind would of course be particularly liable to become torn, were it not for the fact that the delicate tissue is fully supported by the network of the veins which, with the hard strands of the stem and root, form a continuous skeleton throughout the plant.

The second important function of the root is absorption of water from the soil, as witnessed by the rapid withering that ensues when an uprooted plant is left on the surface of the ground. The actual absorption of moisture can be demonstrated by placing a plant of the Shepherd's-purse with its root-system in a tumbler of water, the surface of the latter being covered by a thin layer of oil to prevent evaporation, and its level marked by a strip of gummed paper. A perfectly similar arrangement, but without a plant, should be set up beside it to serve as a control. After some hours the level of the water will be found to have fallen, whereas

no appreciable change is noticed in the control.   In the intact
root this absorption of water is actually effected by the root-hairs.

The stem, besides serving to bear the leaves and inflorescences,
forms the channel through which the water absorbed by the roots
is conveyed to the different parts of the shoot.   By cutting off the
tips of the roots of a complete plant and placing its root-system
in an aqueous solution of light green (Appendix V), the whole
course of the water through the plant can be traced.   If, after
some hours, we split up the main root and stem lengthwise, we
shall find that the green colour is confined to the central core
of the root and to the similar strands which run near the surface
of the stem.   Moreover, the veins of some or all of the leaves
(and even parts of the flower) will be seen to be similarly coloured,
thus proving that the continuous skeleton referred to above also
serves as the water-conveying system of the plant.

The water which is thus brought to the leaves is not pure,
but is a very weak solution of certain mineral substances present
in the soil, and many of these are necessary for the nourishment
of the plant.   Of the moisture reaching the leaves a large volume
escapes as water-vapour from the extensive evaporating surface
which they present.   This is easily demonstrated by the accumulation of moisture on the inside of a bell-jar placed over a healthy
plant, although in order to obtain a reliable result both pot and
soil should be covered with waterproof material (*e.g.* aluminium
foil).   The water retained is built up into the substance of the
plant.   The continual loss by evaporation is made good by absorption through the roots.   A large quantity of water is absorbed,
but this does not determine the amount of mineral salts taken in,
which depends chiefly on the vital activities taking place in the
absorbing cells.

The process of evaporation from the leaves may be also roughly
studied by using filter-paper soaked in a solution of cobalt chloride
and subsequently dried.   Such paper appears deep blue, but readily
turns pink and finally almost colourless on exposure to moisture.
Leaves are placed on a sheet of dry blotting-paper, some with
their upper and some with their under surfaces directed upwards.
Small pieces of the dry cobalt-paper are then laid on each, and the
entire series is covered with a dry sheet of glass to prevent access
of damp air.   It will be noticed that the pieces of cobalt-paper in
contact with the under surfaces of the leaves become colourless
more rapidly than those upon the upper surfaces, thus showing
that more water-vapour escapes in a given time from the under
than from the upper side.

We shall find later that the surface-skin (*epidermis*) on both sides of the leaf is perforated by a large number of minute pores (*stomata*) which are usually far more numerous on the under than the upper surface and whose size varies slightly at different times. The actual pores can be located by sealing up the cut end of the petiole with melted paraffin-wax and immersing the blade in warm water, when owing to the expansion of the air in the leaf the lower surface will become studded with numerous tiny air-bubbles, each marking the position of a stoma. The pores are commonly wide open in the light and almost closed at night, and it is through them that most of the water-vapour escapes. The rate of water-loss is dependent not only on external, but also on internal, conditions and therefore the process is distinguished from evaporation as *transpiration*. It is probably the increasing resistance to the supply of moisture to the internal cell-surfaces that checks this process, when too little water is supplied by the roots. When almost closed the stomata also effectively check transpiration, but in light they may remain open, even when the plant begins to wither. The reduced transpiration from a wilted as compared with a fresh leaf can be shown with the help of cobalt-paper.

The green colour of the leaves is due to a mixture of pigments known as *chlorophyll*, which are of importance in the nutrition of the plant. If a plant is killed by immersion in boiling water and is subsequently placed in alcohol, a solution of the chlorophyll is obtained, leaving the plant itself colourless. If some such leaves are now placed in a solution of iodine (Appendix V), they rapidly acquire a bluish-black colour which is a test for the presence of starch.

It can easily be shown that starch is only to be found in the leaves after the plant has been exposed for some time to the light. Two similar plants are grown in separate pots, the one in the light and the other in darkness. After forty-eight hours a leaf is removed from each plant and decolourised in the way described above. Treatment with iodine shows that starch is only present in the leaf from the illuminated plant.

If this experiment be continued, the plant in the dark assumes a starved appearance as compared with the one in the light, so that starch is evidently an important food-substance. Any new leaves formed in the dark are practically colourless, which shows that light is also necessary for the formation of chlorophyll. If a plant grown in the dark is subsequently exposed to illumination, it will be found that starch soon reappears in the green leaves, but no starch is produced in the colourless leaves until after they have become green. This shows that chlorophyll also is necessary for the processes that lead to starch-production.

It will subsequently become apparent that the starch in the leaves is formed indirectly, with the help of chlorophyll and the radiant energy of light, from the carbon dioxide of the air and some of the water which passes into the leaves, the air obtaining access to the interior through the stomata. Starch is a complex substance, a carbohydrate, composed of the elements carbon, hydrogen, and oxygen, and is formed from simpler carbohydrates like sugars. The presence of carbon in starch can be demonstrated by strongly heating it in a dry test-tube, when most of the carbon remains behind as a black mass. The necessity of carbon dioxide for the production of starch can be shown by an experiment to be described later (p. 208). During the process oxygen is given off.

The process in which carbohydrates are built up from carbon dioxide and water is sometimes spoken of as carbon dioxide assimilation, but, owing to the part which light plays in this complex process, the alternative term *photosynthesis* is now usually employed. This process is the first step in the nutrition of the plant and leads on to the production of the more complicated substances of which it largely consists, and in the formation of which the mineral salts absorbed from the soil play a part.

Another important vital process carried on by the plant involves the taking in of oxygen and the giving out of carbon dioxide. This is the *respiration* common to plants and animals. The exchange of gases is just the reverse of what occurs in photosynthesis, but this latter being a much more active process, respiration is completely masked in the presence of light. Consequently a demonstration of the fact that green plants respire can most easily be obtained in the dark. To show the need for oxygen soaked Peas are placed in a U-tube, one end of which is closed by a rubber cork. The U-tube is then inverted with the Peas resting on the cork and the other end is placed in a solution of pyrogallate of potash (Appendix V). The exposed surface of the solution is at once covered with oil. In the control, water is used to replace the pyrogallate. Whereas the Peas in the control sprout, those in the other apparatus fail to do so, which we may attribute to the pyrogallate having absorbed all the oxygen from the air within the tube. Respiration, in fact, is just as essential for the existence of the plant as for that of the animal.

The substances requisite for the nourishment of the plant are thus obtained from two sources, viz. the soil and the air. The root fi⸱⸱⸱ ⸱⸱⸱ ground and absorbs water which contains a complex series of chemical changes, involving chlorophyll and light-energy, hydrogen from some of the water, and the carbon dioxide are transformed into food-substances. These together with their further products not only serve for the nourishment of the plant, but supply the material for continued growth. In this way the seedling, living at first on food stored within the seed, is able to increase in size and finally to form seeds, capable of giving rise to new individuals. All of these vital processes involve a loss of energy, supplied by that which undergoes transformation during respiration, and hence the importance of the latter for the maintenance of life.

CHAPTER II

PLANT-HABIT AND DURATION

THE life-history of many common plants is compassed in a single year. Some of these (Petty Spurge; *Tropæolum*) circumvent the cold season by dying away in the autumn, leaving only their seeds. These may be termed *summer annuals*, but there is another kind of annual that germinates in the autumn and is able to survive under winter conditions, though it dies with the coming of the summer; such *winter annuals* are exemplified by the annual Buttercup and the annual Forget-me-nots (*Myosotis*). There are some plants, particularly weeds like the Shepherd's-purse (Fig. 1) and the Groundsel (*Senecio vulgaris*), in which the whole life-cycle occupies a much shorter interval of time, so that several successive generations may be produced in a year. Owing to their rapid growth such plants readily establish themselves on disturbed soil. In some annuals the period from sprouting to seed-production does not exceed a few weeks.

The annual uses up all of its available food-materials in the production of seeds, but if this be prevented by removing the flower-buds as they appear, it may often be induced to survive for two or more seasons. There are, however, a large number of plants which in nature normally utilise more than a single year to amass the food-materials necessary for seed-formation. Some of these, which are termed *biennials*, flower only in the second year of their life and soon afterwards perish; examples are furnished by the Mullein (Fig. 5), Canterbury Bell (*Campanula*) and the Carrot. Such plants during the first season's growth do not get beyond the production of a basal rosette (Fig. 5, B). The food-substances formed by these leaves pass into the subterranean portion, which becomes somewhat swollen and serves as a storage-organ (Fig. 65, A, p. 113). During the ensuing winter the leaves, since they lie in close proximity to the soil, obtain a certain amount of protection by surrounding vegetation and inequalities of the surface of the ground. In the following year rapid growth takes place, largely at the expense of the food stored up in the underground parts, and as a result a tall stem bearing numerous flowers is produced (Fig. 5, A). Under certain circumstances, such as growth on very poor soil, the biennial may form a few flowers and seeds already in the first year and then die away, thus behaving like an annual. The "bolting" of Cabbages, Onions, etc., in their first season is a comparable phenomenon due to complex physiological causes, in which temperature-changes often play a considerable rôle.

FIG. 5. The Mullein (*Verbascum thapsus*), a biennial (greatly reduced). B, rosette stage (first year). A, second-year stage.

We can readily imagine a biennial in which the vitality of the plant is not completely exhausted by the production of flowers and fruits, so that sufficient food-material remains to support renewed growth in the following spring. If this goes on from year to year we should obtain a so-called *perennial*, and a large number of plants in nature persist in this manner. Instances are the Stinging-nettle (*Urtica*), the Perennial Sunflower, and the Potato (Fig. 143, B, p. 228). If perennials are grown from seed, some flower already in the first year, whilst most require two or even more years[1] to attain to sufficient maturity before flowers are produced; meanwhile they are accumulating a store of food in their underground organs (Figs. 142 and 143, A, pp. 227, 228).

In the examples above mentioned the aerial parts die down at the end of each season, whilst the subterranean parts persist and by virtue of their store of food-material rapidly produce new shoots in the following spring. When the plant begins to form flowers, it is sufficiently vigorous to provide the necessary food for the resulting seeds, and yet to transfer enough into the underground organs for the commencement of next year's growth. A few perennials of this type, such as the Dandelion (*Taraxacum*) or *Iris*,

[1] There are some long-lived perennials which are like annuals in the fact that they only fruit once and then die (*e.g.* Talipot Palm, *Corypha*).

always retain some of their leaves even during the winter, and the same is true of most Grasses (winter-green perennials). Such plants, which lose part or all of their foliage for a period, form new leaves or lose them at very varying times.

The kinds of perennials hitherto noticed are called herbaceous perennials, since they produce no permanent overground shoot-system. In contrast to these, however, a large number of perennials, namely shrubs and trees, form stems which become hard and woody and persist to form the starting-point for each year's growth, a feature that enables some to attain very considerable dimensions. In the British flora such *woody perennials* are confined to one of the two great subdivisions of Flowering Plants, the so-called Dicotyledons (cf. p. 27), although this habit is also found among the Conifers (*e.g.* Scot's Fir, Yew, etc.). Even in these some part, as a general rule, is shed on the approach of winter, as is seen in the falling of the leaves of plants like the Beech, Hawthorn, etc., which are consequently described as *deciduous*.[1] A few others, such as the Holly and the Scot's Fir, are *evergreen*, bearing leaves throughout the year.

The store of food in these woody perennials is laid down throughout the woody portion of the plant and here again provides for the rapid sprouting which takes place with the advent of spring. Trees are essentially distinguished by their greater height and their frequent possession of a single main trunk.

The form of food-reserve in perennial plants is commonly starch, a fact which may be easily verified by cutting open the underground stem of the Iris or Crocus or a thick branch of the Horse Chestnut in winter, and applying the iodine-test (see p. 8). In other plants (*e.g.* Solomon's Seal and Dandelion) forms of food-material not giving this reaction are found (cf. Chap. VIII.).

The fact that so many plants die back on the approach of winter suggests that this may be related to the onset of colder weather. During winter the temperature of the soil is often so low that absorption of water by the roots practically ceases. If, under these circumstances, the plant were to lose water in transpiration (p. 8) at the same rate as in the warmer period of the year, it would soon wither and die. This evil is, however, avoided by the shedding of the leaves or the dying away of the whole over-ground shoot-system whereby the transpiring surface is greatly reduced. At first sight the evergreen would appear to be an exception to this rule, but it will be noticed that all evergreen

---

[1] For the derivation and meaning of this and other terms applied to plant-structures, see B. D. Jackson, *A Glossary of Botanical Terms.* 4th edit., Duckworth, 1928 (481 pp.).

leaves (*e.g.* the Laurel and the Holly) are of a leathery texture, due to an unusually thick epidermis. As a consequence, transpiration from such leaves goes on slowly at all times of the year, and such little absorption as occurs during the winter is sufficient to obviate severe wilting. It is instructive in this connection to compare the relative rates of transpiration of a deciduous and an evergreen leaf by the aid of the cobalt-method (p. 7).

Plants exhibit a number of diverse habits, of which the erect is by far the most frequent; in this type the aerial shoot-system is so

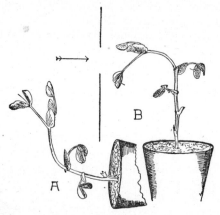

FIG. 6. A, Seedling of Pea, placed horizontally in the dark, showing the shoot bending up under the influence of gravity. B, Ditto, placed vertically and showing a phototropic curvature under the influence of one-sided light, whose direction is indicated by the arrow. (About one-third natural size.)

constructed as to be able to support itself. It is natural to ask why these plants maintain the erect position in nature. If an erect plant be placed next to a window, so that it receives one-sided illumination, the shoot will soon be found to have curved over towards the light (Fig. 6, B). When this has occurred the plant should be turned round through half a circle, whereupon after a further interval the shoot will again bend over towards the window. The erect growth of the stem is dependent on its being exposed to equal illumination on all sides, and one-sided light leads to a bending until equilibrium is again established. The influence of light upon the direction of growth of the plant is spoken of as *phototropism* (*heliotropism*).

It is not difficult to show that other influences play a part in determining the erect position of the shoot, for if we place a plant horizontally in the dark for some hours the tip of the shoot gradually curves upwards till it again assumes a vertical direction (Fig. 6, A); the same thing may be frequently observed in nature, when a plant is blown over by the wind, or a branch sinks down as a result of its own weight. In the plant placed in darkness some agency other than light is evidently at work and, as will be shown later, this is gravity which here has the peculiar effect of causing growth in a direction opposite to that of the gravitational pull. The influence of this force on the direction of growth is termed *geotropism.*

A word or two may be added on the advantages of the erect habit. In the first place, the leaves are thus well exposed to the light and most suitably placed for photosynthesis (p. 9). In addition, the flowers are displayed to the best advantage, a point of great importance, since many plants depend upon insects for the transference of the pollen from the stamens to the stigma. Moreover, the consequent height above the ground greatly facilitates the dispersal of the seeds when, as so frequently obtains, this depends upon the action of the wind.

FIG. 7. Creeping stem (*c.s.*) of the Ground Ivy (*Glechoma hederacea*), showing adventitious roots (*a.r.*) and an erect flowering shoot (*f.s.*) (about half the natural size). The flowering shoot is not shown at its full length.

In marked contrast to erect plants are those which assume a creeping habit, as, for example, the Creeping Jenny (*Lysimachia nummularia*) and the Marsh Pennywort (*Hydrocotyle*). In these the influence of light and gravity on the direction of growth of the shoot must obviously be changed. The principal advantage of this habit lies in the rapidity with which the plant can cover a considerable surface, whilst the close proximity to the soil entails less exposure to atmospheric extremes. On the other hand, such plants run the risk of being overshadowed by surrounding vegetation and forego all the advantages which the erect habit brings with it. These drawbacks are to some extent minimised in certain creeping forms (*e.g.* the Ground Ivy, Fig. 7) by the production of erect flowering shoots from the axils of the leaves of the creeping stem.

There are still other plants which have the tendency to grow

erect, but after reaching a certain size fail to maintain this position
unless they find some additional means of support which in nature is generally furnished by the surrounding vegetation. These *climbers* exhibit diverse methods of utilising such aid The simplest type is afforded by plants like the Goose-grass (Fig. 8, A), the Dog-rose (Fig. 8, B), and the Bramble (Fig. 140, p. 225), which grow vertically for a short time and then, bending over under their own weight, find a suitable support usually in the taller-growing shrubs round about. The apex of such a *scrambler* always tends to grow vertically upwards under the influence of light and gravity but, in the absence of any prop, the stem sooner or later falls on to the ground after which the younger portion again turns upwards; this is repeated until some

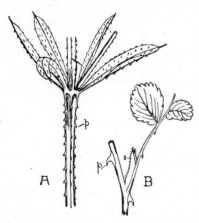

FIG. 8. A, Portion of shoot of Goose-grass (*Galium aparine*) (natural size), to show the prickles (*p*). B, Dog-rose (slightly reduced), with prickles (*p*) on stem and leaf (only a portion of the latter is shown). *s*, stipules.

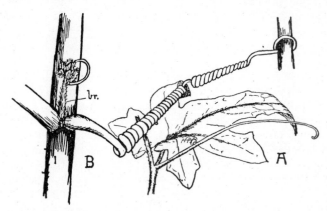

FIG. 9. Tendrils of the White Bryony (*Bryonia dioica*) (natural size).   A, before, B, after clasping the support.   *br.*, branch.

support is found, whereupon the erect part of the stem, in the course of its further growth, is raised above the surface of the soil. The shoot in these plants is provided with curved prickles (Fig. 8, *p*), all of which have their tips directed downwards, so that the plant becomes hooked on to its means of support. In the Bramble and Dog-rose (Fig. 8, B) these structures are very conspicuous, but in the Goose-grass (Fig. 8, A) they are much smaller. Many weak-stemmed plants (*e.g.* the Stitchwort, *Stellaria holostea*), which grow more or less erect when they occur in masses, frequently behave as scramblers, if opportunity serves, but do not possess any very marked equipment for this purpose.

More specialised climbers are those which develop *tendrils*, such as the Sweet-pea (Fig. 169, B, p. 264) and the White Bryony (Fig. 9). These tendrils appear as thin naked green stalks (Fig. 9, A) which, on contact with a branch or twig, twine round it (Fig. 9, B) and in this way the plant, as it grows, becomes attached to its support (cf. Chapter XXIV).

A third method of climbing is adopted by those plants in which the stem itself twines around the supporting object, as in Convolvulus and the Hop (Fig. 10). The shoot here at first grows erect, but after attaining a certain height the tip bends over and revolves in a circle (as indicated by the arrow in Fig. 10), a movement which helps the plant to find an object around which to coil. In these *stem-twiners* the apex of the shoot bears very small leaves (Fig. 10), which soon become separated by remarkably long internodes. As a result of this, twining is accomplished before the leaves are

FIG. 10. Twining stem of Hop (*Humulus lupulus*) (about half the natural size), showing small leaves and long internodes of apical portion. Direction of twining indicated by the arrow.

sufficiently large to interfere materially with the encircling of the support. In the Hop the grip of the climbing stem is greatly aided by the presence of curved prickles similar to those of the scramblers above considered. The Ivy is unusual in climbing by means of roots (Fig. 61, p. 109).

The end attained by the climber is the same as in the erect plant, viz. the exposure of its leaves to adequate illumination, the display of its flowers in a conspicuous position and the placing of its fruits in a situation aloft suitable for seed-dispersal. This type of habit is in nature found more particularly amongst the dense vegetation of hedges (Fig. 11) and thickets, where competition is keen and adequate means of support are available, typical instances being

FIG. 11. Photograph of foot of hedgerow, taken close at hand. *b*, White Bryony; *c*, Chickweed; *g*, Goose-grass; *s*, Stinging Nettle.

furnished by the Honeysuckle and the Black Bryony. The climber enjoys the advantage of being able to dispense with so elaborate a supporting skeleton as that required by the ordinary erect plant, and the material thus economised can be used for rapid growth and the formation of abundant flowers and seeds; on the other hand, its existence turns on the finding of a suitable support and, if this fails, it has little chance of surviving.

Plants of a particular habit are often characteristic of certain situations, climbers of the hedgerow, rhizomatous plants (p. 226) of shifting soils, perennials of cold regions, short-lived annuals of tropical deserts, and annuals of cornfields or other disturbed soil. It is important to recognise that the air becomes drier and the speed of the wind greater with the height above ground. As a consequence the lower the stature of a plant, the less it is exposed to extreme conditions. It will be realised therefore that the level, at which the perennial parts of the plant occur, is a feature of importance; the buds of trees are more exposed than those of shrubs, those of Creeping Jenny which rest on the surface of the ground are less protected than the buds of

Dog's Mercury (*Mercurialis*) which occur just below it, whilst the resting stem of the Cuckoo-pint (*Arum maculatum*) which is often 8 inches under the ground is still better shielded. But the lower the stature of a plant, the less its capacity to compete for light.

This brief review of the various types of plant-habit shows that each has its own advantages, especially in relation to the conditions which obtain in nature. Form and duration are always subservient to the adequate nourishment of the individual, its reproduction and consequent multiplication. Advantages on the one hand are, however, balanced by disadvantages on the other. Thus, if the perennial be able to produce numerous seeds year after year, it also requires a relatively long period of preparation. An apple tree raised from a pip, for example, rarely bears fruit before it is seven years old. Most woody perennials therefore tend to disappear where browsing animals are plentiful, and so it is that with increase of population woody types tend to become replaced by herbs.

So far the evidence from fossil plants indicates that the diverse epochs in the earth's history, since life developed upon it, have been characterised by the preponderance of particular kinds of vegetation. The present is the age of herbaceous plants, and Grasses are probably the most prevalent among living groups, whereas formerly woody plants seem to have dominated the earth's surface, while at an even more remote period the carpet consisted of non-flowering plants, often woody in character and represented by larger and more robust individuals than their relatives of to-day.

CHAPTER III

DICOTYLEDONOUS SEEDS AND SEEDLINGS

MOST Flowering Plants sooner or later produce fruits and seeds which represent the culmination of each season's growth. The seeds eventually come to lie on the rugged surface of the soil. By the action of the summer's heat and winter's frost the soil becomes broken up, and into the numerous crevices thus formed the seeds are washed by rain. Burrowing animals, especially earthworms, contribute to this process and, since in the course of their nutrition considerable quantities of soil are passed through their bodies and become deposited at the surface, they constantly transfer earth from below upwards, leaving corresponding spaces in the soil below. In rainy weather the little streams of water that percolate into the ground wash the seeds downwards, whilst at the end of each season's growth fallen leaves and other vegetable *débris* accumulate on the surface and thus afford added protection. In these various ways the seeds become buried at some slight depth in the soil.

In many plants the seeds remain dormant in the ground until the following spring, when conditions become favourable for *germination*. Seeds only germinate when provided with sufficient moisture, warmth, and adequate oxygen for respiration (cf. p. 9). In nature, the supply of water and oxygen are as a rule sufficient for germination, and it is often the low temperature of the soil that delays this process until the spring.

Many seeds (*e.g.* some Hawthorns), even if placed under suitable conditions, will not germinate immediately after being shed, but require a period of rest during which little-known internal changes take place (after-ripening). In some early-flowering plants (*e.g.* the Field Speedwell (*Veronica arvensis*) and the Poppy) this dormant period is over by late summer or autumn when germination usually takes place, the young plants remaining small throughout the winter (cf. p. 560). Dormancy may, however, be due to delayed development of the embryo, to interference of rigid seed-envelopes with the expansion of the seed-contents, to slow inward diffusion of oxygen, or probably most commonly, to the difficulty with which water penetrates the coat of the seed. In many seeds with

20

comparatively impermeable coats, such as Sweet Peas or Lupins, abrasion of the seed-coat will hasten germination.

We may now study the outward characters of some common seed such as that of the Runner Bean (Fig. 12, A). It is more or less kidney-shaped and is covered with a smooth, tough skin, the seed-coat or *testa*. Along one of the edges of the seed there is a narrow white mark (the *hilum*, *h*) which is the scar where the seed was attached to the pod. At one end of the hilum are two minute swellings (*s*) side by side, whilst near the opposite end is a very small hole (the *micropyle*, *m*) situated at the base of a slight depression.

If some of these seeds be put to soak in tepid water a wrinkling of the seed-coat begins in the neighbourhood of the micropyle and gradually spreads over the whole surface. Still later the testa again becomes smooth, the seed having now increased to about double its original size. The explanation of these changes lies in the fact that water is first absorbed into the seed-coat at the micropyle and subsequently throughout the testa. Since the contents of the seed do not at this stage take up water nearly so rapidly, they show little increase in size, so that the enlarging testa is thrown into numerous folds. Subsequently the seed-contents also absorb water vigorously and swelling up gradually fill out and finally burst the surrounding testa. This swelling is accompanied by the exertion of considerable force, which can be shown by filling a narrow-mouthed glass bottle with dry Beans and placing it in a vessel of water; the seeds, as they swell, become more and more tightly packed, until eventually they burst the glass. This principle is, in fact, often employed for the purpose of removing dents in tin cans, etc.

For the examination of the seed-contents it is most convenient to use seeds which have been previously soaked, although the same features could be made out in the dry condition. On removal of the testa two cream-coloured fleshy lobes, the seed-leaves or *cotyledons*, are disclosed (Fig. 12, B, *c*). If the two cotyledons be carefully separated, a small bud bearing minute yellowish-green leaves (the *plumule* or primary shoot, Fig. 12, B, *p*) will be seen lying between them near to one edge. A close scrutiny shows that each cotyledon is attached to the base of the plumule by a very short petiole, whilst beyond this point the axis of the plumule is prolonged into a short tapering outgrowth, the *radicle* or primary root (*r*). Whereas the plumule is completely hidden between the cotyledons, the radicle after removal of the testa is seen as a projection lying against their edges (cf. Fig. 12, B). The young plant, found within the seed, is termed the *embryo* and includes three types of organs, viz. the radicle, plumule, and cotyledons.

The tip of the radicle fits into a short pocket which arises from

the inner surface of the seed-coat and ends near the micropyle.
This pocket acts like the wick of a lamp in drawing up moisture from

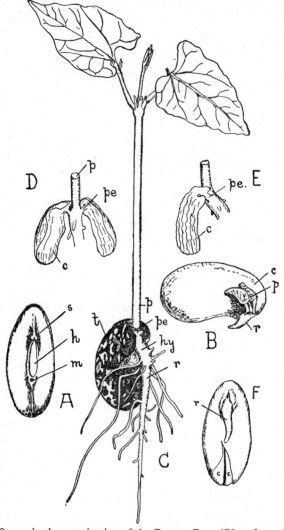

Fig. 12. Stages in the germination of the Runner Bean (*Phaseolus multiflorus*)
(all natural size). A, Soaked seed seen edge on, to show the hilum (*h*), the
micropyle (*m*), and the swellings (*s*). B, Seed with testa and one cotyledon
removed to show plumule and radicle. C, Mature seedling. D, Partially
shrivelled cotyledons, showing attachment to base of plumule. E, Ditto
from side, with completely shrivelled cotyledon. F, First stage in germination. *c*, cotyledon; *hy.*, hypocotyl; *p*, plumule; *pe.*, stalk of cotyledon;
r, radicle; *t*, testa.

the soil and passing it on to the radicle, so that this is the first part of the embryo to receive water and swell to a considerable size.   As a result it is here that the pressure upon the seed-coat is most pronounced and that the bursting of the testa begins.   The radicle, thus freed, grows rapidly downwards (Fig. 12, F) and very soon side-roots arise from it, so that the young plant becomes firmly anchored in the soil.   In the meantime the stalks of the cotyledon are slowly increasing in length (Fig. 12, D, *pe*) and, since the cotyledons themselves remain firmly embedded in the seed on the one hand and the root is fixed in the soil on the other, this elongation has the effect of carrying out the plumule clear of the seed-coat (Fig. 16, A).   Up to this time the plumule has altered little in size, but now a rapid growth in the upward direction begins.   Until after the surface of the soil is reached, the tip of the plumule remains sharply curved, so that it is the more mature region that pushes its way through the ground dragging after it the young tender leaves at the apex (Fig. 16, A).   The curvature rapidly straightens out after the plumule comes above the surface of the soil into the light (Fig. 12, C).

The early stages of germination are accomplished in darkness, and as a consequence the seedling is unable to manufacture food (cf. p. 9).   The early growth of the embryo has in fact taken place at the expense of food-substances which became stored up within its cotyledons whilst the seed was still attached to the parent-plant.   The bulk of this food consists of starch.   If seedlings be examined at successive stages of germination, it will be seen that, as growth proceeds, the cotyledons shrivel up more and more (Fig. 12, D and E) until finally but a shrunken remnant is left.   In the Runner Bean therefore the cotyledons are merely storehouses for nourishment.

An experimental demonstration of the great part played by the food-reserves in early stages of germination is furnished by carefully cutting off the cotyledons from a number of seedlings in which the radicles have obtained a hold upon the soil.   A comparison of normal seedlings with those thus treated will show how great an asset this store of nourishment is to the plant (Fig. 13).

As a second example of a seed we may take that of the Castor Oil plant (Fig. 15, A).   Neither the hilum nor the micropyle are visible on the testa (*t*), owing to their being covered by a warty outgrowth (the caruncle, *car.*), which arises late in development. By splitting the seed lengthwise in the plane of flattening and examining the exposed surfaces of the two halves a thin white leaf-like structure showing midrib and lateral veins will be seen on each (Fig. 15, B, *c*).   These are the cotyledons which in this plant are very thin and only occupy a small portion of the seed-contents

(Fig. 15, C, c). On one or other half, at the narrower end of the seed, will be found a small white peg (Fig. 15, B), the pointed end of which lies nearest the caruncle and constitutes the radicle (r), whilst the opposite blunt end represents the plumule (p). The stalks of the cotyledons are here hardly recognisable.

The embryo of the Castor Oil seed, while showing the same

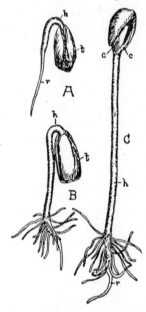

FIG. 13. A, Normal seedling of the Runner Bean. B, Seedling of the same age, from which the cotyledons were removed at an early stage of germination. (Both about half the natural size.)

FIG. 14. Germination of Sunflower (*Helianthus*) (natural size). A, Showing escape of radicle and commencement of elongation of hypocotyl. B, Later stage. C, Hypocotyl straightened and cotyledons about to escape from the seed-coat. c, cotyledon; h, hypocotyl; r, radicle; t, combined fruit-wall and testa.

organs as that of the Bean, is thus much less developed in the resting condition. A further distinction is that the embryo of the Castor Oil only occupies part of the seed and that it is completely surrounded by a white fleshy mass, the *endosperm* (Fig. 15, B and C, e), which is all that one sees when the seed-coat is removed. This is a tissue containing food-reserves for the nourishment of the young plant, and the chief difference from the Bean is therefore that in the latter the food-substances are stored up *in the embryo itself*, whereas in the Castor Oil there is this special food-tissue *outside the embryo.* Seeds which possess this tissue are said to be *endospermic*, whilst those lacking it (*e.g.* the Bean) are described as *non-endospermic.* Treatment with iodine shows that starch is not

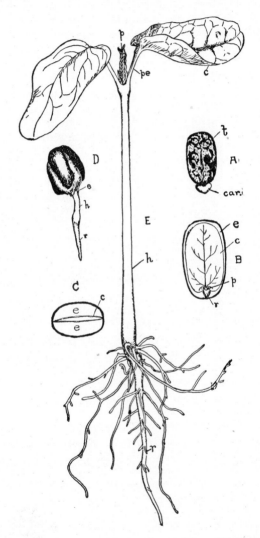

FIG. 15. Structure of seed and germination of Castor Oil plant (*Ricinus communis*) (A, D and E natural size, the others enlarged). A, Entire seed. B, The same halved lengthwise. C, Ditto, cut across. D, First stage in germination. E, Mature seedling. *c*, cotyledon; *car.*, caruncle; *e*, endosperm; *h*, hypocotyl; *p*, plumule; *pe.*, petiole of cotyledon; *r*, radicle; *t*, testa.

present in the endosperm of the Castor Oil seed, its place being taken by the oil which is used medicinally.

The first result of placing these seeds to soak is that the caruncle, which sucks up water like a sponge, increases in size and becomes softer. The seed-coat is so rigid that practically no swelling of the seed as a whole is observed and, since the water absorbed by the caruncle is passed on to the adjacent radicle, this part of the embryo is again the first to swell up, leading to a rupture of the testa at this point. The radicle grows downwards into the soil (Fig. 15, D) and begins to form lateral roots whereby, as in the Bean, the young plant becomes fixed. If a slightly older seedling be examined (Fig. 16, B), it will be noticed that prominent elongation is taking place in a region of the axis situated between the place of origin of the lateral roots and the point of attachment of the cotyledonary stalks. This elongating region has a reddish tinge in contrast to the white root and represents a portion of the stem situated *below* the cotyledons, for which reason it is spoken of as the *hypocotyl* (Fig. 16, B, *h*). Such a hypocotyl is present also in the Runner Bean (Fig. 16, A, *h*), but remains so short that it is difficult to recognise.

The rapid growth of the hypocotyl in the Castor Oil results in its becoming arched upwards (Fig. 16, B), and very soon the top of this arch appears as a loop above the soil. Subsequent to this the hypocotyl begins to straighten as a result of its further growth, and consequently the cotyledons, with the plumule enclosed between them, are dragged out of the ground (Fig. 15, E).

If a seed be examined a little time before the cotyledons emerge, the endosperm will be found to have nearly disappeared. During their long sojourn beneath the surface the cotyledons are occupied in absorbing food from the endosperm for the growth of the seedling, and throughout this period are undergoing a great increase in size, so that when they come above the ground they are many times larger than in the resting seed and have pronounced petioles (Fig. 15, E, *pe*). As the hypocotyl becomes erect the cotyledons spread out their green blades to the light (Fig. 15, E), and now serve as photosynthetic organs; subsequently the plumule forms other leaves and the cotyledons drop off.

The method of liberation of the plumule from the seed is obviously quite different in these two examples (cf. Fig. 16), for, whilst in the Runner Bean this is effected by elongation of the cotyledonary stalks, in the Castor Oil it is the lengthening of the hypocotyl that fulfils this purpose. In both seedlings the delicate tip of the plumule does not push its own way through the soil, the pressure of the soil being received either by the older part of the plumule or by the hypocotyl; in the Castor Oil the risk of injury by friction with the soil-particles is still further reduced owing to the inclusion of the plumule between the cotyledons during its passage through the ground.   Another difference between Runner Bean and Castor Oil lies in the behaviour of the cotyledons, since in the former they remain permanently underground and are said

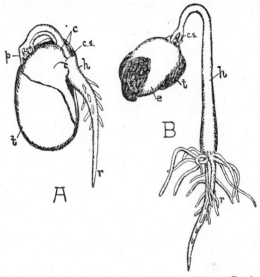

FIG. 16. Liberation of plumule in A, the Runner Bean; B, the Castor Oil (about natural size). *c*, cotyledons; *c.s.*, cotyledon-stalk; *e*, endosperm; *h*, hypocotyl; *p*, tip of plumule; *r*, radicle; *t*, testa.

to be *hypogeal*, whilst in the latter they eventually appear above the surface and are termed *epigeal*.

The two types of seed-structure and germination described in this chapter are characteristic of a large number of Flowering Plants which, owing in part to their possession of embryos with two cotyledons, are grouped together under the name of Dicotyledons. As further examples of non-endospermic Dicotyledonous seeds with hypogeal cotyledons we may mention the Pea and the Acorn, but there are also non-endospermic seeds with epigeal cotyledons, as, for instance, the French or Kidney Bean (*Phaseolus vulgaris*), the Shepherd's-purse (Fig. 1, A and B), and Sunflower (see Fig. 14); the cotyledons here remain within the seed until most of their food-material has been absorbed.   Endospermic seeds may have either hypogeal or epigeal cotyledons; the former are very rare amongst Dicotyledons, whilst examples of the latter are furnished by the Castor Oil and the Buckwheat (*Fagopyrum*).   The dry fruit of the latter has three prominent ridges and exhibits, at the broader end, the remains of the floral leaves. When cut across the middle, the white endosperm is seen occupying the greater part of the interior, whilst the cotyledons appear as an irregular yellowish line. If cut lengthwise, the body of the embryo may also be seen towards the pointed end of the fruit, with the radicle directed outwards. Here, too, the cotyledons are recognisable as a wavy line. Since the hypocotyl is mainly responsible for bringing the cotyledons above the surface of the soil, it is always well developed in epigeal seedlings, whilst in the hypogeal types it generally remains short.

CHAPTER IV

MONOCOTYLEDONOUS SEEDS AND SEEDLINGS

A LARGE number of Flowering Plants, of which the Grasses, the Lilies, and the Palms furnish examples, possess embryos having but a single cotyledon. For this and other reasons such plants are grouped together as Monocotyledons and with the Dicotyledons form the two great subdivisions of Flowering Plants. Apart from the difference in the number of cotyledons, however, the embryo of Monocotyledons shows a similar structure to that of Dicotyledons, and both non-endospermic and endospermic seeds are found, although the latter type is by far the most common.

As a first instance of a Monocotyledonous seed we select the grain of the Maize owing to its large size, but any one of the Cereals (*e.g.* Wheat, Barley, Rye, etc.) would on a smaller scale show the same essential structure and mode of germination. In the dry grain (Fig. 17, A), one end, the former point of attachment to the cob, is more or less tapering whilst the other is broad and rounded, two sides of the grain being generally somewhat flattened. On one of these flat faces a whitish oval depression (*e*) marks the position of the embryo, the remaining yellow part of the contents of the grain consisting of endosperm. Above that end of the oval depression which lies remote from the scar of attachment of the grain, careful examination will reveal a second scar-like projection, the remains of the stigma (*st.*). This shows that the grain of the Grass is still enclosed in the ovary-wall and therefore really represents a fruit containing a single seed. The seed-coat is joined up with the surrounding ovary-wall (cf. p. 474), so that the two cannot be readily distinguished from one another, and as a consequence the micropyle cannot be seen. A little above the middle of the pale patch caused by the embryo, at the end nearest the stigma-scar, a shallow and slightly darker depression, marking the position of the plumule, is frequently recognisable.

After removal of the envelope from a soaked grain, the white embryo and the yellow endosperm are readily distinguished. A faint line runs vertically up the face of the exposed embryo. By

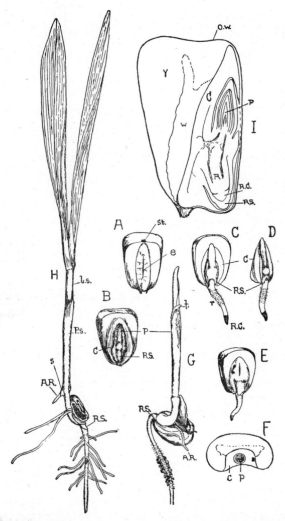

Fig. 17. Structure of grain and germination in the Maize (*Zea mais*) (all figures slightly enlarged, I × 8). A, Entire grain showing outline of embryo. B, Grain with envelope removed and edges of cotyledon folded back to show plumule and radicle. C, Early stage in germination, envelope removed. D, Embryo of same, dissected out. E, First stage in germination. F, Cross-section of grain with envelope removed. G, Late stage in germination showing escape of foliage-leaves from sheath. H, Mature seedling. I, Longitudinal section of complete grain (much enlarged). *A.R.*, adventitious roots; *c*, cotyledon; *e*, embryo; *l.s.*, leaf-sheath; *O.W.*, ovary-wall; *P*, plumule; *P.s.*, coleoptile; *R*, radicle; *R.C.*, root-cap; *R.S.*, root-sheath; *S*, sheath round base of adventitious roots; *St.*, stigma; *t*, tip of coleoptile; *W*, starchy endosperm; *Y*, flinty endosperm.

cutting a shallow slit along this line with the extreme point of a penknife and turning back the two edges of the cotyledon (Fig. 17, B), two peg-like projections are revealed, one directed towards the original point of attachment of the grain and representing the radicle (*R.S.*), the other placed in the opposite direction and constituting the plumule (*P*). The remainder of the white embryo comprises the single large cotyledon (*c*) which is wrapped round both plumule and radicle.

A further insight into the structure of the embryo is obtained by halving the peeled grain lengthwise along the same faint line as before (Fig. 17, I). The embryo is then seen to occupy the whole of the base of the seed, but tapers off to one side above, whilst the cotyledon (*c*) lies in close contact with the endosperm. The short blunt radicle (*R*) (terminated by a darker root-cap, *R.C.*) is now easily recognised and is seen to be enclosed in a special cap-like sheath, the *root-sheath* (*R.S.*, also seen in Fig. 17, B), whilst the plumule (*P*) consists of the central meristem encased in a succession of sheathing leaves (see also *P* in Fig. 17, F). From one side of the axis of the embryo, where plumule and radicle join, the large shield-shaped cotyledon (*c*) arises on a short thick stalk. The whole margin of the cotyledon is drawn out, so as to surround the rest of the embryo (see Fig. 17, F), leaving a slit-like aperture opposite the plumule. Careful examination with a lens shows that the root-sheath and the outermost sheath of the plumule both arise near the point of attachment of the cotyledon.

Around the former point of attachment of the grain is some whitish chaff (representing remains of the Maize flower) which probably facilitates the absorption of water, but the soaked grains of Maize exhibit but a slight increase in size as compared with dry ones. The radicle is again the first part of the embryo to receive water and the first to emerge, bursting through the skin of the grain and growing down into the soil (Fig. 17, E); around its base the split root-sheath can be plainly distinguished (*R.S.* in Fig. 17, C and D). The emergence of the radicle is very soon followed by the outgrowth of the plumule, which pierces the skin by its *own active growth* and pushes its way to the surface (Fig. 17, C and D). The radicle does not grow into a sturdy main root as in the Bean or Castor Oil, but is almost immediately followed by a number of similar roots (Fig. 17, G, *A.R.*), developing near the base of the radicle; these adventitious roots are sometimes recognisable already before germination and often grow more vigorously than the primary one which is soon indistinguishable from them.

The plumule, unlike that of the Dicotyledonous seedlings, remains straight during its passage through the soil, but the soft meristem and the young leaves encasing it are nevertheless amply protected by the outermost sheath (*coleoptile*), the tip of which (*t* in Fig. 17, G) is hard and pointed. It is thus again a structure (viz. the tip of the outermost sheath), already matured within the seed, that has to endure friction with the particles of the soil. On reaching the surface of the ground the sheath becomes exposed to the light and the inner leaves of the plumule burst through (Fig. 17, G and H). In these foliage-leaves we can distinguish two parts, the narrow green blade and a paler portion (the leaf-sheath) which fits closely around the stem (Fig. 17, H, *l.s.*). The coleoptile, having served to protect the plumule whilst piercing the soil, remains as a sheath around the base of the stem (Fig. 17, H, *P.s.*), differing only from the later leaves in the absence of a blade.

During the whole process of germination the cotyledon remains underground within the seed and is actively absorbing nourishment for the growing embryo from the adjacent endosperm. Two regions are distinguishable in the latter, the portion nearest the embryo being white and relatively soft, whilst the remainder is yellow and harder (Fig. 17, I, *W* and *Y*). If we halve a grain lengthwise, the white portion will alone give the starch-reaction with iodine; the remainder of the endosperm consists of thick-walled tissue. In the Sweet Corn the starch is replaced by sugar. As in the Castor Oil, the reserve material will be found to have diminished in grains attached to older seedlings.

The Onion will serve as a second example of a Monocotyledonous seed. In the dry condition this is a more or less wrinkled structure, with three irregular faces and provided with a black testa (Fig. 18, A), one of the edges being prominently concave. If a number of seeds are cut lengthwise, so that the plane of section passes through the concave edge and the opposite face, it will be seen (Fig. 18, B) that, apart from the testa, the seed consists of a mass of greyish-white endosperm (*e*) containing near the margin a whitish coiled embryo; the latter appears to be a uniform structure, but in fact consists of a radicle (R), grading over imperceptibly into the cotyledon (*c*) which completely ensheathes the plumule.

Owing to the hard testa there is no appreciable increase in size when the seed begins to take up water. The first evidence of germination (Fig. 18, C) is as usual the appearance of the radicle (R) at one end of the seed, and this is followed by elongation of the embryo as a whole (Fig. 18, D). The green colouration which is rapidly assumed by the part nearest the seed now distinguishes the cotyledon (*C*), the tip of which remains embedded within the endosperm, from the white radicle (R). In the course of its further elongation the cotyledon becomes prominently arched, this arch being retained for a considerable period, and by its continued growth in the upward direction the seed is often raised considerably above the surface of the ground (Fig. 18, E). At this stage the base of the cotyledon exhibits a slight swelling owing to increase

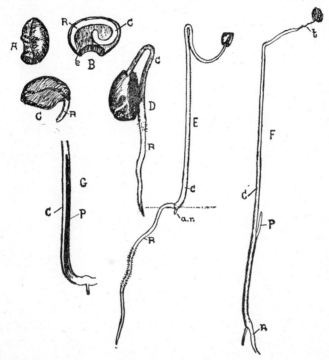

FIG. 18. Structure of seed and early stages of germination of the Onion (*Allium*) (A–D and G considerably enlarged, E and F about twice natural size). A, Entire seed. B, Seed halved lengthwise to show embryo and endosperm. C, Emergence of radicle. D, Elongation of cotyledon. E, Older seedling showing swelling at base of cotyledon due to plumule. F, Appearance of plumule and withering of cotyledonary tip. G, Longitudinal section of base of cotyledon in stage E, to show contained plumule. *a.r.*, adventitious root; C, cotyledon; *e*, endosperm; *P*, plumule; *R*, radicle.

in size of the contained plumule, whilst adventitious roots frequently develop just below this level (Fig. 18, E, *a.r.*). Finally the plumule bursts through the cotyledonary sheath (Fig. 18, F) and commences to unfold its leaves.

Throughout germination the tip of the cotyledon remains within the seed, serving to transfer the food-materials from the endosperm to the growing plant. In late stages, such as that seen in Fig. 18, F, the seed is found to be almost empty and, on cutting it in half, shows apart from the withered tip of the cotyledon only shrivelled remnants of the endosperm. The cotyledon functions, then, in the same way as that of the Maize, but whereas in the latter the entire structure is employed for purposes of absorption, in the Onion the larger part emerges from the seed, becomes green and not only serves as a photosynthetic organ, but also constitutes the means of liberation of the plumule. The Onion thus exhibits a fourth type of germination shown by many other Monocotyledons, *e.g.* Lily, Date.

We have seen that water is a prime necessity for germination,

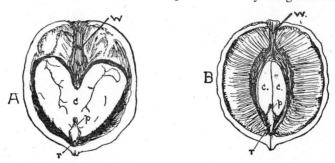

FIG. 19. Structure of the Walnut (*Juglans*) (natural size). A, Section cut lengthwise *between* the two halves of the shell. B, Section cut lengthwise at right angles to the plane of A. *c*, cotyledon; *p*, plumule; *r*, radicle; *W*, wick-like strand.

and that, in order to facilitate its absorption, many seeds are provided with definite mechanisms (*e.g.* the pocket of the Bean, the caruncle of the Castor Oil, etc.). A still more striking example is furnished by the Walnut (Fig. 19), which, when halved longitudinally, shows a prominent wick-like strand (*W*), running from one end of the nut to near its centre and terminating some little distance from the tip of the plumule (*p*). The water diffuses through this strand and from it passes into the thin membranous plates lying between the lobes of the cotyledons (*c*), thus reaching not only the latter, but also the tip of the radicle (*r*), as can be easily seen in fresh Walnuts which have been immersed for some hours in red ink. In the Cress and Mustard the whole seed-coat takes up water, rendering it slimy and adhesive. A number of seeds, again, have marked corrugations or pittings of the surface of the testa —*e.g.* Corn-cockle (*Agrostemma*), Primrose—in which, after wetting, water is readily retained.

The first result of this absorption of water is invariably the escape of the radicle, and in many plants its penetration into the soil is aided by devices for fixing the seeds (*e.g.* the slimy seed-coats already mentioned). The culmination of the process of germination is the liberation of the plumule, which is effected in different ways.

In the previous descriptions attention has been drawn to the fact that the young plumule is always protected in some way or other during its passage through the soil, *e.g.* by its own curvature in the Bean, by the coleoptile in the Maize, etc. The

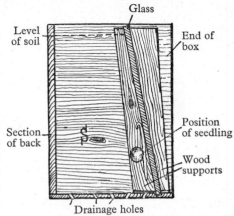

FIG. 20. Diagram of section of box to be used in experiment described on p. 35, showing method of fixing sloping glass front, the position of the seedlings, and the soil (*S*).

straightening of the plumule in the first instance and the bursting through of the enclosed leaves in the second result from exposure to the light on emergence from the soil, and seedlings of either type grown in darkness show no such change. To demonstrate this we can employ a rectangular wooden box which is perforated by a number of small holes to allow of drainage, while one long side is replaced by a sheet of glass sloping inwards from the base at a slight angle (cf. the section in Fig. 20). A thin layer of moist earth is placed on the bottom and seeds are sown in this in close contact with the glass, after which the box is filled with soil. One-half of the glass is covered with black paper, whilst the other remains exposed to the light.

The seeds which develop in darkness germinate in the normal way and sooner or

FIG. 21. Two Maize seedlings. A, Grown exposed to light from beginning of germination. B, Grown in darkness till surface of soil is reached. (Reduced to two-thirds natural size.) See text.

later their plumules appear above the surface (Fig. 21, B). Owing to the inward slope of the glass the plumules remain in contact with it, so that those of the seeds germinating behind the uncovered portion are exposed to the light from the outset, though still beneath the soil. As a result the plumule straightens out or, in the Maize, bursts through the protecting sheath, prematurely. The plumules under these circumstances are so unsuited to force their way through the soil, that they not only fail to reach the surface, but become thrown into folds (Fig. 21, A). This experiment demonstrates that the altered behaviour of the plumule after emergence from the soil is due to illumination, and that without protective devices it would fail to reach the surface. Many herbaceous perennials with underground stems show a similar curvature of the tips of their shoots or of their leaves during their passage through the soil, *e.g.* Dog's Mercury (*Mercurialis*), Moschatel (*Adoxa*), Wood Anemone, etc.

Cotyledons either serve directly as storage-organs or as a means of transference of the food-material from the endosperm. They

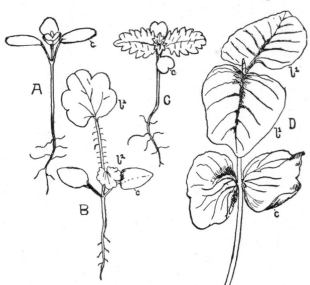

Fig. 22. Different types of Dicotyledonous seedlings (all natural size). A, Garden Spurge (*Euphorbia*). B, Greater Celandine (*Chelidonium*). C, Stinging Nettle (*Urtica*). D, Beech (*Fagus*). *c*, cotyledons; l^1 and l^2, first and second foliage-leaves.

may shrivel after these purposes are fulfilled, or they may subsequently appear above the ground and function for a time as organs of photosynthesis. Such epigeal cotyledons are always simple in form and among Dicotyledonous plants usually differ to a more or less marked extent from the subsequent foliage-leaves (cf. Fig. 22). They are very rarely lobed, as in the seedlings of the Lime and those of the Stork's Bill (*Erodium*). The similarity and simplicity of most cotyledons is doubtless related to the comparative uniformity of the conditions in which they develop and function.

The leaves following immediately on the cotyledons are often simpler in form than those developed later, and this is especially marked in plants whose mature leaves are deeply divided (*e.g.* the Greater Celandine, Fig. 22, B).[1] The foliage may exhibit a progressive increase in complexity as the plant grows older, and a similar transition can often be observed on the shoots of herbaceous perennials, *e.g.* the Musk-mallow (Fig. 23) and the Sheep's Scabious (*Scabiosa columbaria*). Further excellent examples are afforded by young Fern plants (cf. Fig. 254, C, p. 383). Another peculiarity often shown by the first pair of leaves lies in their tendency to arise together from the

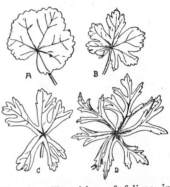

FIG. 23. Transition of foliage in the Musk-mallow (*Malva moschata*) (about half the natural size). A, Radical leaf. B–D, Cauline leaves borne at progressively higher levels on the shoot.

same node, even when those developed later occur singly (*e.g.* in the Beech, Fig. 22, D, and the Runner Bean, Fig. 12, C.)

Even in the mature plant the leaves at the base of a branch (prophylls) not infrequently differ from those produced later. Thus, in *Pelargonium* the first two leaves of each branch arise from the same node, whilst the later ones occur singly; in the Willow (*Salix*) the two scales enveloping each bud are the first two leaves of the shoot to which the latter gives rise.

---

[1] For other examples of transition in seedlings, see p. 263 and p. 509.

CHAPTER V

THE STRUCTURE AND PHYSIOLOGY OF THE PLANT-CELL

EVERY living organism, whether animal or plant, is composed of one or more minute *cells*, and this applies even to those forms of life which are so small that they can only be seen with the help of a microscope. The green powdery covering so often present on tree-trunks and palings consists of multitudes of single-celled plants (Fig. 181, p. 281), whilst millions of cells together form the body of a garden weed or tree. Organisms of the latter type are described as *multicellular*, whilst those consisting of a single cell are termed *unicellular*.

When a strip of epidermis from the inner surface of an Onion-scale is mounted in water and examined under the low power of a microscope (Appendix I), numerous oblong cells connected without intervening spaces to form a *tissue* are seen (Fig. 24, A). The net-work of delicate lines bounding the individual units is constituted by the *cell-walls*. Each cell contains a colourless, granular substance (the *cytoplasm*, Fig. 24, B, *Cy.*) visible particularly round the edge, whilst near the centre or against one side lies a rounded shining body, the *nucleus* (*N*). The cells thus consist of the non-living protective cell-wall (*c.w.*), the cytoplasm, and the nucleus; the last two form the living *protoplast*, composed of protoplasm.

Protoplasm,[1] which usually contains a high percentage of water, is a complex colloid having somewhat of the consistency of the white of an unboiled egg. Its viscosity and rigidity are variable; it can flow or be drawn out into fine threads. It is probably an ultra-microscopic gel, sometimes more like a sol, in which both phases are continuous and interpenetrating. The framework is supposed to consist of filamentous polypeptide chains (proteins) of indeterminate length, with side-chains consisting of phosphatides, lipoids, etc., while the meshes are occupied by a solution of mineral salts and organic substances. Apart from proteins (see p. 72) protoplasm includes carbohydrates and fats. It usually contains large numbers of small

[1] For further details, see A. Frey-Wyssling, *Submicroscopic Morphology of Protoplasm and its Derivatives*. Elsevier Publish. Co., 1948 (255 pp.).

granules which are partly of the nature of food-bodies and partly
waste-products.   The fact that not all, though some, of the properties of living protoplasm are exhibited by cells when ground to
pulp suggest that the particular characteristics of the cytoplasm are

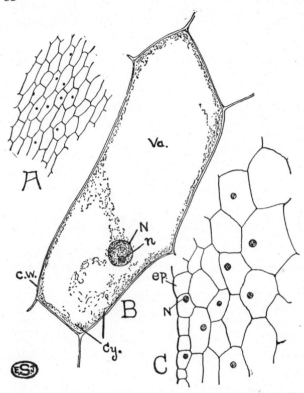

FIG. 24. Epidermis of Onion bulb-scale.   A, Small portion in surface view.
B, A single cell much enlarged.   C, A scale in vertical section.   In A and C
the nuclei are shown black.   *Cy.*, cytoplasm; *C.W.*, cell-wall; *ep.*, epidermis;
N, nucleus; *n*, nucleolus; *Va.*, vacuole.

not entirely an outcome of its chemical constitution, but are to
some extent a consequence of its ultimate structure.   The nucleus
is a most important part of the protoplast, a fact which will become
more apparent when the reproductive processes of plants are
studied.   It appears to be essential for many of the vital activities
of the cell.   A demonstration of this is afforded by the fact that, if
the unicellular animal *Stentor* is broken into pieces, the fragments
which contain portions of the nucleus develop into new individuals,
whilst the others, after a short time, perish.   Moreover, the nucleus

is generally found in that part of the cell which is in process of active growth, *e.g.* at the tip of a growing root-hair.

The structure of the Onion-cell can be more clearly distinguished if the strip of epidermis be stained with a drop of iodine (see Appendix V), and a single cell examined under the high-power objective. The protoplasm will have assumed a yellowish tint, whilst the nucleus appears pale brown. This colour reaction of the protoplast is one characteristic of proteins generally. The nucleus (Fig. 24, B, *N*) is bounded by a thin *nuclear membrane*, whilst within it one or two small round bodies, the *nucleoli* (*n*), are now plainly visible, since they are stained more deeply than the rest. The cytoplasm does not completely fill the cell, but there is a large space or *vacuole* (*Va.*) occupying the greater part of the central region; this vacuole, apparently empty, is in reality filled with a watery fluid, the *cell-sap*. Close observation shows that the cytoplasm is not evenly granular throughout, but that there is a very thin clear layer immediately within the cell-wall, and a similar layer can be detected at the surface abutting on the vacuole. These layers are bounded by the *plasmatic membranes*, which are a result of physical forces operating at the surface of the cytoplasm.

If another strip of Onion epidermis be mounted in concentrated sulphuric acid, the cell-walls will swell and disappear. Subsequent addition of iodine gives a blue colouration to the dissolving walls, a reaction characteristic of *cellulose*, of which most thin cell-membranes largely consist.

It must be realised that the cells just examined, like all plant-cells, are developed in three dimensions, a fact which can be verified by cutting a section transversely across the Onion-scale, when the epidermal cells will appear as flat tabular structures (Fig. 24, C).

As a second example, one of the cells forming the purple hairs (Fig. 25, A) on the stamens of the Common Spiderwort (*Tradescantia*) may be examined.[1] These show the same structure as those of the Onion, but the cell-sap is here of a purple colour. The nucleus, surrounded by a small mass of cytoplasm, is not uncommonly suspended in the middle of the vacuole, the enveloping cytoplasm being connected with that lining the cell-wall by a number of protoplasmic strands (Fig. 25, B). If the granules in these strands are closely observed, they will be seen to exhibit a continuous streaming movement which can be accelerated by *slight*

---

[1] If material of the Spiderwort is not available, a good substitute is furnished by the unicellular hairs lining the inner surface of the corolla-tube of the White Dead-nettle, in which, however, the cell-sap is uncoloured.

warming, but ceases on the addition of a poison (*e.g.* alcohol), whereby the cell is killed. A temporary cessation of the movement can be brought about by mounting the cells in water to which a trace of some anæsthetic (*e.g.* chloroform) has been added. On returning the hairs to ordinary water, however, streaming of the granules is soon resumed. Energy provided by respiration is necessary for such movements. If the cells are mounted in water which has been boiled and subsequently cooled, the cessation of movement shows the necessity of oxygen. The movement is really due to a flowing of the cytoplasm, and this phenomenon betrays the fluid consistency of the latter. No movement can be recognised, however, in the plasmatic membranes, which are therefore probably of a denser character.

All living plant-cells display the features above described, but in many, other structures are present, of which the commonest are bodies known as *plastids.* In those cells of the plant which are exposed to the light the plastids become the depositories of the

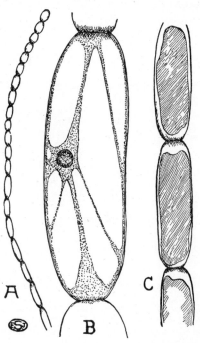

FIG. 25. Staminal hairs of the Spiderwort (*Tradescantia*). A, a single hair; B, a single cell showing the nucleus and strands of cytoplasm passing across the vacuole; C, a hair plasmolysed with sea-water.

chlorophyll, and are then known as *chloroplasts.* On examining a leaf of the Canadian Pondweed (*Elodea canadensis*) under the high power, each of the more or less rectangular cells will be found to contain a number of chloroplasts, which will be seen from one of two aspects (Fig. 26). Some, situated along the sides of the cell, are viewed in profile and appear as flattened ellipses (*O.S.*), whilst others lying against the upper or lower walls, and consequently seen from the surface, present a round or oval form (*Su.*). Each chloroplast is solid and has more or less the shape of a thick saucer containing a number of minute granules.

If attention be centred on a single cell, the chloroplasts lying against the upper face can be brought clearly into view by turning the fine adjustment; on focussing to a lower level, however, another layer of chloroplasts appears belonging to the same cell. Each cell can thus be likened to an oblong box lined along the whole of the inner surface with a thick viscid fluid (the cytoplasm) in which are embedded the chloroplasts, the cavity of the box representing the vacuole (Fig. 26, *Va.*) with its cell-sap.

By watching the chloroplasts, particularly in the elongated cells of the midrib, they will be observed to exhibit movement similar to that of the granules in the cells of the Spiderwort, and here as there this is actually due to a flow of the cytoplasm. Such a streaming movement probably takes place in the cytoplasm of all living cells, but in many it is so slow that it cannot be demonstrated. By its means food-substances, etc., are more quickly distributed from one part of the cell to the other than by mere diffusion.

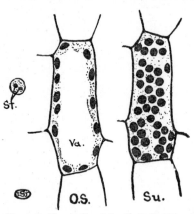

FIG. 26. Two cells of the Canadian Pondweed, one in surface view (*Su.*), and the other in optical section (*O.S.*). The chloroplasts are shown black. At the left a single chloroplast showing starch grains (*St.*). *Va.*, vacuole.

When leaves of the Canadian Pondweed, or those of other plants, are kept in spirit for some little time, all the chlorophyll is removed in solution. The chloroplasts, though now colourless, have undergone no change of shape, and are therefore merely specialised parts of the cytoplasm which hold the chlorophyll.

The green cells of all the higher plants contain numerous chloroplasts, essentially similar in form to those just studied. In the Algæ (p. 295), however, the cells are often provided with but a single chloroplast or a limited number of them, and these are frequently of a much more elaborate pattern. *Spirogyra*, which is exceedingly common in stagnant water, furnishes an extreme instance. The plant here consists of a single thread or filament composed of cylindrical cells joined end to end. According to the species, each cell contains, apart from the cytoplasm and nucleus, one or more chloroplasts in the shape of green spiral bands, usually with a jagged edge (Fig. 27, *ch.*). These spiral chloroplasts are here, again, situated in the lining layer of cytoplasm. At intervals

bright bodies, consisting of protein and known as *pyrenoids*, are
embedded within their substance (Fig. 27, *p.*); but these are more
evident after treatment with iodine, whereupon they become blue,
owing to the fact that each is surrounded by a layer of starch.

Pyrenoids are not found in the chloroplasts
of the higher plants, but are quite frequent
amongst the Algæ (see p. 295).

Returning to the cells in the hairs of
the Spiderwort, we will mount them in
2 per cent. natural or artificial sea-water
(see Appendix VI); the resulting phenomena
could be equally well observed by using any
cells with coloured sap, *e.g.* those forming
the lower epidermis of the Mother-of-
Thousands (*Saxifraga sarmentosa*), or of the
Cyclamen. In the cells thus treated the
lining layer of cytoplasm has contracted
away from the wall, so that a clear region
occupied by sea-water is visible between it
and the wall (Fig. 25, C). In this condition
the cell is said to be *plasmolysed*, and the
phenomenon is spoken of as *plasmolysis*.
If the sea-water be replaced by tap-water,
the cell-sap increases in volume, so that
the cytoplasm regains its original position,
pressed up against the wall, and the cell
resumes its normal appearance. By alternately substituting sea-water and tap-water,
this sequence of events may be repeatedly
observed.

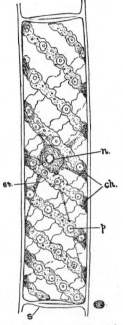

In the normal cell the pressure of the
sap within the vacuole keeps the lining layer
of cytoplasm distended and forced against
the wall, in much the same way as the
bladder of a football, when inflated with

Fig. 27. Single cell of a
Spirogyra-filament
showing the spiral chloroplast (*ch.*), the pyrenoids
(*p.*) surrounded by starch,
and the nucleus (*n.*)
supported by cytoplasmic
strands (*st.*). *S*, separating wall between ad-
jacent cells.

air, is pressed against the leather cover. If the air be allowed to
escape, the bladder shrinks and a space is left between it and the
cover. Similarly, the contraction of the protoplast of the cell,
when surrounded by sea-water, must be attributed to a decrease
in volume of the cell-sap owing to passage of water into the outside
liquid. The recovery, when placed in water, obviously implies an
increase in volume of the sap, and this can only be due to some of
the water around having passed into it.

It is a well-known physical phenomenon (*osmosis*) that, when two solutions of different concentrations are separated by a membrane (which may be of a fluid consistency) that is permeable to the solvent (*e.g.* water) but relatively impermeable to the substances in solution, a passage of water tends to take place through the membrane from the weaker solution to the stronger. Membranes possessing this property are said to be *semi-permeable* with respect to the solutions concerned. This attribute thus depends both upon the nature of the membrane itself and upon the solution in relation to which it is used.

To demonstrate osmosis it is most convenient to use the semi-permeable membrane afforded by the membranous precipitate of copper ferrocyanide which is formed when solutions of copper sulphate and potassium ferrocyanide meet. This membrane is itself too weak to withstand pressure and is most suitably deposited in a supporting membrane of celloidin (see Appendix VII) fitted over the open end of a thistle funnel. The solution whose osmotic potential is to be investigated is placed in such an osmometer, and the whole is immersed in pure water so that diffusion between the two solutions can only take place by way of the semi-permeable membrane. The osmotic potential of the solution can then be calculated from the height to which it rises within a glass tube fitted on to the osmometer, or by means of a suitable manometer.

The lining layer of protoplasm, or probably more correctly the plasmatic membranes, exhibit a varying degree of semi-permeability. Consequently, when cells are surrounded by solutions of substances to which the plasmatic membrane is relatively impermeable and which are more concentrated than the cell-sap, water passes out and the protoplast contracts. On the other hand, when replaced in water, the cell-sap is the more concentrated solution, and the protoplast becomes distended until its further expansion, and further increase in the volume of the sap, is limited by the stretching capacity of the cell-wall. In a healthy plant, supplied with sufficient water, most of the living cells are thus distended, *i.e.* they are *turgid*, a condition which plays an important part in maintaining the stability of herbaceous organs (see p. 143). Absorption of water by the cell may depend to some extent upon imbibition (p. 50) by colloidal substances in the protoplast or cell-sap.

If cells were completely permeable, the concentrations inside and outside would become equal as a result of diffusion; plasmolysis could not occur and osmotic turgidity would be impossible. Cells are, however, relatively impermeable to many substances in solution, although when living cells are left immersed in a plasmolysing solution, the gradual recovery from plasmolysis which is often observed, after a longer or shorter interval, shows that slow inward diffusion of the solute may occur (*endosmosis*). In some plants this is an important means of adjustment to changes of concentration in the soil-solution (cf. p. 566).

The plasmatic membranes exhibit their semi-permeable character, however, only so long as the protoplast remains alive; hence after death both the substances dissolved in the cell-sap can pass outwards, and external solutions can diffuse inwards. If cells of the Spiderwort, etc., mounted in water, are killed by gently heating the slide over a spirit-lamp, the coloured sap will be found to escape into the surrounding liquid; moreover, it will be found impossible to bring about plasmolysis or to render such killed cells turgid. These results, apart from showing that the semi-permeable character of the cytoplasm is altered by death, demonstrate that the cell-wall is readily permeable to substances in solution. The permeability of the cytoplasm, when dead, to the cell-sap may be exhibited on a large scale by placing slices of Beetroot in hot water.

A moment's thought, quite apart from any experimental demonstration, shows that the plasmatic membranes must be permeable to many substances, since most of those dissolved in the soil-water can be detected within the plant. Moreover, plants will thrive for months or years in a solution of mineral salts from which analysis shows that the latter have been absorbed (cf. p. 206).

Were it not for the restraining influence of the wall, which is only slightly extensible, but possesses considerable strength, a plant-cell placed in pure water would increase in size until it became ruptured. This actually occurs when the root-hairs of salt-marsh plants are suddenly transferred to water, for these have a highly concentrated sap. The more concentrated the sap, the more strongly does it absorb water, and the greater will be the pressure upon the wall exerted by the protoplast as it swells. The maximum force with which a solution tends to take up pure water through a semi-permeable membrane is called the *osmotic potential* [1] of the solution.

The cell-sap has a variable osmotic concentration of molecules and ions which confers upon it a potential capacity to absorb pure water, when separated from it by a semi-permeable membrane. When water is absorbed, the consequent swelling of the cell-contents causes an outwardly directed pressure (*turgor pressure*) to be exerted on the wall, which stretches the latter until the increasing pressure of the stretched wall (*wall pressure*) becomes great enough to resist any further increase in the volume of the cell-contents. So long as this limit is not reached, an isolated cell has a power to absorb water (*suction pressure* of the cell), which is equivalent to the difference between the force due to the osmotic concentration of the sap and the wall pressure. It is upon differences in suction

[1] A more apt term for what is commonly called *osmotic pressure.*

pressure that exchange of water between adjacent living cells depends. At any time the intake of water by a cell of a tissue [1] depends on the difference between its absorbing force due to osmotic concentration and the forces tending to remove water from the cell, viz. (a) the pressure of the wall and that of the surrounding cells which oppose any increase in volume, and (b) the suction pressure exerted by the *other* living cells around, which are also competing for water.

Loss of water from cells, as in transpiration, or gain in water, as in absorption by root-hairs, lead to alterations in the suction pressure of the cells concerned, and therefore establish gradients in suction pressure between these and neighbouring cells, by virtue of which movement of water from cell to cell and from one part of the plant to another takes place (cf. p. 193).

By using artificially prepared semi-permeable membranes (see Appendix VII) the osmotic potential of a solution can be determined in terms of atmospheric pressure. In general the osmotic strength of a solution depends upon the number of molecules it contains, though this does not apply to dilute solutions of electrolytes in which the osmotic potential is increased by dissociation into ions. When the molecules are present in equal proportions, two solutions of cane-sugar and grape-sugar, for example, have the same osmotic potential. Such *equimolecular* solutions are obtained by dissolving substances in distilled water, made up to one litre, in proportions equivalent to their molecular weights. If the number of grammes dissolved in a litre of solution is equal to the molecular weight, we have a so-called gram-molecular solution, briefly indicated by M. Solutions of other strengths are indicated as 0.5 M, 0.2 M, etc. Since the weight of a substance depends on the number and mass of the atoms composing its molecule, a 10 per cent. solution of a complex compound, such as inulin or dextrin, will contain fewer molecules than a 10 per cent. solution of a simpler compound, such as grape-sugar or cane-sugar; moreover, cane-sugar which has a higher molecular weight than grape-sugar, will exhibit a lower osmotic potential than the latter when in solutions of the same *percentage* strength. These important facts are illustrated in the following table:

	Molecular weight.	Molar concentration of 10 per cent. solution.	Osmotic potential in atmospheres.
Grape-sugar .	180	0.555	12.43
Cane-sugar .	342	0.292	6.54
Dextrin . .	—	—	ca. 2.2
Albumen ca.	13,000	0.008	0.17

---

[1] Even when a cell forms one of a tissue, it can receive water from all sides as long as the water-supply is normal, since all parts of a healthy plant imbibe water (cf. p. 60).

In order to estimate the osmotic potential within a cell, a solution of sea-water (see Appendix VI), strong enough to bring about plasmolysis, is first obtained. By experimenting with a series of solutions of diminishing strengths, one can eventually be found which just fails to cause plasmolysis, and which is slightly weaker than another which brings about a very slight, but often local, contraction of the protoplast from the wall. The former solution gives the approximate osmotic concentration of the sap at the moment of plasmolysis (for equivalent pressures, see Appendix VI). This value is somewhat higher than that of the sap of the normal cell, since the stretched wall contracts as the turgor-pressure diminishes and water is withdrawn during the experiment. Moreover, it would only be a true value if the membranes were completely semi-permeable. The osmotic potential of a tissue is best computed from the percentages of cells plasmolysed in a series of concentrations. Other accurate methods are indirect and depend on the relation between osmotic pressure and the temperature at which a liquid (*e.g.* the expressed sap of a plant-organ) freezes.

The osmotic concentration of the sap of the individual cells varies, even in a uniform tissue. Moreover, it shows diurnal fluctuations and, with changes in the humidity of the environment,[1] may vary by as much as ten atmospheres in a day. Very low values occur in water-plants, whilst in *Atriplex confertifolia,* a desert plant, 153 atmospheres may be realised.

The full suction pressure can be determined by cutting several small cubes out of a tissue (*e.g.* potato) and, after weighing, immersing them successively in solutions of cane-sugar of differing molar concentration. The suction pressure will equal the osmotic potential of that solution in which the tissue neither gains nor loses weight. When a piece of Dandelion-stalk is split lengthwise into four and the strips momentarily dipped into water, they curl up spirally, since the inner cells have been in a state of compression and the outer in a state of tension. Using circular segments cut from such spirals, a concentration of sea-water that causes neither increase nor decrease in the curvature will give an approximate measure of the suction pressure of the cells. Stems of many herbs can be used in this way.

The protoplast is very readily permeable to a number of organic substances, and these can be used to investigate this phenomenon. Thus, if young shoots of the Canadian Pondweed be placed in a solution of methylene blue, so weak that it has but a very faint tint, the cell contents will after some days be found to have assumed

[1] In *Helleborus fœtidus* osmotic pressures ranging from 10·5 to 66 atmospheres have been observed.

a deep blue colour. This indicates that the dissolved dye has passed through the cytoplasm in considerable amount. If the methylene blue remained unaltered on reaching the vacuole, only sufficient could have entered to bring about a concentration equivalent to that of the solution outside the cells. But the deep blue colour shows that the dye has accumulated within the sap, and this is due to the combination of the methylene blue with the tannin in the latter to form a substance which is completely insoluble in the sap. In this way the concentration of the dye which enters the cell-sap is continually being reduced to a strength below that outside. As a consequence more and more methylene blue diffuses in, and thus the deep blue colour is gradually produced.

A further demonstration of permeability of the cytoplasm is obtained when filaments of *Spirogyra* (and many other Algæ) are placed in a dilute (1 per cent.) solution of caffeine. Under the microscope there is seen to appear in the vacuole a very fine greyish precipitate which, as it accumulates, renders the cell more and more opaque. This precipitate is again a consequence of combination between the tannin in the cell-sap and the caffeine.

Both examples illustrate the very important phenomenon that plant-cells can absorb *and accumulate* considerable quantities of various substances *from very dilute solutions* by diffusion, provided that within the cell they are changed into some other form which is insoluble or does not readily pass through the plasmatic membrane, or that they are adsorbed (see p. 50) by colloidal substances. The accumulation of salts by roots from dilute soil-solutions depends, however, on a high degree of metabolic activity in the cells concerned. The phenomena just discussed also explain the accumulation of food-reserves (*e.g.* starch) in large quantities in the cells of storage-organs. When these reserves are utilised, it is clear that they must be changed into a form which can diffuse to the growing organs, insoluble starch, for example, being transformed into soluble sugar. This process can be simulated by placing leaves of the Canadian Pondweed, whose cell-sap has acquired a deep blue colour in the way above described, in a very dilute solution of citric acid (1 per cent.). The latter passes into the cells and changes the blue pigment into a form capable of diffusing through the plasmatic membrane. Since its concentration inside the cell is greatly in excess of that outside, diffusion takes place and the sap gradually loses its deep blue colouration.

Solutions containing a single salt of sodium, potassium, magnesium or calcium affect the permeability of the protoplasts of plant-cells and, if the action be prolonged or a sufficiently concentrated solution be used, injury will result and may lead to irreversible contraction of the protoplast. Such contractions are not plasmolytic, but are due to a toxic action of the metallic ions of the salt on the plasmatic membranes. Monovalent metallic ions generally increase, while those of higher valency at first decrease permeability. If solutions containing appropriate proportions of salts of mono- and di- or tri-valent metals are employed (*e.g.* sodium chloride and calcium chloride), the toxic effect is greatly reduced. Moreover, it may be still further diminished if a third salt (*e.g.* magnesium chloride) be also added.

The prevention of the poisonous action of one ion by one or more other ions is spoken of as *antagonism* and, as already pointed out, ions of different valencies are most effective. A mixture of cations in solution in such proportions that they exert no toxic effect constitutes a *balanced solution*; when such a solution produces contraction of the protoplast, the effect is a true plasmolysis. Sea-water which is a mixture consisting mainly of chlorides of sodium, magnesium, potassium, and calcium, together with magnesium sulphate, is a naturally occurring balanced solution and when diluted forms a suitable medium for determining osmotic potentials in plant-cells. The rate of entry into a cell of one ion, whether toxic or not, may thus be markedly influenced by the presence of other ions. The complexity of the phenomena of absorption is illustrated by the fact that roots do not absorb compounds in the same proportions as they occur naturally in the soil-solution (p. 208) and that the intake of water and of dissolved salts are both influenced by the rate of respiration.

Of the diverse compounds found within the cells of plants, and continually being transported from one organ to another, some diffuse readily through membranes (*crystalloids*, *e.g.* mineral salts and sugars), while others are indiffusible (*colloids*, *e.g.* gums and proteins). The difference between the two as regards diffusibility is so marked that mixtures of crystalloids and colloids in solution are readily separated by dialysis, *i.e.* by placing the solution in a parchment tray floating on a large volume of water. Crystalloids are usually substances which readily crystallise and form true solutions in which the diameter of the dispersed particles (ions or molecules) is less than a millionth of a millimetre. Many colloids can in various ways also be brought into "solution," like that obtained, for instance, when boiling water is added to starch paste (p. 75). In such a colloidal "solution" or *sol* the particles are many times larger than in a true solution so that they will not pass through the pores of parchment, though they may still pass through filter paper. The particles are probably aggregates of molecules which remain permanently suspended, partly owing to

4

electrical forces. Substances are known which, according to the treatment applied, form either a crystalloidal or a colloidal solution, so that the term colloidal state is more appropriate. Many substances naturally occur in this state.

Sols like those of the metals and supensions of clay in water contain solid particles, which can be precipitated by electrolytes and other agencies (cf. below). In others, like milk and latex (p. 96), the "particles" are minute liquid droplets and the system is known as an *emulsion*. In sols of "emulsoids" such as starch and proteins, the "particles" are liquid, but the phases differ in the main only in consistency or in the proportion of water present.

Sols are distinguished from ordinary suspensions and emulsions by the finely divided state of the particles. These latter can only be detected with the ultra-microscope, and only when relatively coarse; they are then seen to exhibit a constant oscillation due to molecular bombardment (*Brownian movement*), which is also recognisable under the ordinary microscope in particles below a certain size. By various means (change of temperature, addition of electrolytes, shaking, etc.) the suspended particles of a sol may be caused to precipitate, or the whole sol may set to form a jelly-like mass or *gel*. Gel-formation is seen in the setting of sols of gelatine or agar when cooled. More complex is the coagulation of some proteins (*e.g.* white of egg) when heated. Unlike gelation, coagulation is not reversible. The solid particles of a gel probably form a continuous phase, in the interstices of which the liquid is held. Living protoplasm may have the structure of a gel (p. 38) and, like the latter, possesses the important property of imbibing water; it is probably only when it is more or less fully imbibed that it is in a really active condition. The property of imbibition no doubt depends on the hydration of protein ions; it is therefore greatly influenced by various cations and anions and by the acid or alkaline reaction of the medium.

The particles of a sol are nearly always electrically charged. They therefore tend to attract to their surfaces any oppositely charged particles, molecules or ions of foreign substances that come within their domain. Such substances may thus become more or less firmly attached to the surfaces of the colloid, and are then said to be "adsorbed." Adsorption is never complete, but a very large proportion of the substances capable of adsorption may in this way be removed from very dilute solutions. On the large aggregate surface presented by the colloidal complex of protoplasm various substances may become adsorbed so that, even in one and the same cell, large numbers of different chemical reactions may occur simultaneously.

CHAPTER VI

MERISTEMS AND CELL-DIVISION

In some simple plants (e.g. *Spirogyra*) almost every cell may exhibit growth and division, but in most the cells originate in the first instance by division from meristems (growing points) (p. 6), usually situated in a Flowering Plant at the tips of the stem and root and of their respective branches. A similar apical position of the meristem commonly obtains amongst non-flowering plants.

A good example is afforded by the Seaweed *Sphacelaria*, which is found in rock-pools. Here each branch ends in a single large cell (Fig. 28, B, *a*). During the active season this cell is constantly increasing in size, and, when of a certain length, becomes halved by the formation of a cross-wall (*a*, 1). The upper portion again enlarges until a new septum arises, whilst the lower half (termed a segment) divides (2–4) to form the cells of the mature plant. The Seaweed *Dictyota* furnishes another instance of a one-celled growing point (see Fig. 28, A). The daughter-cells in these two Seaweeds are cut off in a single series parallel to one face of the cell.

In most plants having a unicellular meristem the apical cell has the form of a three-sided pyramid with a rounded base directed outwards (Fig. 29, *a.c.*); such a cell is described as *tetrahedral*. Segments are here cut off in succession from each of the three flat inner faces, these segments undergoing further subdivision to form the mature tissues. This type is found in Mosses and Ferns, and can be examined in a longitudinal section through the tip of the stem of *Equisetum* (Fig. 29). In such a section the apical cell (*a.c.*) appears triangular, and two only of the three series of segments are visible. In the roots of Horsetails and Ferns with such a meristem, segments are also cut off parallel to the rounded base, the cells produced by their subdivision forming the root-cap.

The growing regions of Flowering Plants are occupied by a conical or dome-shaped (Fig. 30) mass of small actively enlarging and dividing cells; these replace the single cell found in the groups hitherto mentioned. This *meristem* is best examined in sections cut longitudinally through the middle of the apex of stem or root. In both, the cells of the meristem are arranged in layers, which can be traced back into the different tissues distinguishable in the mature parts. A concentric arrangement is usually evident in

51

roots (Fig. 32) but less distinct in most stems (Fig. 30), although well-marked in *Hippuris* for instance. The thin walls of the polyhedral, meristematic cells fit closely together. As they multiply, those near the apex retain the power of division, while those farther back gradually lose it and pass over into permanent tissue.

In most stems two regions, the tunica (Fig. 30, *t*) and the corpus (*c*), are distinguishable in the apical meristem. The *tunica* consists of one or, more commonly, two (rarely three or more, as in Fig. 30) super-

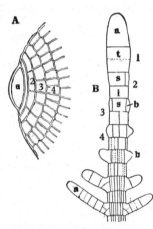

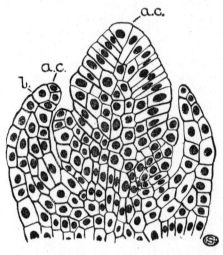

FIG. 28. *A*, Apical cell and adjacent part of thallus of *Dictyota*. *B*, End of a branch of *Sphacelaria*. *a*, apical cells; *b*, lateral branches; *i*, *s*, lower and upper halves of segments of apical cell; *t*, septum; 1–4, successive segments, showing increasing subdivision, cut off from the apical cell. (*A* after Cohn; *B* after Sauvageau).

FIG. 29. Apex of *Equisetum telmateia* in longitudinal section, showing tetrahedral apical cells of stem and leaf (*a.c.*); *l*, leaf.

ficial layers, which divide predominantly perpendicular to the surface (*i.e.* anticlinally). Internal to them lies the *corpus* (*c*), with division-walls less regularly orientated. All the septa in the outermost layer of the tunica are mostly anticlinal, and so this remains a single layer which in the mature region constitutes the epidermis; in the underlying layers there are more or less frequent septa in other directions, especially when a leaf or lateral branch is developing (cf. p. 147). In the corpus a central and subapical group of one or more, irregularly arranged, relatively large, and lightly staining initial cells, which divide infrequently, can often be distinguished, and beneath it a so-called *file meristem* with longitudinally arranged cells (Fig. 30, *f*) which gives rise to the pith. Surrounding the subapical group horizontally are smaller more deeply staining cells which divide actively and further back give rise to the *vascular strands* and the *cortex*.

At the apices of roots the cells are mostly arranged in curved longitudinal rows (Fig. 32), radiating out from a meristematic region covered by the root-cap (Fig. 31, *rc*). The centre of the former is

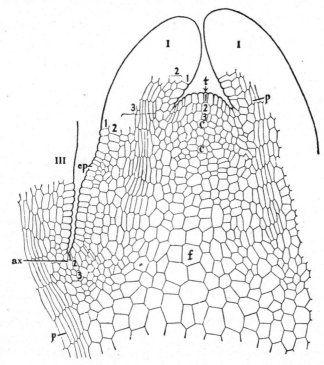

Fig. 30. Longitudinal section of growing apex of *Vinca minor* (after Schmidt). I, III, leaves of two nodes (decussate arrangement). *ax*, primordium of axillary bud; *c*, corpus; *ep*, epidermis; *f*, file meristem; *p*, procambium; *t*, tunica; 1, 2, 3, successive layers of same.

occupied by one or more, somewhat larger, cells (c, c_1) which undergo only occasional divisions but probably replenish the smaller, actively dividing cells producing the main tissues of the root. These cells form an arc-shaped group (c, pe), in which it is usually possible to distinguish separate initials, giving rise to the central vascular cylinder (p), the cortex, and the surface-layer (d) of the young root respectively.[1] The root-cap (rc) may be derived solely

[1] The undifferentiated regions are here often described as plerome, periblem and dermatogen respectively, terms formerly applied also to the regions beneath the apical meristems of shoots. The impossibility of defining them accurately has, however, led to their being abandoned in stems.

from a separate row of initials (calyptrogen) or partly by tangential (periclinal) division of those forming the surface-layer of the root (Fig. 31).

At the base of the internode in Grasses, and at the top of the internode in Labiatæ, occur intercalary meristems, which consist of a transverse plate of small meristematic cells in which no definite regions can be distinguished.

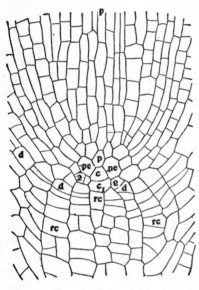

FIG. 31. Longitudinal section through root-apex of *Althæa rosea* (after v. Guttenberg). c, c_1, central cells; d, dermatogen; p, vascular region; pe, initials of cortical region; rc, cells of root-cap; 2, derivatives of pe.

During *cell-division* [1] the nucleus always takes the lead and divides into two daughter-nuclei; after this, division of the cytoplasm usually ensues and a *septum* separates the two new cells. Sometimes the nucleus merely divides by a median constriction, but such direct nuclear division (*amitosis*) is quite exceptional and usually confined to ageing cells. More usually there is a sequence of complex changes during nuclear division spoken of as *mitosis*.[2] All stages are often visible in thin longitudinal sections through the meristems of Flowering Plants (cf. Fig. 32), but in order to observe them readily, it is necessary to employ carefully preserved and suitably stained material (Appendix IV). The phase-contrast microscope, which makes it possible to observe the changes in living cells, shows that they are not artefacts.

The nucleus is usually spheroidal (Fig. 24, B, N) or ellipsoidal (Fig. 35, C) in form and, when not dividing, is spoken of as the *resting* or *metabolic nucleus*; the former term, though widely used, is misleading, since it is improbable that such a nucleus is inactive. Living unstained nuclei often appear almost homogeneous, apart from the nuclear membrane, the structureless nucleoli (p. 40), and

---

[1] For details, see C. D. Darlington, *Recent Advances in Plant Cytology*, J. & A. Churchill, 3rd edit., 1937 (671 pp.); and L. W. Sharp, *Introduction to Cytology*, 3rd edit., McGraw-Hill Book Co., 1934 (567 pp.).

[2] The term *karyokinesis* is now rarely employed.

scattered glistening granules. Sometimes, however, a number of fine coiled threads are just distinguishable in the nuclear sap. These are no doubt identical with the *chromosomes*, which become much more evident during division. In the resting nucleus they

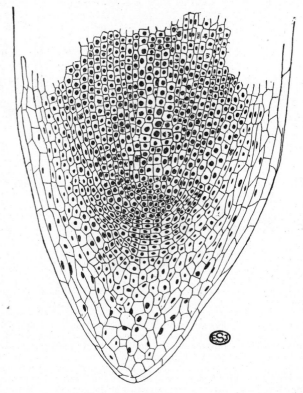

FIG. 32. Root-tip of *Scilla* in longitudinal section showing the meristem and the root-cap. Some of the nuclei (black) exhibit phases in nuclear division.

are usually so highly hydrated that they are invisible, having about the same refractive index as the nuclear sap. The irregular network, with deeply staining granules (chromatin), obtained in stained preparations (Fig. 35, C), is probably an artefact. The marked dehydration, that occurs during early mitosis, leads to rapid contraction of the chromosomes and renders them far less susceptible to change under the influence of preserving fluids so that, with careful fixation and staining, fairly true pictures of the condition in life are probably obtained. The nucleoli stain deeply with basic dyes, while the nuclear sap remains unstained.

The early stages of nuclear division, constituting *prophase,* are relatively prolonged. The first change is that the artificial network referred to above is replaced by a number of thin double strands (Fig. 33, A), the chromosomes. These are always quite separate from one another, as soon as they are recognisable. Each is split

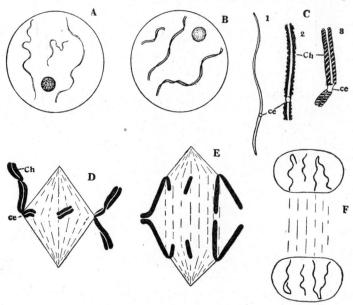

FIG. 33. Diagrams to illustrate mitosis in a haploid nucleus containing three chromosomes. [The normal vegetative nucleus of higher plants is diploid and contains each kind of chromosome in duplicate.] A, Early prophase; each chromosome a double thread. B, Late prophase; the chromatids are thicker, the nucleolus less chromatic. C, 1–3, Diagrammatic representation of a chromosome at successive stages during prophase; in 2 and 3 showing spiralisation. D, Metaphase; chromosomes attached at the equator of the spindle by their centromeres. E, Anaphase; sister chromosomes (the chromatids of the prophase) passing to the poles. F, Telophase; a nuclear membrane has appeared and the chromosomes are becoming decreasingly chromatic. *ce,* centromere; *ch,* chromatid.

(Fig. 33, C, 1) into two closely apposed threads, the *chromatids (ch),* except at one (the *centromere, ce*) or sometimes also at other points (*constrictions*); these consist of unstainable substance, but the rest of each chromatid is uniformly stained. Later the constrictions appear like ligatures in the thickening chromosomes (Fig. 33, B). The bead-like structure, often seen in the latter during prophase in reproductive cells (p. 590), is not usually recognisable in vegetative cells. In the later stages of prophase the split chromosomes shorten (Fig. 33, C) and stain more readily. Finally they are probably only one-tenth to one-twentieth as long as in the earliest stages.

During thickening nucleic acid accumulates in the protein framework of the chromosomes and probably combines with it to form *nucleoproteins*. The nucleic acid is derived from nucleotides, complex organic substances containing phosporus which are abundant in the cytoplasm of cells undergoing mitosis. During prophase the nucleoli gradually stain less deeply (Fig. 33, B), and usually disappear completely before the next stage; perhaps they store some of the nucleotides. The shortening of the chromosomes during prophase is due partly to dehydration and partly to each chromatid becoming coiled in a close spiral (*spiralisation* Fig. 33, C, 2, 3), except where constrictions occur. Towards the end of prophase the chromosomes are commonly arranged on the inner surface of the nuclear membrane which disappears before *metaphase*.

During this stage, which is passed through rather rapidly, the nuclear sap is replaced by a comparatively rigid gelatinous structure, the *nuclear spindle*, shaped like two cones with a common base (Fig. 33, D; 35, A). In the living cell the spindle appears homogeneous, but in fixed material, probably owing to differential loss of water, it often exhibits striations extending from the two apices or poles towards the common base or equator. The striations are probably artificial clefts between longitudinal strands of less strongly hydrated material. The substance of the spindle is so firm that it can be moved as a whole within the fluid cytoplasm. Each chromosome appears attached to the equator of the spindle at a *fixed point* (Fig. 33, D), the *centromere* (spindle-attachment), which was already recognisable in prophase. The centromeres are believed to be directly concerned in forming the spindle.

When the section passes transversely through the equator of the spindle, the chromosomes, in which division into chromatids is now often scarcely perceptible, are seen lying at approximately equal distances. This assemblage, often termed the *metaphase plate* (Fig. 34), affords the easiest means of counting the chromosomes and of recognising their characteristics. The number may be small (Fig. 34, A) or large, but is nearly always uniform in all the *vegetative* cells of a species, constituting one of its most constant characters. The chromosomes may differ in length, in the position of the centromere and in the location and length of other constrictions, if present (Fig. 34, F–J). In certain chromosomes a long constriction (Fig. 34, F, J) separates a short, and usually more or less spherical, terminal part from the rest, such segments being termed *trabants* (satellites). Such chromosomes appear to play a rôle in the formation of nucleoli. Sometimes it is not too difficult to discriminate between the various chromosomes and to recognise that, as a general rule, each chromosome is represented twice (Fig. 34, A, D), although these *homologous chromosomes* often lie widely separated. Small chromosomes are completely embedded in the spindle, but in the longer ones only the centromeres are fixed, the free portions extending into the cytoplasm (Fig. 33, D).

The succeeding stage (*anaphase*) is characterised by the separation of the chromatids, which now repel one another (Fig. 33, E). Separation commences with the splitting of the centromere, whose halves diverge in opposite directions towards the poles and pull the

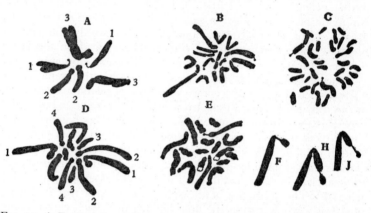

FIG. 34. A–E, Metaphase plates (from various sources). A, *Crepis capillaris*. B, *Crocus sativus* var. C, *C. tournefortii*. D, *Gasteria verrucosa*. E, *Muscari longipes*. F–J, various chromosomes; F, *Aconitum*; H, *Crepis tectorum*; J, *Ribes aureum*. In A and D homologous chromosomes are numbered (1–4).

remaining portions of the chromatids, now the daughter-chromosomes, behind them. According as the centromere is subterminal or median, the separating chromosomes appear **J**-shaped or **V**-shaped, while when the former is nearly terminal, they appear rod-shaped (Fig. 33, E). A pronounced lengthening of the middle of the spindle further separates the diverging chromosomes.

The equivalent halves (chromatids) of the parent-chromosomes thus form two widely separated groups near the spindle poles (Fig. 35, B), which soon become unrecognisable, although the intervening part often persists for a long time. In this final stage (*telophase*) a new nuclear membrane appears around each group of chromosomes, which gradually undergo changes, roughly the reverse of those occurring during prophase (Fig. 33, F). The spiral uncoils and marked lengthening and hydration take place so that the chromosomes lose their visual distinctness and stain less and less readily. When cell-divisions follow rapidly, the chromosomes may in early prophase still show remnants of the spiral of the previous division, but this disappears before the new chromatids undergo spiralisation in their turn. During telophase one or more nucleoli are organised in relation to specific chromosomes (nucleolar organisers), provided with trabants. Two resting nuclei are thus formed, each with the same number of chromosomes as the parent-nucleus. All the vegetative cells [1] thus possess nuclei with an identical chromosome-complement.

As the daughter-nuclei are reconstituted, a diaphragm of modified cytoplasm (the *cell-plate*), at first perhaps of the nature of a semi-fluid film, appears in the equatorial plane and gradually

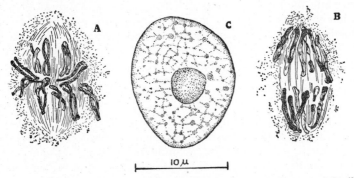

FIG. 35. A, metaphase and B, anaphase in *Vicia faba* (after Fraser and Snell); C, *Alstrœmeria aurantiaca*, resting nucleus (original, Prof. Jane).

extends across the cell dividing the protoplast into two. Deposition of calcium pectate and other substances in this film leads to the formation of a thin membrane, the *middle lamella*, separating the daughter-cells and traversed by fine protoplasmic connections, some of which persist even in the adult plant. Soon further layers, consisting largely of cellulose, are deposited on either side of the original membrane (see p. 63), which is the only part of this separating wall common to the two cells. These additional layers frequently undergo chemical change, but the middle lamella (Figs. 37, 38, *m.l.*) is usually less subject to modification, so that it can be distinguished by its different density, and frequent deeper staining.[2]

When cell-division takes place, therefore, the nuclei of the daughter-cells are derived from that of the parent cell. This fact holds generally throughout the Vegetable and Animal Kingdoms, the nucleus of any given cell always being the product of a pre-existing one. The origin of a new nucleus from the cytoplasm is

[1] For details of nuclear division in reproductive cells, see p. 590.
[2] The separating wall in many Algæ arises as an ingrowing diaphragm (Fig. 183, E, p. 285), and is not always directly related to nuclear division.

unknown. In like manner it is probable that chloroplasts (and other plastids) multiply by division and are derived from pre-existing specialised cytoplasmic bodies. During the enlargement usually following upon cell-division considerable increase of the cytoplasm takes place; but it should be emphasised that new protoplasm is only formed in connection with a pre-existing protoplast, the independent origin of living matter being unknown. In other words, both in the Animal and Vegetable Kingdoms, one generation is merely a continuation of the previous one, the reproductive cells of any one dividing and enlarging to form the body of the next.

We can now consider how the products of the meristem pass over into the mature condition. Most of the polyhedral cells just below the apex have dense cytoplasmic contents, prominent deeply staining nuclei (Fig. 32), and fit closely together without interspaces. A little farther back, representing a maturer phase, they increase appreciably in size and often round off somewhat so that small *intercellular spaces* (Fig. 56, *i.p.*) appear between them, particularly at the angles. Where increase in size involves considerable elongation, the cells may slide by one another (*gliding growth*).

The increase in volume of the cells is largely due to intake of water, which results from the formation of substances that increase the osmotic potential or aid in imbibition. Such substances are produced during the metabolic processes going on in the cells, and, as a consequence of their solution, a number of small vacuoles containing cell-sap appear in the cytoplasm (vacuolisation). Water (so-called *imbibition-water*) also permeates the protoplasm and cell-wall. The vacuoles gradually increase in size, and ultimately coalesce to form one (Figs. 24, 25) or few large ones. Not all the cells at the same horizontal level necessarily undergo these changes simultaneously and, even after vacuolisation, some may retain the capacity for division for some little time. As they mature, however, this capacity is generally lost, though it may be regained through special stimulation, as when a plant is wounded.

The growth of any plant is thus mainly the outcome of multiplication of cells at its meristems, their subsequent increase in volume leading both to a lengthening and gradual widening of the tissues. As they reach maturity the new units mostly become specialised to serve diverse needs, but those which have not undergone profound modification, often retain also the power of division and capacity to develop in different ways as the demands of the organism may dictate. It is the visible enlargement of plants that is popularly spoken of as growth, but in reality this involves the three phases of cell-division, enlargement, and the final differentiation which will form the subject-matter of the next chapter.

CHAPTER VII

THE DIFFERENTIATION OF PLANT-CELLS

FOUR principal types of element [1] are found in vegetable tissues. In herbaceous plants much of the body consists of cells which usually appear rounded or polygonal in transverse sections, and commonly contain a living protoplast. In longitudinal sections they are often rectangular in form, seldom more than two or three times as long as broad, and provided with square or rounded ends (cf. Fig. 84). Such cells, described as *parenchymatous*, frequently have thin walls, and often form extensive tissues known as *parenchyma*.

In contrast to this type are other cells, termed *prosenchymatous*, in which the length greatly exceeds the breadth, such elements being found more particularly in the mechanical and conducting tissues. These cells usually have pointed ends and thickened walls (Fig. 39, C, D), and the width, as seen in transverse section, is commonly small as compared with that of a parenchymatous element (Fig. 39, B). Occasionally forms of cells are encountered which are transitional between these two types.

The elements of the third type are of quite a different character, and are termed *vessels* (Fig. 40). They are the principal water-conducting structures in the wood of Flowering Plants, possess no living contents when mature, and their longitudinal walls are thickened in various ways (p. 67). In the mature condition they appear as long wide tubes or cylinders, but they are actually derived from vertical rows of cells by the more or less complete breaking down of all cross-walls. Perforated septa thus occur at intervals in the course of the vessel, and in woody plants are often obliquely radial with reference to the organ as a whole. The cross-walls may almost entirely disappear (as in the Maple and Oak, Fig. 40, F), but most commonly a distinct rim persists, only the central part being absorbed (*e.g.* the Lime or the Poplar, Fig. 40, E). In still

---

[1] These, and the various modifications described in the present chapter, are most easily studied by teasing out (*i.e.* tearing to pieces with a pair of needles) small portions of a Celery-stalk or Marrow-stem that have been previously boiled for some time in water; the middle lamellæ are thereby dissolved, so that the individual cells readily separate from one another.

other instances the walls break down in such a way that a number of cross-bars remain (*e.g.* the Alder, Fig. 40, D). The original cells are called vessel-segments.

The elements of the fourth type serve for conduction of elaborated food-materials. They are known as *sieve-tubes,*[1] and are located in the phloem, a tissue that in most stems lies just outside the wood. The sieve-tubes, like the vessels, are derived

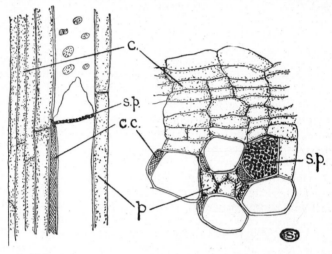

FIG. 36. Phloem-structure of the Vegetable Marrow (*Cucurbita*), in longitudinal (left) and transverse (right) sections. *c.,* cambium; *c.c.,* companion cells; *p,* phloem parenchyma; *s.p.,* sieve-plate.

from vertical rows of cells whose cross-walls are perforated by a large number of fine pores through which the protoplasts of the adjacent segments remain connected. They retain their living contents in the mature condition, and the membranes remain relatively thin (Fig. 36). When the cross-walls are seen from the surface they present the appearance of a sieve, the meshes of which constitute the pores; these walls are spoken of as *sieve-plates* (Fig. 36, *s.p.*).

Before the sieve-plates are fully developed each cell divides longitudinally into two unequal portions. The larger constitutes a segment of the sieve-tube whose nucleus is stated generally to degenerate, whilst the smaller, which retains its nucleus, forms a so-called *companion cell* (Fig. 36, *c.c.*). Sometimes two, or even three, companion cells may be produced before the nucleus of the

[1] See also p. 139. Sieve-tubes of a different type occur in Ferns and Gymnosperms (pp. 372, 412).

sieve-tube segment dies away. The narrow companion cells have dense granular contents in contrast to the wider sieve-tubes, which possess but a thin lining layer of cytoplasm and a large central vacuole, features by which they are often readily recognised in transverse sections.

Behind the meristem the cells have been seen to exhibit a steady increase in size until they attain full dimensions. During the phase of enlargement the walls undergo no appreciable thickening, but surface growth takes place. This is probably accomplished by stretching of the plastic membrane and intercalation of new particles of cell-wall substance between those already present. When fully grown, more or less marked *thickening of the wall* occurs, successive layers formed by the agency of the living protoplast being deposited on the inner surface. Subsequently the wall often undergoes considerable chemical changes, as a result of which it may become more or less impermeable to water, so that the contained protoplast dies. When the thickening is at all conspicuous, the successive layers generally appear more or less distinct (Fig. 37, D; 39, B). This *stratification* is due to the fact that the layers adjacent to one another are of unequal density.

As a general rule the thickening is not uniform over the whole inner surface of the wall, small areas commonly remaining thin (Fig. 37, A). The intimate relation between adjacent cells is evidenced by the fact that such thin areas, interrupting the layers formed by the protoplast of one cell, coincide with the thin areas on the outer sides of its walls, where no thickening has been deposited by the protoplasts of the surrounding cells. In these areas, known as *simple pits*, the original middle lamella (the *pit-membrane*, Fig. 37, A, *pm.*) alone separates the adjacent cells. The majority of the protoplasmic connections (cf. p. 59) pass through these pit-membranes.

Good examples of simple pits are seen in sections of Elder pith (Fig. 37, B). In surface view they appear as more transparent oval or elliptical areas which are irregularly scattered (*Ps.*). In section (*p.*) the walls appear broken at sundry points; but careful focussing shows that the apparent gaps are really bridged by a thin line, the pit-membrane. In the endosperm of the Date (Fig. 37, A), the cotyledon-walls of the Lupine and many other Leguminosæ, and cells of the cortex of the Mistletoe, the thickening is so extreme that the cavity of the cell becomes much reduced, and the pits then appear as deep depressions within the wall. It is in such tissues that the protoplasmic connections between cell and cell can most readily be demonstrated.

The thick-walled elements of the plant are of considerable

mechanical importance, since they form skeletal tissues which
are mostly devoid of intercellular spaces. When such mechanical
elements occur in young growing organs, where too great a rigidity

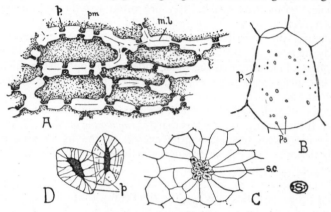

FIG. 37. Thickened cell-walls. A, Portion of the endosperm of the Date
(*Phœnix*) in section. B, Pith-cell of the Elder. C, A group of stone-cells of
the Pear, together with a small part of the adjacent flesh. D, Two isolated
stone-cells. *m.l.*, middle lamella; *p.*, pits seen in section; *pm.*, pit-membrane;
Ps., pits in surface view; *s.c.*, stone-cells.

is disadvantageous, they take the form of *collenchyma* which differs
from other strengthening tissues in the fact that its cells are living.
Collenchyma is frequent immediately beneath the epidermis in

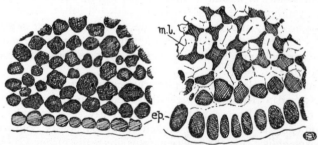

FIG. 38. Collenchymatous tissue from the stems of the Burdock (*Arctium*)
(left) and Dead Nettle (*Lamium*) (right). *ep.*, epidermis; *m.l.*, middle lamella.
Both in transverse section. The cell-contents are shaded.

young stems (Fig. 80, A, *s*), in the midribs of young leaves (Fig. 98,
M), and in the adult stems of some herbs. In its most typical form it
is characterised by extreme thickening of the corners of the cells,
as seen in transverse section (Fig. 38), the thickened angles appearing
bright and shining owing to their highly refractive character.

Sometimes, however, collenchyma exhibits uniformly thickened walls, interrupted only by pits. The thickening, unlike that of most mechanical elements, is practically unaltered *cellulose*, which possesses considerable stretching power, so that collenchyma is well suited to act as a support in young growing organs (cf. p. 67).

All cellulose-walls [1] are extensible and, moreover, readily permeable to water and many substances in solution. Cellulose is a polysaccharide (p. 76), with a molecule consisting of a straight chain of numerous anhydrous glucose groups linked through oxygen atoms. These chains are aggregated into bundles (micellæ), which are united by a colloidal matrix and, according to one view, form a three-dimensional lattice-work. Cellulose-walls are scarcely coloured by iodine, but treatment with strong sulphuric acid causes swelling and ultimate solution, one of the products then giving a blue colour with iodine. Other tests for such walls are the blue colour and swelling produced by chlor-zinc-iodide and their solution by ammoniated copper oxide (Appendix V). Hæmatoxylin (Appendix IV) colours cellulose-walls deep purple.[2]

The remaining mechanical elements form tissues termed *sclerenchyma*, distinguished from collenchyma by a chemical change of the thickened walls known as *lignification*, in consequence of which the cell-contents ultimately die. Such lignified walls are much harder and stronger than those consisting of cellulose. They possess relatively little plasticity, and when wet are not readily permeable to water and practically impermeable to air. Substances, collectively spoken of as lignin, are deposited in, or chemically combined with, the cellulose framework and cause marked differences in reaction. Thus, such walls are insoluble in cuprammonia, whilst the lignin is dissolved by Eau de Javelle (Appendix V) and also by sodium sulphite. Iodine solution stains lignified walls brown, and a similar colouration is obtained with chlor-zinc-iodide. Aniline chloride, or sulphate, which does not colour cellulose-walls, yields a brilliant yellow colouration and, as it does not stain starch, is particularly useful when that substance is present. An alcoholic solution of phloroglucin, followed by strong hydrochloric acid, produces a scarlet colouration. Lignified walls stain yellow or brown with hæmatoxylin, and are deeply stained by gentian violet, which is effective in combination with Bismarck brown, the wood and other sclerenchyma becoming violet and the ordinary cell-walls brown.

There are two principal types of sclerenchymatous elements,

---

[1] See R. D. Preston, *The Molecular Architecture of Plant Cell Walls*. Chapman & Hall, 1952 (223 pp.).

[2] Mingled with the cellulose in many plant-cells, especially those of succulent fruits and storage roots, are pectic substances which are soluble in water.

viz. stone-cells and fibres; of these the former are more or less parenchymatous, the latter prosenchymatous in shape. The gritty character of the flesh of some Pears is due to *stone-cells* which, in a thin section, can be seen to occur as little clusters (Fig. 37, C) irregularly scattered through the thin-walled parenchyma forming the flesh. The cavity of each stone-cell is very much reduced and inconspicuous owing to the strong thickening of the wall (Fig. 37, C and D, *s.c.*). This shows distinct stratification, and is traversed by a number of dark lines (*p.*) radiating from the centre and branching as they approach the surface. These are the pits which serve for the transference of nourishment to the protoplast during the process of thickening, on the completion of which the living matter dies.

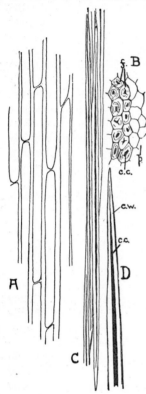

FIG. 39. Collenchyma of Dead Nettle stem in longitudinal section (A), and fibres from the stem of the Hop in transverse (B) and longitudinal sections (C, D). *c.c.*, cell cavity; *c.w.*, cell-wall; *f*, fibres; *p*, parenchyma.

The *fibre* is a narrow, very much elongated, cell with tapering pointed ends, and in the adult condition its protoplast is frequently dead. The walls are in general strongly thickened and lignified (Fig. 39, B–D), and usually bear a number of oblique slit-shaped pits. In the mature plant fibres are generally the most important form of mechanical element, being frequently present in the cortex and composing a large proportion of the wood of thicker branches (cf. p. 175). The cortex in the young stems of many woody plants exhibits a continuous mechanical ring composed of alternating groups of fibres and stone-cells.

Plant-fibres can undergo some elongation and can bear heavy stresses without losing the power of resuming their original length; loads as great as 14 to 25 kilogrammes per square millimetre are required to produce permanent lengthening. The powers of fibres in this respect may be compared with those of metal rods (*e.g.* of wrought iron and steel) which, whilst they become permanently stretched under similar stresses, exhibit far less extension before the limit of their elasticity is reached. Fibres will thus permit bending on the part of a plant-organ (under the influence of the wind, for example), and will not give way, even under considerable stress; moreover, their elasticity will bring about a return to the normal position as soon as the stress is relieved. Whilst the breaking stress (10–12 kg. per sq. mm.) for collenchyma is not much less than for many fibres, it exhibits permanent elongation under quite low tension, so that it is especially suited to the mechanical needs of a growing organ where constant extension is taking place.

Owing to their great strength, fibres of sufficient length for spinning are used for the manufacture of textiles, rope, etc. They are usually prepared from herbaceous plants by removing the softer tissues or allowing them to rot away. Important fibre-yielding plants [1] are the Flax (*Linum usitatissimum*), in which the fibres may attain a length of over 50 mm., New Zealand Flax (*Phormium tenax*), Hemp (*Cannabis sativa*), and Jute (species of *Corchorus*, mainly cultivated in Bengal). Manila hemp used for high quality ropes is obtained from the leaves of a Banana (*Musa*) cultivated in the Philippines, while Sisal hemp is made from the fibres of a species of *Agave*. Coir, used mainly for matting, etc., is derived from the Coconut, whilst Raffia-tape or bast is obtained from the Palm *Raphia*.[2] Moreover, fibres treated in various ways are the source of wood-pulp and other paper-making materials.

The main function of *vessels* (Fig. 40) is water-conduction, but they also assist in mechanical support on account of their thick walls. These are necessitated by the frequent existence of negative (reduced) pressures (p. 203) in the conducting tracts, such as obtain, for instance, when transpiration is active. At these times collapse of the vessels, under the positive pressure exerted by the surrounding elements, is prevented by the rigidity of the vessel-walls. The type of thickening varies greatly, depending largely on whether the vessel is formed in a part of the plant that is still growing or in one that is mature. In the former the thickening must admit of stretching of the wall, which would otherwise be ruptured.

The first-formed vessels of the wood (*protoxylem*), which differentiate a short distance behind the meristem, exhibit continuous spirals or disconnected rings of thickening (*spiral* and *annular* vessels, Fig. 40, A, B). These are deposited on the inner side of the original vessel-wall, to which, however, they are often

---

[1] Regarding economic plants, see R. Good, *Plants and Human Economics*, Cambridge University Press, 1933 (202 pp.); J. M. Hector, *Introduction to the Botany of Field Crops*, 2 vols., Central News Agency, Johannesburg, 1936; H. S. Redgrove, *Spices and Condiments*, Pitman & Sons, 1933; F. N. Howes, *Nuts*, Faber & Faber, 1948; also the work of Lindley and Moore, cited on p. 609.

[2] Regarding cotton, see p. 159.

only attached by a narrow connection, as can be seen in optical section (Fig. 40, C). As the organ elongates the spirals are drawn out like a spring, and the rings become more widely separated, by the gradual stretching of the unthickened part of the wall. If, however, growth in length is very considerable (as, for instance, in many Monocotyledons and aquatics), complete rupture may ultimately take place, so that in the mature plant only an irregular

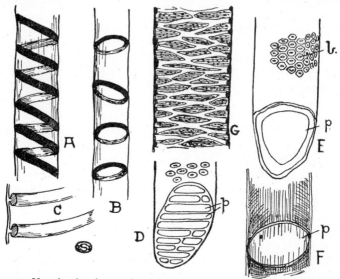

FIG. 40. Vessels showing various types of thickening and perforation. A, spiral; B, annular; C, portion of A in longitudinal section showing attachment of thickening to wall; D, end of vessel of Alder (*Alnus*) showing ladder-like perforation; E, vessel of Poplar (*Populus*); F, vessel of Oak (*Quercus*); G, reticulate vessel of Marrow (*Cucurbita*). *b.*, bordered pit; *p.*, perforations between segments of vessel.

canal remains to indicate where the protoxylem was situated (Fig. 85, A, *P.c.*).

The vessels formed after completion of growth often exhibit *reticulate* thickening (Fig. 40, G), which appears as a more or less irregular network of ridges deposited on the inner side of the original wall. Careful examination shows that the meshes of this reticulum often possess the characters of bordered pits.

Such *bordered pits* are common on the vessels in the later-formed wood. An examination of the surface of the vessel-wall under the high power of the microscope shows that each pit is provided with a broad *border* (Fig. 40, E, *b.*; also Fig. 41, B, *b*). This is either circular in outline, or more commonly polygonal when the pits are crowded, the actual aperture of the pit appearing round (Fig. 41, B, *p*) or more or less slit-shaped. In section the border is recognised as a dome-shaped cover formed by the thickening of the wall, which around the pit arches away from the middle lamella (*i.e.* pit-membrane); the top of this low dome is perforated by the aperture leading into the pit (cf. also Fig. 280, D, p. 413). Where two vessels adjoin one another, such a perforated dome

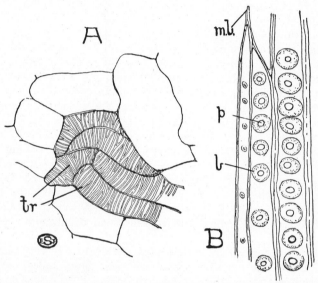

FIG. 41. Tracheids. A, Spiral type, from the leaf of Dog's Mercury (*Mercurialis*). B, Bordered-pitted, from the stem of the Scot's Fir (*Pinus*). *b*, border of bordered pit; *m.l.*, middle lamella; *p*, aperture of bordered pit; *tr.*, tracheids.

occurs on either side of the common wall, so that these bordered pits coincide. The pit-membrane may possess a central thickened area (*torus*) which, owing to its modified character, is impervious alike to air and water.

When the pit-membrane, which is easily displaced, is forced to one side or the other, the torus closes up the aperture of the dome, and thereby any passage of water or of air from one vessel to the other is prevented. Such displacement will occur when the pressure in one vessel differs from that in the adjacent one, so that the bordered pits operate as safety-valves whereby differences of pressure in the wood become localised.

The conduction of water in the higher plants is mainly effected by means of vessels, but another kind of conducting element, the *tracheid*, which is likewise dead, is also found in the wood of thicker branches and, more commonly, in leaves. Each tracheid is formed from a *single* cell which is more or less elongated in form, and usually bears bordered pits (Fig. 41, B) or spiral thickening (Fig. 41, A). The wood of the Fir and other Conifers is entirely made up of long tracheids, similar in appearance to fibres, but bearing pronounced bordered pits (Fig. 41, B). Very narrow bordered pits appearing as oblique slits are not uncommon in wood fibres.

The walls of mature cells often undergo chemical changes other than lignification, some of which (*e.g.* the change affecting the cells of the cork, p. 186) will be described later, but a few special instances may conclude the present chapter. In a number of plants the thickening of the walls of certain cells takes the form of layers of *mucilage* of varying chemical constitution. These, in the dry condition, are hard and horny, but in the presence of moisture they soften and swell up considerably. Indeed, such mucilaginous walls possess a remarkable power of absorbing and holding water, and are particularly prevalent in plants characteristic of dry situations. The slimy character of many Seaweeds is due to the mucilaginous nature of nearly all the cell-walls, and here the change in bulk, as between the dry and wet condition, is especially evident. Mucilaginous walls stain deeply and rapidly with aniline blue.

The *gums* formed by certain plants are probably very similar chemically to the mucilages, and, like them, often appear to arise as a result of chemical alteration of the cell-wall. Diverse species of *Acacia* yield gums of economic importance, *e.g.* gum arabic (from *A. senegal*), catechu used in tanning (from *A. catechu*), etc.; gum tragacanth, which is far less soluble, is obtained from species of *Astragalus*.

Another frequent modification consists in the deposition of mineral substances within the cell-wall. For example, in the Horsetails (*Equisetum*) and most Grasses the membranes of the outer cells are impregnated with silica, to which many Grass-leaves owe their sharp cutting edges. This *silicification* increases the stability of the plant and also serves as a protection against snails, etc. A siliceous envelope is very characteristic of certain minute unicellular Algæ known as Diatoms (cf. p. 294).

Sometimes the surface of the plant is encrusted with carbonate of lime, as in some Stoneworts (*Chara*) and certain other lowly members of the Vegetable Kingdom (cf. p. 292). Local deposits of lime on special ingrowths of the walls are not uncommon in the epidermal cells in certain Flowering Plants. The resulting structures are known as *cystoliths*, and are well seen in the leaves of the Stinging Nettle (Fig. 42, *C*) and of various kinds of Fig (*e.g.* in *Ficus elastica*). If sections of the leaves are placed in weak acetic acid, the carbonate of lime dissolves with effervescence and the framework of the cystolith becomes visible.

In the mature plant the different types of elements are grouped

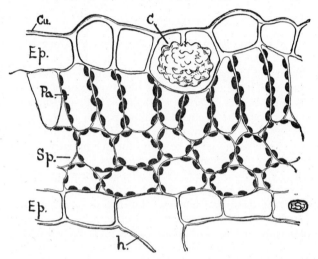

FIG. 42. Transverse section of the leaf of a Nettle (*Urtica*) showing a cystolith (*C*). *Cu.*, Cuticle; *Ep.*, epidermis; *h*, hair; *Pa.*, palisade tissue; *Sp.*, spongy parenchyma.

together to form *tissues* subserving diverse functions. Thus, for instance, one tissue, which is always superficial and has the general function of protecting the underlying parts, constitutes the epidermis. The vascular tissues, comprising the wood or xylem and the phloem, form the principal conducting systems for water and mineral salts, and for elaborated food-substances, whilst others —largely parenchymatous in character—go to form the general matrix or ground tissue. It must not be supposed, however, that, because there is one general function, the component elements of these and other tissues are necessarily uniform in character.

CHAPTER VIII

FOOD-RESERVES AND ENZYMES

APART from the living constituents, cells usually contain numerous substances which are either dissolved in the sap or, when insoluble, occur as solid bodies or suspended drops. These substances can for the most part be grouped as food-bodies or as by-products, according as they are known to be employed in the nutrition of the plant or are supposed to be of no further nutritive value.

Among the commoner *food-substances*[1] are various carbohydrates (*e.g.* sugars, starch, etc.), oils, and proteins, all of which have been built up by the plant from simple inorganic compounds by a series of complex changes. During the earlier part of the season such food-substances are used directly to supply the necessary materials for growth, but subsequently, with decreasing demands, a large proportion are stored up for future use. In perennial herbs they accumulate in those organs which persist from year to year (*e.g.* bulbs, tubers, etc.), whilst in woody perennials they are stored in the stem- and root-systems (see p. 226). Similar food-substances are, moreover, laid up within the cotyledons or endosperm of all seeds. Carbohydrates are organic compounds built up of the elements carbon, hydrogen and oxygen, the last two being present in the same ratio as in water. Oils have an analogous composition but contain proportionately less oxygen. Proteins are far more complex containing, in addition to carbon, hydrogen and oxygen, the elements nitrogen and sulphur.

One of the most important food-substances is *starch*, which is insoluble in the cell-sap and is often the first easily recognisable product of photosynthesis. On microscopic examination the starch appears as very small shining grains, mainly within the chloroplasts (Fig. 26, *St.*). These grains gradually increase in amount during the day, but generally disappear over-night, and are consequently spoken of as *transitory starch*. Their gradual accumulation on a bright day is due to the conversion of the soluble sugars, produced more rapidly than they can be removed, into insoluble starch. In

---

[1] For reference-books, see p. 97.

darkness, when photosynthesis ceases, the accumulated starch is changed back into sugar and transferred to other parts of the plant.

In contradistinction to this transitory starch, that which accumulates in storage-organs usually takes the form of rather large grains which originate within colourless plastids, known as *leucoplasts*. The latter occur in those cells which are not exposed to light, and differ from chloroplasts only in the absence of chlorophyll, which is generally not produced in darkness. Leucoplasts, however, readily change to chloroplasts. When a Potato-tuber, for instance, is exposed to light, it turns green through the formation of chlorophyll within the leucoplasts. Large starch-grains may actually be produced within green plastids (*e.g.* in a greenhouse plant, *Pellionia*), and these provide particularly appropriate material for studying the mode of formation of the grains.

In a transverse section of the stem of *Pellionia* the outermost cells (Fig. 43, *a*) are seen to contain chloroplasts (*ch.*), in some of which there is a bright shining dot, the transitory starch-grain (*s*). The larger starch-grains, seen nearer the centre in various stages of development, may be supposed to have originated likewise, as small bodies within the chloroplasts there situated (Fig. 43, *b*). But in the mature condition these grains have enlarged to such an extent that the enveloping chloroplasts appear merely as green caps to one side of them (Fig. 43, *c*, *ch.*).

The large starch-grains that can be scraped out of a Potato are more suitable for the study of details of structure. Examined in a drop of water, each shows a number of asymmetrical layers arranged around the darker *hilum*, or point of origin (Fig. 43, *d*). This stratification indicates the manner of growth of the starch-grain, the successive layers, often rather faint, being distinguished by different kinds of chemical constituents. In the grains of the Potato (Fig. 43, *d*) and *Pellionia* (Fig. 43, *c*) the point of origin is towards one end (*excentric* type). On the other hand, the hilum, in those from the cotyledons of the Pea or Bean, lies in the centre (*centric* type, Fig. 43, *f* and *g*), and the layers are arranged symmetrically around it. The dry grains of Pea, Bean, etc., exhibit a number of radiating cracks, which appear as dark irregular lines (Fig. 43, *g*); these seem to be due to the drying up of some of the imbibed water which permeates the substance of all starch-grains.

Whilst most of the grains of Potato-starch show but a single hilum, an occasional one will be found to possess two or three, each with its own system of layers (Fig. 43, *e*). This results from the development of several grains within the same leucoplast, growth of each occurring independently until they meet; deposition of starch sometimes continues with the formation of layers common to the whole group (Fig. 43, *e*). Such structures are called *compound grains*. In many cereals numerous grains arise in

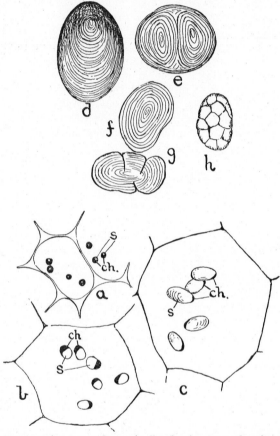

Fig. 43. Starch-grains. *a–c*, Stages in the development of grains within the chloroplasts of *Pellionia*; chloroplasts shown black. *ch.*, Chloroplasts; *s*, starch-grains; *d* and *e*, Potato starch; *f* and *g*, Pea starch; *h*, Compound starch-grain of Rice.

each leucoplast, so that the compound structure may even consist of numerous units. Thus a starch-grain of the Rice (Fig. 43, *h*) or Oat is marked out into a number of small areas, each representing a constituent unit.

Starch-grains consist of two polysaccharides (cf. p. 76), amylopectin and amylose, the former probably predominating in the inner and more highly refractive part of each of the successive layers of which the grain is composed. They may be separated by treatment with dilute caustic soda or by the action of enzymes (p. 83). Both consist of a large number of glucose units linked together through oxygen atoms (cf. cellulose, p. 65), but amylopectin has a larger and more complex molecule than that of amylose. With iodine the latter takes on a reddish colour by contrast to the deep blue assumed by amyopectin. When boiled with water starch-grains swell and provide a starch-paste or an opalescent "starch-solution," which is considered to be a solution of amylose thickened by a gelatinous suspension of amylopectin. This "solution" is colloidal in character (p. 50), and therefore will not diffuse through an organic membrane. Examination with X-rays shows the molecules of starch-grains to have a random distribution. Under polarised light they exhibit a black cross with the hilum as its centre. Comparatively few dyes colour starch, although gentian violet and eosin are notable exceptions.

The accumulation of starch-reserves by plants is a feature of the greatest economic importance, constituting as they do a very important article of human diet.[1] The cereals, the pulses, and Potatoes, all of which contain a high percentage of starch (cf. p. 83), furnish a sufficient illustration. Cereals [2] are the fruits of Grasses; of these the most widely consumed are Rice (*Oryza sativa*), Millet (*Pennisetum typhoideum, Sorghum, Panicum, Setaria*), and Maize (*Zea mais*), cultivated in tropical countries, whilst Wheat (*Triticum*), Oats (*Avena*), Barley (*Hordeum*), and Rye (*Secale cereale*) are grown in temperate climates. Tapioca is obtained from the root-tubers of the Cassava or Mandioc (*Manihot utilissima*, a member of the Spurge family, widely grown in the Tropics), whilst sago is the starch found in the pith of various Palms (mainly species of *Metroxylon*, cultivated in the Malay region), from which it is extracted after the appearance of the inflorescence. Buckwheat (*Fagopyrum*, Polygonaceae) is used as a chicken-food.

The wide distribution of starch as a form of storage of carbohydrate material can probably be related to its insoluble character, so that it does not affect the osmotic potential. The small amount of moisture in seeds renders them unsuited to the storage of soluble carbohydrates, and doubtless explains the frequent occurrence of starch in the endosperm and cotyledons. In succulent storage organs, on the other hand, soluble carbohydrates often occur. One of the most important is *inulin*, another of the complex polysaccharides, which has a molecular weight similar to that of amylose. It is owing to this that, in spite of its solubility and frequent high concentration, inulin has but little effect on the osmotic potential of the cells containing it (*cf.* p. 46).

Inulin is found especially in the Compositæ and the allied family of the Campanulaceæ, but also in the bulb of the Wild Hyacinth (*Scilla non-scripta*) and in other Monocotyledons. Soluble

[1] See the reference-books, listed on p. 67.
[2] Of these cereals there are many races in cultivation which differ not only as to their yield, their resistance to climatic extremes and to diseases, but also as to their properties. Thus some Wheats, grown chiefly in continental climates, produce a high proportion of gluten and yield "strong" flour.

carbohydrates of a similar chemical constitution are, moreover, encountered in many members of the latter group (*e.g.* the graminin of Grasses, the irisin of the Iris, etc.).

In a fresh tuber of the *Dahlia* or Jerusalem Artichoke (*Helianthus tuberosus*), the intact parenchymatous cells contain inulin dissolved in the sap. On placing relatively thick sections in spirit, the inulin is deposited as a finely granular precipitate. In material kept for some weeks in spirit, so that the latter has only penetrated slowly into the tissues, the inulin will be found as big spherical or lobed masses deposited on the cell-walls. These *sphere-crystals* (Fig. 44, *In.*) usually show concentric layers, whilst radial lines

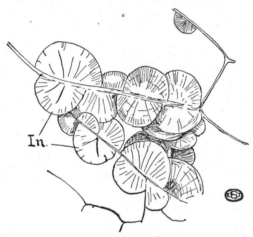

FIG. 44. Sphere-crystals of inulin (*In.*) in the cells of the tuberous root of a Dahlia.

traversing them indicate the numerous component needle-like units. On warming in water, the sphere-crystals of inulin readily dissolve. Sections treated with orcin (in alcohol), followed by concentrated sulphuric acid, acquire a deep orange-red colour.

Sugars are among the most important of the soluble carbohydrates present in plants. They possess much simpler molecules than the polysaccharides just considered, being either monosaccharides with the general formula $C_6H_{12}O_6$, or disaccharides with the formula $C_{12}H_{22}O_{11}$. Disaccharides and polysaccharides are so called since they respectively split up, under certain circumstances, into two or many molecules of monosaccharides.

Among the *monosaccharides* found in plants, the commonest are dextrose or glucose (popularly known as grape-sugar) and fructose or levulose (fruit-sugar), whilst of the *disaccharides* sucrose or saccharose (cane-sugar) and maltose (malt-sugar) deserve mention. Owing to their relatively simple molecules they induce a high osmotic potential, although for solutions of equal strength this is greater for monosaccharides than for disaccharides. For this reason no doubt grape-sugar and cane-sugar, the two which function as food-reserves, are only found in very minute quantities in seeds (except for the cane-sugar in the Sweet Corn, a variety of Maize). On the other hand, grape-sugar is one of the principal carbohydrate-reserves in the bulb of the Onion, whilst cane-sugar occurs in the Sugar Beet (*Beta*), in the pith of the stem of the Sugar Cane (*Saccharum officinarum*), and in the Sugar Maple (*Acer saccharinum*) (see p. 177). The sugar is extracted from the sliced Beet with the aid of warm water, whilst in the Sugar Cane the juice is crushed out of the canes with the help of rollers. In both the crude sugar is subjected to subsequent processes of refinement. The impure uncrystallisable residue is known as molasses.

Fructose is most abundant in succulent fruits, and is an important constituent of nectar; in both, however, it is mixed with, usually smaller amounts of, grape and cane sugars. Such sugars are, of course, not of the nature of food-reserves, but serve a biological purpose in connection with seed-dispersal and pollination.

All the four sugars above mentioned are found in foliage-leaves, though in proportions that vary greatly both during the day and night and at different seasons of the year. By the use of isotopes it has now been established that sucrose is the first free sugar to be formed in photosynthesis. Fructose is produced earlier, but only as an ester (fructose diphosphate), not at first as a free sugar. Maltose and glucose, like the transitory starch, are secondary products. *Maltose* may frequently be formed during the breakdown of starch for utilisation within the plant and is found not only in foliage-leaves, but in germinating Barley (malt) [1] and other starch-containing seeds.

Cane-sugar is readily split (in the presence of water, so-called hydrolysis) into two molecules of monosaccharide by boiling the solution with a few drops of some mineral acid (*e.g.* hydrochloric acid); one molecule of glucose and one of fructose are obtained, the mixture being known as *invert sugar*. Cane-sugar is similarly converted into invert sugar by the agency of an enzyme *invertase* found in most plants. In the same way the polysaccharides above discussed can be split up with the formation of disaccharides or

---

[1] The malt is obtained by allowing moistened Barley to germinate at a moderate temperature, after which the latter is raised so as to kill off the Barley, the conversion of starch into sugar continuing through the agency of enzymes (see below).

monosaccharides, as the case may be. For instance, a starch "solution" boiled with a few drops of a mineral acid becomes clearer, and the ordinary reaction to iodine gradually disappears; the colour assumed with this reagent is now reddish, owing to the presence of simpler polysaccharides known as *dextrins*. If the boiling be continued, the whole of the starch "solution" ultimately breaks down into glucose. Similarly inulin gives rise to fructose. In the plant starch and inulin are acted upon by enzymes, *diastase* and *inulase* respectively, which effect like changes, except that diastase breaks down starch into the disaccharide maltose, which in its turn is acted upon by an enzyme *maltase* with the production of two molecules of glucose.

The sugars are readily distinguished from one another by certain characteristic reactions. Thus glucose, fructose, and maltose all reduce Fehling's solution (which contains cupric oxide, Appendix V) with the formation of a red precipitate of cuprous oxide, and are consequently known as reducing sugars. Sucrose, on the other hand, is a non-reducing sugar, giving no precipitate with Fehling's solution, until it has been inverted by boiling or enzyme-action. It may be added that neither inulin nor the dextrins effect reduction of this reagent.

For microchemical purposes, especially when but small quantities of sugars are present, the following procedure is more advisable. The sections are mounted in a drop of a solution of phenylhydrazine hydrochloride (Appendix V) in glycerine with which a drop of a solution of sodium acetate in glycerine is thoroughly mixed. The preparation is heated for about half an hour (although a longer period is often necessary) and allowed to cool. The phenylhydrazine reacts with many of the sugars to form insoluble yellow crystalline compounds, known as *osazones*. Glucose and fructose produce the same osazone, whose crystals appear as long needles arranged in sheaves (Fig. 45, A); that of maltose forms rosettes or plates of broad needles (Fig. 45, B), whilst cane-sugar produces no osazone.

Another method of storage of carbohydrate-material takes the form of strongly thickened cell-walls (cf. p. 63 and Fig. 37, A), as in many seeds (Date, Lupine, Coffee, etc.). Such walls consist of so-called *reserve-celluloses*, polysaccharides which differ somewhat from ordinary cellulose and break down more readily into simple sugars.

Of very common occurrence in plants are complex compounds known as *glucosides*, most of which consist of glucose combined with one or more aromatic or other organic substances. On boiling with dilute mineral acids they split up into their constituents (hydrolysis). The decomposition of the glucoside within the plant is effected by special enzymes which generally occur in distinct cells, so that the chemical process is not initiated until, for some reason (*e.g.* injury), enzyme and glucoside come into contact. Thus a glucoside amygdalin occurs in the seeds of the Bitter Almond (but not in the cultivated form), whilst the appropriate enzyme *emulsin* is situated in the skin; on crushing the seeds decomposition of the amygdalin into glucose, benzaldehyde, and prussic acid takes place, this last being responsible for the poisonous properties. The hot taste of many members of the Cruciferæ (*e.g.* Horse Radish, Cress) is due to the formation of mustard oil (together with glucose and potassium hydrogen sulphate) by the action of an enzyme *myrosin* on another glucoside *sinigrin* (myronate of potash).

In the two instances just given the glucosides undoubtedly render the plant distasteful to animals, but often they seem to serve as a means of storing glucose in a form which does not diffuse readily. Thus the leaves of many Willows contain a glucoside salicin which, during the night, is split up by the enzyme *salicase* into glucose and saligenin; the former is removed, whilst the latter combines with the new sugar formed the next day. To the glucosides also belong:—the saponins found in the Soapwort (*Saponaria*), *Quillaia*-bark, and many other plants, and easily recognised by the formation of a froth when shaken up with water; the active principles of the Foxglove (*Digitalis*), the most important being digitalin, which has a profound effect on the action of the

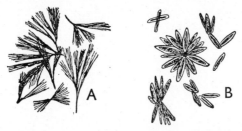

FIG. 45. Osazones. A, of glucose; B, of maltose (after Plimmer).

heart; and the indican of the Woad (*Isatis tinctoria*) and of the Indigo-plant (*Indigofera*), the latter being the source of natural indigo.[1]

Oils or *fats* constitute another important group of reserve-substances. They are formed from carbohydrates and are found especially in those seeds in which the latter are either scanty or absent (*e.g.* Castor Oil, Sunflower, etc.). Drops of oil are, however, not uncommon in the ordinary vegetative cells. The vegetable fats are compounds (esters) of glycerine with various fatty acids (palmitic acid, oleic acid, etc.), and are decomposed by enzymes known as *lipases* into their two constituents. They occur widely as fluids, although the fat of the Cocoa (*Theobroma cacao*), the so-called Cocoa-butter, forms an exception to this. In correspondence with their low specific gravity, fats are a frequent form of non-nitrogenous food-reserve in seeds depending on wind-dispersal.

The oil appears in the cell-sap or protoplasm as shining globular drops of varying size which are readily soluble in ether, benzene, etc.; some are even soluble in alcohol (*e.g.* those in the seeds of the Castor Oil). When a considerable quantity of fat is present (*e.g.* in the Brazil-nut), it can be squeezed out

---

[1] Vanillin, the cause of the aroma of Vanilla (obtained from the pod of *Vanilla planifolia*, a tropical Orchidaceous climber), is an aldehyde, similar to those often combined with glucose to form glucosides.

by pressure on to a piece of filter-paper, producing a greasy mark. The oil-globules turn pink or red on treatment with Scharlach Red (Appendix V), and assume a blackish colouration with osmic acid, which, however, also stains proteins and tannins. If sections of oil-containing material be placed in a solution of concentrated potash and ammonia in equal proportions, the globules after some time lose their sharply defined outline, and often become replaced by needle-shaped crystals. The change, spoken of as saponification, is due to the breaking up of the oil into glycerine and the fatty acid, the latter uniting with the alkali to form the corresponding salt.

Many plant-fats are of considerable economic importance; thus, olive oil is obtained from the fleshy fruit-wall of the Olive (*Olea europæa*, mainly cultivated in the Mediterranean region); coconut oil, used in the preparation of margarine, from the ripe seeds of the Coconut Palm (*Cocos nucifera*) [1]; Castor Oil from the seeds of the Castor Oil plant (*Ricinus communis*); and Palm Oil from the African Palm (*Elæis guineensis*). Cotton-seed is an important source of oil used largely in the manufacture of oil-cake, whilst the "drying oils" used in the paint industry are also obtained from the seeds of plants, such as Linseed (*Linum usitatissimum*), Sunflower seed, Poppy seed, or the fruits of *Aleurites* (tung-oil). Pea-nuts (*Arachis hypogæa*, with 38–50 per cent. of oil), and Soja-beans (*Glycine* spp.) are also important sources of oil. The oil is often extracted after crushing, the ultimate residue forming so-called "oil-cake," which is extensively used for the feeding of cattle. Various vegetable oils are, moreover, employed in the manufacture of soap.

The carbohydrates or fats found in the various storage-organs are always accompanied by nitrogenous food-reserves, the most important and widespread of which are the *proteins*. We have already seen that very complex combinations of proteins are organised to form the living protoplasm, but simpler proteins often occur as non-living constituents of the ordinary vegetative cells, and are especially abundant in the diverse storage-organs. In the former they may either be dissolved in the cell-sap or appear as crystal-like bodies, termed *crystalloids*, which may even be lodged in the plastids or nuclei. Succulent storage-organs, such as tubers, often likewise contain dissolved proteins, or these may take the form of crystalloids, as in the outer layers of a Potato; but not uncommonly a considerable part of the nitrogenous matter in these is a mixture of simpler compounds known as *amides* (*e.g.* asparagin in the Potato and glutamin in the Beetroot).

In seeds proteins generally occur as small grains which are well seen in the cotyledons of a Pea or the endosperm of the Castor Oil. If a section of the former be treated with iodine, the minute protein granules take on a brown colouration, in sharp contrast to the blue or blackish starch-grains with which they are intermingled. On warming a section in a few drops of Millon's reagent (Appendix V), the whole assumes a brick-red colour which microscopic examination shows to be due to the proteins. Heating with concentrated

---

[1] Copra is the commercial name for the dried kernel of the Coconut.

nitric acid gives a yellow colouration which, on addition of ammonia, changes to orange (xanthoprotein reaction).

The proteins of oil-containing seeds (*e.g.* Castor Oil, Brazil-nut) occur in the form of especially large granules, known as *aleurone grains*. These appear to arise, as the seed dries during ripening, from the entire contents of vacuoles rich in protein-substance. Although the structure of aleurone grains is relatively complicated, they exhibit the characteristic protein-reactions mentioned above. If a thin section of the Castor Oil or Brazil-nut (from which the fat

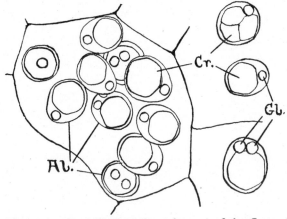

FIG. 46. Aleurone grains (*Al.*) from the endosperm of the Castor Oil plant (*Ricinus*), showing the globoid (*Gl.*) and crystalloid (*Cr.*).

has been removed by soaking in alcohol and benzene respectively) be stained with iodine, the brown-coloured grains are readily seen under the microscope. Each shows a bounding membrane, the original membrane of the vacuole, enclosing amorphous protein in which two or more bodies are embedded. One of these, the crystalloid (Fig. 46, *Cr.*), is large and more or less angular, whilst the other, the globoid, is smaller and rounded (Fig. 46, *Gl.*); both consist of protein, but in the globoid, of which more than one may be present, this is combined with a double phosphate of calcium and magnesium. By mounting sections in water the amorphous ground-mass of the aleurone grain may be dissolved, and the bounding membrane rendered clearly visible; treatment with dilute potash causes bounding membrane and crystalloid to swell and disappear.

The protein-granules of Pea, Bean, etc., are often regarded as small aleurone grains and similar grains occur in abundance in the aleurone layer found at the periphery of the endosperm of Grasses (Wheat, Maize, etc., Fig. 47). When the coat of the grain is

6

detached, the protein-containing layer generally comes away with it, hence the greater nourishing properties of wholemeal bread. For the same reason peeled potatoes are not as nutritious as those boiled in their skins, since the outer layers of the tuber contain protein-crystalloids.

Some plant proteins (albumins) are soluble in water, others (globulins) in dilute solutions of certain salts or (prolamines) in 70 per cent. alcohol; several kinds usually occur side by side. Their complex molecules render them practically indiffusible and, before they are transported to parts where growth is occurring (*e.g.* germinating seeds), they become converted into simpler diffusible compounds. This conversion is brought about by *proteases* (*proteolytic enzymes*), which occur in seeds and green leaves, for

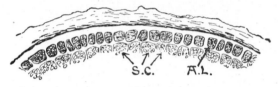

FIG. 47. Aleurone layer (*A.L.*) of Wheat as seen in a transverse section. The starch-containing cells (*S.C.*) lie immediately beneath.

instance, and in function resemble those occurring in the digestive tracts of animals. *Pepsins* break down proteins into peptones and polypeptides, compounds which still possess some characteristics of proteins, while *erepsins* (*peptidases*) hydrolyse these to amino-acids, which lack these properties. Enzymes (papain, bromelin), resembling the pancreatic trypsin and converting proteins into amino-acids, are found in the Papaw (*Carica papaya*) and Pine-apple (*Ananas*). Amino-acids abound in growing parts (*e.g.* leucin in Horse Chestnut buds, tyrosine in Lupine-seedlings, etc.).

Digestive enzymes, secreted by the surfaces of the cotyledons in endospermic seeds, change the food-materials of the endosperm into simpler diffusible substances. There is usually no special secretory layer, although in Grasses the columnar epidermal cells of the cotyledon are glandular in character. These same cells also serve to absorb the digested food-substances.

Many plant-products, rich in the diverse food-reserves above considered (see p. 83), furnish important sources of human food. They also provide many of the essential *vitamins*. Green vegetables Oranges, Guavas, Black Currants and Rose Hips constitute important sources of the antiscrobutic vitamin C (ascorbic acid), while Carrots contain the carotin (p. 91) which is the precursor of vitamin A, and Cereals provide vitamin B. Vegetable products, moreover, supply important trace-elements (see p. 208).

APPROXIMATE FOOD-CONTENT OF VARIOUS PLANT-PRODUCTS

(In percentages of the fresh weight)

			Starch.	Fats.	Proteins.[1]
Cocoa	.	.	.	4·2	50·4	13·3
Maize	.	.	.	68·4 [2]	4·5	9·8
Oat .	.	.	.	58·0 [2]	5·2	10·4
Rice .	.	.	.	75·0	0·5	9·0
Wheat	.	.	.	67·9 [2]	1·8	12·3
Potato-tubers	.	.	20·0	0·15	1·9
Lettuce	.	.	.	2·2	0·3	1·4
Broad Bean	.	.	.	48·0 [2]	1·6	23·0
Pea-nuts	.	.	.	5·2	44·0	30·0

Since *enzymes* [3] are of fundamental importance in metabolism and universally present in living cells, their nature and mode of action may be briefly considered. Large numbers are now known, but some (*e.g.* zymase, p. 241, A) that were formerly regarded as single substances, have proved to be enzyme-complexes.

Most enzymes are soluble in cold water or in dilute glycerine and can be dissolved out of the crushed plant or material ground to a fine powder. If finely powdered malt (*i.e.* germinating Barley) is shaken up thoroughly with water, an impure solution of the enzyme-complex acting on starch is obtained. On slowly adding 90 per cent. alcohol to about 25 c.c. of the filtrate, the enzymes are precipitated and separated from many accompanying substances. If the precipitate is filtered off and redissolved in water, a preparation with higher activity is obtained, and this can be further purified by fresh precipitation with alcohol or by dialysis. These crude methods are applicable to many enzymes, but very elaborate procedures are necessary to obtain a really pure product.

A solution of invertase which will invert cane-sugar is readily obtained, according to Plimmer,[4] in the following manner. A quantity (100 grams) of ordinary Yeast is ground up with about 6 grams of calcium carbonate. The resulting paste is treated with 5 c.c. of chloroform or ether (to liberate the enzymes), and allowed to stand exposed to the air for three or four days, after which the enzyme is precipitated from the filtrate with an equal volume of alcohol. An impure solution of invertase, which will bring about the inversion of cane-sugar, can, however, be obtained by simply mashing Yeast in water with a little ether, and filtering off the solid matter through an asbestos filter.

Lipase can be prepared from the seeds of the Castor Oil by cutting up the endosperm into small pieces, and soaking these for a short time in a small quantity of ether in order to remove the oil. The material is then ground into a pulp with a very dilute (0·5 per cent.) solution of acetic acid, which sets free the enzyme. The insoluble matter is filtered off, washed till the filtrate gives

---

[1] Percentages mostly calculated for entire nitrogenous organic matter.

[2] Total carbohydrates.

[3] For further details, see the works of Stiles and Thomas cited on p. 193 and that of Baldwin, cited on p. 236.

[4] *Practical Organic and Biochemistry*, 2nd edit., 1918, p. 401.

no acid reaction, and the residue is shaken up with a small amount of water. If some of this suspension be added to a little olive oil, an acid reaction will soon be obtained owing to the formation of fatty acids.

Many enzymes have been obtained in an apparently pure and sometimes crystalline state. All contain a colloidal protein component (*apo-enzyme*) of very high molecular weight and rapidly destroyed by temperatures above 50° C., as well as a highly reactive chemical group. The latter may be part of the protein molecule when the enzyme is a chemical entity; or, it may be a second simpler substance tightly bound to the protein; or, a less firmly attached simpler substance, capable of removal by dialysis and not readily affected by higher temperatures, known as a *co-enzyme*. Some of the most important co-enzymes are phosphoric esters. Zymase (p. 241, A) can be dialysed into a colloid fraction containing many enzymes and a crystalloid fraction containing the co-enzymes; neither is active by itself. Some vitamins (*e.g.* ascorbic acid, thiamin) act as co-enzymes or are essential parts of co-enzymes.

All enzyme-reactions are such as require appreciable time, so that their rate can be measured under any given conditions. A most important aspect of enzyme-activity is the small quantity of enzyme necessary to bring about a pronounced change; thus, invertase is stated to invert 200,000 times its weight of cane-sugar. Further, at the end of the reaction the amount and characteristics of the enzyme are unaltered. In both respects enzymes resemble chemical *catalysts*, as exemplified by the small quantities of manganese dioxide used to accelerate the liberation of oxygen from potassium chlorate, and the effect of colloidal platinum black in causing the combination of oxygen and hydrogen at ordinary temperatures. Both reactions would take place without the catalyst, but at a very much slower rate. Similarly, the changes brought about by enzymes might also occur in their absence, but so slowly as not generally to be detectable. Much the same change as is produced by the enzyme can often be achieved with other catalysts (*e.g.* boiling with small quantities of mineral acids).

Although the enzyme appears unaltered at the end, some combination with the substrate or substance undergoing change evidently occurs. Adsorption probably takes place on the large surface of the colloidal component, where the substrates enter into chemical combination with the active group or co-enzyme which is also adsorbed. After a cycle of changes the products are set free.

The kinds of chemical changes in which enzymes are concerned often effect hydrolysis of the substrate, that is to say, it is broken down with the addition of the elements of water, thus:

$$C_{12}H_{22}O_{11} + H_2O = C_6H_{12}O_6 + C_6H_{12}O_6 \ [1]$$

cane-sugar   water   glucose   fructose

$$(C_6H_{10}O_5)n + nH_2O = nC_6H_{12}O_6$$

inulin   water   fructose.

The following are some of the hydrolytic enzymes found in plants:

Enzyme	Substrate	Products
Diastase (amylase α, β)	Starch	Dextrin and Maltose
Maltase	Maltose	Glucose
Invertase	Cane-sugar	Glucose and Fructose
Inulase	Inulin	Fructose
Cellulase	Cellulose	Cellobiose
Cellobiase	Cellobiose	Glucose
Cytase (hemicellulase)	Reserve-cellulose	Glucose, etc.
Emulsin, Myrosin, etc.	Glucosides	Glucose, etc.
Lipases	Oils (fats)	Glycerine and Fatty Acids
Proteases (proteolytic enzymes)	Proteins	Peptones, Polypeptides and Amino-acids

Amylase and maltase are everywhere responsible for the change from starch to sugar. The starch grains are rendered soluble; amylose is broken down by β-amylase into maltose, and amylopectin by α-amylase into dextrins, which are converted into maltose. In seeds containing reserve-celluloses in their thick walls (*e.g.* Date), the cytase acts so gradually that germination is very slow.

Starch can, however, be broken down by *phosphorylase*, which also acts on other polysaccharides. Here the substrate reacts with phosphates, the end-product being a compound of glucose and phosphoric acid (glucose-1-phosphate) which can be split by another enzyme into its two components. Both the amylase and phosphorylase systems can operate in the down-grade direction, the former more rapidly at lower, the latter at higher acidities, but only phosphorylase can bring about appreciable synthesis (cf. p. 86).

Other examples of non-hydrolytic enzymes are those concerned in alcoholic fermentation (p. 241, A) and those catalysing oxidative processes. Many compounds, which remain unaltered in air or molecular oxygen, are rapidly oxidised by living plant-tissues. An alcoholic solution of gum guaiacum is only very slowly changed in air, but is rapidly oxidised giving a blue colour on addition of the sap of a Potato or of other plants containing such enzymes. Cut surfaces of these plants (*e.g.* Apples, many Fungi) often show colour changes, owing to oxidation of polyphenolic substances in the cells, when exposed to air. Many plants, however, lack *oxidase-systems* of this kind and their tissues do not discolour in air. When guaiacum is applied to the cut surface of a Horse Radish root, blueing only ensues if hydrogen peroxide is also supplied.

[1] Although the formulæ for glucose and fructose are the same, these two compounds differ in the arrangement of the atoms within their molecules.

This is due to a *peroxidase*, which markedly increases the oxidising properties of the peroxide. Peroxidases probably play a part in biological oxidations.

Most enzymes act only on a restricted range of substances possessing a similar type of chemical linkage. Marked specificity is exhibited by invertase, while all fats are hydrolysed by lipases and all proteins by proteases. The speed of a reaction depends upon the concentrations of the enzyme and substrate, and many other factors. It is usually doubled or trebled or more with every rise of 10° C., but, above temperatures of about 50° C., most enzymes are rapidly destroyed so that the rate diminishes. This thermolabile property is due to their protein-component. Cooling, sufficient to kill protoplasm, on the other hand, leaves them unharmed, so that active enzymes can be extracted from frozen and subsequently thawed material. Strong light rapidly destroys enzymes, an effect seemingly mainly due to the violet rays. Optimum activity is usually shown only within certain narrow limits of hydrogen-ion concentration, and marked acidity or alkalinity may destroy an enzyme. Enzyme-action may be arrested by narcotics (chloroform) or poisons (prussic acid, mercuric chloride) and by various, more or less specific, *inhibitors*. Moreover, unless the products are removed, as usually happens in the plant, a retardation of the action is soon evident. Continued action of amylase, for example, depends upon the removal of maltose. Accumulation of the products may actually exert a poisonous effect, as, with the alcohol produced by Yeast.

The chemical processes influenced by most enzymes are balanced reversible reactions. Where hydrolytic enzymes are concerned, for example, hydrolysis or synthesis may predominate according to the conditions of supply and demand, the direction always being towards the position of equilibrium of the reacting substances. Various syntheses have been carried out with enzymes outside the plant (*e.g.* that of fats by lipase), while more recently starch has been synthesised by the action of phosphorylase on glucose-1-phosphate (p. 85). A proof of synthesis in the plant is difficult because as a general rule the small amounts of synthesised products are at once removed from the scene of the reaction.

The rapid chemical changes constantly taking place in living organisms thus depend on enzymes. These catalysts operate in every living cell and are concerned both in building up complex substances from simpler ones and in the breaking down of the former. Since the rate of reaction depends on the concentration of enzyme present, which is no doubt regulated by the living cell, it may be intimately related to the momentary requirements of the organism.

CHAPTER IX

BY-PRODUCTS AND SECRETORY ORGANS

THE by-products comprise chemical compounds [1] formed during the metabolism of the plant which either play no further part at all or are only indirectly concerned in the elaboration of food-substances. This does not, however, mean that they fulfil no useful functions in the living organism, for they may be of importance in warding off the attacks of preying animals, in the creation of attractive mechanisms, etc. Examples are furnished by the bright colouring-matters of many petals, the ethereal oils of many sweet-smelling herbs and flowers, and the alkaloids found in many plant-organs.

One of the most widespread of the by-products is *calcium oxalate*, which may occur in practically every organ and tissue. It is produced by the neutralisation of the oxalic acid formed during metabolism and, being insoluble, appears as crystals which assume diverse forms. Large *solitary crystals* (Fig. 48, C), each occupying the greater part of the cell-contents, are very common, but more frequent are radiating clusters, or rosettes, of crystals (Fig. 48, A). Another widespread type takes the form of bundles of needle-shaped crystals (*raphides*), generally situated in enlarged cells containing mucilage (Fig. 48, B). This last type is particularly characteristic of the Monocotyledons, though by no means lacking in Dicotyledons (*e.g.* Enchanter's Nightshade). In the Solanaceæ, the oxalate of lime is deposited in the form of a powder-like mass of numerous very minute crystals (so-called *crystal-sand*).

Crystals of calcium oxalate are, if present, always found in quantity where active metabolism is going on. In old stalks of Rhubarb a gritty texture is produced by their abundance. They are often very plentiful in the tissues adjoining actively secreting organs (cf. p. 92); also in the leaves of deciduous plants, just prior to leaf-fall, features which respectively emphasise that this substance is a by-product, and that it is not generally useful to the organism.

[1] For reference-books, see p. 97.

The crystals of calcium oxalate are not soluble in acetic acid, but readily dissolve in sulphuric acid, with the production of calcium sulphate. The latter, being itself insoluble, becomes deposited promiscuously in the form of needle-like crystals. These tests serve to verify the presence of oxalate of lime, but usually their application is unnecessary, since crystals of other compounds are very rare.

Many substances occur in solution in the cell-sap, and of

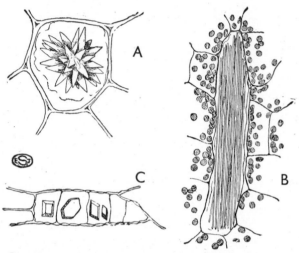

FIG. 48. Crystals. A, Cluster crystals from leaf of Dog's Mercury (*Mercurialis*). B, Raphides from leaf of Enchanter's Nightshade (*Circæa*). C, Solitary crystals from phloem of Horse Chestnut (*Æsculus*).

these the commonest are diverse *organic acids* and bodies known as tannins. The former are responsible for the familiar acid reaction of the sap, and are especially abundant in unripe fruits. As examples mention may be made of malic acid (in Apples), citric acid (in Lemons), tartaric acid (in Grapes), etc. The name of *tannins* is given to diverse organic substances, whose chemical constitution is not fully established, but all of which possess an astringent taste and are characterised by the following reactions: They reduce Fehling's solution, are precipitated by the salts of many metals (*e.g.* basic lead acetate), and take on a blue-black or greenish colour with ferric chloride. Dilute iodine solution, together with a little 10 per cent. ammonia, gives a brilliant red colour even with small quantities of tannins, whilst they are readily precipitated by dilute solutions of caffeine (cf. p. 48).

Tannins are particularly common in the bark of trees (*e.g.* Oak,

Wattles), in unripe fruits (*e.g.* Pear, Acorn), in leaves (*e.g.* Bracken), and occur abundantly in certain abnormal growths (*e.g.* Oak-galls). They are often accompanied by a yellow or reddish pigment which facilitates recognition of the cells in which they occur. The bark of certain trees (*e.g.* Oak), owing to the large quantity of tannin present, has long been employed in the conversion of hide into leather, which process depends on the coagulation, by the tannin, of the protein substances contained in the animal skin. The reactions of tannins with ferric salts have been extensively used in the preparation of ink.

Another group of by-products, encountered particularly in certain families of Flowering Plants (*e.g.* Ranunculaceæ, Scrophulariaceæ, Solanaceæ, Umbelliferæ), are the *alkaloids*. These are complex basic organic compounds containing nitrogen, which are either dissolved in the cell-sap or present in the solid state; in the plant they are often combined with organic acids. The alkaloids are of such importance, owing to their poisonous and medicinal properties,[1] that the following list of some of the more familiar is given:

Alkaloid	Action	Source, etc.
Aconitine .	. Poisonous (used as an antipyretic).	Leaves, root, etc., of Monkshood (*Aconitum napellus*).
Atropine .	. Poisonous (various medicinal uses).	All organs of Deadly Nightshade (*Atropa belladonna*), seeds especially of Thornapple (*Datura stramonium*, Fig. 49) (Solanaceæ).
Cephaeline	. Emetic (active principle of ipecacuanha).	Root of *Psychotria ipecacuanha* (Fam. Rubiaceæ, Brazil).
Cocaine .	. Local anæsthetic.	Leaves of *Erythroxylon coca* (Fam. Linaceæ, Bolivia and Peru).
Coniine .	. Poisonous (paralytic effect).	Seeds of Hemlock (*Conium maculatum*, Umbelliferæ).
Hyoscine .	. Poisonous (sedative).	Henbane (*Hyoscyamus niger*), *Atropa belladonna*, *Datura stramonium* (Fig. 49).
Morphine	. Narcotic (active principle of opium).	Young fruits of Opium Poppy (*Papaver somniferum*).
Nicotine .	. Poisonous.	Leaves of Tobacco (*Nicotiana tabacum*, Solanaceæ).
Quinine .	. Febrifuge.	Bark of *Cinchona* spp. (Rubiaceæ).
Strychnine	. Poisonous, heart and respiratory stimulant.	Seeds of *Strychnos nux-vomica* (Fam. Loganiaceæ).

The alkaloids as a whole are not characterised by any very specific reactions, but they are precipitated from solution by many different reagents (*e.g.* iodine in potassium iodide, tannic acid). They give very marked colour-reactions with various substances; thus a section of the rhizome of the Monkshood

---

[1] For further details of the economic importance of these and other substances mentioned in this chapter, see the works cited on p. 67.

treated with a little 50 per cent. sulphuric acid shows a bright red colouration in the parenchyma adjoining the vascular strands, as a result of the presence of aconitine.

The *ptomaines*, which are basic in character, are compounds produced during the decomposition of flesh, etc., by the agency of Moulds and Bacteria, but the effects of so-called "ptomaine-poisoning" are usually due to bacterial toxins. Such stimulants as the caffeine of tea-leaves, coffee-beans, cocoa-beans, and Kola (*Cola acuminata*), and the theobromine present in the Cocoa, are derivatives of purine and very similar to the alkaloids.

FIG. 49. Photograph of part of the shoot, including two fruits, of the Thorn-apple (*Datura stramonium*), which contains the alkaloids atropine and hyoscine.
[Photo. E. J. S.]

The characteristic and often pleasing odour of many Labiatæ (*e.g.* Lavender, Mint, etc.) and Umbelliferæ (*e.g.* Fennel, *Fœniculum*), as well as of flowers, is due to the presence of so-called *volatile* or *ethereal oils*, which are composed of mixtures of hydro-carbons (*i.e.* compounds containing carbon and hydrogen only), known as terpenes, and of their oxygen derivatives. Examples are: lavender oil from the flowers of the Lavender (*Lavendula*); pepper-mint oil, which contains the antiseptic menthol, from the Pepper-mint (*Mentha piperita*); bergamot oil, used in the manufacture of Eau de Cologne and other perfumes, from the Bergamot Orange (*Citrus aurantium* var. *bergamia*), a variety of the ordinary Orange;

oil of aniseed from the Aniseed (*Pimpinella anisum*); and the numerous oils from the many species of *Eucalyptus* (Myrtaceæ).

Many of these are used commercially in the preparation of perfumes. Similar oils are the essential principles of such spices as Cloves (*Eugenia caryophyllata*), Cinnamon (the bark of young twigs of *Cinnamomum zeylanicum*), Ginger (the rhizome of *Zingiber officinale*), Pepper (the berries of *Piper nigrum*), etc. Moreover, the active principle of the Hop (*Humulus lupulus*), which is contained in special hairs (cf. p. 161) borne on the bracts of the female catkins, and that causing the odour of Tea, likewise belong to the ethereal oils.

Camphor is a solid terpene-derivative obtained from the wood of the Camphor-tree (*Cinnamomum camphora*), whilst turpentine is a mixture of terpenes which flows from the resin-passages (cf. p. 411) in the trunks of various species of Pines (especially *Pinus pinaster*) and of the Spruce Fir (*Picea abies*), when cuts are made in the surface. After the oil of turpentine has been distilled off, the solid residue left is rosin.

Most of the terpenes are colourless, highly refractive liquids, which evaporate completely if sections containing them are heated on a slide for about ten minutes. They are readily soluble in alcohol, chloral hydrate, glacial acetic acid, etc. The ethereal oils are sometimes combined with glucose, etc., in the form of glucosides (*e.g.* the mustard oil of Cruciferæ, cf. p. 79), and become liberated only after coming in contact with the appropriate enzyme.

The tints of many petals are due to *anthocyanidins*, which usually occur as glucosides (*anthocyanins*) dissolved in the cell-sap, their colour depending on the reaction of the sap (red when acid, blue or violet when alkaline), as well as on the presence of tannins and other substances. They also occur in vegetative parts (Beetroot, leaves of *Saxifraga sarmentosa*). Their development often accompanies the accumulation of sugars and appears also to be stimulated by intensive transpiration and strong illumination, such as occur in alpine and arctic regions where high colouration is a conspicuous feature.

The yellow and red colours of certain flowers (*e.g. Tropæolum*) and fruits (Tomato) are, however, due to pigments (carotenoids, etc.) lodged in special plastids, termed *chromoplasts*, in which they are often deposited as crystals. They occur in considerable quantities in Carrot-roots, to which they impart the orange colour and, owing to their conversion into vitamin A within the animal body, render this vegetable a valuable diet. Diverse plants are the source of dyes; thus, the dried stigmata of *Crocus sativus* yield saffron, and the rhizome of *Curcuma longa* (tropical Asia) the yellow dye turmeric.

Increase of knowledge has shown that some of the substances above considered may be of more importance in relation to essential life-processes of plants than was formerly thought probable and that the term by-products may not always be warranted. It is likely, however, that substances like alkaloids, tannins, and resins may be indirectly beneficial by rendering plants containing them distasteful to herbivorous animals. Similarly, the antiseptic character of resin may well be of service in protecting a wound over which it has congealed. The common occurrence of ethereal oils in plants of dry situations has been regarded as bringing about a lessening of transpiration in sunshine. It may be, however, that some of the substances here referred to constitute a means of storage of food-material, and this may apply to some of the tannins and anthocyanins which have the structure of glucosides.

In many plants by-products like those considered above collect as so-called *secretions*. This term is also applied to the sugary liquid produced by the nectaries of flowers, to the watery exudations appearing at different points on leaves under certain conditions, etc. Secretions are very commonly the result of the activity of specialised cells or groups of cells, which may be classed under the general heading of *secretory organs* or *glands*. Their products may pass direct to the exterior, or may be retained in special cavities or canals within the body of the plant. Many of the secretory organs are superficial, and some of these are developed as hairs (cf. p. 160).

Secretions of the nature of ethereal oils, resins, etc., are frequently lodged within the body of the plant. When they are found in isolated cells (*secretory cells*; *e.g.* Bay Laurel, *Laurus nobilis*), the latter often differ, apart from their contents, in shape and in their larger size from the cells of the surrounding parenchymatous tissues. Typical instances are furnished by the so-called tannin-sacs, which are generally characterised by a slightly elongated form; extreme examples are found in the cortex and pith of the Elder (*Sambucus*).

More striking are the *secretory cavities*, *i.e.* large intercellular spaces, approximately isodiametric in form, and again usually lodged in parenchymatous tissues. Often such appear as transparent dots when leaves containing them are held up to the light, a phenomenon well seen in the St. John's Wort (*Hypericum perforatum*) and in the Rue (*Ruta graveolens*). The cavities are filled with an oily secretion, to which these plants owe their peculiar odour. In cross-sections of the leaves of the St. John's Wort the cavities appear more or less circular, each being lined with a layer of thin-walled, somewhat flattened cells (the *epithelium*, cf. Fig. 50, B, *S*.), which discharge the secretion into the central space. The cavities of this plant originate by a gradual separation of the cells, a type of development spoken of as *schizogenous*, and recognisable even at maturity by the presence of a well-defined epithelium; similar schizogenous cavities are encountered in the leaves of the Myrtle (*Myrtus communis*).

In those of the Rue, on the other hand, the cavities arise by a disorganisation of the secreting cells whose remains (cf. Fig. 50, A) persist at the periphery, this mode of origin being described as *lysigenous*; thus at maturity no epithelial layer is present. Similar lysigenous cavities are encountered in the flower-buds known as Cloves (*Eugenia caryophyllata*, Fig. 50, A) and in the skin of the Orange. The secretory cavities of the Rue immediately adjoin the upper epidermis of the leaf, and the secretion in this instance

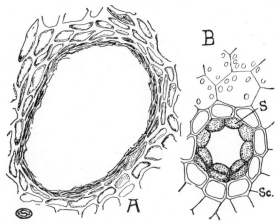

FIG. 50. Secretory organs. A, Lysigenous secretory cavity of the Clove (*Eugenia caryophyllata*). B, Schizogenous secretory canal of the Ivy (*Hedera helix*) in transverse section. *S.*, secretory epithelium; *Sc.*, sclerenchyma sheath.

gradually escapes to the exterior through a zigzagged slit surrounded by four cells; bending of the leaves (*e.g.* by the wind) leads to momentary distortion of the secretory space and consequent emission of part of the secretion. In the Mallows (*Malva* spp.) many parts of the plant contain irregular lysigenous cavities due to the confluence of cells with mucilaginous walls.

In many plants, and especially in the stems and roots, the secretions are present in elongated structures, the *secretory canals*, which are generally schizogenous in origin, the bounding epithelium being developed throughout their entire length. In cross-sections these canals appear as rounded (Fig. 50, B) or oval cavities, whilst in longitudinal sections they are seen to be extensive sinuous tubes which frequently branch and fuse, thus forming a system often pervading all the parenchymatous tissues. The secretory canals are commonly (*e.g.* leaf of the Scots Fir, *Pinus sylvestris*; petiole of the Ivy) enveloped by a sheath of thick-walled cells (Fig. 50, B, *Sc.*), which prevents compression or collapse through turgor of the surrounding tissue. They often occur in the immediate neighbourhood of the phloem of the vascular bundles, as in the Ivy (*Hedera helix*) and the Umbelliferæ. In the St. John's Wort and certain other plants the secretory cavities of the leaf are replaced by canals in the stem, but the difference is one of shape, not of kind.

It is a familiar fact that in some plants a milky, though sometimes coloured, juice (brilliant orange in the Greater Celandine, *Chelidonium majus*) issues from every cut or broken surface. This latex is especially found amongst British plants in members of the Poppy family (Papavaraceæ), Spurge family (Euphorbiaceæ), Harebell family (Campanulaceæ), a tribe of Compositæ, and in the White Convolvulus (*Calystegia sepium*); but it is still more characteristic of certain tropical genera. The latex is contained in much elongated tubes which constitute a branched system throughout the thin-walled tissues of the plant and which conform to one of two types.

In the Spurges (*Euphorbia*) the laticiferous tubes can be recognised already in the embryo as several isolated cells, situated just outside the rudimentary vascular system of the cotyledonary node. Each of these *laticiferous cells* elongates considerably as the seedling develops, insinuating itself between the surrounding parenchymatous cells, and this process of growth continues throughout the life of the plant. Thus, even in the adult condition, the number of laticiferous cells remains the same as in the embryo. In the course of their elongation the laticiferous cells develop frequent branches which follow a more or less longitudinal course into all the organs, including the different parts of the flower, but the branches do not fuse with one another. In spite of this extensive growth, which leads to the penetration of the latex-tubes even into the ultimate branches—in tropical Spurges as much as 50 feet above the ground—no cross-walls arise in these elements. On the other hand, as elongation and branching occur, repeated nuclear division takes place, the numerous minute nuclei in the adult laticiferous cell being embedded in the lining layer of cytoplasm which envelops a continuous vacuole occupied by the latex.

In transverse sections through the mature stem of a Spurge, the branches of the laticiferous cells (Fig. 51, *l.*) will be seen at the outer limit of the phloem (*ph.*) as a number of large circular elements with thick white walls. Longitudinal sections, cut tangentially to the phloem, show the characteristic form of the tubes, and branching can often be recognised (Fig. 51, B). The granular latex, which has been coagulated by the preservative (spirit), contains curious starch-grains somewhat resembling minute knuckle-bones.

These, and the thick walls of the tubes, are peculiar to the Spurges, but in other respects the features just described are applicable to all laticiferous cells.

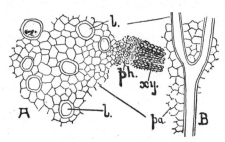

By contrast *laticiferous vessels*, which are characteristic of Papaveraceæ, Campanulaceæ, and Compositæ, are formed from rows of cells (which may run in any direction, though prevalently longitudinal) by the partial, or usually complete, breaking down of the cross-walls. Laticiferous vessels are usually not

Fig. 51. Laticiferous cells (*l.*) in the stem of a Spurge (*Euphorbia*), in transverse (A) and longitudinal (B) sections. *pa.*, parenchyma of cortex; *ph.*, secondary phloem; *xy.*, secondary xylem.

recognisable in the embryo, but arise at a later stage in development. They too form an extensive system in all parts of the plant, most commonly near or within the phloem. They are readily distinguished from the laticiferous cells, however, by the occurrence of frequent fusions between their branches, as a result of which they form a highly irregular network (Fig. 52, C). The mode of origin of these elements can seldom be recognised in the adult condition, but in *Chelidonium majus* longitudinal sections show quite clearly remains of the partially absorbed transverse septa.

Laticiferous vessels are abundant in the fleshy roots of the Dandelion (*Taraxacum*) or Salsify (*Tragopogon*, Fig. 52, A); in transverse

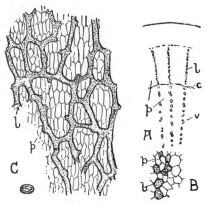

Fig. 52. Laticiferous vessels in the root of the Salsify (*Tragopogon*). A, Diagrammatic representation of a small part of a transverse section, showing the distribution of the laticiferous vessels (*l.*), in relation to the cambium (*c.*), and the vessels of the xylem (*V.*). B, a small part of the secondary phloem enlarged. C, Longitudinal section. *p.*, parenchyma.

sections of preserved material they are plainly recognisable by their brown contents. They have comparatively thin walls and present a very irregular shape (Fig. 52, B, *l.*), which is due to the plane of section often more or less coinciding with that of a cross-connection between the vertical components of the system; moreover, owing to the thin walls of the laticiferous vessels, the pressure of the surrounding elements leads to distortion. The dense irregular network resulting from the numerous cross-connections is a very prominent feature in a radial longitudinal section (Fig. 52, C, *l.*).

Latex, like milk, is an emulsion, the fluid basis of which is a solution of diverse substances (mineral salts, sugars, proteins, tannins, etc.). Sometimes it includes an important active principle of the plant; for example, in *Papaver somniferum* the alkaloid morphine. The suspended particles include on the one

FIG. 53. Row of Para-rubber trees (*Hevea brasiliensis*) on Galley Beach Estates, Ceylon. (Reproduced by permission of the proprietors of the *Indiarubber Journal.*)

hand oil-drops, on the other granules of resin, gum, protein, and caoutchouc, whilst, as already noted, starch-grains occur in the latex of the Spurges. On exposure to air latex as a general rule congeals rapidly, a change often accompanied by discolouration. The latter feature is especially marked in the latex of the Lacquer-tree (*Rhus vernicifera*), where the action is due to an oxidising enzyme (cf. p. 84) which converts the white juice into a dark shining varnish. The "setting" of latex is partly due to evaporation of water, but mainly to a confluence of the oil-globules and suspended particles. The coagulation of the latex, like that of blood, is of advantage in protecting and rapidly covering a wounded surface; moreover, the "dressing" in this case is even antiseptic. The laticiferous elements further serve as food-reservoirs, and in this connection it may be noted that the latex of starved plants becomes thin and watery. Moreover, the frequent association of these elements with the phloem, and the often intimate contact between them and the photosynthetic tissues, seem to indicate a rôle in the storage and transport of elaborated food-material. The by-products, which are not uncommonly present in considerable quantity in the latex, probably render these plants distasteful to animals.

Those plants, whose latex contains a considerable percentage of caoutchouc-particles, are of great economic importance, since they are the source of the *rubber* and *gutta-percha* of commerce. Para-rubber is obtained from a member of the Euphorbiaceæ (*Hevea brasiliensis*, Fig. 53) in which, however, the latex is contained in laticiferous vessels. Other kinds are Ceara-rubber (from *Manihot glaziovii*, Euphorbiaceæ), African rubber (from species of *Landolphia*, family Apocynaceæ), and those obtained from the Indiarubber plant (*Ficus elastica*) and from *Castilloa elastica* (Central America). Gutta-percha is derived from diverse members of a tropical family, the Sapotaceæ, but here the latex is contained in vertical rows of cells.

The latex of rubber trees is obtained by making cuts in the bark and collecting the exuding juice in a small cup. The flow is maintained by paring off thin slices from the lower edges of the cuts, so that the latex-tubes are kept open. After the latex has been artificially coagulated it is washed, and thereupon the raw product is vulcanised. The process of vulcanisation or curing involves a combination of sulphur in varying proportions, according to whether soft rubber or vulcanite is required.

[For further details relating to plant-chemistry, see P. Haas and T. G. Hill, *An Introduction to the Chemistry of Plant Products*, 2 vols., 2nd edit., Longmans, Green & Co., 1922; J. Bonner, *Plant Biochemistry*, Academic Press, Inc., 1950].

CHAPTER X

THE ROOT AND ITS FUNCTIONS

THE two chief functions of the root are attachment to the soil and absorption of water and dissolved nutrients. We may now consider the suitability of the root for these purposes. In the root of a young Bean- or Pea-seedling (Fig. 54) we can distinguish, as in the Shepherd's-purse, root-cap (*r.c.*), root-hairs (*r.h.*), and lateral roots (cf. Fig. 13 of the Bean). The two former are best seen if the seedlings have been kept for two or three days in water.

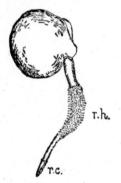

The root-cap serves the purpose of protecting the delicate cells of the meristem at the tip of the root from injury whilst the latter is forcing a passage through the soil. In a longitudinal section the cap is found to consist of a number of concentric layers of thin-walled parenchymatous cells, whose arrangement becomes less regular towards the outside (Fig. 32). During elongation of the root the outermost cells of the root-cap gradually become mucilaginous and break down so that the root-tip glides easily between the particles of soil. The substance of the cap is constantly renewed from the underlying meristem.

FIG. 54. Young Pea-seedling with radicle showing root-hairs (*r.h.*) and root-cap (*r.c.*) (about twice natural size).

There is a varying extent of bare root between the apex and the region occupied by the root-hairs (Fig. 54). It is in this region, and here only, that increase in length is taking place in the new units formed by division of the cells of the meristem (p. 52). To demonstrate this fact we take a number of seedlings having straight radicles (see Appendix X) about an inch long and, using Indian ink, mark off horizontal lines (see Appendix XI) along the root, at intervals of one millimetre from the apex backwards (Fig. 55, A). The seedlings are then attached to a piece of cork

by pins passing through the cotyledons and fixed with the roots
pointing vertically downwards in the neck of a jar, the sides of
which are lined with wet blotting-paper. The whole is left in a
warm dark place for about forty-eight hours.

At the end of this time it will be found that the marks are
unequally spaced (Fig. 55, B). Little elongation has taken place,
for example, between the lines at the extreme tip, or between those
adjacent to the seed. On the other hand, the distance between the
fourth and fifth marks has increased very considerably, while the
intervals above and below have elongated to a less and less extent
until we reach the regions at base and apex where no alteration has
taken place. It is thus apparent
that growth in length of the root
takes place in a very restricted zone,
situated a little way behind the apex,
and that growth involves the distinct processes of cell-division at
the meristem and the subsequent
enlargement in the zone of elongation.

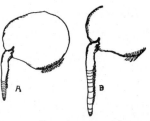

FIG. 55. Experiment to demonstrate region of growth in radicle
of Broad Bean (about half the
natural size). A, At the beginning
of the experiment. B, Forty-eight
hours later.

In order to pierce its way through
the soil, the growing root must
obviously be capable of exerting
considerable force. This force is a
result of the increase in size of the
cells in the zone of elongation and in nature, where the older part
of the root is firmly fixed by root-hairs and lateral roots, it serves
to drive the apex downwards. Moreover, owing to the restriction
of growth in length to a short region, the driving power is
exerted close to the apex and therefore the direction of application
of the force and the moving tip tend to remain in the same straight
line; thus a maximum effect is secured.

The root-hairs arise above the elongating portion of the root,
and the advantage of this is clear when it is remembered that their
purpose is to absorb water from the soil (p. 7), a function which
could not be fulfilled if their position were continually altering
with the growth of the root. Moreover, under such conditions
the delicate root-hairs would become torn and useless. As it is,
however, they develop from that part of the root which has just
concluded its growth in length. The root-hairs, which are narrow
tube-like outgrowths of the surface-cells (Fig. 116, p. 194), in-
sinuate themselves between the small particles of the soil (Fig. 340,
p. 490), with many of which they come into very close contact.
It is owing to this that, even after careful washing beneath a tap

of running water, small soil-particles still cling to the finer branches of the roots.

It is, however, not only the front part of the root that is devoid of root-hairs, for the latter usually occupy but a short zone and the hinder part is again bare (Fig. 54). This is because root-hairs are mostly transient structures [1] lasting only a few days, new hairs sprouting out in front as the older ones die away behind. The new hairs arise from surface-cells in which elongation has just ceased and thus, whilst the part occupied by root-hairs always remains at the same distance from the root-apex, the zone follows the growing tip as it penetrates through the soil. Since root-hairs are developed in exactly the same way on the lateral roots, the growth of the whole root-system carries the region of absorption into an ever-increasing and unexploited periphery.

The general structure of the root [2] can best be studied in a cross-section through the mature region, the Creeping Buttercup (*Ranunculus repens*) furnishing a suitable example. Under the low power of the microscope the broad parenchymatous *cortex* (Fig. 56, *C.*), whose cells contain numerous starch-grains (*s.*), and the central conducting strand, are sharply contrasted. At the edge of the section is a layer of shrunken cells (Fig. 57, *r.*), some of which are prolonged into shrivelled root-hairs. This epidermis withers above the zone of root-hairs and, since its chief function is their production, it is more usually termed the *piliferous layer*. It is only in sections cut nearer the growing tip that its cells are as yet uncontracted, and can be seen to form a single layer.

The *root-hairs*, each arising from a separate cell (Fig. 57, *r.*), appear as tubular unbranched outgrowths with bluntly rounded tips. The greater part of any root-hair is occupied by a large vacuole continuous with that of the epidermal cell and filled with sap. There is consequently only a thin lining layer of cytoplasm, which is best seen near the tip where the single nucleus usually lies embedded.

Beneath the withered piliferous layer, in the older part of the root, lies the *exodermis* (Fig. 57, *Ex.*), a layer of protective cells

[1] The root-hairs of some plants may persist and function for two or three years.

[2] Important reference-books, dealing with plant-anatomy are: A. De Bary, *Comparative Anatomy of the Vegetative Organs of the Phanerogams and Ferns* (transl. by F. O. Bower and D. H. Scott), Oxford, 1884 (659 pp.); A. J. Eames and L. H. MacDaniels, *An Introduction to Plant Anatomy*, McGraw-Hill Book Co., 2nd edit., 1947 (427 pp.); G. Haberlandt, *Physiological Plant Anatomy* (transl. by M. Drummond), Macmillan & Co., 1914 (777 pp.). A comprehensive taxonomic account is given by C. R. Metcalfe and L. Chalk, *Anatomy of the Dicotyledons*, 2 vols., Clarendon Press, 1950. A similar volume on Monocotyledons is in process of preparation.

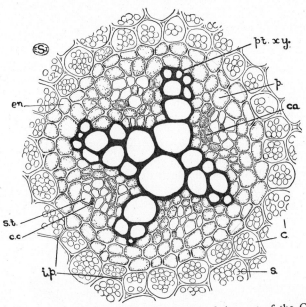

FIG. 56. Transverse section of the central part of the root of the Creeping Buttercup (*Ranunculus repens*). The walls of the xylem elements are shown black. *C.*, inner part of cortex; *ca.*, cambium; *c.c.*, companion cell; *en.*, endodermis; *i.p.*, intercellular spaces; *p.*, pericycle; *pt.xy.*, protoxylem; *s.*, starch; *s.t.*, sieve-tube.

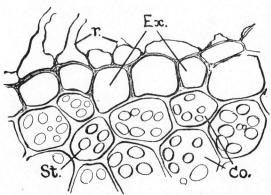

FIG. 57. Piliferous layer (in part withered) and exodermis of the root of the Creeping Buttercup (*Ranunculus repens*). *Co.*, cortex; *Ex.*, exodermis; *r.*, root-hairs arising from cells of piliferous layer; *St.*, starch.

which are on the whole rather smaller than the adjacent cells of the cortex. Their brownish, slightly thickened walls are chemically changed (*i.e.* suberised, cf. p. 186) in such a way that they are almost impermeable to water; but this alteration does not usually take place till the root-hairs begin to wither, so that the water they absorb can readily pass inwards to the vascular cylinder. Sometimes, however (*e.g.* most Monocotyledons), where the exodermis differentiates at an early stage, thin-walled passage-cells (Fig. 64, *P.*), through which the water travels, occur at regular intervals.

The cell-walls of the *cortex* become thinner towards the centre, and intercellular spaces (Fig. 56, *i.p.*) are abundant. The latter form a continuous system which permits of gaseous exchange with the aerial parts of the plant. The vascular strand is delimited from the cortex by two well-defined layers of cells, an outer, the endodermis (*en.*), and an inner, the pericycle (*p.*) (cf. below).

In sections stained with aniline chloride a four-rayed group of yellow elements, composing the lignified wood or *xylem* (Fig. 56), occupies the greater part of the conducting strand. In the bays between the four arms of the xylem are oval groups of small-celled unstained tissue, the *phloem*, in which the wide and empty-looking sieve-tubes (*s.t.*) are plainly distinguished from the narrower companion-cells (*c.c.*) with their dense contents (cf. p. 62). Each phloem-group is separated from the adjacent xylem by one or two layers of parenchyma (*ca.*).

The xylem consists chiefly of dead, empty-looking elements, the vessels, of which those at the centre of the conducting strand are the largest, whilst the remainder become progressively smaller in passing outwards along any one of the rays. The end of each xylem-arm, immediately beneath the pericycle, is thus occupied, by a strand of the narrowest vessels (Fig. 56, *pt.xy.*). In cross-sections, through younger parts of the root, a larger or smaller number of the central vessels will appear thin-walled and un-lignified, showing that differentiation of the xylem takes place from without inwards. The small peripheral elements are the *proto-xylem*, and the larger later-formed ones are termed the *metaxylem*.

Longitudinal sections passing through one of the xylem-arms will show that the vessels of the protoxylem are spirally thickened, whilst those of the metaxylem bear bordered pits. The walls between the larger vessels, in the transverse section, exhibit a thin dark line down the middle (the middle lamella), with the thickening layers on either side. These latter are not homogeneous, however, but appear to consist of short dark lengths alternating with lighter and narrower portions, where the pits are seen in optical section.

The cells of the *endodermis* (Fig. 56, *en.*) are distinctly smaller than the adjacent cortical cells and somewhat flattened. Their radial walls are thicker and look darker than the others, although when sharply focussed in optical section they appear bright owing to their highly refractive character. On treatment of a section with strong sulphuric acid, the membrane swells and dissolves, except for the radial walls, which persist unaltered, implying that they are chemically different from the other walls of the endodermal cells. These features of the radial walls are commonly exhibited by the endodermis of roots, and a layer with similar thickenings is found in the stems of aquatics (cf. p. 544). These thickenings form hoop-like bands extending over both vertical and horizontal walls of each cell. They collectively constitute an impervious network, the meshes of which are occupied by the protoplasts.

The purpose of the endodermis is still obscure. The firm lateral connection of the cells due to the thickening renders this layer an efficient sheath to the vascular system. The considerable thickening of the entire endodermal wall, which obtains in some roots (cf. below), suggests a probable mechanical value. In the unthickened state this layer may serve to cut off the water-conducting strand from the air-spaces of the cortex, a delimitation rendered necessary by the frequent differences in pressure (due either to root-pressure or "negative pressure", pp. 194, 204) on its two sides. Moreover, all liquids must necessarily pass through the protoplasts of the endodermal cells. Not uncommonly the layer of cortical cells next to the endodermis develops characteristic thickenings on the transverse and radial walls, a feature well seen in the roots of many Cruciferæ (*e.g.* White Mustard), and no doubt of mechanical value.

The *pericycle* which lies immediately within the endodermis is another continuous layer not characterised by any structural peculiarities (Fig. 56, *p.*).

Many of the features just described are typical of roots generally, viz. the aggregation of the vascular tissue near the centre; the alternation of phloem and xylem resulting in a radial structure; the peripheral location of the protoxylem; the wide cortex; the presence of an endodermis with its special differentiation; also the occurrence of exodermis and piliferous layer. Roots differ among one another in two principal respects—namely, as to the number of phloem- and xylem-strands, and in the presence or absence of parenchyma (pith) in the centre of the conducting tissue. As regards the former feature, there may be two or more of such strands, roots being described as *diarch, triarch, tetrarch* (Fig. 56), *pentarch* (Fig. 59), etc., according as the number of alternating xylem- and phloem-groups is two, three, four, or five, etc., whilst when they are numerous the structure is said to be *polyarch* (Fig. 58). Thus the root just examined is tetrarch, that of the Wallflower diarch, and that of most Monocotyledons polyarch. A *pith* composed of parenchyma, which is sometimes thick-walled, is frequent in the roots of herbaceous Dicotyledons (Fig. 59) and

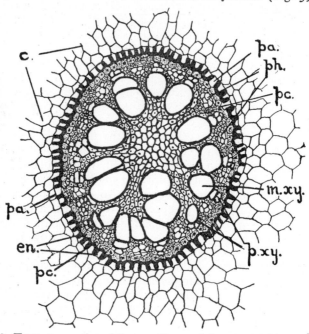

FIG. 58. Transverse section of the central part of the root of *Iris.   C.*, cortex; *en.*, endodermis;   *m.xy.*, metaxylem;   *pa.*, passage cells;   *pc.*, pericycle;   *ph.*, phloem;   *p.xy.*, protoxylem.

in Monocotyledons (Fig. 58), but in woody Dicotyledons and Conifers the xylem-groups often meet at the centre. Roots also vary in the manner of thickening of the mature cells of the endo-dermis and the number of layers constituting the pericycle.

A transverse section of the root of the *Iris* illustrates these features. It exhibits the typical Monocotyledonous structure, viz. a central pith and numerous alternating groups of xylem and phloem (Fig. 58). The endodermis (*en.*) is conspicuous owing to the marked thickening of all but the outer walls of most of its cells. Opposite the protoxylem groups (*p.xy.*), however, the endodermal cells are often thin-walled, and such *passage-cells* (*pa.*) serve for the transference of water through the endodermis, which is elsewhere impermeable. A thickened endodermis interrupted by thin-walled passage-cells is found particularly amongst Monocotyledons (see also Fig. 64, *Pa.*).

The side-roots arise at some considerable distance from the tip of the main root (Fig. 12, C; Fig. 15, E), and careful observation shows that they have burst through the outer covering of the latter (Fig. 59). The mode of origin of the laterals can be readily

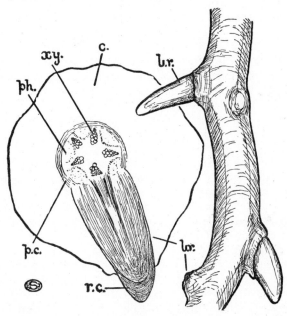

FIG. 59. The root of a Bean seedling in surface-view and in transverse section showing the origin of the lateral roots (*l.r.*). *C.*, cortex; *ph.*, phloem; *p.c.*, pericycle; *r.c.*, root-cap; *xy.*, xylem.

studied in longitudinal sections through a Bean root. The lateral roots arise by division of pericycle cells, either opposite the protoxylem strands (Fig. 59, *l.r.*), or between these and the phloem, so that in Dicotyledons they form vertical series equal to or double the number of xylem groups. In Monocotyledons, owing to the numerous protoxylem-strands, and the early decay of the tap-root, this arrangement is often obscured.

A short distance behind the apex young laterals, which have not yet reached the surface, are distinguishable. In the course of their further development, the side-roots push their way through the cortex, so that, by the time they emerge at the surface, the protective root-cap is fully formed (Fig. 59, *r.c.*). This so-called *endogenous* origin contrasts with the superficial origin of the branches of the stem, and can be related to a need for protection, until the young root has developed sufficiently to withstand the resistance of the soil.

All, even the finest members of a root-system, show an identical structure, and the principal difference between the main root and its branches lies in their direction of growth. The factors causing the downward growth of the main root can be investigated by the following experiments.

A number of healthy seedlings having straight radicles (Appendix X) are pinned parallel to one another to the surface of a large cork; the latter is then fixed edge on to the bottom of a light-tight box in such a way that the radicles are horizontal and free to bend. The entire inner surface (including the lid) is lined with wet blotting-paper, and the whole is left in a warm place for about twenty-four hours. The tips will then be found to have curved downwards into a vertical position. It is plain that the roots were subjected equally on all sides to moisture, warmth, supply of air, and darkness, and the only one-sided influence is the force of gravity. The root then, unlike the shoot of most plants (cf. p. 15), grows in the direction of this force and is thus led to penetrate deeper and deeper into the soil. On the other hand, light which plays an important part in determining the direction of growth of the shoot, has little influence on the roots of most plants.

Examination of the root-system of such plants as the Shepherd's-purse and the Pea discloses the fact that the laterals diverge at more or less of an acute angle from the main root, so that they grow outwards and downwards (Figs. 2, 12, 15). In order to observe readily the growth of the root-system we can employ a rectangular wooden box, provided with drainage-holes as described on p. 35; one long side of the box is replaced by a sheet of glass which slopes *inwards* from the top at a slight angle. The box is filled with soil and seeds are planted at the surface in close contact with the glass, the whole being placed in darkness. Owing to the positive geotropism of the root-system the main root and its laterals remain in close touch with the glass surface. The box is propped up so that its floor is at an angle of 45° with the ground, and the experiment left for about three days. It is then observed that the tip of the main root, as in the preceding experiment, has curved down into the vertical position; the tips of the laterals have also curved, so that these tips now lie at the same angle as before with the new direction assumed by the growing part of the main root—a fact which can be verified by measuring the old and new angles with a protractor. The direction of growth of the laterals is thus also influenced by gravity, but forms a constant angle with that of the main root.

Arising from the laterals of the first order are smaller roots of the second order, and in a strongly developed root-system there may even be branches of a higher order (Fig. 2). These ultimate members of the root are unaffected by gravity and generally extend into the soil in all directions. Hence the volume of soil occupied by the root-system is very completely exploited by its numerous ramifications.

Apart from gravity, there is, however, one other factor that markedly influences the direction of growth, especially of the finer branches of the root-system, and that is the distribution of moisture. To demonstrate this fact we use the same box as in the last experiment with the following modification (Fig. 60): A small clean

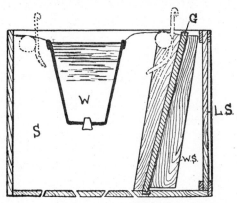

FIG. 60. Experiment to demonstrate hydrotropism in roots. The box is shown in section; the final appearance of two seedlings is indicated by dotted lines. S, soil; W, water in central pot; G, sloping glass front of box; L.S., light-shield. W.S., wooden supports for glass front.

flower-pot, the hole at the base of which is firmly plugged to prevent leakage, is filled with water and embedded up to its rim in the soil which otherwise fills the box and which should be moderately dry. Soaked seeds (*e.g.* Pea, Bean) are planted against the glass as before, but some are also placed in the surface layer of the soil in other parts of the box. Water is supplied to the soil only by way of the flower-pot which is kept full. After having remained in darkness[1] for about ten days, the roots of the seedlings planted against the glass are scarcely visible and, on uprooting them carefully, it will be seen that this is due to their having curved more or less markedly towards

[1] This can be effected by means of a wooden light-shield, shown in Fig. 60.

the pot which is the only source of moisture in the soil (see Fig. 60). Moreover, the seedlings which have developed from the seeds planted elsewhere in the box will, if carefully uprooted, also show a marked curvature of their roots towards the pot.   The success of the experiment depends on the realisation of a correct moisture gradient.   The influence of unequal distribution of moisture on the direction of growth of roots is described as *hydrotropism*.

The type of root-system with which we have hitherto become familiar (*e.g.* in the Shepherd's-purse, Fig. 2) is characterised by the possession of a prominent main root (often spoken of as a *tap-root*) growing vertically down into the soil and bearing numerous branches that become progressively smaller.   This type is most commonly found in Dicotyledons.   In Monocotyledons, on the other hand, as well as in many Dicotyledons, the root-system consists of a number of members in which we cannot distinguish any single one as specially prominent; such a root-system is described as *fibrous*, and good examples are furnished by the Strawberry (Fig. 139, p. 224), the Hyacinth and Grasses (Fig. 65, C).   We have already met with an instance of this kind in considering the germination of the Maize (p. 31).

The radicle, which usually gives rise to the tap-root, in all fibrous root-systems fails to develop to any considerable extent.   The tuft of roots originates either by outgrowth from the base of the stem (Grasses, Strawberry, etc.) or from the hypocotyl (Groundsel, Sanicle).   Owing to the fact that they do not arise from roots, these laterals are described as *adventitious*.   Another good example of such adventitious roots is seen in the Ivy (Fig. 61), where they appear on the side of the stem adjacent to the wall and serve to fix the plant. The propagation of plants by cuttings (*e.g.* Geraniums, Osier-willows) is dependent upon the development of adventitious roots from the part of the stem placed in the soil.   In many Willows the rudiments of such roots are already visible as little knob-like swellings beneath the nodes of the uncut stem.

We may now consider how the structure of the root is related to its two principal functions, the absorption of the soil-solution and the anchorage of the plant.   Absorption of water takes place mainly through those regions in which the piliferous layer is still intact and living.   The outgrowth of its cells into root-hairs, the chief organs of absorption, affords an enormously increased surface over which the latter can take place.   The size and number of the root-hairs tend to decrease with increasing wetness of the soil, and in some marsh-plants (*e.g.* Marsh Marigold) and a considerable number of aquatics they may be altogether absent.   Here, owing to the ready availability of water, enlargement of the absorbing surface is unnecessary. Not uncommonly root-hairs arise from special shorter cells of the piliferous layer, often distinguishable by their denser protoplasm and larger nuclei, and recognisable already just behind the apex. The older part of the root, which is amply protected by the exodermis, plays no appreciable rôle in absorption.

In plants in which the overground organs persist and form a woody skeleton, the development of this aerial system is accompanied by a similar change in the root. Most trees at first possess a tap-root, but, as the plant becomes older, the laterals near the surface of the soil frequently develop more strongly and form a horizontal platform which serves to support the plant and distributes the pulling strain (due to the action of the wind) over a wider area. Such roots often appear above the surface of the ground as a system radiating from the base of the main trunk, this

Fig. 61. Portion of a climbing shoot of Ivy (*Hedera helix*), showing the adventitious roots and three nodes (somewhat reduced).

being due to their own increase in thickness, as well as to erosion of soil by rain. The bulk of such a woody root-system no longer serves the purpose of absorption, this function being restricted to its finest branches. It is a familiar fact that the foliage of most trees affords a more or less efficient shelter from rain, the water draining off from the edge of the canopy. Since the roots develop *pari passu* with the crown of foliage, their absorbent branches are thus usually located beneath the drip of the tree.

The root is suited to its anchoring function by its more or less extensive branching, and the central location of the mechanical elements which enable it to withstand the pulling strain to which it is subjected. In most roots the mechanical tissue is constituted merely by the xylem, as well as by the pith when the latter is thick-walled, but in the Pea and other Leguminosæ groups of fibres are developed in relation to the phloem. When roots serve not only for anchoring, but also for the support of the plant, a modified structure may obtain.

In the Maize, after the plant has reached a certain height, additional adventitious roots arise from the stem, some little way above the surface of the ground, and grow obliquely downwards into the soil (Fig. 62, C). These *prop-roots* serve the purpose of augmenting the somewhat feeble primary root-system which is insufficient to maintain the tall Maize plant in the erect position. Better examples are furnished by the tropical Mangroves which

grow in loose shifting estuarine mud subjected to tidal inundation.

A cross-section of a *prop-root* of the Maize (Fig. 62, A) contrasts
with one of an ordinary root of this plant in the presence of a
special cortical ring of mechanical elements and the larger size
of the central cylinder, so that the xylem also is more peripheral.

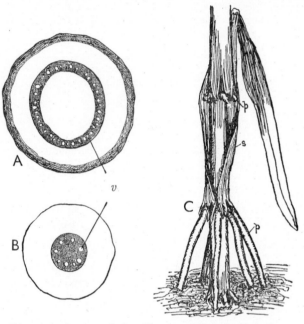

FIG. 62. Diagrams of a normal absorbing root (B) and of a prop-root (A) of
the Maize (*Zea mais*).   The sclerenchymatous tissues are indicated by shading.
v., vessels; *C.*, lower part of plant of Maize, showing prop-roots (*p*) arising
from two nodes, the upper ones in an early stage of development (about natural
size); *s*, sheath of lowest leaf.

In both these respects the mechanical construction of such a prop-
root approaches that of a stem (cf. p. 144).

Many plants characteristic of soils rich in humus exhibit an
intimate relation of fungal threads with their roots or other underground organs.   In some these threads form a dense weft over the
whole surface (*ectotrophic mycorrhiza, e.g.* Beech, *Monotropa,* etc.),
and appear to replace the absent root-hairs.   In others the Fungus
can be seen occupying a definite zone *within* the cortex [*endotrophic
mycorrhiza, e.g.* Bird's Nest Orchid (Fig. 63, *m.*), Heather, etc.].
The advantage of association with the Fungus would appear to
depend mainly on the power of the latter to break down and absorb

the organic material which is then in part utilised by the Flowering Plant (cf. p. 218).

Many tropical Orchids which grow high up in the forks of trees possess tufts of roots protruding into the humid air. These *aerial roots* exhibit a modification of structure in correspondence with their special functions as organs of absorption and photo-

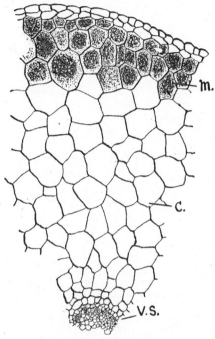

FIG. 63.—Transverse section of the outer part of one of the underground branches of the Bird's Nest Orchid (*Neottia nidus-avis*), showing the vascular strand (*V.S.*), the cortex (*C.*), and the mycorrhizal zone (*m.*).

synthesis. The cortical cells frequently contain chlorophyll, a feature doubtless related to their growth in light, since ordinary terrestrial roots (*e.g.* those of the Pea) will often become green when exposed to illumination. In extreme instances (*e.g. Tænio-phyllum*) the entire photosynthesis is carried out by means of aerial roots, which assume a leaf-like appearance, whilst the true leaves are mere scales. The absorption of water in such roots is accomplished with the aid of a tissue formed by a remarkable development of the epidermis (the *velamen*, Fig. 64, *V.*). This generally divides so as to form several, or many, layers of cells, which ultimately lose their living contents and often exhibit a spiral or reticulate thickening. Moreover, large holes frequently develop in the walls of many of the cells, as a result of which any moisture falling or condensing on the surface is rapidly absorbed. The exodermis (Fig. 64, *Ex.*), situated at the inner edge of the velamen, is interrupted by thin-walled passage-cells (*P.*) for the

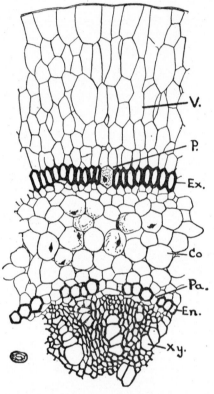

FIG. 64. Transverse section through part of a root of an epiphytic Orchid (*Dendrobium*), showing the velamen (*V.*). *Co.*, cortex; *En.*, endodermis; *Ex.*, exodermis; *P.* and *Pa.*, passage cells; *Xy.*, xylem.

inward transference of the water absorbed. In dry weather air fills the cells of the velamen, so that they appear white and opaque; but when occupied by moisture they become translucent and the green colour of the cells beneath is visible.

In biennials and herbaceous perennials the roots frequently serve as storage-organs for the food-materials, laid up for subsequent growth (see Chapter II), and in consequence become more or less swollen. Frequently it is the tap-root which enlarges in this way, and good examples are furnished by the Carrot (Fig. 65, A), the Parsnip, and the Dock. The swollen structure in the Turnip (Fig. 65, D) consists largely of a tap-root, but in the formation of the uppermost portion the hypocotyl and the base of the stem appear to participate, since remains of leaves are often

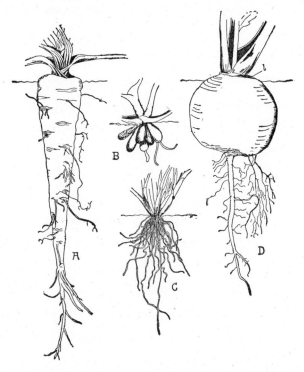

FIG. 65. Different types of root-systems (reduced to about half natural size). A, Carrot. B, Lesser Celandine. C, Grass. D, Turnip. The level of the ground is in all cases shown by a black line. *l*, leaf-scar.

found in this region (Fig. 65, D, *l*). In the Dahlia and Lesser Celandine (*Ficaria verna*, Fig. 65, B), on the other hand, many of the members of the fibrous root-system are swollen, and the enlarged roots are often spoken of as *root-tubers*. The tubers of a Lesser Celandine bear near their tip an axillary bud from which new growth ensues in the following spring. The underground tubers of British Orchids are swollen adventitious roots which arise upon an axillary bud. The examples just given include a number of our common vegetables which owe their utility to the large quantities of food-reserves contained in the storage-organs, and

8

as further instances we may add the Radish, the Beetroot and the Mangold wurzel (*Beta vulgaris* var.).

The slight variation in the morphology and anatomical construction of roots can be related to the comparatively uniform environment, the soil, in which they develop. Indeed, as we have seen, the only marked departures from the normal structure are associated with special functions.

Roots not only absorb water, but also take in nutrient ions by a process of ionic exchange. In addition they are known to secrete into the soil organic substances, which may be of the nature of antibiotics and check the root-growth of their competitors and the activity of bacteria. Sometimes such secretions provide the chemical stimulus that causes the cysts of Eelworms to develop (*e.g.* those of the Potato Eelworm) or the seeds of the parasitic Broomrapes (p. 217) to germinate. Or again the amides, secreted by the rootlets and root-hairs, provide the stimuli to which Wireworms respond in seeking their food.

CHAPTER XI

THE ARCHITECTURE OF THE SHOOT

THE shoot usually grows erect in response to the directive influences of light and gravity (p. 14), though occasionally it may exhibit a prostrate or climbing habit. The shoot differs greatly in appearance from plant to plant. This variety of form is determined by the way in which the stem branches, as well as by the shape and mode of arrangement of the leaves, and to understand the architecture of the shoot these features must be considered separately.

It is easiest to study the mode of branching in the first place on woody plants, because the succession of events is more clearly seen in them than in herbs which frequently do not branch much until the time of flowering. If we examine a woody shoot, as for instance one of the larger branches of the Beech, in winter-time (Fig. 66, A), we find that it is terminated by a long, slender and pointed structure of a brown colour, the *terminal bud* (*t.b.*); this contains in miniature and telescoped together next year's continuation of the branch. Along the sides of the latter are a number of perfectly similar buds (the *lateral buds*, *l.b.*), each capable in the next season of growing out into a side-branch. Beneath each lateral bud the bark shows a smooth scar (*l.s.*), generally well defined and bearing a curved band of dots. Each scar marks the former position of a leaf (*i.e.* it is a *leaf-scar*, see also Fig. 67), and the dots on its surface are the broken ends of the vascular strands that joined stem and leaf. The lateral buds, therefore, are all axillary (p. 3) to leaves of past seasons, the terminal buds alone having no subtending leaf-scars. In some plants (*e.g.* some Willows) more than one bud (*accessory buds*) may arise in a leaf-axil, either above or on either side of the usual one (cf. also p. 264).

Other external features of the twigs are the *lenticels* (Fig. 66, A, *l*; Fig. 67), small generally lighter-coloured projections of varying shape, which are irregularly distributed on the bark of woody plants and serve the purpose of gaseous interchange between the interior of the branch and the atmosphere, prevented except at these points by the impermeable bark.

The most fundamental distinction in the mode of branching lies in the behaviour of the terminal bud. In a considerable number of trees, of which the Conifers furnish excellent examples, the original plumule of the seedling steadily continues its growth year by year, lengthening out in the spring and producing a new

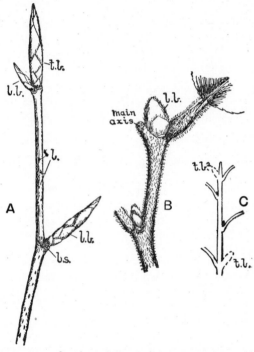

FIG. 66. Winter state of twigs of Beech (A, about natural size) and Elm (B, somewhat enlarged). C, Diagram to explain behaviour of terminal bud in the Elm or Lime. *l.*, lenticels; *l.b.*, lateral buds; *l.s.*, leaf-scar; *t.b.*, terminal bud; *t.b.* and *t.b.*[2] in Fig. C, terminal buds of successive seasons which die away.

terminal bud in the autumn, so that a tall, straight, main axis (or monopodium) is produced. A certain number of lateral buds develop into side-branches of the first order, but these are all subsidiary to the central shaft and again branch in the same manner. Moreover, in this method of *monopodial* branching the oldest and largest laterals are farthest from the growing tip, whilst the youngest and smallest are close to it. As a result of this very regular branching, such plants often exhibit a very symmetrical conical shape, well seen in a good specimen of a Christmas tree.

The most essential characteristic of the type just considered is the persistence of the meristem of the main axis from year to year, and herein lies the distinction from so-called *sympodial* branching. This latter is seen in its simplest form in the Elm (Fig. 66, B and C) or Lime. If a branch of one of these trees be examined in the course of the summer, it will be found to possess a well-marked terminal bud, but as the season advances this bud

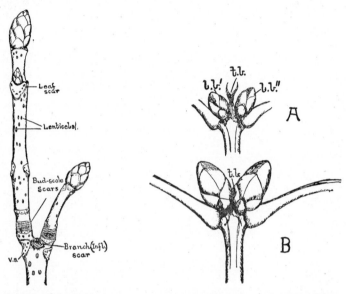

FIG. 67. Portion of twig of Horse Chestnut (*Æsculus*) showing buds, leaf-scars and lenticels (about two-thirds natural size). *v.s.*, vascular strands.

FIG. 68. Twigs of Lilac (*Syringa vulgaris*) illustrating dichasial branching and dying away of terminal bud. A, Young stage, about natural size. B, Older stage, slightly enlarged. *l.b'*, *l.b.''*, lateral buds; *t.b.*, terminal bud.

begins to show signs of withering, while the axillary bud situated just beneath it increases in vigour. Ultimately, when the winter arrives, this axillary bud will be found to occupy a position at the extreme end (Fig. 66, B, *l.b.*), the true terminal bud being represented by a small shrivelled remnant or scar (main axis in Fig. 66, B) at one side. Careful examination even at this time, however, shows that the bud at the end of the branch is not a true terminal one, since beneath it is found a leaf-scar.

The lateral buds which thus always come to occupy the ends of the branches in the Elm or Lime continue the growth of the latter in the following season, so that as the years go on there is

built up a composite axis or sympodium, consisting of a succession
of lateral branches, so adjusted as to form an apparently continuous
whole (cf. Fig. 66, C). In some plants, however, sympodial
branching does not take place with complete regularity.

In the Horse Chestnut (Fig. 67), for example, frequent monopodial branching takes place, and sympodial
branching occurs only in connection with
flowering. The inflorescence (p. 5) of this
tree forms the termination of the branch upon
which it is borne; when flowering and fruiting are over, the stalk of the inflorescence is
shed and leaves a large round somewhat
sunken scar (Fig. 67, infl. scar). The nearest
lateral bud grows into the line of continuity
and in the next season replaces the branch
whose further growth terminated with the
production of flowers. Circular scars marking
the former attachment of inflorescences are
always to be found on branches of the Horse
Chestnut (Fig. 67).

FIG. 69. Branch of
the Field Spurrey
(*Spergula arvensis*),
showing dwarf-shoots
(*d.s.*) (about two-thirds
natural size).

The Lilac (Fig. 68) shows a slightly
different type of sympodial branching. Here
the terminal bud usually, though not invariably, either dies, or its existence is terminated
by the formation of an inflorescence, as in
the Horse Chestnut. The difference, as compared with the previous examples, is that two
lateral buds, instead of one, grow out to
replace the main axis, so that it looks as if the
latter had forked.[1] This so-called *dichasial*
branching is also well seen in the Mistletoe
and occasionally in the Horse Chestnut.

The extent of branching varies greatly;
on the one hand are plants, like most
Monocotyledons, in which it is practically restricted to the region
of the inflorescence, whilst on the other are richly branching trees,
such as the Beech or Elm. In all woody plants, however, the
materials available for growth suffice for the development of only
a small number of buds, a very considerable percentage being
doomed to inactivity, either permanent or temporary. These
inactive or *dormant buds* retain their vitality often throughout
the life of the tree or shrub and are ready to grow out into
branches, should occasion demand. That the presence of the

[1] Cf. Dichotomy, p. 288.

terminal buds is largely responsible for preventing further development is easily seen if we remove these from the branches; thereby lateral buds borne lower down upon them which would otherwise remain dormant are caused to sprout (cf. p. 249). Upon this depends the principle of hedge-making, in which by cutting off the tops of the upper branches numerous laterals are caused to develop, so that a dense growth results.

In a few plants (*e.g.* Scot's Fir, Field Spurrey, Fig. 69) most of the lateral branches do not elongate in the normal way, but remain quite short owing to the non-development of the internodes; such branches are termed *dwarf-shoots* (Fig. 69, *d.s.*). Most of our fruit-trees exhibit a similar phenomenon, but here a few of the lower internodes are developed, so that these *spur-shoots* do not remain quite as short as typical dwarf-shoots.

In all the above examples we have spoken of shoots as arising from normal buds developed in the axils of leaves. Exceptionally, however, shoots may originate in another way, as, for example, from the cut stumps of trees, from roots (*e.g.* in the Bindweed and Poplar) or from foliage-leaves (*e.g. Cardamine pratensis*). The term *adventitious*, which has already been applied to roots (p. 108), is used also for such shoots, developing in an unusual position.

The majority of plants exhibit but a single leaf at each node, an arrangement described as *alternate*, but there are quite a large number (*e.g.* Lilac, Fig. 68; Hop, Fig. 10; Hedge Woundwort, Fig. 70, C) in which a pair of leaves arise together, when the leaf-arrangement is said to be *opposite*. Such pairs of leaves almost invariably occur at right angles to one another at successive nodes (Fig. 70, C), *i.e.* they are *decussate*. Occasionally, as in the Teasel (*Dipsacus*) and Yellow Centaury (*Blackstonia*), the bases of the opposite sessile leaves are joined together so as to surround the stem, a condition described as *connate*. If more than two leaves occur at a node the group is spoken of as a *whorl,* examples being seen in the Oleander (*Nerium*) and the Water Milfoil (*Myriophyllum,* Fig. 388); here again the leaves of one whorl usually alternate with those above and below. A result of such alternation between the leaves of successive nodes is the prevention of undue overshadowing, and the same advantage accrues from the spiral arrangement of alternate leaves (cf. below).

In many herbaceous plants (*e.g.* Dandelion, Shepherd's-purse, Fig. 1) a large number of leaves arise close together from the base of the stem, just above the surface of the soil; such leaves are usually collected in the form of a rosette and are described as *radical* leaves (Fig. 1, *r.l.*), in contrast to those borne on the upper part of the stem, the *cauline* leaves (Fig. 1, *c.l.*).

The simplest possible type of alternate arrangement is for one leaf to be separated by half the circumference of the stem from that at the next node, so that the leaves form two vertical rows. This *distichous* arrangement is well seen in the Hazel (Fig. 70, A), in Grasses and in the Ivy (Fig. 61) and is often expressed simply by the fraction $\frac{1}{2}$. In the Beech and in the Sedges, for instance, the leaves are closer together, forming three vertical rows on the stem and being separated from one another by only one-third of the circumference; the arrangement is therefore *tristichous* and can be briefly represented by the fraction ⅓. One of the commonest types is for successive leaves to follow at intervals approximately equal to two-fifths of the stem's circumference (Fig. 70, B).

In plants having a spiral leaf-arrangement the interval between successive

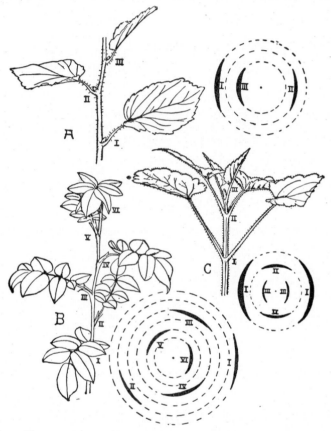

FIG. 70. Shoots and diagrams to show leaf-arrangement. A, Hazel (*Corylus*) (leaf-arrangement ½). B, Dog-rose (leaf-arrangement ⅖). C, Hedge Wound-wort (*Stachys sylvatica*, leaf-arrangement decussate). In the diagrams the dotted circles represent successive nodes, the leaves being indicated in black and numbered in correspondence with the leaves on the shoots.

nodes is often not a constant one, so that, for instance, a ⅖ arrangement below may give place to a ⅓ above (*e.g.* in the Poplar). It is, however, important to realise that alternate leaves are not scattered irregularly on the shoot, but are disposed according to some definite, even though slightly variable, plan.

The external form of the stem often varies with the arrangement of the leaves upon it; thus, although in most plants having alternate leaves the stem is cylindrical, the ⅓ arrangement in Sedges is associated with a triangular stem, whilst in plants with decussate leaves the stem is often square (*e.g.* Labiatæ, Fig. 70, C; Scarlet Pimpernel).

The leaves of erect shoots or of rosettes retain throughout life the position which they occupied at their first development and which is generally well suited to prevent overshadowing. But on horizontal branches of trees and shrubs the conditions are different; the leaves show the same original arrangement as on the upright

FIG. 71. Photographs of two branches of the Hornbeam (*Carpinus*); on the left a horizontal branch showing leaf-mosaic, on the right an upright shoot showing radial arrangement of the leaves. [Photo. E. J. S.]

branches, but during development the orientation of the blades is adjusted so that it becomes more suited to the direction of illumination. This is very clearly seen, if one compares an upright and horizontal branch of a Privet or *Forsythia*. On the erect branch the decussate character is quite distinct, but on the horizontal one the leaf-stalks have twisted, so that the blades are placed more or less horizontally at right angles to the light, the original position of the leaves being only made out by a careful scrutiny of their mode of attachment.

The same feature can be observed in the Beech and Hornbeam (Fig. 71), where on the side-branches the leaves all appear in one plane instead of being radially disposed in a number of vertical

series. Whilst leaves are able to adjust their position in this way
before they attain to maturity, this is not usually possible after the
leaf is fully grown (see, however, p. 266); a position is therefore
taken up during development, such as is well suited to light-
reception.

The preceding considerations indicate that we must distinguish

FIG. 72. Photograph of seedling Sycamore (*Acer pseudoplatanus*)
taken from above, to show leaf-mosaic.   [Photo. E. J. S.]

between the *radial* shoots of most erect plants in which the leaves
and branches spread out in all directions from the axis, and *dorsiventral* shoots in which the leaves and branches lie in one plane,
as in horizontal and creeping stems.   In the latter, the axillary
buds tend to grow out in the plane of the leaves, as in horizontal
branch-systems of Hornbeam (Fig. 71), Elm, or Beech.   Here
there is an almost continuous expanse of leaf-surface, smaller leaves
being situated between larger ones and those of neighbouring
branches overlapping only to a very slight extent, so that we can
speak of a *leaf-mosaic*.   This feature is pronounced in trees with a
dense canopy and in smaller plants growing in the shade of larger
ones.   Such leaf-mosaics are also exhibited by radial shoots
(Fig. 72) and radical rosettes.

CHAPTER XII

LEAVES AND BUDS

THE foliage-leaf as a general rule consists of three parts: the base or slightly enlarged attachment to the stem, the stalk or petiole whose upper surface is generally grooved (Fig. 101), and the blade or lamina. Occasionally the petiole is absent (*sessile*,[1] *e.g.* Shepherd's-purse, Fig. 3, E), but the majority of leaves are *petiolate*. The petiole plays an important part, not only as an organ for spreading out the blade to the light and air, but also, as seen at the end of the last chapter, for placing the latter in the most suitable light-position.

The leaf-blade may consist of one continuous undivided surface, when it is described as *simple* (Fig. 73, A, B, E); or it may be cut up into a number of lobes connected with one another by an undivided portion, when the leaf is said to be *lobed* (Fig. 72; Fig. 73, D); or again it may be completely segmented into a number of separate leaflets, *i.e.* compound (Fig. 70, B; Fig. 73, C and H).

Diverse terms are used to describe the various shapes of leaves and leaflets. A prolonged description is, however, unnecessary, since Fig. 73 shows clearly what is meant by *linear* (*e.g.* Grass-leaves, Fig. 73, G), *lanceolate* (*e.g.* Privet, Fig. 73, I), *ovate* (*e.g.* Chickweed, Fig. 73, B), *obovate* (*e.g.* Garden Spurge, Fig. 73, F), *cordate* (*e.g.* Hedge Woundwort, Fig. 73, A), *reniform* (*e.g.* Ground Ivy, Fig. 73, E) and *hastate* (*e.g.* Convolvulus, Fig. 73, J). The obovate form is merely the ovate inverted, and similarly there are certain plants in which the blades have the shape of an inverted heart (*obcordate*, *e.g.* the leaflets of the Wood-sorrel, Fig. 173, p. 268). A peculiar type of leaf, termed *peltate*, is seen in the Pennyworts and the Garden Nasturtium (Fig. 117, B), the petiole being here attached to the centre of the round blade. A somewhat similar form occurs in the Garden Geranium (*Pelargonium*) in which the base of the lamina forms two lobes which almost meet in the middle line (*orbicular*). As a general rule the two halves of the blade are similar in size, but when one is larger than the other (*e.g.* Lime or Elm) the leaf is said to be *asymmetrical*.

Terms are similarly employed to describe the margin of the leaf; this may be either *entire* (Fig. 73, B, F, I), *i.e.* with a smooth uncut outline, or *serrate* (Fig. 73, A) with forwardly directed, or *dentate* (*e.g.* Enchanter's Nightshade,

---

[1] Regarding the terms used in the description of plant-structure, see B. D. Jackson, *A Glossary of Botanical Terms.* Duckworth, 4th edit., 1928 (481 pp.).

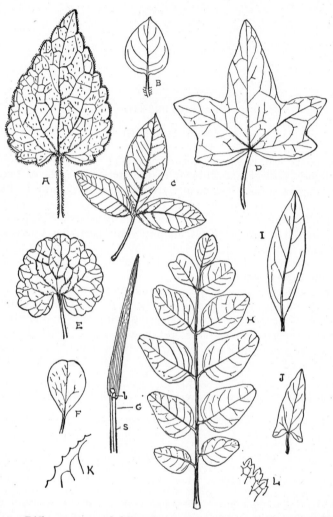

FIG. 73. Different types of foliage-leaves (all about one-half natural size). A, Hedge Woundwort (cordate, acute). B, Chickweed (ovate, acuminate). C, Laburnum (trifoliate). D, Ivy (palmately lobed). E, Ground Ivy (reniform, crenate). F, Garden Spurge (obovate, obtuse). G, Grass (linear). *l*, ligule; *s*, leaf-sheath. H, False Acacia (*Robinia*) (pinnate with mucronate leaflets). I, Privet (lanceolate, entire). J, Field Convolvulus (hastate). K, Enchanter's Nightshade (showing dentate margin only). L, White Deadnettle (showing biserrate margin only).

Fig. 73, K) with outstanding teeth, or *crenate* (Fig. 73, E) with rounded projections.   When the margin is provided with fine hairs, as in the Woundwort
(Fig. 73, A) it is said to be *ciliate*, whilst when there are teeth of two sizes it is
described as *biserrate* (*e.g.* White Dead-nettle, Fig. 73, L) or *bidentate*.

The nature of the leaf-tip also varies, but the figures will make quite clear
what is meant by *acute* (Fig. 73, A and I), *obtuse* (Fig. 73, F), *acuminate* (*i.e.*
tapering to a point, Fig. 73, B) and *mucronate* (*i.e.* with a small point arising
from an almost straight edge, as in the leaflets of the False Acacia, Fig. 73, H).
The surface of the leaf is either *leathery* (Laurel), without hairs (i.e. *glabrous*,
Privet), *hairy* (Woundwort), or *glaucous* (*i.e.* with a waxy bloom, Sea Holly).

It was noticed in the Shepherd's-purse (p. 4, Fig. 3) that the extent of
lobing of the leaf-blade varies greatly, and this shows that there is no essential
difference between a serrate or crenate margin on the one hand and a deeply
lobed margin on the other.   In many plants, however, the character of the
margin is quite constant, and therefore it is often convenient to employ special
terms for deeply cut leaf-blades, *e.g.* the *sinuate* margin of the Oak or the
palmately lobed leaves of the Ivy (Fig. 73, D) and Sycamore (Fig. 72), in which
the lobes are arranged like the fingers of a hand.

There are two principal types of compound leaf: that in which
the leaflets or *pinnæ* are arranged in two rows, one on either side
of the leaf-stalk (*pinnate*, Fig. 73, H; Fig. 70, B), and that in which
all the leaflets come off from the same point (*palmate*, as in the
Lupine).   In the former type the petiole either terminates in a
leaflet (*e.g.* Ash, Rose, Fig. 70, B), or rarely such a terminal pinna
is wanting.   A common form of leaf is that shown by the Strawberry
(Fig. 139) and Laburnum (Fig. 73, C), etc., in which only three
leaflets occur, when the blade is said to be *trifoliate*.   Occasionally
the leaflets of compound leaves themselves exhibit subdivision, so
that blades may be *bipinnate* (*e.g.* Beaked Parsley, *Acacia*, Fig. 174)
or even *tripinnate* (*e.g.* many Ferns).   Compound leaves are readily
distinguished from branches bearing small leaves by the presence
of a bud in the axil of the main stalk, by the absence of axillary
buds to the individual leaflets, and by the absence of a terminal bud.

The transition of foliage already noticed in the Mallow (p. 37)
indicates that the leaves of an individual are not necessarily all alike
in form, and some plants indeed, as for instance the Ivy and the
Scabious, regularly produce foliage of two types.   In the former
the lower leaves are palmately lobed, whilst those upon the flowering
branches are more or less oval in outline.

As regards the arrangement of the veins (*i.e.* the *venation*)
each leaf may show a prominent main vein or midrib, giving off
a number of lateral veins which by continued branching form a
network throughout the lamina (Fig. 3).   Such *reticulate* venation
is characteristic of the leaves of most Dicotyledons, but differences
are found as regards the way in which the prominent veins are
distributed.   Most commonly a single midrib is predominant and

from it laterals of smaller size arise on each side (*pinnate* venation, Fig. 73, B and I and Fig. 365), but occasionally there are several veins of equal prominence branching out from the base of the blade like the fingers of a hand (*palmate* venation, Fig. 73, D and E). In most Monocotyledonous leaves a totally different type of venation is found; the blade is traversed by several veins of similar size running side by side and connected with one another by numerous cross-branches (*parallel* venation, Fig. 73, G).

The *leaf-base* [1] exhibits great variety of form and fulfils a number of different functions. In a large number of plants it appears merely as a more or less marked enlargement at the base of the leaf (*e.g.* Lime). This enlargement is sometimes extensive, forming a prominent cushion or *pulvinus*, and in such leaves the base often retains the power of bending throughout life, so that they are able to adjust their position repeatedly with reference to the light; examples are furnished by the pulvinus at the base of the petiole in the Runner Bean (Fig. 74, F, *p*) and at the base of the leaflets in the Wood-sorrel (Fig. 173). In these plants the laminae change their position at night (cf. p. 268).

Plants possessing large blades often exhibit special modifications of the leaf-base which strengthen them to withstand sudden strain entailed by the resistance offered to wind and rain by the leaf-surface. A simple example is afforded by the Sycamore, in which this is met by a mere swelling of the leaf-base, but in a large number of plants (*e.g.* Burnet Saxifrage, Fig. 74, C, and other Umbelliferæ) the base is expanded to such a degree that it extends round the stem on either side as a more or less close-fitting *leaf-sheath* (Fig. 74, C, *l.b.*); in Grasses the margins [2] (Fig. 73, G, *s*) actually overlap. Since the lower edge of such a sheath is attached to the node along its whole circumference, a much firmer connection between leaf and stem is obtained without loss of elasticity. An extreme type is seen in the Sedges (*Carex*) where the leaf-sheath forms a closed tube enveloping part of the internode above, the blade, as in Grasses, actually diverging from the stem only at some distance above the node. A further increase of the connection with the stem is found in the Mullein (*Verbascum*, Fig. 74, G) and Cotton-thistle (*Onopordon*), where the lower part of the sessile blade is continued down the axis (*decurrent*).

In all plants in which the leaf-base is enlarged it affords a

---

[1] For details, see the work of Goebel, cited on p. 1.

[2] A peculiar structure, of varying size and shape and generally of a membranous texture, is present at the junction of blade and sheath in Grasses (Fig. 73, G, *l*). The purpose of this *ligule* is not properly understood, but it may be protective in function.

certain amount of protection to the axillary bud, and this is very
pronounced in the swollen sheaths of Umbelliferæ (Fig. 74, C).
A very efficient protection of axillary buds is shown by the Ivy
(Fig. 61), the Plane-tree and the Syringa (Fig. 75, B), in all of which
the hollow leaf-base more or less surrounds the bud, so that the
latter is not visible until the leaf has been removed (see right-hand

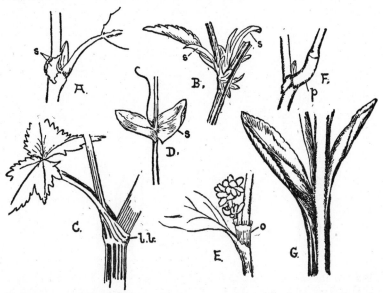

FIG. 74. Leaf-bases and stipules of various plants (all about natural size).
A, Willow, summer-shoot. B, Pansy. C, Burnet Saxifrage (*Pimpinella
major*). D, Meadow Vetchling (*Lathyrus aphaca*). E, *Polygonum persicaria*.
F, Runner Bean. G, Mullein (decurrent leaves). *l.b.*, leaf-base; *o*, ochrea;
p, pulvinus; *s*, stipule.

diagram in Fig. 75, B).   The value of the leaf-base as a protective
structure depends in part on the fact that this portion of the leaf
reaches maturity very early, and this is specially important in those
plants in which it bears leafy outgrowths or *stipules* (Fig. 74, A
and B) helping to shield the axillary bud.   Leaves possessing such
structures are described as *stipulate* in contrast to leaves in which
they are absent, which are said to be *exstipulate*.

Simple forms of such stipules are found on the summer-shoots
of Willows (Fig. 74, A, *s*) and in the Cherry, whilst larger ones,
which are deeply lobed, are seen in the Pansy (Fig. 74, B, *s*).   The
Rose-leaf (Fig. 8, B, *s*; Fig. 70, B) has its stipules joined with the
petiole, so that the base of the latter appears winged.   In many
plants the stipules are green and thus assist in the photo-

synthetic function of the blade; such stipules generally remain attached throughout the life of the leaf (*persistent*), whilst when merely protective they are often leathery or membranous and usually fall off at an early stage (*caducous*). Plants in which the blade is modified for other purposes (*e.g.* to form tendrils for climbing, as in the Meadow Vetchling, Fig. 74, D), often exhibit a

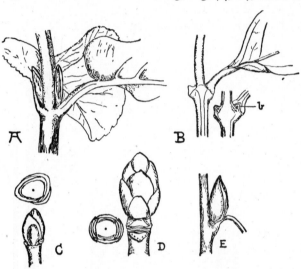

FIG. 75. Bud-protection (all figures about natural size). A, Wayfaring Tree (*Viburnum lantana*) (naked buds). B, Syringa (*Philadelphus*) (bud in hollowed petiole). C, Lime-bud, with plan of bud-scale arrangement above. D, Horse Chestnut-bud, with plan of bud-scale arrangement at side. E, Goat-willow (*Salix caprea*). *b*, bud.

great development of the stipules which then constitute the only photosynthetic portion of the leaf.

As a general rule stipules can be easily recognised as arising directly from the leaf-base, but occasionally they appear rather as outgrowths from the stem on either side of the node; they can, however, be distinguished from leaves by the fact that there is no bud in their axil. A very peculiar instance of this kind is furnished by the Goose-grass (Fig. 8, A) and the Bedstraws (*Galium*) in which each node appears to bear a whorl of leaves; but only two of these leaves situated opposite to one another ever possess axillary buds, and we can consequently infer that the other members of the whorl are stipules. The Persicaria (Fig. 74, E) and the Docks furnish other instances in which the stipules are not at once obvious, since here they are joined together so as to form a short membranous tube (*ochrea*) surrounding the axillary bud and the base of the internode above.

Material for the study of the early development of the shoot is furnished by every bud. The essential structure is always the same and may for the sake of convenience be examined in a Brussels Sprout,[1] a bud in which, owing to its large size, all the parts are easily recognised. Outwardly we see merely a series of overlapping leaves, but a more complicated structure is presented when the bud is halved lengthwise (Fig. 76). The central portion is occupied by the axis which tapers to the meristem (*g.pt.*) above. Below the latter are seen series of developing leaves (p', p'', p''', etc.), the youngest and smallest nearest the meristem, the oldest and most advanced farthest from it. A very short distance behind the meristem minute buds (*ax.b.*) are seen arising in the axils of the young leaves and, farther from the apex, the buds become more and more prominent until each is recognised as having the structure of the whole in miniature. The young leaves are closely crowded

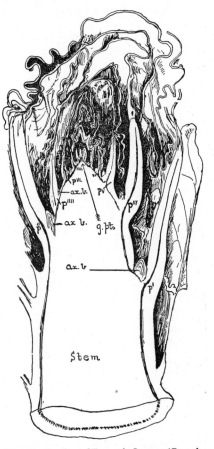

Fig. 76. Section of Brussels Sprout (*Brassica oleracea*) (considerably enlarged). *ax.b.*, axillary buds; *g.pt.*, meristem of main axis; p', p'', p''', etc., leaves of successive ages.

together and the upper internodes are scarcely developed; consequently there is insufficient room for the enlarging leaf-blades which become thrown into numerous folds, and thus the familiar compact structure of a bud is developed.

[1] The Cabbage is likewise a huge bud, each Brussels Sprout being a Cabbage on a small scale.

9

The Brussels Sprout is an example of a summer-bud in which the close packing gives sufficient protection to the young structures developing within, although even here the whole is enveloped in maturer leaves.　In buds which have to withstand the rigour of winter additional protection is, however, necessary and this is provided in a number of different ways.　Most commonly the bud is covered in by close-fitting leathery or membranous scales (the *bud-scales*), which are frequently brown (*e.g.* Beech, Oak), but sometimes black (*e.g.* Ash), and usually exhibit the same arrangement as the leaves upon the stem (Fig. 75, C and D).

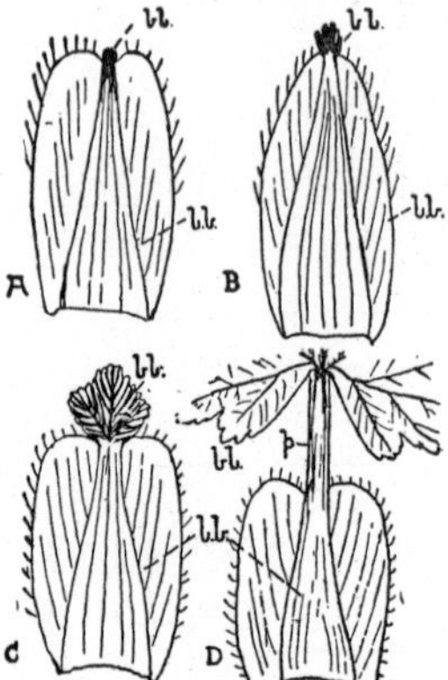

At first sight a bud-scale appears to differ very much from a foliage-leaf, but a comparative examination of the parts of the opening buds of the Flowering Currant will enable us to deduce that the one is but a modification of the other. If, starting at the outside, the bud-scales are removed in succession, a gradual transition will be found between them and the foliage-leaves within the bud (Fig. 77).　The outermost scales are oval with a minute black apex (Fig. 77, A, *bl.*); a little farther in, the scales show a somewhat larger tip which on careful scrutiny is seen to be a rudimentary or arrested leaf-blade (Fig. 77, B, *bl.*); still farther in, the latter becomes more prominent (Fig. 77, C), and so by successive stages we come to the first foliage-leaves in which a petiole (Fig. 77, D, *p*) appears and in which the scaly enlargement at the base (*l.b.*) shows a diminution in size. In the innermost leaves of the bud this scale is seen to have contracted into a small leaf-base, such as is found in the mature foliage-leaves of the plant.　All these transitions may not be present in a single bud.

FIG. 77. Transition between bud-scales and foliage-leaves in Flowering Currant (*Ribes sanguineum*); the successive stages are marked A–D and are all about twice natural size. *bl.*, blade; *l.b.*, leaf-base; *p*, petiole.

The bud-scales of the Flowering Currant are therefore nothing else than modified leaves with a much enlarged leaf-base and a more or less completely arrested lamina.　The same deduction can be made regarding the bud-scales of the Sycamore, Ash, Horse Chestnut, etc.　It is not always the whole leaf-base, however, that forms the bud-scale, for a study of opening buds of the Beech (Fig. 78) or Elm will show that caducous stipules are the protecting structures.　Whereas the inner scales are seen to arise in pairs

from the bases of the unfolding leaves, a variable number of the
outer scales, though likewise paired, have no corresponding blades.
As in the buds of the Flowering Currant, therefore, the laminæ of
the outermost leaves are arrested, only the part necessary for protection (here the stipules, there the leaf-base) being represented.

Another type of bud-scale is seen in the Lilac and Privet in

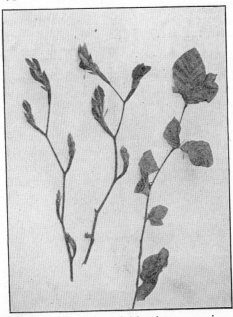

FIG. 78. Photographs of Beech-twigs showing successive stages of bud-
expansion.   In the right-hand twig the stipular bud-scales can be seen adhering
to some of the foliage-leaves.   [Photo. E. J. S.]

which, if the structures composing the bud are removed in succession, it will be found impossible to say exactly where to draw
the line between bud-scale and foliage-leaf.   In fact the bud-scales
here are entire leaves of small size and leathery consistency.   In
the Willow the two bud-scales (Fig. 75, E) represent the first leaves
of the shoot (p. 37).   The bracts found in the region of the inflorescence (p. 427) are frequently modified structures comparable
to bud-scales, often representing an enlarged leaf-base with a
rudimentary lamina at the apex (e.g. *Helleborus*).

Bud-scales are not always the only special protection of the
winter-bud, for not uncommonly there is a layer of sticky varnish
(*e.g.* Horse Chestnut, Poplar), which further reduces the risk of
excessive transpiration (cf. pp. 8 and 13) from the young leaves

within. Moreover, the latter are often equipped with numerous protective hairs, appearing as a white wool in the Horse Chestnut or as a dense brown covering in the Plane Tree (p. 159). A few plants, of which the Wayfaring Tree (Fig. 75, A) and the Alder Buckthorn (*Frangula alnus*) are the only British examples, rely solely on such a felt of hairs, their buds being naked without enveloping scales.

Returning to the study of the Brussels Sprout we may follow up the stages in the development of the foliage-leaf. Even with a lens, some of the leaf-rudiments nearest the meristem appear as perfectly uniform structures, as yet showing no signs of the three parts of the mature leaf. Farther from the apex a distinction can be made between leaf-base and leaf-blade. It is only at a much later stage of development that intercalary growth takes place between the two regions resulting in the formation of the short petiole.

FIG. 79. Diagram to explain method of folding of the young foliage-leaves; in all cases the blade is shown in section. *a*, Fern. *b*, Violet. *c*, *Polygonum*. *d*, Lady's Mantle (*Alchemilla*). *e*, Laurel. In *b–e* the lower surface of the leaf is shown uppermost.

If we examine the buds of a number of different plants, we shall find that the way in which the young foliage-leaves are folded varies greatly (see Fig. 79, B–E). These folds often persist to some extent, for a brief period, after the leaf has emerged from the bud (*e.g.* Beech, Lady's Mantle, etc.), the young blade thus not exposing its full surface until the tissues have matured.

With the arrival of spring all the different parts within the bud begin to expand, the hitherto short internodes commence to lengthen and the leaves to unfold, this taking place at the expense of the food-materials which are stored up in the woody branches (p. 13). As a result the whole bud swells (Fig. 78), the bud-scales are forced apart, and the shoot begins to elongate. No lengthening of the internodes between the bud-scales usually takes place; they consequently remain as a crowded group at the base of the growing shoot. Sooner or later they drop off, leaving a number of broad flat scars which, on superficial observation, look like a series of closely set rings encircling the stem; since such *bud-scale scars* (see Fig. 67) are necessarily formed only at the beginning of each season, the intervals between successive series mark as many years' growth of the branch.

The shoot is generally in an advanced state of differentiation within the bud, in some early flowering plants (*e.g.* Lilac, Horse Chestnut, Flowering Currant) even including an inflorescence in which most of the parts are already present in miniature; the changes subsequent to opening are chiefly in the direction of a rapid increase in size of the different organs. In trees and shrubs most of this growth takes place in a few weeks, and during the remainder of the summer the buds (terminal and lateral) for the next year are being constructed. The enlargement of the shoot-system in a given season is therefore more or less dependent on the nature of the preceding one, and this applies especially to the extent of flowering in those plants in which the flowers are already formed in the winter-buds; of the latter many fruit-trees afford excellent examples. It must be borne in mind that new leaves, and particularly new flowers, may be initiated months before they actually expand. In so far as external conditions, such as weather, are important, they must therefore be considered, not with respect to the time of leaf-expansion or flowering only, but also with respect to the period when the leaf and flower rudiments are actually formed.

CHAPTER XIII

THE STRUCTURE OF THE YOUNG STEM

STEMS, as contrasted with roots, develop under very diverse conditions as regards mechanical stresses, illumination, loss of moisture, etc,. and correlated with this display a much more varied structure. The general plan of construction, moreover, differs from that of roots in several important respects.

The organisation of a Dicotyledonous stem [1] can be studied in a cross-section through the uppermost internode of a young Sunflower (Fig. 80, A). The most obvious feature is that the vascular tissue is a ring broken up into distinct *vascular bundles*. In each the thick-walled xylem (*xy.*) is towards the inside and the thin-walled phloem (*ph.*) towards the outside, the two thus lying on the same radius (constituting a *collateral* bundle), in contrast to the alternate arrangement of these tissues obtaining in the root. By the disposition of the vascular bundles in a ring the ground tissue is marked out into three regions, namely, the *cortex* (Fig. 80, A, *c.*), the *rays* (*r.*), and the *pith* (*p.*). The terms *pith, cortex,* and *rays* are, however, purely topographical, and do not necessarily imply any differentiation between the component cells, which in fact are largely thin-walled and parenchymatous in all three regions (cf. Fig. 82, *Co.* and *p.*). The edge of the section is bounded by the *epidermis* [2] which differs from that of the root in having strongly thickened outer walls. It forms a continuous layer except where interrupted by the presence of stomata or lenticels (p. 189). Its function is to protect the more delicate internal tissues, and in correspondence with this it does not wither at an early stage like the piliferous layer. Occasional cells grow out into hairs (Fig. 80, A, *h.*), but these are quite different in character from the root-hairs.

Immediately within the epidermis in this stem are several layers of collenchymatous cells (Fig. 80, A, *s.*), thickened mainly on the tangential walls, whilst between the cells of the inner layers are

---

[1] Reference-books on plant-anatomy are listed on p. 100.
[2] For a detailed consideration of epidermis and stomata, see the next chapter.

relatively large intercellular spaces. Such spaces are also abundant in the ground tissue generally, and appear as small triangular cavities between the polygonal cells of the pith.

At the inner limit of the cortex there is a single layer of cells distinguished by the frequent presence of large starch-grains (Fig. 82, *sh.*), which can be rendered more prominent by staining with iodine. The layer in question bends outwards around each vascular bundle, and so presents a sinuous outline. Such a *starch-*

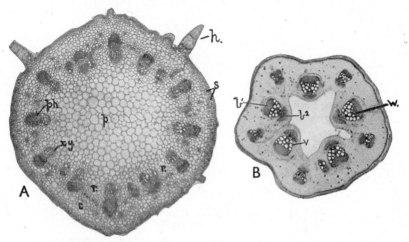

FIG. 80. Photomicrographs of transverse sections of A, the young stem of the Sunflower (*Helianthus*); B, of the Marrow (*Cucurbita*). b^1, b^2, phloem; *c.*, cortex; *h*, hair; *p.*, pith; *ph.*, phloem; *r*, rays; *s*, collenchyma; *v*, vessel; *w, xy.*, xylem.

sheath is not uncommon in herbaceous Dicotyledonous stems (cf. also Fig. 103, *S.s.*). The central cylinder, which is separated off from the cortex by this sheath, is termed the *stele*, and comprises the vascular bundles and the accompanying ground tissue.

The zone of tissue between the starch-sheath and the phloem constitutes the *pericycle*, which, in the Sunflower, is composed of groups of fibres (not fully thickened in the young internode) opposite the bundles (Fig. 81, *f.*; Fig. 103, *F*), and elsewhere of parenchyma (Fig. 80, A). In other plants the pericycle is often parenchymatous throughout, consisting of one or more layers of cells. The term, as in the root, is a purely topographical one, being applied to the region situated between the conducting strands and the starch-sheath or a similar continuous layer of cells.

In the individual bundles the phloem can be distinguished by the shining appearance of the cell-walls, which resemble those of the young fibres, as well as by the unequal size of its component elements (Fig. 81). The large, empty-looking sieve-tubes, exhibiting an occasional sieve-plate (*s.p.*)[1] and associated with small companion cells (*c.c.*), which have dense contents, are intermingled with ordinary parenchyma-cells (*phloem-parenchyma, ph.p.*). Two or three layers of flattened thin-walled cells, situated between the phloem and the xylem, constitute the region of the *cambium*

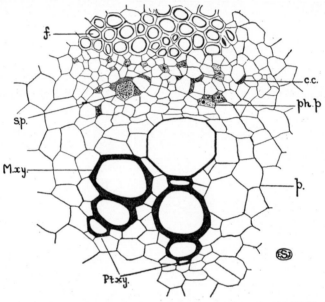

FIG. 81. A single vascular bundle from the stem of the Sunflower (*Helianthus*) in transverse section. *c.c.*, companion cells (shaded); *f.*, fibres of the pericycle; *M.xy.*, metaxylem; *p.*, parenchyma of the rays; *ph.p.*, phloem-parenchyma; *Pt.xy.*, protoxylem; *s.p.*, sieve-plate.

(cf. Fig. 103, *C*, p. 171), a meristematic zone which becomes active in the older stem and forms additional vascular tissue (cf. Chapter XVI).

The wood consists of radial files of vessels separated by rows of smaller parenchymatous cells (the *wood-parenchyma*, Fig. 81). The vessels (*Pt.xy.*), situated nearest the pith, are the *protoxylem* (cf. p. 67), while the larger metaxylem-elements (*M.xy.*) are towards the outside, a further point of contrast to the root. The wood-parenchyma cells have more or less thickened walls, which are lignified like those of the vessels, but they nevertheless retain their living contents. Small cells resembling the wood-parenchyma,

[1] The sieve-plates are not readily recognised in the Sunflower.

but not lignified, form a sheath (the *medullary sheath*, Fig. 80, A) at the inner edge of each bundle.

A longitudinal section of a Sunflower-stem passing radially (*i.e.* parallel to a radius) through one of the bundles will show the same succession of tissues and enable us to complete our picture of the various elements (Fig. 82). The short and somewhat bulging epidermal cells are succeeded by those of the collenchyma, which are many times longer than broad, and have strongly

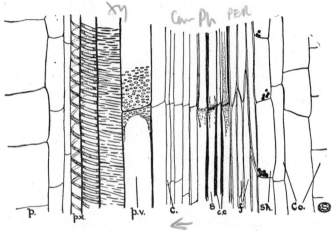

FIG. 82. Longitudinal section through a vascular bundle of the Sunflower (*Helianthus*). *c.*, cambium; *c.c.*, companion cells; *Co.*, cortex; *f.*, fibres of pericycle; *p.*, pith-parenchyma; *p.v.*, pitted vessel of metaxylem; *px.*, spiral vessel of protoxylem; *s.*, sieve-tube; *sh.*, starch-sheath.

thickened longitudinal walls (cf. Fig. 39, A, of Dead-nettle). The thin-walled rectangular cells of the cortex (Fig. 82, *Co.*) are much shorter. Next come the starch-sheath (*sh.*), recognisable by its large starch-grains, and the typical fibres of the pericycle (*f.*). The detailed structure of phloem and cambium (*c.*) will be studied in another stem, but in the former the long, apparently empty, sieve-tubes (*s.*) and the narrow, densely granular, companion cells (*c.c.*) are readily distinguished. The vessels of the metaxylem (*p.v.*) bear very dense spirals or occasionally bordered pits, whilst in the protoxylem the thickening takes the form of rings or of a loose spiral (*px.*). The narrow elongated elements sometimes seen between are the wood-parenchyma cells.

Further insight into the structure of the Dicotyledonous stem will be afforded by a study of that of the Vegetable Marrow (*Cucurbita*) (Fig. 80, B; 83). The transverse section differs from that of the Sunflower in the hollow pith, in the presence of a broad ring of sclerenchyma (*Scl.*) some little way beneath the epidermis, and in the arrangement and construction of the vascular bundles. A pith-cavity is a frequent feature in the stems of herbs (*e.g.* Labiatæ, Umbelliferæ, Gramineæ, etc.), and can be related to cessation in the growth of the pith-cells, so that rupture occurs as a result of the continued enlargement of the stem.

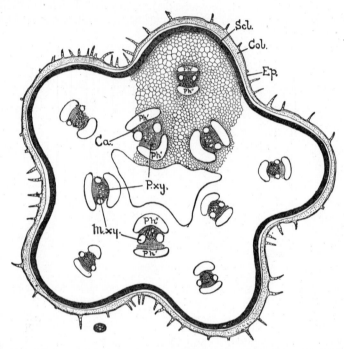

FIG. 83. Diagram of a transverse section of the stem of the Vegetable Marrow (*Cucurbita*). *Ca.*, cambium; *Col.*, collenchyma; *Ep.*, epidermis; *M.xy.*, metaxylem; *Ph.'*, outer phloem; *Ph."*, inner phloem; *P.xy.*, protoxylem; *Scl.*, sclerenchyma (black).

In the stem of the Marrow there are two rings of vascular bundles of which the larger and inner alternate with the smaller and outer (Fig. 83). Two groups of phloem occur in each bundle, one external (*Ph.'*), separated from the xylem by the cambium (*Ca.*), the other internal (*Ph."*), separated from the protoxylem (*P.xy.*) by ordinary parenchyma or sometimes by a second cambium. Such bundles, termed *bicollateral*, are not uncommon in certain families of Flowering Plants, such as the Cucurbitaceæ (to which the Marrow belongs), and the Solanaceæ, and offer a marked contrast to the normal collateral type seen in the Sunflower.

Both inner and outer phloem are composed of the same elements as in the Sunflower, though these are much larger than usual. The general structure has already been described on p. 62 (Fig. 36). In some of the sieve-tubes the plane of the section passes through one of the almost horizontal and deeply stained sieve-plates (*s.p.*). Under high power this exhibits an irregular network of thickening, each mesh being occupied by a large pore, traversed by a thick strand connecting the cytoplasm of adjacent segments. In the longitudinal section, in which the sieve-plates are seen in optical section (Fig. 36, left; 84), they present an interrupted appearance, due to the alternation between the pores and the bars of thickening. The connecting cytoplasmic strands are each encased in a cylinder of callose (cf. below) and are continuous with the cytoplasm lining each surface of the sieve-plate, as well as the longitudinal walls of the segments. This cytoplasm includes plastids, forming a starch which is coloured red by iodine, as well as persisting nucleoli of the disorganised nucleus of the segment, while the vacuole contains a proteinaceous colloidal slime (cf. p. 146), which in preserved material often accumulates on the sieve-plates. In young sieve-tubes denser and more conspicuous "slime-bodies" commonly precede the appearance of slime in the vacuole. Functionless sieve-like areas are sometimes present on the longitudinal walls (Fig. 36).

Thick, highly refractive masses, composed of the carbohydrate *callose* may cover one or both surfaces of the plates. Callose is insoluble in ammoniated copper oxide, but soluble in 1 per cent. caustic potash; it is coloured reddish-brown by chlor-zinc-iodide and becomes deeply stained by prolonged action of eosin or of a dilute aqueous solution of aniline blue. Deposits of callose arise sooner or later in the sieve-tubes of most plants and are often permanent, marking the end of the activity of the element in question. In some woody plants (e.g. *Vitis*) and in many Monocotyledonous rhizomes this is, however, a periodic phenomenon, callose being formed in the autumn and becoming redissolved at the advent of spring. This, as well as the fact that plasmolysis is possible, suggests that, despite the absence of a nucleus, the cytoplasm remains alive until the sieve-tube collapses.

Here and there the plane of the section passes through a companion cell (Fig. 36, *c.c.*) in contact with its sieve-tube. The former tapers off towards the sieve-plates above and below, so that its length coincides with that of the sieve-tube segment from which it was cut off. The large nucleus can generally be seen embedded in the dense cytoplasm which completely fills the cell. The phloem-parenchyma cells (Fig. 36, *p.*) are readily distinguished by their shape from the other elements. The cells of the cambium (Fig. 84, *Ca.*) appear much elongated in the longitudinal section and have chisel-shaped ends.

In the transverse section of the *wood* one can recognise, as in the Sunflower, small protoxylem-elements towards the interior (Fig. 83, *P.xy.*), large metaxylem-vessels beyond (*M.xy.*), and numerous intermingled wood-parenchyma cells. Where two vessels are in contact, the middle lamella between the pitted thickening layers of

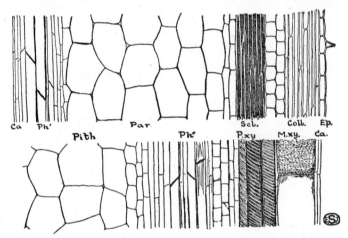

FIG. 84. Longitudinal section through the stem of the Vegetable Marrow (*Cucurbita*). *Ca.*, cambium; *Coll.*, collenchyma; *Ep.*, epidermis; *M.xy.*, metaxylem; *Par.*, parenchymatous cortex; *Ph.'* and *Ph."*, outer and inner phloem; *P.xy.*, protoxylem; *Scl.*, sclerenchyma. The right-hand end of the lower figure joins on to the left-hand end of the upper.

the common wall can be clearly made out. In longitudinal sections the broad metaxylem-vessels (Fig. 84, *M.xy.*) show reticulate thickenings which are in marked contrast to the spiral thickenings of the protoxylem-vessels (*P.xy.*); the slight constrictions occurring at short intervals mark the limits of the vessel-segments, and, in thick sections, the ring-like remnants of the original septa can often be distinguished. The exceptionally large vessels are a marked feature of many other climbers besides the Vegetable Marrow.

Stems of Monocotyledons (of which the Maize furnishes a typical instance) usually exhibit a large number of bundles which frequently appear scattered throughout the whole of the ground tissue, so that a definite cortex and pith cannot be distinguished, *i.e.* there is often no sharply circumscribed stele as in the ordinary Dicotyledon. The bundles (Fig. 85, A), though differing in certain details, show the same general structure, being collateral

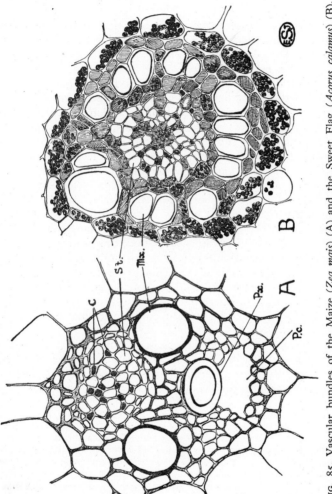

Fig. 85. Vascular bundles of the Maize (*Zea mais*) (A) and the Sweet Flag (*Acorus calamus*) (B). *C.*, companion cells; *Mx.*, metaxylem; *P.c.*, protoxylem canal; *Px.*, protoxylem; *S.t.*, sieve-tubes. Note the envelope of thick-walled cells surrounding the bundle of the Maize.

with xylem and phloem on the same radius and with the protoxylems (*p.x.*) directed inwards.

The phloem (Fig. 85, A), which often has similar shining cell-walls to that of the Sunflower, is an oval or rounded group of tissue composed of sieve-tubes (Fig. 85, A, *S.t.*) and small companion cells (*C.*). The latter are more rounded than is usual in Dicotyledons, and this, combined with the absence of parenchyma,[1] leads to the remarkably uniform appearance of the phloem. There is no cambium between the xylem and the phloem, an important respect in which the Monocotyledonous bundle usually differs from that of the Dicotyledon. The shape of the xylem as a whole is often roughly that of a **Y**, the stem of which is occupied by a radial row of protoxylem-vessels (Fig. 85, A, *Px.*), whilst the arms are formed by a pair of large metaxylem-vessels (*Mx.*). The phloem tends to be sunk between the latter (cf. Fig. 85, A), but the degree of sinking varies considerably in different stems, and in extreme instances the phloem may even be completely surrounded by the xylem (as in the Sweet Flag, *Acorus calamus*, Fig. 85, B). As usual, a certain amount of wood-parenchyma occurs between the vessels. In the stems of the Maize and many other Monocotyledons which exhibit rapid elongation, the protoxylem-vessels undergo early rupture and give rise to an irregular cavity (cf. p. 68) (Fig. 85, A, *P.c.*), in which remnants of the spiral or annular thickenings are recognisable. The bundles are commonly enveloped in a sheath of small, thick-walled cells (often fibres, *e.g.* in the Maize, Fig. 85, A), a feature also encountered in some Dicotyledons (*e.g.* Buttercup).

The typical Monocotyledonous stem thus differs from that characteristic of Dicotyledons in the large number, scattered arrangement, and general form of the bundles, in the usual absence of a cambium, and in the detailed structure of the phloem.

Certain Dicotyledons (*e.g.* Buttercup and its allies), however, show resemblance to Monocotyledons in the shape of the bundle, in the absence of phloem-parenchyma, and the very feeble development of the cambium. Moreover, the stem of the Dicotyledon may exceptionally possess a relatively large number of scattered bundles (*e.g.* Meadow Rue, *Thalictrum*), whilst that of Monocotyledons may in its turn exhibit a ring-like arrangement of the bundles (*e.g.* Black Bryony, *Tamus*, Fig. 86) and a feeble development of cambium (cf. p. 170).

In certain Dicotyledons which possess a normal ring of vascular bundles additional ones occur in pith (e.g. *Rumex crispus, Oenanthe crocata*) or cortex (e.g. *Buxus sempervirens*). Such *medullary* and *cortical* bundles are often probably merely strands entering from the leaves which have not yet taken their normal place in the vascular cylinder (cf. p. 168). These bundles either show

---

[1] Phloem-parenchyma is present in some Monocotyledons.

the normal orientation (*i.e.* with the xylem towards the inside), or they exhibit the reverse arrangement; in many plants, moreover, they consist of phloem only.

The way in which the stem fulfils its functions may now be considered. The elements of the xylem and other mechanical tissues such as collenchyma, whilst giving appreciable support to the immature stem, are inadequate to confer rigidity in the youngest parts where they are yet poorly developed. Such parts depend for their support on an adequate water-supply and, when this is

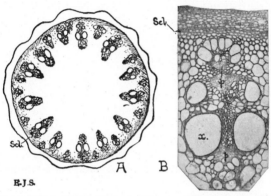

R.J.S.

FIG. 86. Stem of the Black Bryony (*Tamus communis*). A, Diagram of transverse section. B, Photograph of a small portion on a larger scale. *p.*, phloem; *Scl.*, sclerenchyma-ring; *x.*, metaxylem vessel.

lacking, as happens on a hot summer's day, they droop and commence to wilt, although they readily recover when provided with more water. It should be recalled (p. 44) that every living cell of a healthy plant is turgid and, when this is so, it is as firm as an inflated cycle-tyre or a toy balloon. The plant being largely composed of such turgid cells, the whole forms a stiff structure which only becomes flaccid when water is deficient. Part of the liquid can be readily withdrawn from the turgid cells by placing herbaceous plants (*e.g.* any seedling) in a strong solution of salt for some minutes, when they become quite limp, though subsequent immersion in water restores the original firmness.[1]

[1] The recovery of a flaccid shoot when water is sucked into it can be demonstrated with the help of the apparatus shown in Fig. 122 (p. 200), by using a one-holed rubber cork on the flask, provided with a piece of glass tubing bent as in the figure. The upper end of the flaccid shoot is removed and the cut surface, thus produced, is attached to the long arm of the glass tube, whilst the lower end of the shoot is placed in water. In order to prevent the entry of air by way of the stomata, both surfaces of the flaccid leaves should be vaselined. As a consequence, the suction generated within the flask (cf. p. 199) operates in causing a rapid flow of water through the shoot. After a short time the leaves become turgid.

Differences between the various tissues in the extensibility of the cell-walls, and consequently in their wall-pressure (p. 45), also play a part in the stability of herbaceous plants. To study this select young Elder-shoots (or in winter the flowering stems of Narcissus or Daffodil) and cut off a piece about 8 inches long with straight ends. The hard outer portion is then completely removed in four longitudinal strips, leaving only the juicy central pith of the stem. If we now compare the length of the original piece with that of one of the outside strips and with that of the pith, we shall find that the former is a little shorter and the latter slightly longer. This indicates that in such a stem the pith is in a state of compression, while the outer tissues are under tension. Such *tissue-tensions* can be imitated as follows.

A weak spiral spring (such as can be made by twisting thin steel wire round a piece of wood), about 8 or 9 inches long, and a similar length of an inner tube of a cycle-tyre are obtained. Neither is capable of supporting itself when erect; if, however, the spring is slipped into the rubber tube and the former slightly compressed, so that the ends of the tube can be firmly tied, the two combined form a structure of considerable rigidity. Here, just as in the stem, the inner part is in a state of compression while the outer is extended.

It is in consequence of such tissue-tensions that many herbaceous shoots, when halved lengthwise, exhibit a curvature of the two halves with the exterior on the concave and the interior on the convex side; similarly the cut ends of the flower-bearing stalks of Dandelions and other plants, when kept in water, split from below upwards into strips which coil up with the inner tissues facing outwards, owing to their higher suction pressure.

The shoot of the erect plant is chiefly liable to bending, and thus contrasts with the root, which is exposed chiefly to pulling strains. When a stem is bent, the tissue on the convex side is stretched out, whilst that on the concave side is pressed closer together, and the farther we pass from the centre the greater will be the extension and compression respectively. Resistant tissue situated at the outside therefore renders a stem best able to withstand bending; and since the stresses to which a shoot is subjected, as a result of the force of wind and rain against the leaves, may operate in any direction, the advantage of an equal and symmetrical distribution of the strengthening tissue on all sides is obvious. Related to this the *mechanical tissues* of the stem are more or less symmetrically arranged near the periphery. In the young stem the upright position is maintained by the combined support afforded by sub-epidermal collenchyma (Figs. 38, 80, and 83), the xylem, and the turgidity of the living cells. As the stem matures, additional mechanical tissue is often furnished by the development of pericyclic fibres (*e.g.* Sunflower, Fig. 81, *f.*), of a thick-walled sheath to the bundles (Monocotyledons, Fig. 85, A; Buttercup), or of a zone of sclerenchyma in the cortex (*e.g.* Vegetable Marrow, Fig. 83, *Scl.*). Even in the ordinary Monocotyledonous stem the bundles are far more numerous near the edge; moreover, Monocotyledons frequently exhibit a copious development of peripheral sclerenchyma, to which, for instance, the hardness of a

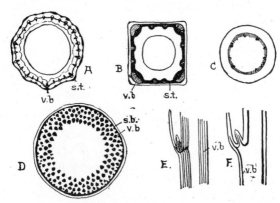

FIG. 87. Diagrams of stem-structure. A–D, cross-sections (considerably enlarged). A, Bishop's-weed (*Aegopodium*). B, *Stachys*. C, Dicotyledon stem with continuous ring of wood. D, *Asparagus*. E–F, longitudinal sections through stem, leaf, and axillary bud; E of *Asparagus*, F of *Stachys*. *s.t.*, non-vascular supporting tissue; *v.b.*, vascular strands.

Bamboo is largely due. The presence of mechanical elements immediately beneath the epidermis often results in a ribbed or fluted appearance of the stem (as in many Umbelliferæ, Fig. 87, A), whilst in the Labiatæ (Fig. 87, B) this strengthening tissue forms a continuous square tube in which the vascular strands themselves are embedded.

In slender underground stems aiding in the attachment of the plant, and therefore chiefly exposed to tension, a much more centralised disposition of the mechanical elements is observed than in the upright shoot. This is well seen in many Sedges and Grasses. An extreme condition is reached in water-plants, where, related to the prevalent pulling strain, such mechanical tissue as is present becomes concentrated at the centre of the stem (cf. p. 543).

Most young stems exhibit *chloroplasts* in the cortical cells (even when these are collenchymatous, as in the Campion), the carbon dioxide requisite for photosynthesis being obtained from the intercellular spaces between them, which communicate with the atmo-

10

sphere by means of occasional stomata in the epidermis. The
outer cortical zone sometimes (*e.g.* Umbelliferæ) consists of alternating bands of mechanical and photosynthetic tissues, the former
occupying the ridges, the latter situated beneath the furrows.
Here the stomata are restricted to the strips of epidermis overlying
the photosynthetic tissue.

Varied evidence (p. 199) shows that the vessels are the
channels by which water and mineral salts are passed from the
root into the leaves. The phloem, on the other hand, serves to
conduct elaborated food-substances (proteins, carbohydrates) which
seem to travel mainly by way of the sieve-tubes. If the stem of
the Marrow be dipped into boiling water so as to coagulate the
contents, the abundant proteins in the sieve-tubes can be demonstrated by heating longitudinal sections with Millon's reagent.
The storage of food-substances in perennial organs (*e.g.* rhizomes,
tubers, etc.) is effected chiefly by the thin-walled ground tissue.

Whilst it has been seen that the arrangement of the tissues
differs materially in root and stem, the ground tissues in the two
organs pass over imperceptibly into one another. The protoxylem-
strands are directly continuous, whilst the metaxylem is developed
towards the exterior in the stem and towards the interior in the
root, and occupies a more or less intermediate position in the region
(*i.e.* the hypocotyl) where the *transition* from the one to the other
type of structure takes place. The phloem is similarly continuous,
and the transition from root to stem mainly involves a lateral and
outward displacement accompanying the enlargement of the vascular
cylinder (Fig. 88). The transition between the two organs is,
however, often very complex, being accompanied by splitting or
union of conducting strands, as a result of which the number of
protoxylem-groups in stem and root do not necessarily correspond.

Some reference has already been made (p. 60) to the development of the axis below the apical meristem. In cross-sections
at this level through a young Dicotyledonous stem a ring of meristematic tissue is often recognisable between the vacuolising cells of
pith and cortex. It is within this ring that the future vascular
tissue develops, commonly as several discrete strands, the *procambial strands*, although not infrequently (*e.g.* Foxglove) a complete
procambial ring is formed. The procambial tissue consists of long,
narrow, thin-walled cells (Fig. 30, *p*), which have tapering ends,
dense protoplasmic contents, and prominent nuclei and arise by
repeated longitudinal division of the cells of the ring, accompanied
by marked elongation. In roots the procambial elements originate
within the central tissue, which is usually regarded as constituting
a single procambial strand.

The vascular elements differentiate progressively from the enlarging procambial strands.   In stems the innermost procambial cells give rise to spirally thickened protoxylem-vessels, while the outermost, usually at a slightly higher level, develop into the first-formed phloem (*protophloem*).   As the strands are traced farther and farther from the apex (*i.e.* from younger to older stages) the differentiation of xylem and phloem proceeds towards the middle of each.   Ultimately all that remains is a narrow strip of thin-walled cells between xylem and phloem, which in Dicotyledons gives rise to the cambium.

In diverse herbaceous and woody Dicotyledons, however, a continuous vascular ring, with primary xylem and phloem arranged concentrically and interrupted by narrow rays, is found already in the young stem.   Such a cylinder arises either from a procambial ring or by the early intercalation of accessory strands between those primarily formed. Not uncommonly pericyclic fibres originate from the outer part of the same procambium as produces vascular tissue.   In the root alternating groups of protoxylem and protophloem arise at the periphery of the procambial strand, whilst the later-formed elements and the pith, if present, develop from the central region.

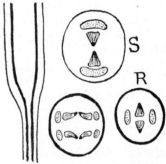

FIG. 88. Diagrams showing one type of transition from the vascular structure of the root to that of the stem. The dotted areas represent phloem and the shaded xylem; protoxylem shown black. *R.*, root; *S.*, stem; the remaining cross-section, hypocotyl.

Both leaves and branches originate close behind the apex of the stem as superficial outgrowths (*i.e.* are *exogenous*, Figs. 29, 30), a mode of development contrasting markedly with the internal (endogenous) origin of lateral roots.   Leaf-rudiments arise at definite intervals by rapid division of the cells of the tunica and of the adjacent underlying cells of the corpus (cf. p. 53 and Fig. 30). Longitudinal divisions within the latter initiate procambial tissue (*p*) at an early stage, the foliar procambial strands being developed in intimate relation to those arising in the stem, so that in the mature condition (p. 168, Fig. 102) the vascular tissues of leaf and stem are continuous.   As the leaf-primordium enlarges, formation of procambial tissue advances acropetally.   The vascular strands of stipules are branches of those in the leaf-base.   The strands arising in the young branches also become connected with those in the stem.

CHAPTER XIV

THE EPIDERMIS

THE surface of the shoot is protected by the epidermis, composed of one layer of living cells which possess certain marked characteristics. In transverse sections the cells usually appear somewhat flattened with slightly convex outer walls; moreover, they fit closely together without intercellular spaces (Figs. 42 and 89, *Ep.*). The epidermal cells have living contents, usually contain plastids, and possess large vacuoles filled with watery, generally colourless, sap (Fig. 89, *Ep.*). Chloroplasts are not developed in the cells in well-illuminated situations, but are often present in the epidermis of submerged aquatics or of land-plants when growing in the shade (cf. pp. 522, 550).

The outer epidermal walls are usually more strongly thickened than the others, and so changed (*cuticularised*) as to render them much less permeable to water vapour and gases. The exact nature of the modification is obscure, but it appears to consist essentially in impregnation with substances of a fatty character; these are most abundant in the outermost region of the external walls, which together form a relatively impermeable layer, continuous over the whole epidermis (except for the stomata), known as the *cuticle* (Figs. 89 and 92, *Cu.*). Where the walls are strongly thickened an intervening zone (the cuticularised layers), in which cuticularisation has not progressed to the same extent, can sometimes be distinguished between the cuticle and the unaltered cellulose on the inside. The cuticle is often yellowish in colour, whilst the cuticularised layers, when present, appear faintly yellow and less transparent than the colourless cellulose. The cuticle may be quite smooth, but in some leaves (e.g. *Helleborus fœtidus*) it presents numerous minute ridges which appear as faint striations in surface sections. Cuticularisation may sometimes extend to the lateral walls, which then are generally thickened, so that in section they appear as pegs projecting inwards.

The cuticle is insoluble in cuprammonia and concentrated sulphuric acid, being the only part of the epidermis that does not dissolve in the latter reagent. With iodine and sulphuric acid it yields a brown colouration, and it is easily stained with Scharlach red, probably as a result of the presence of fatty substances.

Owing to its toughness, the cuticle, especially when strongly developed, renders the epidermis more efficient as a protection against mechanical injury and infection; but its chief function is

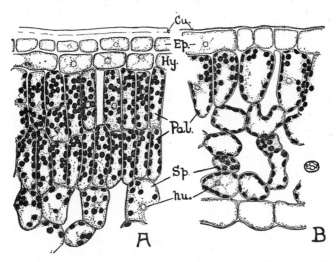

FIG. 89. Transverse sections through the leaves of the Holly (A) and *Ranunculus auricomus* (B). In the former only half of the vertical extent of the leaf is shown. *Cu.*, cuticle; *Ep.*, epidermis; *Hy.*, hypodermis; *Nu.*, nucleus; *Pal.*, palisade layers; *Sp.*, spongy parenchyma. The chloroplasts are shown black.

to restrict transpiration mainly to the stomata. In correspondence with this its thickness varies with the nature of the habitat; thus the cuticle is most strongly developed in plants of dry situations (*e.g.* Gorse, Fig. 345, B; *Ammophila*, Fig. 397, A, etc.), whilst it is extremely thin in or absent from submerged aquatics (Fig. 382), where absorption of water takes place over the whole surface. Most young organs, before they have attained their full size, possess but a very thin cuticle and exhibit considerable cuticular transpiration; hence the necessity for other means of reducing water-loss (*e.g.* hairs, folding of leaves, etc.). Even a very thick cuticle is, however, not completely impermeable. Its efficiency in reducing transpiration is sometimes augmented by a covering of *wax* secreted by the epidermal cells; when present in any considerable quantity (*e.g.* leaves of the Sea Holly, fruit of the Plum, etc.), this gives the surface a bluish tinge. Such coverings of wax also prevent the collection of moisture on the surface of the plant. They are readily rubbed off, but may be subsequently renewed.

Not uncommonly the epidermis can be easily stripped off and so examined in *surface view*, when it will again be seen to form a continuous layer (Fig. 90, B–D) without intercellular spaces, the only gaps being the pores of the stomata. The shape of the cells in such surface sections is very varied. In stems (Fig. 90, D) and in the leaves of most Monocotyledons (Fig. 90, C) they are usually considerably elongated parallel to the longitudinal axis, whilst in most Dicotyledonous leaves they are roughly isodiametric (Fig. 90, B). Where the lamina is thin the lateral walls of the epidermal cells are often undulated (Fig. 90, B). Through this wavy outline the cells interlock, so that the surface of contact is increased, and the risk of tearing by the wind is diminished. The lower epidermis, which has numerous points of weakness constituted by the stomatal perforations, generally exhibits this undulation to a more marked degree than the upper.

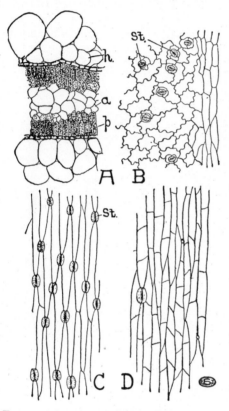

FIG. 90. Structure of the epidermis. A, Transverse section of leaf of Silver Goosefoot (*Halimione portulacoides*) showing bladder-like hairs (*h.*), the aqueous tissue (*a.*), and the palisade layer (*p.*). B, Surface section of leaf of Ground Ivy (*Glechoma hederacea*). C, Surface section of leaf of Onion. D, Surface section of stem of Runner Bean (*Phaseolus multiflorus*). *St.*, stomata.

The epidermis in the young plant keeps pace with the increasing size of the underlying tissues by the division and growth of its cells, but usually all the septa are at right angles to the surface, so that it remains a single layer. This subdivision is plainly recognisable in the stem of the Runner Bean, where the spindle-shaped epidermal cells, after reaching a certain size, become divided by transverse septa (Fig. 90, D).

In plants of dry habitats the epidermal cells may attain a considerable size (*e.g.* in the Sea Purslane, *Honkenya peploides*) and serve for the storage of water, which is possibly always a function of this layer, though here to a much greater extent than normally. In extreme instances water may be stored in localised enlargements, which often project as water-containing *hairs* or bladders (*e.g.* the Ice-plant, *Mesembryanthemum crystallinum*, and the Silver Goosefoot, *Halimione portulacoides*, Fig. 90, A, *h.*).   In times of drought the adjacent photosynthetic tissues withdraw moisture from these cells, which consequently contract, the side walls becoming undulated; when water again becomes plentiful, the cells fill and the walls gradually straighten out.   The epidermis is not uncommonly aided in the storage of water by the development of one or more additional layers, which may be formed by the division of the epidermis (*Ficus elastica*), or by differentiation from the underlying tissues (as in the Holly, Fig. 89, A, *Hy.*).   The cells of such a *hypoderm* resemble the epidermal cells in the possession of large vacuoles and the absence of chloroplasts, but usually have thinner walls. It will hence be realised that leaf and young stem are always surrounded by a water-jacket tending to diminish the heating effect of the sun.

Water may also be retained by thick mucilaginous internal walls (cf. p. 70) developed by the epidermal cells (*e.g.* Hollyhock, Sycamore, etc.).   These often project deeply into the photosynthetic tissues when swollen with water.   This feature tends to retard the evaporation of water during periods of drought.

The pronounced thickening and cuticularisation of the outer walls of the epidermal cells, and the absence of intercellular spaces between them, endues the epidermis as a whole with considerable strength.   It hence serves as a mechanical protection, but also (in combination with the hypoderm, when present) as a light-screen for the underlying chlorophyll.   Moreover, the polished cuticle, especially characteristic of tropical plants, serves to reflect a large part of the light and heat rays falling upon it.   Most important of all, it checks evaporation from the general surface of the plant, and indeed, where the cuticle is thick, transpiration is almost entirely restricted to the stomata.

Certain *modifications* of the epidermis are associated with special physiological functions.   Thus in many shade-loving plants the outer walls of the epidermal cells are markedly convex (*e.g.* Wood Sorrel; Moschatel, *Adoxa*, Fig. 91).   Each cell, then, functions as a plano-convex lens focussing a localised patch of bright light at its base. It has been suggested that this acts as a mechanism for the orientation of the leaf, since, when the direction of illumination is altered, the position of the patch of light likewise changes. The protoplasm upon which this light falls is assumed to be sensitive, so that an adjustment of the leaf follows until the patch of light is again located in the normal position. But quite apart from any value that this may possibly have in enabling the plant to place its leaves at an appropriate angle to the light, the concentration of the latter may well be of value in connection with photosynthesis.

FIG. 91. Transverse section through part of the upper epidermis and palisade layer of the leaf of the Moschatel (*Adoxa moschatellina*). The chloroplasts are shown black.

The general characteristics of *stomata* are readily studied by stripping off a piece of the epidermis from a fresh leaf of the *Iris*. Scattered among the colourless elongated cells are oval stomata, each consisting of two bean-shaped *guard-cells* (Fig. 92, C, *g.c.*; see also Fig. 90, C) surrounding the narrow elliptical *pore* by means of which the intercellular spaces of the leaf communicate with the external atmosphere. The guard-cells contrast with the ordinary epidermal cells in containing numerous chloroplasts and starch-grains, and are especially distinguished by the uneven thickening of their walls, which are thin on the side away from the pore, but markedly thickened around the latter. Each guard-cell has a well-developed protoplast and a prominent nucleus. The ordinary epidermal cells almost meet above the guard-cells, so that the latter are only plainly visible on focussing to a lower level (Fig. 92, C); in this way the pore comes to be situated at the bottom of a miniature hollow (*vestibule*) constituted by the surrounding cells, and the stoma consequently occupies a sheltered position. This feature is especially marked in plants of dry situations, but in those growing in damp, shady habitats the guard-cells are often level with or raised above the adjacent epidermis (Fig. 345, C, D).

The overarching of the guard-cells by the adjoining epidermal cells is equally obvious in a transverse section (Fig. 92, D) of the *Iris*-leaf. Here each guard-cell appears approximately oval in form and provided with thick walls, the thickening being especially marked adjacent to the pore, and giving rise to a slight upwardly projecting ridge at the outer edge of the aperture. In many plants, however, the walls of the guard-cells are not so uniformly thickened, those remote from the pore being relatively thin, whilst those towards the aperture show a marked decrease in thickness opposite the middle of the pore (*e.g.* Onion, Fig. 92, E); in such stomata the outer ridges are well marked, and there is frequently a second pair of ridges on the inner side. As a result of this unequal distribution of the thickening, the cavities of the guard-cells taper abruptly in the direction of the pore, so that a maximum thickness is obtained

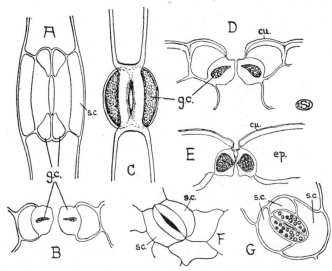

FIG. 92. Structure of stomata. A, C, F and G, in surface view; B, D and E, in transverse section. A, B, Millet-Grass (*Milium effusum*). C, D, *Iris germanica*. E, Onion (*Allium cepa*). F, Madder (*Rubia peregrina*). G, *Sedum spectabile*. *cu.*, cuticle; *ep.*, epidermal cell; *g.c.*, guard-cells; *s.c.*, subsidiary cells.

towards the upper and lower sides (Fig. 92, E); in some plants this is so marked that the whole cavity merely appears as a slit (*e.g.* Grass, Fig. 92, B). Beneath the stoma lies an air-space, the *respiratory cavity* (Fig. 98, *R.*), serving for the immediate interchange of gases and water-vapour between the intercellular system of the plant and the air around.

The vertical leaf of the *Iris*, in which both surfaces are alike, bears almost the same number of stomata on each. Moreover, the latter are all placed parallel to the axis, as in most Monocotyledons (Fig. 90, C) and the epidermis of young stems; in the latter, however, the stomata are often few in number (Fig. 90, D). Those of horizontal dorsiventral leaves (*e.g.* most Dicotyledons) are chiefly situated on the lower surface, being sometimes altogether absent from the upper (*e.g.* most trees), and, moreover, exhibit an irregular arrangement (Fig. 90, B).

The number of stomata per unit area apparently bears no relation to the need for economy of water. Actually the frequency of stomata for a particular species may vary greatly in different parts of the same leaf, and especially in leaves growing under different conditions. The frequency appears to depend almost entirely on the species concerned and the extent to which the stomata are separated by the growth of the intervening epidermal cells, and as a consequence the leaves of plants growing in dry habitats usually have more numerous stomata than those of the same species when growing in humid conditions (cf. p. 522).

TABLE OF STOMATAL NUMBERS

	Average Upper Epid.	Average Lower Epid.
TREES		
Oak (*Quercus Robur*)	o	450
Beech (*Fagus sylvatica*)	o	236
Birch (*Betula alba*)	o	184
SHRUBS		
Barberry (*Berberis vulgaris*)	o	400
Hazel (*Corylus avellana*)	o	225
Whortleberry (*Vaccinium myrtillus*) . . .	16	120
Elder (*Sambucus nigra*)	o	90
Guelder Rose (*Viburnum opulus*)	o	79
HERBS		
Brachypodium sylvaticum	240	o
Wild Hyacinth (*Scilla non-scripta*) . . .	55	51
Daffodill (*Narcissus pseudo-narcissus*) . . .	65	68
Dog's Mercury (*Mercurialis perennis*) . . .	o	82
Lesser Celandine (*Ficaria verna*) . . .	21	75
Goldielocks (*Ranunculus auricomus*) . . .	16	59
Lilium martagon	o	30
AQUATICS		
Water Plantain (*Alisma plantago*) . . .	50	36
Water Forget-me-not (*Myosotis palustris*) . .	7	91
Frog Bit (*Hydrocharis morsus-ranæ*), floating leaves .	89	o

The stomatal apparatus originates from a mother-cell which is cut off by means of a curved septum from one of the ordinary epidermal cells. Soon a vertical wall is formed parallel to the long axis of the mother-cell, separating the future guard-cells, which gradually acquire their distinctive thickening. Meanwhile the middle lamella between them breaks down, except at the two ends, to form the pore. In some families the guard-cells are accompanied by so-called *subsidiary cells* (two in the Rubiaceæ,

Fig. 92, F, *s.c.*, three or more in the Crassulaceæ, Fig. 92, G, *s.c.*) which differ in size and shape from the other epidermal cells, and probably form part of the mechanism of the stoma.   Subsidiary cells are usually cut off from the mother-cell before the guard-cells are produced, but in some plants they are formed by division of the surrounding epidermis.

On mounting a strip of fresh epidermis in water, the open pores of the stomata are conspicuous, being usually occupied by air.   On transference to glycerine or a 5 per cent. sugar solution, which will reduce the turgor of the guard-cells, the width of the pores decreases appreciably (*i.e.* they "close"), but when returned to water the turgor is restored and they again open.   Measurement shows that, though there is usually no marked change in length, there is an appreciable increase in width, when the stoma opens (cf. Fig. 93).   The alteration in form of the guard-cells, to which the variation in the size of the stomatal aperture is due, is thus primarily determined by changes in turgescence.

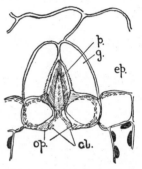

FIG. 93. Half of a stoma seen in perspective, showing the positions of the guard-cells in the open (*op.*, firm lines) and closed (*cl.*, dotted lines) conditions. *ep.*, epidermis; *g.*, guard-cell; *p.*, pore.

The *mechanism* is, however, directly dependent on the unequal distribution of thickening which, in transverse section, has been seen to be mainly localised around the upper and lower edges of the pore;   on the other hand, the middle of the convex wall next to the pore, as well as the curved wall remote from the pore, remain comparatively thin (Fig. 92, E).   When the guard-cells are turgid and the thin walls stretch, the pull exerted separates the thick walls, thus opening the pore (Fig. 93, *op.*).   As seen in section, opening of the stoma is accompanied by a flattening of the convex walls on each side of the pore and an increased convexity of the unthickened walls.   As a result there is movement of the guard-cells at the lines of junction with the adjacent epidermis both above and below, due to the bulging of the walls away from the pore.   Where both the outer and the inner walls of the epidermal cells are thickened, there is at the points of junction with the guard-cells a sudden thinning which admits of their movement (*e.g.* Onion, Fig. 92, E); but when the external wall alone is thickened, such a hinge occurs only on the outside (*e.g.* Iris, Fig. 92, D).   The flattening of the convex walls adjacent to the pore is aided by the thin middle part, which forms a similar hinge.

An action, resembling that of a stoma and likewise depending on unequal distribution of thickening, can be obtained by halving longitudinally a short length of Daffodil-stalk or internode of Dog's Mercury and rendering the halves flaccid by immersion in a strong salt-solution. The flaccid strips, with the original outer surfaces in contact, are firmly tied together at the two ends. When immersed in water, they become turgid and gradually arch apart, in other words, the pore of the artificial stoma opens; a return to the salt-solution once more results in closure and this sequence of events can be repeated.

The *influence of external conditions* on the size of the pore can be indirectly studied with a *porometer* (Fig. 94). This consists of a T-tube (*t*), one horizontal arm of which can be closed by a clip (*c*), while the other is connected in an air-tight manner with the under side of the leaf (*l*); this is simply done by pressing the melted end (*a*) of thick-walled rubber tubing against the leaf or by connecting the tubing with a glass cup pressed onto the leaf through a gelatine washer (Appendix XVII). The vertical arm is joined to the tube *e*, into which water is raised by applying suction at *f*. When the clip is closed, the water-column in *e* slowly falls, as air passes from the uncovered part of the leaf through the air-spaces into *t*, the rate of fall (measured against a scale) being directly proportional to the width of the stomatal pores, although also dependent on the changing resistance to flow of air through the intercellular spaces of the leaf. Depletion of carbon dioxide beneath the cup causes the enclosed stomata to open more widely than those outside, so that for accurate work it is necessary to use a special cup through which a current of ordinary air can be passed between readings.

A direct method is to immerse leaves, immediately after detachment, in strong alcohol which fixes the guard-cells in their momentary condition. The average size of the pores is then measured under the microscope (Appendix II) on a strip of epidermis. Such measurements can also be made on the living plant.

The opening and closing of stomatal pores is primarily influenced by light and water-supply. If the latter is adequate, the stomata of some plants (*e.g.* Potato, Cabbage) remain open throughout the 24-hour period, while in most thin-leaved plants (*e.g.* Cereals) they open during the day and close at night. In them the sensitiveness of the stomata to light is such that, even the effect of temporary shading, as by a big cloud, can be observed with the porometer. This shows that alteration in turgidity of the plant as a whole is not necessarily involved. Moreover, Fungi, which have no stomata, also exhibit diminished transpiration in darkness.

The normal rhythm of stomata may, however, be markedly altered when a shoot becomes flaccid owing to water-deficiency. This is often due to excessive transpiration, the rate of which depends mainly upon external factors, like wind and the humidity of the air (p. 202), but also upon the water-content and temperature of the leaf. On dry sunny days the stomata of diverse plants have been found to close round about midday and, with increasing water-stringency, the period of opening may be more and more curtailed. At the onset of wilting, however, stomata may temporarily open more widely, while in many plants (including shade- and marsh-plants, *e.g.* Water Plantain) they remain open even in flaccid shoots. Though they ultimately respond to wilting, closure is often so long delayed that the check is ineffective (see also p. 203).

The changes in shape of the guard-cells are apparently due largely to changes in osmotic potential of the sap which may be five times as great in the open as in the closed stoma. These changes result from alterations in the relative proportions of sugar and starch. In light, when starch is hydrolysed and the sugar-content and osmotic concentration of the sap increase, the stoma opens; in darkness starch is formed from sugar and the pore closes. There is some evidence that, in wilting leaves also, synthesis of starch in the guard-cells is promoted. The effect of light is probably indirect and related to changes in hydrogen-ion concentration. In light the carbon dioxide of respiration does not accumulate (p. 9), the hydrogen-ion

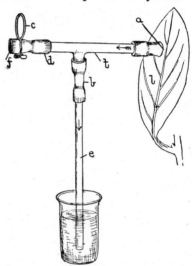

FIG. 94. Porometer, for description see p. 156.

concentration is less and the conversion of starch into sugar is favoured. In darkness the accumulating carbon dioxide increases the acidity and starch is formed. Lower acidity is believed to favour diastase which mainly hydrolyses, while increased acidity favours phosphorylase and so promotes condensation (p. 85). There are indications, however, that the starch-sugar hypothesis is inadequate by itself. Changes in permeability and hydration of the cytoplasm may also be involved.

A modified stoma is found in the Gramineæ and Cyperaceæ (Sedge-family). The much elongated guard-cells surround a pore having the form of a flattened hexagon (Fig. 92, A). In the middle of each guard-cell the outer and inner walls are so strongly thickened as to leave only a small slit-shaped cavity (Fig. 92, B), but the end-portions are thin-walled (Fig. 92, A, *g.c.*). The stomata are flanked by thin-walled subsidiary cells (*s.c.*), which, together with the terminal

portions of the guard-cells, function in much the same way as the
thin-walled part of an ordinary guard-cell, whilst the thick median
portions correspond to the thickened walls of the latter.

Not uncommonly a few, or even many, of the epidermal cells
(cf. Fig. 83) grow out into more or less elongated, often branched,
processes called *hairs*, which are especially common on leaves and,

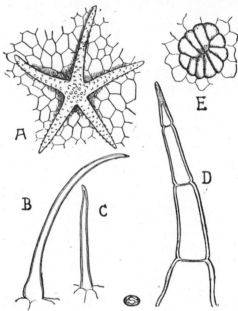

FIG. 95. Hairs. A, of *Deutzia*; B, of *Cynoglossum*; C, of Shepherd's
Purse (*Capsella*) (unbranched type); D, of Vegetable Marrow
(*Cucurbita*); E, of Hop (*Humulus*).

when numerous, very obvious. They may remain unicellular
(Fig. 95, B, C), or become multicellular (Fig. 95, D) by the formation of septa. Nearly every type of hair, whether branched or
not, may be, in one plant or the other, uni- or multi-cellular
without any appreciable difference in outward form; but the
presence or absence of septa, as well as the structure of the hair,
are often characteristic of whole groups. The walls of the hairs
are of varying thickness, and either consist of cellulose or have
undergone chemical alteration.

One of the most important *functions* of hairs, when numerous,
is to bring about a decrease in the rate of transpiration in wind.
The moist air entangled between these hairs is sheltered, so that

it is not readily removed by air-currents, nor does it diffuse rapidly into the dry atmosphere around. As a result of the presence of this moisture-laden air in the immediate neighbourhood of the leaf-surface, transpiration of water-vapour from the interior through the stomata is retarded. These *covering hairs* are usually dead and, at maturity, occupied only by air; such dead hairs often appear white, showing that a large proportion of the light falling upon them is totally reflected, hence they also afford protection against the heating effect of the sun and against excessive illumination. Hairs thus serve to reduce transpiration and act as a screen to the underlying chloroplasts. An analogy could be drawn with the interior of a woodland, where beneath the trees the air is cool, shady, and damp, just as it is beneath the hairs on a leaf. Not uncommonly hairs are only present on the young leaf, falling off as the latter matures (*e.g.* Plane, Horse Chestnut, etc.).

The simplest type of covering hair is unbranched and usually tapers towards the tip (Fig. 95, B–D). Short stiff hairs of this kind are found in some Boraginaceæ (*e.g.* Forget-me-not, etc.), but they are often much longer, and either interwoven to form a woolly tangle (*e.g.* Coltsfoot, Thistles, young leaves of the Horse Chestnut, etc.) or all disposed in the same direction, giving a silky appearance to the surface of the leaf (*e.g.* Silverweed, *Potentilla anserina*). Long unbranched hairs from the seed-coat of the Cotton-plant (*Gossypium* spp.), a member of the Mallow-family (Malvaceæ), are the source of cotton.[1] They are unicellular and may reach a length of 2–5 centimetres and serve for the dispersal of the seeds by wind. Similar hairs, with the same function, occur on the seeds of the Willow, Willow-herb (*Epilobium*), and many other plants.

The epidermal cells of many petals are drawn out into very short processes, or *papillæ*, which are the cause of the velvety surface and prevent wetting. A similar production of papillæ is not uncommon on the stomatal surface of the leaves of tropical plants growing in damp situations (*e.g.* tropical rain-forest).

Branched hairs assume very diverse forms, only a few of which can be mentioned. In the Mullein and Plane they are tree-like, and consist of an erect multicellular axis from which numerous tapering branches radiate at intervals. More frequent are so-called *stellate hairs*, in which there is but one set of radiating branches terminating a short stalk which, however, is sometimes practically absent (e.g. *Deutzia*). Multicellular hairs of this kind are typical of the Lime-family (Tiliaceæ) and Mallow-family (Malvaceæ), whilst unicellular ones are exemplified in *Deutzia* (Fig. 95, A). Stellate hairs are also found in the Cruciferæ (Fig. 4, C), but here they are accompanied by simpler forms with only two or three branches and by unbranched hairs.

A very efficient transpiration-check is afforded by the *peltate hairs*, which are well seen in the Sea Buckthorn (*Hippophaë*, Fig. 96) and in *Elæagnus*,

---

[1] The walls of these hairs are practically pure cellulose. Many hairs, which from their length might be used for the manufacture of textiles, are slightly lignified, and consequently too brittle to spin. Kapok of commerce is obtained from the slightly cuticularised hairs lining the fruit of the Silk-Cotton tree (*Eriodendron anfractuosum*), which is common in the Tropics.

where, owing to the large number of these scale-like structures, the under-surface of the leaf has a characteristic silvery appearance. The short stalk of these hairs is surmounted by a horizontal expansion, consisting of a large number of unicellular rays which are joined together at their base but free at their tips.

Certain climbers (p. 17) are materially aided in clinging to their support by the possession of stiff hairs. Thus the ridges on the stem of the Goosegrass (*Galium aparine*) bear numerous reflexed unicellular hairs, shaped like a hook. In the Hop the ridges are similarly beset by stiff hairs, with two arms situated in the vertical plane, on a small elevation of the epidermis. Extreme types of multicellular climbing hairs are furnished by the prickles of the Rose and Bramble.

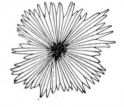

FIG. 96. Peltate hair of Sea Buckthorn (*Hip-pophaë rhamnoides*).

Whilst the walls of the ordinary covering hairs are generally not appreciably thickened, both branched and unbranched hairs may possess thick walls which are frequently silicified or calcified; when thus stiffened, they constitute a *chevaux-de-frise* against small animals (*e.g.* slugs). Good examples are afforded by the unbranched bristle-hairs of many Boraginaceæ (*e.g.* Borage, Comfrey, etc.) and the branched types found on Stocks and other Cruciferæ. Their effect is often accentuated by the presence of numerous minute teeth on their surface (Fig. 95, A).

One of the most striking examples of hairs acting as a deterrent to animal attacks is, however, furnished by the unicellular *stinging hairs* of the Nettle (*Urtica*) (Fig. 97, D). Each is borne on a multicellular stalk in which is embedded the thin-walled swollen base of the actual stinging hair. The upper part of the latter is comparatively thick-walled and tapers gradually to near the apex, where it suddenly enlarges to form a tiny bead-like tip (Fig. 97, E). The lower part of the wall is calcified, the upper part silicified. The living protoplasmic contents often show distinct streaming movements, and include a large vacuole filled with acrid sap. When an animal brushes against one of these hairs, the little tip breaks off, leaving exposed a fine needle-like point formed by the upper tapering part of the hair. As a result of the pressure of contact, this fine tube penetrates the skin, and the compression of the bladder-like base injects the contained fluid into the wound.

The hairs of many plants produce secretions [1] which are often of the nature of ethereal oils (cf. p. 90). Such *glandular hairs* are

[1] Water- and sugar-secreting hairs are considered in Chapter XVIII.

multicellular and generally consist of a basal cell, which is usually sunk in the epidermis, a projecting stalk, and a glandular head (cf. Fig. 118, *g.h.*), but are otherwise of very diverse form. In the Chinese Primrose (*Primula sinensis*, Fig. 97, A–C) and the Garden Geranium (*Pelargonium*), the head is formed by a single cell and the stalk by a varying number of cells. In the Labiatæ (*e.g.* White Deadnettle) the head is composed of four or more

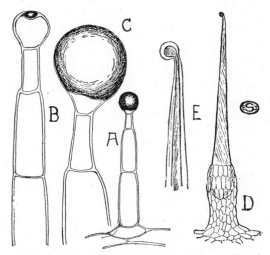

FIG. 97. Glandular hairs of Chinese Primrose (*Primula sinensis*, A–C) and Stinging Hair of Nettle (*Urtica*, D, E). In A–C the secretion is shaded, and in C and E only the greatly magnified tip of the hair is shown.

cells disposed in a plane parallel to the surface of the leaf. Extended division of the head leads to the peltate type of glandular hair, such as is seen in the Hop (Fig. 95, E) and the Black Currant.

All the cells of such glandular hairs are living, those of the head which are concerned in active secretion being specially characterised by dense protoplasmic contents and large nuclei. Small droplets of secretion can often be recognised within the young glandular cells, but in the mature condition the ethereal oil is found deposited between the cuticle and the cellulose-layer of the outer wall (Fig. 97, B), so that after solution of the oil by means of alcohol a space is evident beneath the cuticle. The volatile oils produced by these glands are the cause of the fragrant perfume of many herbs (*e.g.* Lavender).

CHAPTER XV

THE STRUCTURE OF THE LEAF

THE detailed structure of dorsiventral leaves is most easily realised in a transverse section. Beneath the colourless epidermis (Fig. 98, *Ep.*) of the upper side are one or more layers of vertically elongated cells constituting the *palisade tissue* (*Pa.*), which is especially concerned with photosynthesis; its cells are deep green owing to the numerous chloroplasts. Between the palisade layer and the lower epidermis lies the loose "*spongy*" tissue (*Sp.*), which is composed of irregular cells separated by many and often conspicuous intercellular spaces (*In.*). This tissue contains fewer chloroplasts and communicates with the external atmosphere by way of the stomata. Palisade and spongy tissues together constitute the ground-tissue, or *mesophyll*, of the leaf. Here and there the section will pass through *veins*, some cut transversely, others obliquely or longitudinally; the veins include the vascular tissue with xylem towards the upper and phloem towards the lower side, and each is surrounded by a well-defined layer of cells, the *bundle-sheath* (*Sh.*).

Good material for a detailed study is furnished by the *Fuchsia*. The features of the epidermis have been fully described. The *palisade* cells are four to six times as long as broad and form a single layer (Fig. 98, *Pa.*). They are attached on the one hand to the upper epidermis, and on the other to the rounded cells constituting the uppermost layer of the spongy parenchyma. Narrow intercellular spaces, extending the whole depth of the palisade layer, occur at intervals between the cells, but these spaces are only apparent here and there in the transverse section (cf. Fig. 98, *Pa.*). In sections parallel to the surface of the leaf the palisade cells appear rounded (being cut transversely, Fig. 99, A), so that they have the form of a number of closely packed cylinders placed side by side and interspersed with regularly disposed vertical spaces (*i.p.*), where the curved surfaces are not in contact.

The numerous lenticular *chloroplasts* form an almost continuous

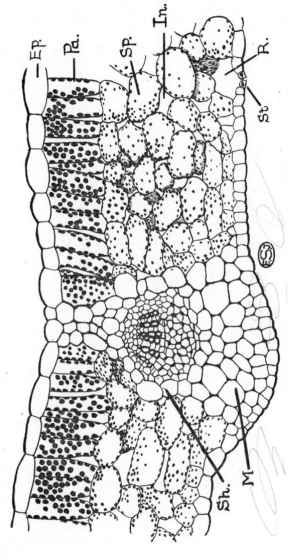

FIG. 98. Transverse section of the leaf of *Fuchsia* passing through a vein. *Ep.*, epidermis; *In.*, intercellular space; *M.*, collenchyma of the midrib; *Pa.*, palisade layer; *R.*, respiratory cavity; *Sh.*, sheath of vascular bundle; *Sp.*, spongy parenchyma; *St.*, stoma.

layer in the cytoplasm lining the vertical walls, a feature well seen
in both transverse and surface sections (Fig. 98, *Pa.*; Fig. 99, A;
see also Fig. 89). This peripheral position is clearly favourable
to the rapid absorption of carbon dioxide from the adjacent intercellular spaces. Moreover, the chloroplasts, as a result, present
their edges to the light so that the chlorophyll is less exposed to
the injurious effects of excessive illumination. Owing to the
considerable length of the palisade cells, there is accommodation
for a large number of chloroplasts in each. In some plants,

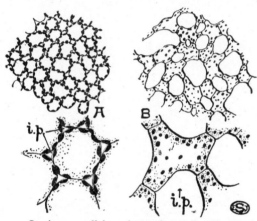

FIG. 99. Sections parallel to the surfaces of a *Fuchsia* leaf, cut
respectively through the palisade layer (A) and through the spongy
parenchyma (B). In each the lower figure shows a small portion
on an enlarged scale. *i.p.*, intercellular spaces.

moreover, the chloroplast-bearing surface is increased by the
development of special infoldings of the wall [*arm-palisade, e.g.*
in the leaves of the Elder (Fig. 100, *a.p.*)].

In the transverse section of the leaf of the *Fuchsia* two or three
palisade cells frequently join by their lower ends on to one and
the same cell of the spongy parenchyma (Fig. 98; see also Fig. 100,
c.c.; Fig. 346). The cells in question are usually broadened
at their upper ends, so that they are more or less funnel-shaped.
Presumably the photosynthetic products (carbohydrates, etc.)
formed in the palisade cells pass into these *collecting cells* and from
them diffuse, via other spongy elements, to the veins.

The *spongy parenchyma*, in its most typical form (*e.g.* in
Euphorbia amygdaloides), consists of irregularly lobed cells attached
to one another by their projecting arms (cf. Fig. 346), so that wide
intercellular spaces occur between them. In the *Fuchsia* and in
many leaves, however, the cells are more rounded and the inter-

spaces consequently smaller (Fig. 98, *In.*; Fig. 99, B). The rather few chloroplasts in the spongy, as compared with the palisade, parenchyma may be related to the fact that the former tissue receives relatively less light. The layer in contact with the lower epidermis is not uncommonly continuous (except for the gaps constituted by the respiratory cavities, Fig. 98, *R.*), and its cells may even show a palisade-like form when they generally contain rather numerous chloroplasts (*e.g.* Corn Cockle), and serve to utilise the light reaching the under side of the leaf.

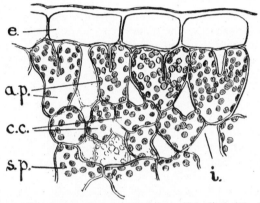

FIG. 100. Transverse section through part of the leaf of the Elder (*Sambucus*) showing the upper epidermis (*e.*); the arm-palisade cells (*a.p.*); the collecting cells (*c.c.*); and the spongy parenchyma (*s.p.*). *i.*, intercellular space.

The spongy tissue creates an extensive intercellular system communicating on the one hand with the external atmosphere by way of the stomata, and on the other hand with the entire aerating system of the rest of the plant. The spongy cells also serve to conduct elaborated food-materials in various directions to the adjacent veins, whilst their cell-sap provides a reserve supply of water which may be partially surrendered to the palisade cells, with their higher suction pressure.

The structure of the mesophyll just described is characteristic of *dorsiventral leaves* generally, the following being the chief modifications. The palisade tissue not uncommonly consists of several layers (*e.g.* Holly, Fig. 89, A), a feature especially encountered in leaves exposed to strong illumination, whilst leaves developed in dull light may have little or no palisade tissue. In some plants (*e.g.* the House-leek) the photosynthetic cells are elongated parallel to the midrib, whilst in transverse section they appear more or less rounded.

Variegated leaves usually exhibit a similar structure to that of the normal foliage of the same species, except that the pale areas lack chlorophyll and may have smaller epidermal cells. It need hardly be said that the structure of reduced foliage-leaves (*e.g.* scale-leaves of rhizomes, bud-scales, etc.) is of a much simpler character. Such are usually colourless with a homogeneous mesophyll, and often possess no veins.

Movement of chloroplasts in conformity with the intensity of illumination is seen in a few plants (*e.g.* Duckweed, *Lemna*; Moss-leaves, etc.). In these the chloroplasts occupy a profile position on the vertical walls when the light is intense, whilst when weak the chloroplasts pass to the horizontal walls, so that their full surface is presented towards the source of illumination.

The *vascular tissue* of the leaf is very extensive, forming a network in Dicotyledons and a parallel system in most Monocotyledons.[1] The repeated branching facilitates not only the delivery of water and mineral salts to all parts of the leaf, but also the rapid removal of elaborated food-substances. The vascular system, however, also constitutes a supporting skeleton for the lamina, in which it is often aided by accompanying mechanical tissues; the latter are found especially in the larger veins, and consist of strands of collenchyma (Fig. 98, *M.*) or sclerenchyma, which run both above and below the vascular bundles or sometimes on the lower side only.

A transverse section through one of the larger veins of the leaf shows a single bundle enveloped in a sheath of one or more layers of large transparent thin-walled parenchyma-cells (Fig. 98, *Sh.*; cf. also Fig. 346, *V.*); the accompanying collenchyma (*M.*) is developed especially on the lower side. The xylem, which is adjacent to the palisade tissue, consists of rows of vessels alternating with wood-parenchyma, the protoxylem being directed towards the upper epidermis; phloem of the normal type here lies on both sides of the xylem, although in most leaves it is found only on the lower side. Between xylem and phloem a cambium can often be recognised (Fig. 98), especially in evergreen leaves (*e.g.* Holly) which remain on the plant for more than one year.

In passing to the finer and finer ramifications of the vascular system a gradual simplification in structure is apparent. The differentiation of the phloem becomes less and less distinct, its place being taken by a more or less uniform tissue of thin-walled elongated cells, whilst at the ultimate terminations of the bundles it often disappears completely. Similarly the xylem-vessels gradually give place to relatively short spiral or reticulate tracheids (Fig. 41, A,

---

[1] The Cuckoo-pint (*Arum maculatum*) and Black Bryony (*Tamus communis*), for instance, have a venation similar to that of Dicotyledons.

p. 69), the amount of wood-parenchyma diminishing till it dies out. Thus the *bundle-ends* usually consist only of tracheids surrounded by the single-layered parenchyma-sheath.

In larger leaves (*e.g.* Sunflower) the *midrib* often contains several bundles, and in the Docks (*Rumex*) and the Rhubarb (*Rheum rhaponticum*) quite a large number of strands occur. On the whole the vascular supply is proportional to the size of the leaf, and this is

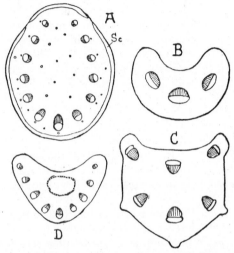

FIG. 101. Diagrams showing the petiolar structure of A, Sea Holly (*Eryngium maritimum*); B, Dog's Mercury (*Mercurialis perennis*); C, Black Bindweed (*Polygonum convolvulus*); D, Bishop's Weed (*Ægopodium podagraria*). The shaded part of the bundles represents xylem, the unshaded part phloem. *Sc.*, sclerenchyma.

true also of the *petiole*. Small leaves (e.g. *Cerastium*, Fig. 102) frequently possess but a single petiolar strand orientated as in the lamina, whilst larger ones usually have several bundles grouped in an arc, with its opening towards the concave or flattened upper surface (Fig. 101, A, B, D) and the protoxylems directed inwards. In such petioles the strands commonly vary appreciably in size and number at different levels owing to frequent anastomoses, while accessory strands may traverse the pith or the often widened upper angles (Fig. 101, C). Sometimes (e.g. *Pelargonium*) the bundles form a ring, while the vertically flattened petioles of the Aspen (*Populus tremula*) are traversed by three superposed concentric strands.

The bundles of the petiole can be traced backwards some little distance into the cortex of the stem, following a slightly oblique course, so that, in sections cut transversely just below the nodes, the one or more bundles (*leaf-trace bundles*) passing from the leaf into the stem appear cut obliquely in the cortex. After penetrating some little way into the latter the bundles turn abruptly downwards and run vertically through one or more internodes, ultimately, with (Fig. 102) or without previous branching, fusing laterally with strands derived from other leaves. The bundles traversing the stem are therefore merely downward continuations of those found in the leaves. In the region of the nodes the vascular system may be very complex and not uncommonly forms a more or less continuous network of vessels or tracheids with diverse orientation. The vascular supply of the axillary bud often arises from the central cylinder as two separate strands which soon unite to form a ring. These strands usually pass off horizontally and at a higher level than those entering the subtending leaf.

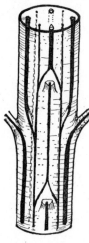

FIG. 102. Diagrammatic representation of the vascular system in a small portion of the stem of *Cerastium* (modified from Prantl). Only the bases of the leaves, with a single vascular strand, are shown.

In Monocotyledons the sheathing leaf-bases completely encircle the axis, numerous strands passing from each leaf into the stem. The median vascular bundles often pass almost to the centre of the stem before they bend downwards; subsequently they pursue a longitudinal direction, at the same time returning obliquely towards the periphery. The more laterally placed strands follow a similar course, but do not penetrate to the same depth. As a result the vascular bundles from the successive leaves usually appear irregularly scattered through the cross-section (cf. p. 140), but tend to be more densely crowded near the outside (Fig. 87, D, p. 145).

The mechanics of the leaf differ in several respects from that of the stem. The petioles of most leaves, when at rest, have to withstand a one-sided stress acting mainly from above and due to the weight of the blade, which may be much increased during rain. The arrangement of the mechanical tissue in the form of an inverted arch, open on the upper side (see Fig. 101, B, D), gives considerable strength to meet the usual bending stresses from above, but is not so rigid as the closed tube found in stems. It therefore allows of a certain flexibility, so that the leaf readily assumes a streamline position during gusts of wind. In such leaves as the Sycamore (Fig. 72), Wood-sorrel (Fig. 173), and Garden Nasturtium (Fig. 117, B), in which the petiole is attached more or less centrally and at right angles to the blade, the stress is almost equally distributed over the leaf-stalk and the arrangement of the vascular strands is more like that of a stem (cf. Fig. 101, C). In radical leaves (*e.g.* Daisy) which rest on the ground, the open arch arrangement is greatly flattened out.

The tearing action of wind and hail is to a large extent obviated by the strengthening network formed by the veins, and especially by the occurrence of marginal mechanical elements. The latter are either vascular strands, linking the finer veins and running parallel to the margin (Red Currant) or consist of bundles of fibres (e.g. *Iris*) occupying the same position. Moreover, the epidermal cells at the edge of the leaf are usually especially thickened and have a pronounced cuticle.

The leaves so far considered exhibit a marked difference of structure and appearance between the upper and lower surfaces (dorsiventral type), which is probably related to the horizontal position. In the *Iris* and other Monocotyledons, where the leaf-blades stand vertically and both surfaces receive an equal amount of light, the structure is identical on the two sides (isobilateral type). The structure of most Monocotyledon leaves is in fact more comparable to that of the Dicotyledon petiole than to that of the leaf blade. In still other instances (*e.g.* Onion, White Stonecrop, *Sedum album*), the leaves are more or less cylindrical, and, apart from the dorsiventral arrangement of the vascular bundles, exhibit radial organisation, with a palisade layer extending uniformly round the periphery (centric type).

CHAPTER XVI

SECONDARY THICKENING

It was pointed out in the preceding chapter that the vascular supply of the leaf is roughly proportional to its size (p. 167), and in the same way the vascular system of the stem is correlated with the area of leaf-surface which it bears. With the annual increase of foliage exhibited by all woody perennials, a need for additional conducting elements arises, and this want is supplied through the activity of a meristem (the cambium, p. 136) situated between the xylem and phloem of the bundles. *Cambium* is found in this position in all Dicotyledons and Conifers (see p. 412), but in Monocotyledons is present only occasionally as a vestige (*e.g.* in the leaf-sheaths of the Maize and in the leaves of many other Grasses). The division of the cells of the cambium leads to the formation of additional conducting elements, accompanied by a gradual increase in the size of the stem, spoken of as *secondary thickening*. Enlargement does not, however, always imply cell-division, since in some Palms, where no active cambium occurs, there is increase in girth mainly due to enlargement of the cells already present.

The cambium may be regarded as arising from an unaltered portion of the procambium (cf. p. 147), which has retained its powers of division, but until it becomes active it is difficult to recognise. The actual cambium is established by the appearance of two parallel tangential walls in the persisting procambial elements. There is thus cut out a single layer of radially flattened cells (Fig. 103, A, C.) which have dense protoplasmic contents and prominent nuclei and, as seen in longitudinal section (Fig. 84, Ca.; 103, B), have an elongated form and tapering ends. Subsequent division of these cells takes place parallel to the two tangential faces whereby files of segments are produced, both on the outer and inner side, those adjacent to the phloem becoming differentiated as additional (secondary) phloem, those adjacent to the xylem as additional (secondary) xylem. In certain sectors, however, the cambial cells divide transversely to form groups of isodiametric cells which appear spindle-shaped in tangential section and from which the rays (p. 173) are produced (Fig. 103, B, *r*).

According to the character of the procambial tissue (cf. pp. 146, 147), the cambium at first consists either of separate strips which subsequently join laterally, or it appears as a complete cylinder from its inception. In the former state, subsequent to the

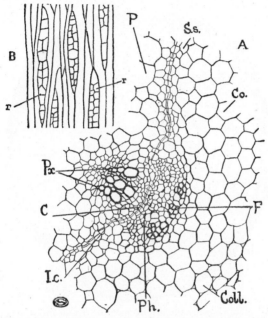

FIG. 103. *A*, Transverse section of a small portion of the hypocotyl of the Castor Oil plant (*Ricinus communis*). *C.*, intrafascicular cambium; *Co.*, cortex; *Coll.*, collenchyma; *F.*, pericyclic fibres; *I.c.*, interfascicular cambium; *P.*, parenchyma; *Ph.*, phloem; *Px.*, protoxylem; *S.s.*, starch sheath. *B*, Tangential section through cambium (diagrammatic) showing cambial cells and ray-initials (*r*).

development of the cambium within the bundles, division by two tangential walls takes place progressively in certain cells of the rays, and, where a starch-sheath is present, these occur in the pericycle (*e.g.* hypocotyl of the Castor Oil plant, Fig. 103, *I.c.*). The cambium between the bundles (*interfascicular*, Fig. 103, *I.c.*) links up with that within the bundles (*intrafascicular*, Fig. 103, *C.*) to form a complete meristematic ring. In woody perennials the cambium resumes its function each year, although division is arrested during the winter months.

The secondary wood thus added on the inside forms a larger and larger core each year (Fig. 104). Since it is composed of hard persistent tissue, there is practically no compression of the wood, which progressively augments, so that the increase in girth of the stem serves as a rough measure of the amount of tissue added. To this enlargement the secondary phloem contributes but little, since this tissue is mainly thin-walled, and the outer earlier-formed elements become compressed more and more, as a consequence

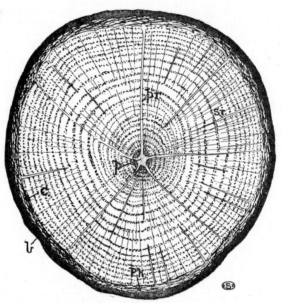

FIG. 104. Diagram showing the arrangement of tissues in a transverse section of a woody trunk, about twenty-four years old. The large vessels of the early wood of each growth ring are shown as black dots. *b.*, bark; *c.*, region of cambium; *p.*, pith; *Ph.*, secondary phloem; *pr.*, primary ray; *Sr.*, secondary ray.

of the increasing pressure resulting from the growth of the wood and the annual formation of intercalated phloem. The cambium keeps pace with the enlarging circumference of the secondary wood, mainly by radial division and growth of its cells or by transverse divisions and gliding growth (p. 60).

The pressure on the outer tissues, due to the *interpolation of secondary vascular elements* between the primary xylem and phloem, becomes more and more marked as the years go by and its effects are most pronounced in the cortex. Moreover, the steady increase in size of the woody core results in a gradual enlargement of its circumference, so that the softer tissues beyond become tangentially stretched. This tension can be readily demonstrated by making an extended vertical incision through the cortex of a three-year-old twig of the Ash. The edges of the cut are seen to separate immediately owing to transverse contraction of the thin-walled tissues. In nature the tangential tension is exemplified by the irregular longitudinal fissures which are so marked a feature of the older bark of many trees.

In regions where the cambium consists of groups of isodiametric cells (p. 170), the segments cut off are parenchymatous, and differ from the other elements of the wood and phloem in being radially and not longitudinally elongated (Fig. 106, A, *m.r.*). In transverse sections of a secondarily thickened stem these *parenchyma rays* appear as a number of radiating streaks, one or more cells in width (Fig. 104, *pr.* and *Sr.*). Some of these rays extend from cortex to pith (*pr.*) and, since they correspond in position to the original rays between the vascular bundles, are called *primary* rays; others (the *secondary* parenchyma rays, *Sr.*), however, though traversing the greater part of the secondary phloem, penetrate only to a varying depth towards the centre. In some plants (e.g. *Aristolochia*) the primary rays are very wide, and practically the whole of the interfascicular cambial strips participate in their formation.

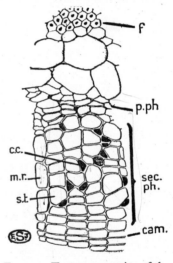

FIG. 105. Transverse section of the outer part of the stem of the Horse Chestnut (*Æsculus*), showing the secondary phloem (*Sec. ph.*) and the cambium (*Cam.*). *c.c.*, companion cells; *f*, fibres of pericycle; *M.r.*, parenchyma ray; *P.ph.*, primary phloem; *s.t.*, sieve-tube.

The *secondary wood* is composed of four main types of elements, viz. vessels, tracheids, wood-fibres, and wood-parenchyma, but transitions between the different types are not infrequent. The component elements often exhibit a distinct radial arrangement (*e.g.* Horse Chestnut), though this may be somewhat obscured when the vessels are large and numerous (*e.g.* Lime, Elm). The *vessels* of the secondary wood usually bear densely crowded bordered pits (Fig. 106, *V*; Fig. 40, E, *b*, p. 68), often arranged in distinct vertical series, and not uncommonly show additional reticulate or spiral thickenings deposited on the inner surface of the wall. The perforated septa are frequently oblique (Fig. 106, C, *V*) with reference to the radial plane, a

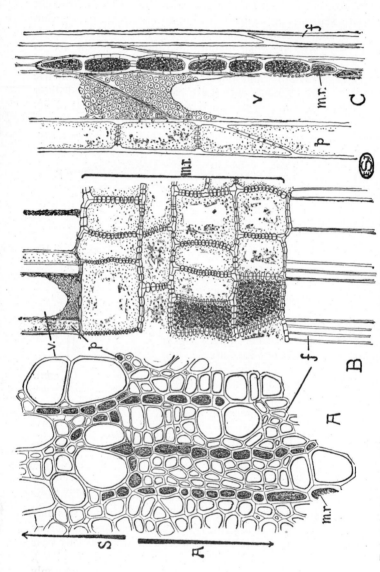

FIG. 106. Structure of the secondary wood of the Horse Chestnut (*Æsculus*). A, Transverse section showing the early wood (S.) of one, and the late wood (A.) of the preceding growth ring. B, Radial longitudinal section. C, Tangential longitudinal section. *f*, fibres; *m.r.*, parenchyma rays; *p*, wood-parenchyma; *V*, pitted vessels of secondary xylem.

feature which can be related to the peculiar form of the cambial segments from which the vessels are derived. The perforations are varied (cf. p. 61 and Fig. 40, D–F), but the type in which a number of cross-bars remain is commoner than in the primary wood. *Tracheids* (cf. p. 70) differ from vessels in being derived from single segments of the cambium, which show no open perforations in the end-walls; they are usually much shorter than the vessels, but of about the same width. The vessels and tracheids are the water-conducting elements of the secondary wood, and the former are generally much more numerous than the latter; in fact, tracheids may be almost absent (*e.g.* Willow).

The typical *wood-fibres* closely resemble those described on p. 66, having pointed ends and more or less thickened walls, which bear occasional oblique slit-shaped simple pits (Fig. 106, *f.*). As the pit-apertures on the two sides of the wall are often inclined in opposite directions, a X-like appearance is commonly presented. Fibres of this type are connected by transitions with others which bear bordered pits with oblique slits (*e.g.* Beech), and differ but little from the fibrous tracheids of the Conifers (see p. 412). In the typical wood-fibres the walls are lignified and the contents dead; but fibre-like cells with living protoplasts occur in the secondary wood of the Sycamore and of many herbs. Such fibres are occasionally septate (*e.g.* Vine) and constitute transitions to wood-parenchyma. Where vessels are in contact with the ordinary mechanical fibres, pits are not developed on the walls.

The *wood-parenchyma* cells of the secondary xylem resemble those of the primary xylem, in form and in the possession of a living protoplast; the walls are, however, commonly thicker and often lignified, the horizontal ones showing prominent pitting (Fig. 106, *p.*). Wood-parenchyma cells may be generally distributed throughout the wood (*e.g.* Birch, Beech), or more especially confined to the summer-formed wood and the immediate vicinity of the vessels, sometimes completely ensheathing them (*e.g.* Ash). The parenchyma in contact with the vessels bears simple pits corresponding in position to pits of the vessel wall, which latter are here either simple (*e.g.* Oak) or bordered (*one-sided bordered pits*), like the remaining pits of the vessel wall.

The structure of the *parenchyma rays* can only be fully appreciated by a study of their appearance in transverse and in longitudinal sections, both radial and tangential. In the transverse section the cells, except for the fact that their long axis is placed radially and not vertically, are very similar to those of the wood-parenchyma, though not uncommonly having somewhat thinner walls. The latter bear simple pits which are often particularly numerous on the tangential walls (Fig. 106, B; Fig. 108, m.). The simple pits of the radial walls and the bordered pits of the vessels combine to form one-sided bordered pits like those described above.

Attention has already been drawn to the variable width of the rays. In general the secondary parenchyma rays are narrow and often only one cell wide; the primary ones in most trees do not greatly exceed the secondary in width, but in many herbs the contrast is extremely marked. Each ray is a plate of cells of which the full vertical extent is seen in tangential longitudinal sections (Fig. 106, C, m.r.). The secondary parenchyma rays are very limited in this direction, rarely exceeding ten or twelve cells in height, whilst the primary rays usually extend through an entire internode. Each ray, as seen in tangential section, is somewhat spindle-shaped as a result of the tapering of the cells at the upper and lower margins (Fig. 106, C, m.r.).

In radial longitudinal sections the secondary rays are cut parallel to their flat faces, and appear as so many narrow paren-chymatous strips passing at right angles across the longitudinal grain of the wood (Fig. 106, B). The detailed structure of the ray here somewhat resembles that of a brick wall, the alternation of the cells simulating the "bond" of the bricks. The component cells show plainly the radial elongation referred to above, but sometimes those at the upper and lower margins are short and not markedly lengthened (e.g. Willows). The radial, like the vertical, extent of the secondary rays is seen to be limited (cf. p. 173). Should the radial section pass through one of the primary rays, the latter will be seen to show a far greater development, both in the vertical and radial directions.

Apart from the occasional presence of fibres with protoplasmic contents, the wood-parenchyma and the parenchyma rays are the only living constituents of the secondary wood. The living cylinder constituted by the phloem and cortex is thus connected with numerous inwardly directed plates of living tissue, the paren-chyma rays. Of these, however, only the primary ones extend to the pith, where they are linked up by a second cylinder of living cells, the *medullary sheath* (p. 137), which invests the inner margins of the primary xylem tissue. The radiating plates formed by the secondary rays are, however, not isolated, even where they pass between the dead elements of the secondary wood, since they are connected both vertically and horizontally by bands of wood-parenchyma cells.

The mass of vessels and fibres is thus permeated by a con-tinuous system of living elements connected with the food-conducting tissues and seemingly fulfilling at least two functions: firstly, to conduct elaborated food-substances to the cambial region, the living cells of the wood, and the medullary sheath; secondly, at certain times of the year, the cells serve for the *storage* of food-substances, *e.g.* starch, as can be shown by the application of iodine to a section of a twig in autumn. When this starch is utilised during the sprouting of the buds in spring, it is changed into sugar, and is then transferred in the water ascending the vessels to the growing regions, hence the sweet character of the sap which exudes in bleeding.[1] The aeration of the secondary tissues is effected by narrow intercellular spaces which are more particularly associated with the living elements.

The major part of each annual addition to the secondary wood usually consists of vessels and fibres, but the proportion of these latter varies with the kind of plant and during each season's growth. The wood formed in spring (*early wood*, Fig. 106, A, S.) mostly contains a much larger percentage of vessels than that formed in summer (*late wood*, A.); its vessels, moreover, are often larger and have thinner walls, and the same may be true of the fibres. This difference may be related to the sudden demand on the water-supply in the spring on the part of the newly-expanding leaves, whilst later in the season provision is possible for the growing mechanical requirements [2] of the plant by an increased proportion of fibres. As a consequence there is often a sharp boundary between the dense small-celled late wood of one season and the wide-celled early wood of the next (Fig. 106), and this leads to the marking out of the secondary wood into a succession of *growth rings* (Fig. 104), by means of which the approximate age of a trunk can be estimated. In Evergreens and some other trees in which the seasonal leaf-production is not so marked, the vessels tend to be more evenly distributed. Such wood is termed *diffuse-porous*, in contrast to the *ring-porous* type previously described.

Occasionally, when a new set of leaves is produced to replace a first crop killed by frost or devoured by caterpillars, their expansion is accompanied by the formation of a second zone of early wood, so that two "annual rings" are formed in a single season. The width of the growth ring is mainly determined by nutrition, often influenced by climate, though the variations in thickness in one and the same ring are probably the result of mechanical stresses.

---

[1] Cf. p. 194. Maple-sugar is derived from the evaporated sap of *Acer saccharinum* (North America), obtained by tapping the trees in spring.

[2] A feature that is probably also connected with the growing mechanical stress is the increased length of the fibres in the later-formed growth rings.

Such asymmetrical growth rings, with a maximum development on the upper or lower side, are commonly found in horizontal branches. Extreme asymmetry is seen in the "buttress-roots" observed in many tropical trees (*e.g.* species of *Ficus*).

The constant addition of new wood is perhaps mainly necessitated by changes in the central earlier-formed xylem, as a result of which it becomes useless for purposes of conduction, although such changes often increase its value as a mechanical support; it is then spoken of as *heart-wood* in contrast to the active *sap-wood* beyond. The elements of the heart-wood often become impregnated with tannins, resins, etc., which are frequently accompanied by dark-coloured pigments; in some trees the latter are extracted and afford useful dyes, *e.g.* the logwood (hæmatoxylin) obtained from *Hæmatoxylon campechianum* (Tropical America). The employment of mahogany, walnut, etc., in cabinet-work is largely due to the rich colouration of the heart-wood and the high polish which its hard character enables it to take. In the Ebony-tree (*Diospyros*) the sap-wood is white and not especially hard, the ebony of commerce being the mature, very hard, and almost black heart-wood. In some plants (*e.g.* Beech) little heart-wood is formed, much of the xylem remaining functional.

The impregnating substances are often antiseptic, and prevent decay by inhibiting the development of Fungi and Bacteria, thus increasing the durability of the wood. Teak (*Tectona grandis*) owes its value as a tropical timber to the presence of a substance which renders it immune from the depredations of wood-boring insects; it is also the cause of its peculiar scent. The liability of many Willows to develop hollow trunks at an early stage may be attributed to the absence of antiseptic substances from the older wood.

The cavities of the water-conducting elements in the heart-wood are frequently blocked in various ways, most commonly by the ingrowth of structures known as *tyloses* (Fig. 107). These are bladder-like intrusions through the pits, from the wood-parenchyma cells, into the vessels, and are sometimes so numerous as to fill the latter completely with a false tissue resembling parenchyma. They are bounded by the extended thin-walled pit-membrane, which undergoes a certain amount of surface growth, and occasionally becomes thickened and lignified (e.g. *Robinia pseudacacia*). Each of the young tyloses is living, containing cytoplasm, cell-sap, and sometimes also a nucleus; but when they have reached their full size both the tyloses and the wood-parenchyma cells [1] of the heart-

---

[1] The latter are invariably dead in the mature heart-wood, even when no tyloses are formed.

wood die, so that the whole of the latter consists of dead elements. Tyloses are also produced in herbaceous stems (*e.g.* Vegetable Marrow, Fig. 107), but here their function is obscure.   The plugging of the vessels of the heart-wood is, however, not always effected in this way, since in other plants mineral deposits (lime in the Elm) may take their place.

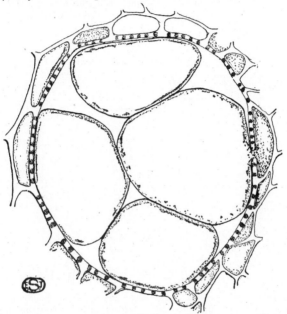

FIG. 107. Tyloses in a vessel of the Vegetable Marrow (*Cucurbita*) as seen in transverse section. On the right the connection with the wood-parenchyma is shown.

In tree-trunks, which have been cut across, the vessels look like small pin-pricks on the smooth surface of the wood and the growth rings are often clearly recognisable.   Traversing the cross-section like the spokes of a wheel are the rays (cf. Fig. 104).   In a block of wood which has been cut radially, we can recognise the long tubes formed by the vessels and irregularly shaped silvery bands passing across them (the silver grain of the Oak), which are the rays.   When the wood is cut tangentially, the same features may be made out, the rays now, however, appearing as short vertical streaks.

The mechanical properties of *timbers* [1] depend largely on the proportion of fibres, on the number and size of the vessels, and on the thickness of the

[1] See A. L. Howard, *A Manual of Timbers of the World*.   Macmillan & Co., 2nd edit., 1934 (672 pp.); F. W. Jane, *The Structure of Wood*, Blacks, 1953.

fibre walls. Thus, close-textured (close-grained) woods (*e.g.* Box, Holly) are characterised by having abundant fibres and small vessels, whilst the coarse or open texture of wood (seen in Oak, Ash, etc.) is due to the large number of wide vessels and often to the thin character of the fibres as well. The "softwoods" of commerce are obtained from Conifers whose wood is solely composed of long narrow tracheids (cf. p. 412), usually having thinner walls than the fibres of hardwood trees.

The employment of timber for commercial purposes is determined by such qualities as closeness of texture, ease of working, elasticity, toughness,

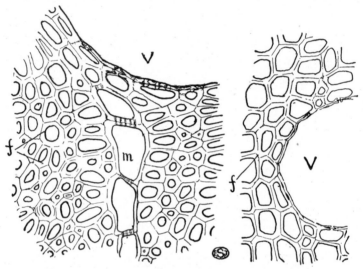

Fig. 108. Transverse sections of the secondary wood of the Sycamore (*Acer pseudoplatanus*) (right) and the Oak (*Quercus*) (left). Note the fibres (*f*), which are much thicker-walled in the latter than in the former. *m*, parenchyma ray; *V*, vessels.

durability, colour, figure, etc. Thus the resilience of the wood of certain types of Willow is responsible for their use in the manufacture of cricket-bats, whilst the ancient esteem of Yew (*Taxus baccata*) for bows, and the use of Ash where bending is required, are the outcome of the elasticity and toughness of these woods. The elastic limit of Ash is only reached under a stress of about 5000 lb. per square inch as compared with 3500 lb. for Douglas Fir. Such qualities are probably not only the result of length of fibre, but also one of physical or chemical constitution of the xylem walls. Liability to splitting is often due to straightness of the constituent elements, while it is their small size that renders the timber of the Hornbeam (*Carpinus*) so suitable for cogwheels, etc. The "figure" of timber, for which many woods are chiefly prized, is largely dependent on the direction of the fibres and the prominence of the parenchyma rays when cut in certain planes.

To render timber suitable for use, the cut log needs to undergo a process of *seasoning*, which involves the drying out of the sap and water, a process that in the open occupies from six months to a year or even longer in hardwoods, and about half the time for Coniferous timber. Artificial means (*e.g.* heating in special sheds or by electricity) are now frequently employed in order to shorten this period. The greatest care is necessary in seasoning to avoid undue stresses and strains, which bring about warping and splitting of the timber, defects that commonly develop if the process be unduly hastened. This is partly due to the fact that the tangential shrinkage is often nearly double that of the radial. For this reason radial cracks, that open wider and wider as the trunk dries, are not uncommon.

Other common defects are the "*knots*," which are constituted by the vascular tissues of lateral branches that have become embedded in the wood of the trunk; in forestry their development is checked by dense planting.

In the following list are enumerated some of the more important timbers, their principal uses, and the trees from which they are derived:—

A. Coniferous.

Douglas Fir or British Columbia Pine .	*Pseudotsuga taxifolia* (Pacific N. America) (constructional work, joinery, plywood).
Larch . . .	*Larix decidua* (Europe) (mining timber, marine constructional work).
Pitch Pine . .	*Pinus palustris*, etc. (U.S.A.) (constructional work).
Red Deal, Scots Pine	*Pinus sylvestris* (N. Europe) (constructional work, sleepers, pit props, etc.).
European Whitewood, White Deal .	*Picea abies* (N. and Central Europe) (joinery, paper pulp, scaffold poles).
White Pine, Yellow Pine . . .	*Pinus strobus* (N. America) (Pattern making, joinery).

B. Dicotyledonous.

Ash . . .	*Fraxinus excelsior* (Europe) (wheelwright's work, tool-handles, etc.).
Beech . . .	*Fagus sylvatica* (Europe) (furniture, tools).
Birch . . .	*Betula* spp. (Europe, N. America) (plywood, furniture).
Elm . . .	*Ulmus* spp. (Europe, N. America) (wheelwright's work, coffin boards).
Hickory . . .	*Carya* spp. (N. America) (tool handles, spokes).
Jarrah . . .	*Eucalyptus marginata* (W. Australia) (constructional work, flooring, wood block paving, etc.).
Lignum vitæ . .	*Guaiacum* spp. (America) (underwater bearings).
Lime and Basswood	*Tilia* spp. (Europe, N. America) (carving, matches).
Mahogany, African	*Khaya ivorensis* (W. Africa) (furniture, cabinet work).
Mahogany, American	*Swietenia* spp. (Tropical America) (same uses as last).
Maple and Sycamore	*Acer* spp. (Europe, N. America) (flooring, turnery, rollers, etc.).
Oak . . .	*Quercus* spp. (N. Hemispheres) (furniture, flooring, etc.).
Poplar . . .	*Populus* spp. (Europe, N. America) (lorry bottoms, floors, matches, plywood).
Tasmanian oak .	*Eucalyptus* spp. (Australia) (flooring, furniture).
Teak . . .	*Tectona grandis* (Indo-Malaya) (shipbuilding, etc.).
Walnut . . .	*Juglans* spp. (Europe, N. America, Asia) (furniture, cabinet work, gun stocks).
European Boxwood .	*Buxus sempervirens* (Europe) (wood engraving blocks, tool handles, etc.).
Willow . . .	*Salix* spp. (Europe) (cricket bats, artificial limbs, etc.).

The *secondary phloem* (Fig. 105), like the primary, consists of parenchyma, sieve-tubes, and companion cells, but these last are commonly larger and fibres are often present. The septa in the sieve-tubes are not uncommonly oblique and provided with several perforated areas separated by bar-like thickenings (*compound sieve-plates*). In some plants the phloem-parenchyma and sieve-tubes, with their companion cells, are produced in such regular sequence as to form alternating tangential bands. The fibres are likewise often disposed in layers separating the zones of thin-walled elements (*e.g.* Lime, Mallow, etc.). Vertical series of phloem-parenchyma cells, occupied by crystals of oxalate of lime, and elongated secretory elements (*e.g.* tannin-sacs, cf. p. 92) are not uncommon. The older secondary phloem of woody plants, which has passed out of use, is not infrequently shed with the bark (p. 190).

The parenchyma rays of the secondary phloem are continuous with those of the xylem and exhibit the same general structure, except that the component cells remain thin-walled. In certain Flowering Plants (*e.g.* Lime, etc.) the outer ends of the primary parenchyma rays exhibit a marked V-shaped enlargement, whereby the secondary phloem becomes divided up into a number of wedge-like groups.

A transverse section of any unthickened Dicotyledonous *root* will show a narrow band of two or three layers of parenchymatous cells between each phloem-group and the adjacent xylem. Prior to the commencement of secondary growth tangential division-walls arise in these cells, leading to the production of a *cambium* (Fig. 56, *ca.*, p. 101) like that of the stem. In this way there originate as many cambial strips (Fig. 109, A, B, C.) as there are groups of phloem, and, by the active division of the former, secondary xylem is produced on the inside and secondary phloem on the outside. Differentiation of the cambium is at first confined to the inner surface of each phloem-group, but by slow degrees it extends along the sides of the xylem-arms till finally, by the development of tangential division-walls in the cells of the pericycle opposite the protoxylems, a complete lobed cylinder of cambium is established. Owing to the late development of the cambium opposite the protoxylem-groups, secondary thickening is at first more extensive in the bays, so that the outline of the cambium, at first lobed, gradually becomes circular.

The root soon comes to possess a broad ring of secondary wood and phloem (Fig. 109, C), similar to that of the stem, and, as in the latter, traversed by primary (*P.r.*) and secondary *rays.* The former, which, especially in herbs, often attain a considerable width, are situated along the same radii as, and are equal in number to, the primary xylem-groups (*P.xy.*). When these primary rays are broad and consist only of parenchyma, the secondary vascular tissue appears as separate wedges. The radial extension of the parenchymatous rays is not so marked as that of the wood, so that certain diarch roots, after secondary thickening, sometimes exhibit a band-like structure (*e.g.* Nettle). The secondary rays, like those of the stem, are generally narrow.

The vessels and wood-parenchyma of the *secondary wood* of the root are relatively more numerous and more evenly distributed

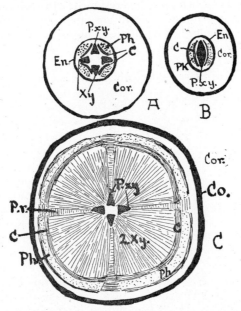

FIG. 109. Diagrams showing secondary thickening in the root. A, a tetrarch, and B, a diarch root, before thickening, showing the position of the cambium (*C.*). C, a tetrarch root after secondary thickening has been going on for some time. *Co.*, cork; *Cor.*, cortex; *En.*, endodermis; *Ph.*, phloem; *P.r.*, primary ray; *P.xy.*, protoxylem; *Xy.*, primary xylem; 2*Xy.*, secondary xylem.

than in the stem, so that the growth rings are usually less conspicuous. In its detailed structure the *secondary phloem* is similar to that of the stem, and, except for the points already mentioned, the same is true of the secondary wood. In the root, as in the aerial axis, the production of secondary tissues forces the primary phloem progressively farther from the centre. Old, secondarily thickened roots resemble stems very closely, but, when the central tissues are preserved, the original root-structure can be traced by following down the primary rays and locating the protoxylem-groups at the periphery of the metaxylem.

The storage of food in *fleshy roots* is effected by thin-walled parenchyma, which is often copiously developed both in the secondary phloem and in the secondary xylem. The vessels of the latter then form isolated groups, which are either scattered or arranged in radial files (*e.g.* Salsify, *Tragopogon*, Fig. 52, A) in the storage tissues, a distribution facilitating rapid transference from the storage cells when growth is resumed. In such roots the limits of secondary xylem and phloem are often difficult to distinguish, unless the cambium be first located; moreover, the primary xylem is often indistinguishable.

The process of secondary thickening so far described is that normally found in the vast majority of Dicotyledons and Conifers, but a few so-called *anomalous types* merit a brief consideration. In many members of the Spinach-family (Chenopodiaceæ) the normal cambium functions only for a short time and, after forming a narrow strip of secondary xylem and phloem, ceases to divide. Thereupon another cambium arises in the inner part of the cortex, and a new strip of xylem and phloem is produced till this cambium in its turn ceases to be active. This process is repeated again and again, each successive cambium forming xylem on the inner and phloem on the outer side. In the root of the Beet (*Beta*) the successive cambia form continuous rings of xylem and phloem, its fleshy character being mainly due to the extensive development of the latter tissue. In most stems showing this kind of abnormal thickening, however, xylem and phloem are produced only in certain sectors, and appear as secondary bundles separated by the thick-walled ground-tissue, developed from the remaining parts of each cambium (e.g. *Halimione portulacoides*).

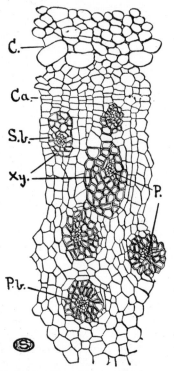

FIG. 110. Transverse section of a portion of an old stem of *Dracæna* showing secondary thickening. *C.*, cortex; *Ca.*, cambium; *P.*, phloem; *P.b.*, primary bundle; *S.b.*, secondary bundle; *Xy.*, xylem.

Another uncommon method, shown by certain Monocotyledons

which exhibit marked secondary increase in girth, is well illustrated
by the Dragon-tree (*Dracæna*), the stems of which may attain a
diameter of ten feet or more.   The bundles of the young stem here
exhibit the usual scattered arrangement; but in the cortex, immediately beyond the vascular region, there arises a cambium
(Fig. 110, *Ca.*) which cuts off segments mainly towards the inside,
the small number cut off on the outside forming an addition to the
cortex (*C.*).   Some of the inner segments divide and undergo
gradual differentiation to form *secondary bundles* (*S.b.*), whilst the
remainder, retaining a somewhat radial arrangement, become
thickened and lignified.   The secondary bundles embedded in this
thick-walled tissue are concentric with centrally placed phloem (*P.*),
which is often very scanty in amount; the xylem contains no vessels,
consisting of fibrous tracheids only.

Very complicated types of anomalous thickening are exhibited
by the woody climbers (*lianes*) of tropical forests.   In many of
these the old trunks develop cambial rings about several centres,
each such cambium producing a separate xylem-core, so that a
rope-like structure composed of several intertwined woody strands
results.   Most of these woody climbers are characterised by the
large size of the vessels, as is well seen in the wild *Clematis*.

The activity of the cambium, which is responsible for the normal
processes of secondary thickening, is always seasonal in the shoots
of plants living in temperate latitudes, being completely arrested
during the winter and restricted to a few of the warmer months.
In winter the cambium can only be distinguished with difficulty
as a somewhat shrunken layer just outside the wood, but with the
resumption of activity in spring the cells become turgid and translucent.   Division of the cambial cells commences just below the
expanding buds and from there gradually spreads basipetally down
the internodes.   It is recognisable in the shoot some time before
it becomes evident in the root, and here is seen in the main root
before spreading to the branches.   Cessation of cambial activity
follows the same sequence.   There is evidence that small traces of
chemical substances (auxins, see p. 253), diffusing in a downward
direction, are responsible for the initiation and apparent downward
extension of cambial activity in the various parts of the axis.

CHAPTER XVII

CORK-FORMATION AND THE BARK

ONE result of secondary thickening is a marked enlargement of the periphery of stem or root, in consequence of which the outer tissues are subjected to increasing tension (cf. p. 172). These, the epidermis and cortex, ordinarily have but a limited power of stretching, and, as soon as this limit is reached, they rupture and no longer form an effective covering for the underlying tissues. This function is henceforth fulfilled by a protective tissue, the *cork*, formed by the active division of a secondary meristem, the phellogen or cork-cambium, which arises in the cortex. In a few plants (e.g. *Acer striatum*) the epidermal and cortical cells are capable of limited growth and division, and here the formation of a cork-cambium is correspondingly delayed.

Cork-formation takes place in essentially the same way in both stem and root. The *phellogen* invariably arises by the formation of two successive tangential walls, in the stem most commonly in the cells of the subepidermal layer (Fig. 111). The cells are thus each divided into three segments, of which the central constitute the actual cork-cambium (*c.c.*), whilst the outer form the first layer of cork and the inner the first, and often the only, layer of a tissue known as *phelloderm* (*Ph.*). Whilst the outer and inner segments undergo no further division, the cells of the phellogen divide again and again, one of the two products of each division becoming differentiated as cork or phelloderm, while the other remains as the cell of the cork-cambium. Usually, however, these divisions of the phellogen lead to the cutting-off of cells on the outside only, so that no further formation of phelloderm takes place.

The activity of the phellogen results in the development of a continuous cylinder of tissue consisting of numerous radial files of cells, each file (Fig. 111, 1–6) representing the product of one cork-cambium cell. This tissue is the cork and, apart from the absence of intercellular spaces between its cells, it is especially characterised by a chemical modification of the cell-walls spoken of as *suberisation*. This latter renders them practically impervious alike to gases and to liquids, features to which cork owes its utilisation in closing bottles.

Suberisation is due to the deposition of a layer of fatty compounds on the inner surface of the wall, and hence cork is coloured by the same reagents (Scharlach red, etc.) as stain fats. A yellowbrown colouration is assumed with chlor-zinc-iodide, and a yellow one with strong potash. On boiling with concentrated potash,

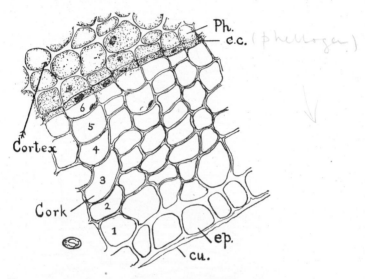

FIG. 111. Transverse section through the cork layer in the stem of the Elder (*Sambucus*). *c.c.*, cork-cambium; *cu.*, cuticle; *ep.*, epidermis; *Ph.*, phelloderm; 1–6, successive segments of the cork in order of production.

large yellow globules often escape from the walls. Suberised membranes, moreover, are highly resistant, being insoluble both in cuprammonia and concentrated sulphuric acid. Suberisation of the walls ensues soon after the cork-cells are cut off from the phellogen, and it is almost unnecessary to add that, as a result, the cells die, their contents ultimately consisting of air or more rarely of pigmented bodies (often tannins and their derivatives). The characteristic white appearance of the surface of the Birch (*Betula*) is due to the presence in the cells of the cork of solid granules of a substance known as betulin.

The cells of the *cork* vary considerably in shape, although very commonly flattened. The walls are often relatively thin. The radial walls are frequently thrown into folds, whilst the tangential ones are often almost straight (cf. Fig. 111). These features of the cork-cells can be related to the tangential tension and radial compression set up by the increasing girth of the enclosed axis.

In a few plants (*e.g.* Currant, Fig. 112, Laburnum, etc.) a more or less extensive *phelloderm* (*Ph.*) is formed. The cells of this

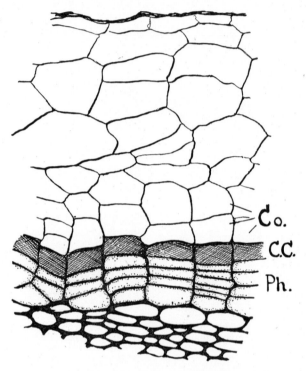

FIG. 112. Transverse section through the peripheral part of the stem of the Currant (*Ribes*), showing the cork (*Co.*), the cork-cambium (*C.C.*), and the extensive phelloderm (*Ph.*), of four to six layers of cells. Beyond the cork are seen cortex and epidermis.

tissue also are arranged in radial files, but the walls remain unsuberised. The phelloderm consists of living cells, and thus merely serves to augment the primary cortex, although where the walls are thickened it has an additional mechanical value.

Whilst the cork-cambium most commonly develops in the subepidermal layer of cells, it not infrequently arises in deeper-seated cortical layers (Fig. 112) or even in the pericycle. A good instance is furnished by the Barberry (Fig. 113), where the phellogen (*C.C.*) develops just inside the ring of mechanical tissue (*Sc.*) occupying the inner part of the cortex. In roots, too, it almost invariably arises in cortical cells in the immediate neighbourhood of the pericycle (Fig. 109, C, *Co.*).   The origin of a cork-cambium from the epidermis is seen in Willows, as well as in the Rose, Apple, Hawthorn, and other members of the Rosaceæ.

The cork not only prevents the excessive transpiration which would ensue after rupture of the epidermis consequent upon secondary thickening, but also takes over other protective functions of that tissue.   Suberised walls possess considerable strength, though their elasticity is slight, and the cork consequently forms a mechanical envelope whose efficiency is heightened by the close connection between its cells.   The frequent presence of air in the latter retards excessive heating by day or excessive cooling by night.   Moreover, the waste substances commonly encountered in the walls or cavities of the cork-cells are antiseptic, excluding access of various parasites to the living tissues within. As soon as cork-development commences, therefore, the parts concerned become ensheathed in an almost impermeable protective layer which would practi-

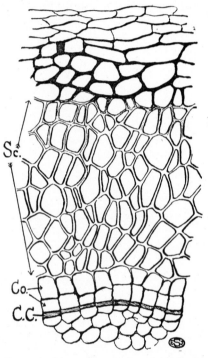

FIG. 113. Transverse section through the deep-seated cork in the stem of the Barberry (*Berberis*) showing two layers of cork-cells (*Co.*) situated between the cork-cambium (*C.C.*) and the zone of sclerenchyma (*Sc.*).

cally sever all direct communication between the internal tissues and the atmosphere, but for the formation of localised patches of loose tissue, the *lenticels,* whose development often commences slightly before that of the cork (see Fig. 67).

The first lenticels usually arise beneath the stomata of the young stem, where strips of cambium are formed in the subepidermal layer by the customary tangential divisions.   These cambial strips divide very actively, cutting off segments on both sides.   Those on the inner give rise to radial rows of phelloderm, whilst those on the outer remain thin-walled and unsuberised, but sooner or later round off and frequently lose all connection with one another (Fig. 114, *l*.).   This loose tissue [1] is formed in considerable bulk, so that it leads to a gradual elevation and ultimate rupture of the overlying epidermis.   The tissue of the lenticel is thus exposed, and air from the external atmosphere can freely circulate between its cells and, by way of the narrow air-spaces between the cells of the phellogen and phelloderm, into the intercellular spaces of the cortex.   The rounding-off of the constituent

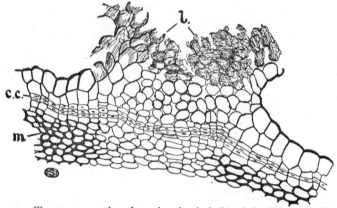

Fig. 114. Transverse section through a lenticel (*l*.) of the Elder (*Sambucus*).
c.c., cork-cambium; *m*, mechanical tissue.

cells and consequent development of the intercellular spaces vary considerably, so that the lenticel may be spongy (*e.g.* Elm, Birch) or relatively compact (*e.g.* Willow, Spindle-tree).   In some lenticels alternating zones of loose and compact tissue are formed.   The strips of cambium giving rise to the lenticels subsequently become continuous with the cork-cambium (Fig. 114).

Where the cork is deep-seated, the tissues external to it are practically cut off from all sources of food and all connection with the interior, and therefore die away.   These dead tissues, on the outside of the cork, are shed sooner or later, leaving the latter exposed as *bark*.   In some plants (*e.g.* Beech, Oak) the same cork-cambium continues to divide year after year, although inactive during the winter, so that a thick mass of cork is formed.   This is also true of the Cork Oak (*Quercus suber*), which is the main source of the commercial article.   In this tree the first cork, which here arises subepidermally, is of no value, being removed when the tree is ten to fifteen years old.   The cortex thus exposed forms a

[1] Forming the so-called " complementary tissue."

new phellogen which gives rise to the thin-walled cork of commerce. This is peeled off every eight to twelve years. The corks for bottles are cut in such a way that the long dark lenticels traverse them transversely.

In most woody plants the first-formed phellogen ceases to divide, and indeed itself becomes changed into a layer of cork, at a comparatively early stage. A new cambium then arises at a deeper level in the cortex, produces a fresh zone of cork, and then in its turn passes out of action, to be succeeded by another situated still deeper. The bark formed in this way consists of alternating layers of cork and dead cortex, and comprises all the tissues beyond the most recently established phellogen. When the original cork-cambium is deep-seated, the subsequent cambia are continuous cylinders; whilst when the first is superficial, the later ones are often merely curved vertical plates whose margins are in contact with one another. As the bark gets thicker and thicker the outer portions are subjected to a growing tension, so that, being dead tissue, fissures appear at the surface as irregular longitudinal furrows well seen in the Oak and Elm. In many plants, however, the oldest bark is shed, and this takes place either as rings (*ring-bark*, *e.g.* Birch, Cherry) or as scales (*scale-bark*, *e.g.* Plane, Scot's Fir), according as the successive cork-cambia are continuous cylinders or separate plates.[1]

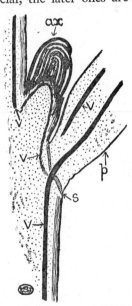

FIG. 115. Diagrammatic longitudinal section through part of a node of the Sycamore (*Acer pseudoplatanus*), showing the abscission layer (*S.*). *ax.*, axillary bud; *p.*, petiole; *V.*, vascular bundles.

After the shedding of the first-formed cork, lenticels may develop from any part of an active phellogen. As a result of subsequent stretching they assume various forms, which are often characteristic of individual species. Thus, on the bark of the Birch and Cherry they appear as slightly raised horizontal lines, whilst in the Poplar they are usually lozenge-shaped. The *cork-wings* developed in many varieties of woody plants (*e.g.* Cork Elm, Cork Maple, etc.) are due to the copious formation of cork which, consisting as it does of dead cells, necessarily splits at the surface; the regularity of the fissures may,

---

[1] Regarding commercial uses of bark, see pp. 79, 89, 91.

however, depend in part on excessive local activity of the cork-cambium.

It will have become apparent that cork serves to protect surfaces which would otherwise be exposed, and indeed it is even found covering wounds and the scars left by the shedding of leaves, flowers, branches, etc. The fall of leaves is preceded by the differentiation of a definite separating layer (*abscission layer*) which is produced, with or without division, from the cells at the base of the leaf-stalk (Fig. 115, *S*.). The layer in question is generally recognisable by the smaller size of its cells, and its position is often indicated externally by a slight constriction of the petiole. Subsequently the middle lamellæ between its cells break down, sometimes becoming mucilaginous, and for a time the leaf is connected with the stem solely by the epidermis and the vascular bundles. Beneath the abscission layer a protective layer is formed by lignification and suberisation of the underlying cells (Lime, Sweet Chestnut) or of cells formed by a number of cambial divisions (Goat Willow, *Populus balsamifera*). After leaf-fall the scar (Fig. 67) becomes covered by a smooth layer of cork, which subsequently becomes continuous with that of the stem. It is interrupted only where the vascular bundles are broken across and here the vessels are usually plugged by tyloses (p. 178). The detachment of flowers and the phenomenon of self-pruning, by which small branches of certain trees (*e.g.* Poplar) are regularly shed, is due to a similar development of a definite abscission-layer.

Prior to their detachment there is considerable transport of inorganic and organic materials from the leaves into the stem. This often commences with the removal of carbohydrates and a temporary accumulation of sugars, during which red colouring matters (anthocyanins, p. 91) tend to be formed. Later the green pigments disappear and the accompanying yellow ones (p. 209) become conspicuous, often associated with the anthocyanins. Changes of these kinds are responsible for the brilliant *autumn-colours* displayed by the foliage of many trees. The fallen leaves often contain large quantities of calcium oxalate crystals and other by-products.

CHAPTER XVIII

THE PLANT IN RELATION TO ITS WATER-SUPPLY [1]

IT has been emphasised that the root subserves several functions, of which the most important are anchorage and absorption. The latter takes place mainly through the root-hairs, which not only considerably increase the absorbing surface, but are juvenile, constantly renewed, cells and therefore very actively metabolising. Since transpiration under most conditions takes place from all the exposed surfaces of the shoot, a gradient is maintained throughout the plant so that water travels from the absorbing surface of the root towards the leaves. Further water from around the contiguous soil-particles therefore passes into the root-hairs and is replaced from the surrounding soil. So long as a gradient of suction pressure (p. 45) exists across the root-cortex, water will pass inwards from the diluted sap of the root-hair in the direction of the arrows in Fig. 116. When plentiful water is available, all the cortical cells in the absorbing zone may be more or less fully turgid. Even then, provided the xylem-vessels contain a higher concentration of solutes than the soil-solution, movement of water from the soil into the xylem can occur from osmotic causes, although this involves a passage of water into the vessels from the cortex against an osmotic gradient. There may be the necessary gradient in suction pressure, though not in osmotic potential. Absorption of water and mineral salts is known to depend on active root-respiration, which probably provides the energy for forcing salts to move against their diffusion gradients and so establishing the osmotic gradients necessary to move the water. The forcing of water into the xylem may actually be mainly due to hydrostatic pressure.

The rate of absorption of water is greatly affected by the temperature of the soil, diminishing rapidly as it becomes colder,

[1] Important books on general physiology of plants are: W. Stiles, *An Introduction to the Principles of Plant Physiology*, 2nd edit., Methuen, 1950 (615 pp.); M. Thomas, *Plant Physiology*, 3rd edit., Churchill, 1947 (504 pp.). The water-relations of plants are considered in detail in N. A. Maximow, *The Plant in Relation to Water* (transl. by R. H. Yapp). Allen & Unwin, 1929 (451 pp.).

although plants differ markedly as regards their capacity to absorb at lower temperatures. A phenomenon known as *root-pressure* manifests itself at times of active root-metabolism and respiration. It can be demonstrated in the following way: The stem of a Fuchsia or Vegetable Marrow growing in a pot is cut off about 2 inches above the soil. To the cut stump one of the horizontal arms of a T-tube is firmly connected by pressure tubing, both joints being wired on. To the other horizontal arm is attached about 3 inches of similar tubing, the free end of which can be closed by a clip. After filling

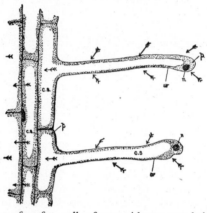

Fig. 116. Diagram of surface-cells of root with two root-hairs (very considerably magnified). The direction taken by the water is indicated by arrows. *c.s.*, cell-sap; *n*, nucleus; *p*, cytoplasm; *w*, cell-wall.

the T-piece with water, a mercury manometer is joined on to the third arm, taking care to exclude all air-bubbles. The clip is then closed. The soil is well watered and the apparatus is kept in a warm place. Very soon the mercury in the manometer will register an increasing pressure and, in a sturdy plant, this may reach nearly an atmosphere.

It will be obvious that, when such root-pressure exists, it must help in forcing water up the stem, particularly when the latter is of no considerable height; an effective root-pressure is, however, in nature not often realised except in spring. At such times liquid may exude, and even overflow, from cut stems, as may be well seen in the Cress, the Vine and in trees felled in spring. The sap exuded in *bleeding* is often rich in sugars (p. 177), formed from the rapid conversion of reserve-starch, and also contains mineral salts, facts which again suggest that there may be an active passage from living cells into the dead vessels.

On damp warm nights, when there is abundant absorption and

transpiration is at a minimum, a considerable positive pressure results. The excess of moisture, in many plants, then escapes through special organs called *hydathodes*, over which it frequently collects as small drops of liquid. The hydathodes are usually situated on the margins of the leaves, *e.g.* at the ends of the principal veins of the peltate blade of the Garden Nasturtium (Fig. 117, B), at the tip of the leaf in Grasses (Fig. 117, A), or upon the leaf-teeth in the Marsh Marigold and Fuchsia. If any one of these

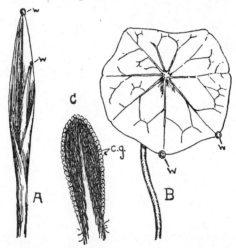

FIG. 117. Leaves with water-pores. A, Maize. B, *Tropæolum* (peltate leaf). C, Saxifrage with chalk-glands (*c.g.*). *w*, the drops of water above the water-pores.

plants, in a well-watered condition, is placed beneath a bell-jar in a warm moist atmosphere, the drops of liquid marking the positions of the hydathodes soon appear. They can be demonstrated more rapidly by the application of a negative pressure in the surrounding atmosphere (cf. p. 200, Fig. 122, C).

In some plants the hydathodes take the form of glandular hairs, their cells possessing dense protoplasmic contents and large nuclei. Good examples are found on the leaves of the Runner Bean (Fig. 118, A), where they are bent, club-shaped structures situated near the veins and consisting of a row of thin-walled cells, the terminal cell often being divided into two by a vertical wall.

A hydathode, exhibiting quite a different mechanism, is much commoner among British plants. These hydathodes occur generally above the bundle-endings, being especially located at the leaf-apex (Grasses) or on the tips of the leaf-teeth (Lesser Celandine). In these the water escapes from so-called *water-pores*, which are situated in the epidermis of the hydathode (Fig. 120, *St.*) and

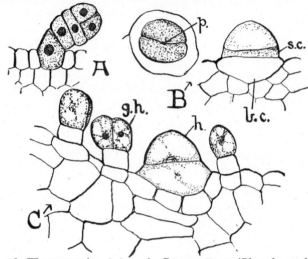

FIG. 118. Water-secreting hairs. A, Runner Bean (*Phaseolus multiflorus*). B, Yellow Rattle (*Rhinanthus*). C, Toothwort (*Lathræa squamaria*). The left-hand figure of B from the surface, the others in vertical section. *b.c.*, basal cell; *g.h.*, glandular hair; *h.*, hydathode; *p.*, pore; *s.c.*, stalk cell.

resemble ordinary stomata, except that they are often larger and that their pore remains permanently open in correspondence with

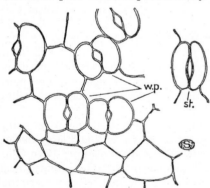

FIG. 119. Water-pores (*w.p.*) of the Lesser Celandine (*Ficaria verna*) seen from the surface; *st.*, a normal stoma on the same scale for comparison.

the absence of the characteristic thickenings in the guard-cells; in surface sections they chiefly differ in their more rounded form (Fig. 119). In some plants but a single water-pore is associated with each hydathode (*e.g.* Enchanter's Nightshade, *Fuchsia*), but in others they are numerous (*e.g.* Wild Strawberry), and occasionally grouped in shallow depressions that can be recognised with the unaided eye (*e.g.* Marsh Marigold).

In a longitudinal section through an entire hydathode of this type (Fig. 120) the end of the vascular bundle, which is here seen to consist of tracheids only, usually enlarges somewhat, often in a cup-shaped manner. Between the tracheids and the overlying water-pores there is commonly a small-celled tissue, the *epithem* (*ep.*), composed of cells with prominent nuclei and dense cyto-plasmic contents; there is often, however, a space immediately beneath the epidermis. The epithem is traversed by a system of fine intercellular spaces through which, under sufficient pressure, the water passes from the tracheids to the water-pores.

Hydathodes can often be recognised at a very early stage, and are probably most active in the young leaf, which develops in an almost saturated atmosphere within the expanding bud. Active

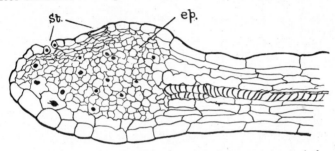

FIG. 120. Hydathode of Lesser Celandine (*Ficaria verna*) in vertical section (after Salisbury). *ep.*, epithem tissue; *St.*, water-pores.

exudation of water takes place when the hydrostatic pressure within the plant becomes excessive. The hydathodes can therefore be regarded as safety-valves which avert damage to the immature cells. The liquid exuded from hydathodes is not pure water, but usually contains a very small percentage of dissolved salts. In some plants, however, the amount of the latter may be so consider-able that they remain behind as an incrustation when the water evaporates. Thus in the Saxifrages (*Saxifraga*) and the Sea-Lavender (*Limonium*) a little white scale consisting of carbonate of lime is often found in dry weather on the leaf-teeth over each of the hydathodes.

The exudation of water from hair-like hydathodes is due to active secretion on the part of the protoplasts of the constituent cells. As a consequence secretion of water ceases, if the cells be killed by painting the surface of the leaf with a solution of corrosive sublimate or other poison. Hydathodes possessing water-pores are, however, mainly passive in their action, the water being forced out by hydrostatic pressure through the intercellular spaces of the epithem, and not by active secretion on the part of the living protoplasm.

Nectaries of flowers (cf. p. 451) represent a form of secretory organ comparable to the hydathodes just considered. The nectar is produced by the active secretion of cells belonging either to the modified epidermis (usually palisade- or papilla-like, e.g. *Anemone nemorosa*) or to the underlying tissue. The nectary of the Hogweed or other common member of Umbelliferæ, forming the disc on the top of the ovary (Fig. 428, B, *n*), consists in cross-section of a mass of small glandular cells having the customary thin walls,

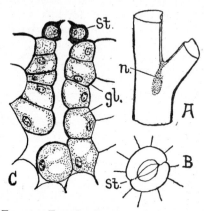

abundant protoplasm, and large nuclei, and covered by an epidermis containing numerous stomata. The prominent cuticular ridges often exhibited by the epidermis of these nectaries may serve to retain the secreted fluid *in situ*. In the Buttercup the secreting tissue at the base of the petal is similarly composed of small cells, but there are no stomata, so that the nectar only escapes by filtration through the outer membrane.

FIG. 121. Extrafloral nectary of the Bracken (*Pteridium aquilinum*) (after Lloyd). A, The fork of a frond showing the nectary (*n.*). B, A stoma from the nectary in surface view. C, The nectary in section. *gl.*, glandular cells; *St.*, stoma.

Nectaries always produce a sweet sugary fluid which at first is very concentrated (being thick and syrupy), but subsequently becomes more and more diluted by absorption of liquid from beneath. We can imitate this mechanism in a simple way by scooping out two hollows in an unpeeled Potato and filling one of them with powdered sugar. After about an hour the latter cavity will be found full of syrup which may even overflow, whilst the other is dry and empty. In this way nectaries may serve to withdraw excess of water from the plant.

Extrafloral nectaries on the vegetative organs occur in quite a number of plants, *e.g.* on the under-surfaces of the stipules of the Broad Bean (*Vicia faba*), on the leaf-bases of the Black Bindweed (*Polygonum convolvulus*), at the forks of the fronds of the Bracken (*Pteridium aquilinum*, Fig. 121, A), and on the upper part of the petioles of the Cherry and Guelder Rose (*Viburnum opulus*, Fig. 315, F, p. 452). In the first-named plant the nectary appears as a dark depression, which when cut across is found to be composed of a palisade-like layer of secreting hairs, each consisting of an oblong head of several cells, borne on a short stalk. Those of the Guelder Rose are supplied with vascular tissue, the secreting surface resembling that of the floral nectary of the Hogweed. The structure of the Bracken-nectary is shown in Fig. 121, C.

The osmotic substances secreted by extrafloral nectaries tend to cause water to pass out from a turgid plant and these organs, which are most active in moist air, may well serve primarily as hydathodes. Floral nectaries, however, have the additional important function of attracting insects.

The experiment described on p. 7 demonstrates that the xylem is the channel for the *conduction* of water, which is also proved by the fact that a branch, from which all the tissues outside the wood have been removed for a short stretch (so-called ringing), remains healthy for weeks, no matter whether it is left on the tree or kept in water. Conduction through the pith cannot be assumed, since this tissue often disappears in older stems (p. 138); moreover, removal of a length of pith does not interfere with water-conduction.

A further experiment shows that the water travels mainly through the cavities of the conducting elements. The ends of two similar shoots are allowed to dip for about ten minutes, into melted paraffin-wax and into water kept at the same temperature, respectively. After cooling, the extreme end is shaved off each, whereby all the plugged parenchyma-cells are removed, although the vessels and tracheids will remain blocked. If the shoots are then placed in water, the plugged branch fades after a few hours, while the control remains fresh.

The rate of flow of the water through the wood varies greatly from plant to plant and, for instance, with the same driving force is appreciably less through a Coniferous than through most Dicotyledonous stems, a fact which can be shown in the following way (Fig. 122, A): A round-bottomed flask is provided with a two-holed rubber cork, through each hole of which a piece of glass tubing twice bent at right angles is inserted (as in the figure). The one arm of each glass tube should project only for a short distance below the cork, while the other free arm should be considerably longer. To the open end of the latter a short piece of stem (in the one case of a Conifer (g), in the other of an Elm (d), both being of equal length) is fitted by rubber tubing, so as to make an air-tight connection. Each piece of stem should be previously coated, all except its two ends, with a layer of melted paraffin-wax, so as to close up all apertures and scars. The rubber cork with attached tubing is now taken out of the flask and the latter is half filled with water which is heated until it has boiled for a minute or two. Whilst vapour still fills the flask, the rubber stopper is fitted into it, after which the flask is placed in a vessel of cold water, the unattached ends of the two stems being allowed to dip into beakers of water (Fig. 122, A). The reduced pressure within the flask, resulting from the condensation of the contained aqueous vapour, leads to a strong suction, and as a result columns of water which have traversed the two stems will form in the tubes above their upper ends, the height of each being proportional to the rate of flow (Fig. 122, A).

A great part of the water reaching the leaves escapes in *transpiration*. Comparative transpiration-rates are often estimated by the cobalt-method (p. 7), rendered more exact by using standard colour-strips [1] representing the initial (dry) and final (moist) conditions. The much greater rapidity of transpiration from the lower surface of many leaves (*e.g.* Lilac) can be shown by this method, as well as in the following way: Choosing two healthy leaves, the

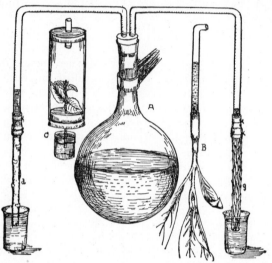

FIG. 122. A, Apparatus for comparing the rate of flow of water through the wood of two shoots (*d*, Elm; *g*, Conifer). B, Modification of same to show that gases can pass in and out of the stomata of a leaf. C, Modification for the demonstration of water-pores. For details, see text, pp. 199, 237.

ends of the petioles, and in one the lower surface of the blade, in the other the upper surface, are covered with vaseline, after which the two are hung up in a warm room. A few hours later the blade vaselined on the upper side will be more or less withered, whilst the other will have remained almost fresh. Comparison in the same way of thin and leathery leaves with the lower surfaces vaselined demonstrates the importance of a thick cuticle.

A measure of the rate of absorption of a cut shoot can be obtained with the help of an instrument known as a *potometer*. As absorption under normal conditions is closely parallel to the rate of transpiration, it can be regarded as an indirect measure of the latter. The shoots employed in experiments with the potometer should be removed from the plant some hours previously and kept in water; before use

[1] For details as to their preparation, see Henderson, *Annals of Botany*, l, 1936, pp. 321–324.

the lower 3 inches of the stem should be cut off.   The potometer
(Fig. 123) consists in general of a three-way glass tube; to one arm
the plant is attached, to the second a funnel serving as a reservoir
and capable of being closed by a stopcock, while the third arm is
connected to a piece of capillary glass tubing bent downwards at the
end and resting on a graduated scale.   To prepare the instrument
for use the stopcock is opened and water is poured into the funnel
until it fills the apparatus and flows from the end of the capillary
tube, whereupon the stopcock is closed.

A perforated rubber stopper is carefully passed over the end of

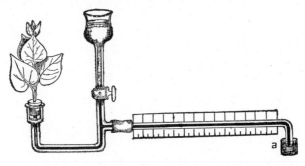

FIG. 123. Potometer.   For description, see text.

a leafy shoot (see Appendix XIV) and fitted into the arm designed
to take the plant so that the end of the stem is in water.   The open
end of the capillary tube dips into a reservoir a.   If this be removed
for a short interval, a small air-bubble is introduced which will be
seen to creep along it; this is due to the fact that the moisture lost
in transpiration from the leaves is replaced by absorption.   By
opening the stopcock, until the column of air has been driven back,
and again closing it, the potometer is prepared for a fresh observation; and, if we record (with the help of a stop-watch) the time
taken for the end of the air-column to pass over a measured distance
on the scale, the average of several readings will give an estimate
of the rate of absorption from the shoot employed.

In this way we can indirectly determine and compare the rates
of transpiration from shoots of different plants, the contrast afforded
by evergreen and deciduous types being specially instructive.   If
half the leaves of a shoot are removed or vaselined, it will be found
that, as a result of the reduced transpiring surface, the rate of
absorption is much decreased.   We may also compare shoots
exposed to different conditions, such as a hot and a cold room, dry
and moist air, moving and still air, and in each instance we shall find

that the first alternative induces more active absorption, implying that transpiration is accelerated by heat, dry air and wind.

The approximate amount of transpiration can be found by determining the loss of weight of a plant after a given interval and making a correction for the gain due to photosynthesis and the loss due to respiration (cf. p. 240). The method is only applicable to a plant grown in a pot, which like the soil must be covered with water-proof material. Alternatively, the transpired moisture can be absorbed by a weighed amount of dry calcium chloride, contained in a small vessel and placed together with the plant beneath a bell-jar, whose lower edge is greased to make an air-tight connection; the control is similar, but without a plant. If the two lots of chloride are reweighed after some time, the difference between the weights indicates the amount of water-vapour lost by the plant.

Most of the water-vapour given off in transpiration is that which has evaporated from the walls of the mesophyll-cells bordering on the intercellular spaces of the leaf. As the walls lose water, more passes into them from the cytoplasm which in its turn is supplied from the vacuole. This increases the suction pressure of the cell as compared with that of the next cell in the path, from which therefore water diffuses into the evaporating cell. This process is repeated in all the cells extending up to the xylem of a vascular bundle. The water passes down the gradient in its own diffusion potential, which is lowered by evaporation from the walls of mesophyll-cells and maintained by the supply in the xylem. If the supply cannot keep up with the demand there will be an increase in the osmotic concentration of the sap of the mesophyll-cells. The lowering of vapour pressure due to this is, however, far from sufficient to account for the resulting reduction in evaporation. Perhaps quite slight shrinkages of the cells considerably increase the resistance to movement of water from the cell-interiors to their surfaces and thus reduce the transpiration rate.

The most important external factors affecting transpiration are wind and the saturation-deficit of the air, the latter mainly influenced by the amount of water in the air and by temperature. Water-loss can, however, take place even into a saturated atmosphere, if the temperature of the interior of the leaf be above that of its surroundings. Hence a hairy covering may reduce transpiration by checking rise of temperature of the leaf-cells through insolation.

Cuticular transpiration is very slight in the mature shoot, and most of the water-vapour passes out through the stomata. Since diffusion through such minute apertures is greater at the margins, the rate tends to be proportional to the diameters and not to the areas of the pores. If stomata are crowded, the diffusion-systems from neighbouring pores interfere with one another. Mostly, however, the pores are so distributed as to afford a maximum number of epidermal apertures with minimum interference, so that, when the pores are wide open, diffusion takes place as readily as though the intercellular spaces were fully exposed. It remains doubtful whether in most plants stomatal closure normally plays any great part in restricting transpiration (cf. p. 157). Considerable reduction in the width of the pores may occur before loss of water-vapour is appreciably reduced. The risk of excessive loss of moisture and consequent wilting is inevitable with a large area of leaf-surface suited to the needs of photosynthesis.

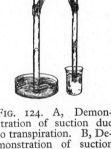

The manner in which water is raised in plants is still debated. Since any theory must explain the rise in tall trees, such phenomena as root-pressure (p. 194) and capillarity can only play a very small part. Participation of the living cells, everywhere associated with the wood, has often been urged, but, since trees placed with their severed trunks in coloured poisonous solutions, have continued to raise liquid into their uppermost leaves long after such cells must have been killed, this view finds little support. Much evidence points to *water-conduction* being a purely physical

FIG. 124. A, Demonstration of suction due to transpiration. B, Demonstration of suction due to evaporation from a porous mass (*p*). For details, see text.

process, depending on suction of the transpiring shoots and the cohesive strength of water, an hypothesis known as the *cohesion theory*.[1]

The experiment shown in Fig. 124, A, demonstrates that a transpiring shoot may bring about upward water-movement. A leafy shoot, cut under water and with the surface of the stem vaselined, is fixed by pressure tubing into a long narrow glass tube which is filled with water (Appendix XIII) and dips into mercury. As the shoot transpires, the mercury slowly rises and replaces the absorbed water. That this is a purely physical phenomenon can be shown by substituting for the shoot some porous mass like Plaster of Paris (Fig. 124, B), which is *loosely* packed into the bulb of a thistle funnel (*p*) and, in setting, expands sufficiently to fill it completely. In experiments of either kind the mercury may rise to a level above that supported by ordinary atmospheric pressure.

This effect must play an important part in the upward passage of water. The osmotic potentials of transpiring leaf-cells are always

[1] See H. H. Dixon, *Transpiration and the Ascent of Sap in Plants*, Macmillan, 1914 (216 pp.).

considerable and in tall trees may attain to high levels, especially on the higher branches. As a consequence water diffuses into them from the xylem and passes continuously from the latter to the leaf-surfaces. Removal of water from the xylem reduces the pressure in the tracts and, in tall plants, creates an actual pull amounting to many atmospheres. Owing to the cohesion of water this pull is transmitted to the water-column in the stem and is thought to suffice to lift it to the tops of the highest trees.

Above about 34 feet from the ground the transpiration stream in the xylem must always be in a state of tension increasing with height. Even in small plants a reduced pressure or even a tension (negative pressure) may arise when transpiration exceeds absorption. If a stem is then cut open beneath a solution of light green, the solution penetrates to a considerable distance into the vessels. It is instructive to compare a plant that has received little water with a well-watered one.

Plants gathered on a hot summer's day, when such a reduced pressure is almost invariably realised, often wither even though soon placed in water. This is due to the taking up of air into the vessels and their consequent loss of conducting power. If two shoots are cut, one under water and the other in the air, from a plant in which a reduced pressure has been demonstrated, the former will remain fresh, while the latter may soon fade when placed in water. Hence the necessity of cutting shoots for transpiration experiments under water.

The concept that the water in the conducting tracts of stems and leaves forms a continuous moving column (the *transpiration stream*), pulled up the plant by the transpiring leaves, requires a system with considerable tensile strength. The cohesion between the molecules of a mass of water is stated to exceed 500 atmospheres, although there is some difference of opinion about this; strong forces of adhesion also exist between the water and the water-saturated walls of the conducting elements. There remains an element of doubt whether these forces suffice to prevent rupture of the water-columns at times of excess transpiration and great tension. Even in wilted plants, however, the conducting elements may contain unbroken columns of water. When transpiration diminishes, as at night, or water is absorbed in excess of that lost, the tension in the water columns gradually decreases and may even be replaced by a positive root-pressure.

Plants absorb far more water than is directly needed and the excess is lost in transpiration. By maintaining the transpiration-stream, this process provides a current of water serving to carry the mineral salts absorbed from the soil. It also has an effect in lowering the temperature of the leaves.

CHAPTER XIX

PHYSIOLOGY OF NUTRITION

THE water and the mineral salts dissolved in it help in one way or another to build up the body of the plant. The water retained is employed for diverse purposes, viz. (i) in combination with the carbon dioxide of the air to form the starting-point of the organic substance of the plant, (ii) to keep the cells in a turgid condition (cf. pp. 44 and 143), (iii) to serve as a medium for transference of soluble materials from one part to another, and (iv) as imbibition water permeating the cell-walls and protoplasm. Uncombined water thus constitutes a great part of the plant, as can be readily seen by comparing the weight of a fresh and a dried plant.

To ensure a more accurate comparison a considerable quantity (*e.g.* about 100 grams) of fresh material is cut up into small pieces, put into an evaporating dish of known weight, and the two weighed together. The dish is now placed over a water-bath and heated until the weight is constant. The final weight of the material is far less than the original one. Since the temperature of the water-bath would be only sufficient to drive off the uncombined water, the loss of weight recorded corresponds to the amount of the latter; the weight of the remaining substance is consequently known as the *dry weight* and is usually expressed in percentages of the fresh weight.

The dry weight varies considerably according to the kind of plant or the portion of it used; thus, in a woody plant it amounts to about 50 per cent., in an herbaceous plant to about 30 per cent., and in a water-plant (as well as in many edible fruits) to little more than 5 per cent. In all but woody plants, therefore, the major part of the plant's substance consists of water. This does not, however, apply to dormant seeds in which the dry weight usually represents about seven-eighths of the total, and we can consequently understand why, as a preliminary to germination, so large an amount of moisture has to be absorbed (cf. p. 21).

In order to study further the composition of the plant we

place the dried material in a weighed crucible and heat it strongly for several hours over a Bunsen burner, but the temperature should not be so high as to cause it to glow. The mass first becomes charred and then gradually assumes a greyish-white colour like that of tobacco-ash. During this heating process all the carbon, hydrogen, oxygen, and nitrogen compounds composing the plant are broken down and escape, chiefly in the form of various simple gases (*e.g.* carbon dioxide, water-vapour, free nitrogen, etc.), and the matter that remains (the so-called *ash*) consists of the mineral constituents of the plant (*e.g.* silica, potassium carbonate, etc.).

If, after cooling, the weight of the ash is ascertained, it will be found to represent but a small fraction of the original dry weight (*e.g.* about 4 per cent. in a Potato, about 7 per cent. in the Clover, and as much as 17 per cent. in Tobacco-leaves). In order to obtain a fairly accurate estimate of the ash the heating must be repeated until no further decrease takes place. Analysis of the ash (Appendix VIII) of a large number of plants has shown that it always contains compounds of the following elements, though present in varying amounts: aluminium, calcium, chlorine, iron, magnesium, phosphorus, potassium, silicon, sodium, sulphur. To these must be added the elements carbon, hydrogen, nitrogen and oxygen, which were present in the dried material before its conversion into ash, so that compounds of a considerable number of chemical elements enter into the composition of plants. An adequate supply of certain of these, as well as slight traces of others, is known to be essential for healthy growth.

This can be established by means of *water-cultures* (Fig. 125 and Appendix IX) set up in large jars, the interiors of which have been sterilised by first rinsing them out thoroughly with commercial nitric acid and then washing out the latter with boiled water, until it gives no indication of an acid reaction with litmus. The sides of the jars are then covered with black paper to exclude light, and each is fitted with a cork pierced by three holes; through two of these a short length of glass tubing is inserted, whilst the other is left open to receive the plant. The jars are filled to about four-fifths of their height with solutions appropriate to the line of enquiry to be pursued. The following solution supplies all requisite elements except carbon and the oxygen for respiration.

Potassium nitrate	.	.	.	2 grams.
Magnesium sulphate .	.	.	.	½ gram.
Calcium sulphate	.	.	.	½ gram.
Ferric phosphate	.	.	.	½ gram.

These salts are added to two litres of glass-distilled water, the whole being shaken up or thoroughly stirred, until the bulk of the ingredients have passed into solution. A small quantity of undissolved matter may remain, but this is later dissolved by the roots of the plants.

A young seedling (preferably, if a rapid result be desired, of some plant with scanty food-reserves in its seeds) is now inserted through the middle hole of the cork in each jar, so that its roots just dip into the water, the plant being kept in position by packing it round with cotton-wool. The glass tubes, whose upper ends are closed with plugs of cotton-wool, serve for the daily aeration of the liquid in the jar and also for the addition of fresh distilled water, when necessary. Adequate aeration is of great importance.

Many diverse plants have been grown successfully and for long periods in culture solutions like that described on the previous page, whereas in distilled water only stunted growth is obtained. Such culture solutions therefore provide all the requisite mineral nutriment, but if others are prepared, individually lacking *one* of the elements in the above formula (Appendix IX), it can be proved that each is necessary for healthy growth. Thus, if nitrogen be absent (which can be effected by substituting potassium sulphate for potassium nitrate in the culture-solution given on the previous page), the seedlings fail to reach any considerable size and sooner or later die. This shows that the great volume of free nitrogen in the atmosphere cannot be used directly by the ordinary plant.

In the absence of a suitable supply of nitrogen no proteins or protoplasm can be formed and growth is impossible after the food reserves in the seed are exhausted; for a similar reason, if sulphur or phosphorus be lacking, little growth ensues. Potassium,

FIG. 125. Water-culture.

which is found in considerable quantities in leaves and in meristematic tissues, is seemingly, like calcium, concerned in the synthesis of protoplasm. Enrichment of soil with potassium salts stimulates vegetative growth, whilst shortage, for instance, produces "leaf scorch" as in Apple trees. Calcium is requisite for the calcium pectate of the middle lamella. Magnesium is found in some proteins and is a constituent of chlorophyll, while the latter is not produced when iron is lacking. When compounds of these elements are altogether absent (which is difficult to secure owing to the presence of iron as an impurity in most chemicals), the leaves become cream-coloured or *chlorotic*. In nature, in the presence of a high calcium-content in the soil, magnesium and iron may be deficient in the plant owing to difficulties of absorption and thus chlorotic effects may result. The individual elements certainly fulfil functions additional to those just indicated.

Nine elements (calcium, hydrogen, iron, magnesium, nitrogen, oxygen, phosphorus, potassium, sulphur), apart from carbon (cf.

p. 9), must therefore be supplied in appreciable amounts for adequate nourishment. All are absorbed from the soil as simple soluble inorganic compounds like those in culture-solutions. The salts used in preparing the latter, however, unless specially purified, always contain minute traces of other chemical elements, some of which are just as important as the main nutrients. The absence of such *trace elements* [1] may cause serious deficiency diseases. Thus, boron and manganese are essential for the proper development of many, and perhaps all, plants. Zinc-deficiency causes certain pathological symptoms in trees, traces of copper are necessary for healthy growth of Sunflower and Flax, and minute amounts of molybdenum for Tomatoes. The cobalt present in plants is necessary for higher animals whose intestinal flora derives its supply from the plant-food. Only minute quantities of trace elements are necessary, in fact several (*e.g.* copper) are toxic in larger amounts. The increased surface provided by the root-hairs may be of importance for the absorption by base-exchange of the trace elements in the soil.

Continued absorption of mineral salts probably depends on the maintenance of a high state of metabolic activity in the root-cells, as well as transference of the absorbed substances to other parts or their utilisation in metabolism (cf. p. 48). Salts may, however, be accumulated against a considerable concentration gradient without change, and this must involve appreciable expenditure of energy. An adequate oxygen-supply admitting of active root-respiration is, indeed, known to be a necessity for salt-absorption. Other influencing factors are the temperature, water-content and acidity of the soil, and the composition of the soil-solution. Neighbouring plants take up substances in very different amounts from a soil. Thus, the ash of Grasses is rich in silica, which produces the hard surface, whilst other meadow-plants contain but little. On the other hand, the same species from different soils may show appreciable variation in the proportions of the elements present in the ash.

The ordinary green plant derives its carbon from atmospheric carbon dioxide, of which there are about three parts in 10,000 of air. In aquatics this is provided by the carbon dioxide or carbonates in the water. If a land-plant is deprived of carbon dioxide in the surrounding air, the leaves form no starch. This is shown by keeping it, together with a quantity of soda-lime, beneath a bell-jar to which air obtains access through a U-tube filled with the same substance. In the control pieces of chalk replace the soda-lime.

In the process of *photosynthesis* in green leaves the carbon

---

[1] See W. Stiles, *Trace Elements in Plants and Animals.* Cambridge, 1946 (189 pp.).

dioxide obtains access almost entirely through the stomata (p. 152). If Lilac-shoots placed in water are kept in the dark until all starch has disappeared, none will be formed on exposure to light in those in which the under sides of the leaves are vaselined. The continued inward diffusion of carbon dioxide depends on a gradient being maintained between the outer air and the walls of the photosynthetic cells, where the carbon dioxide becomes dissolved in imbibition-water. So long as the stomatal pores remain appreciably open, absorption of carbon dioxide probably takes place almost as rapidly as if there were no epidermal covering (cf. transpiration, p. 203). The rate may increase in moving air.

That photosynthesis takes place only in the presence of *chlorophyll* is shown by the absence of starch in the non-green parts of variegated leaves (*e.g.* variegated Privet, p. 166; cf. also p. 8). The chloroplasts contain two green pigments (chlorophylls *a* and *b*), as well as several yellow carotenoid pigments (carotin, xanthophylls), the former, except in gold-leaved varieties, being present in considerably greater quantity than the latter. The chlorophylls differ but slightly and are probably the pigments mainly concerned in photosynthesis. They are complex compounds of carbon, hydrogen, oxygen, nitrogen, and magnesium, the last forming the central atom of the molecule. The yellow pigments are simpler (carotin $C_{40}H_{56}$, xanthophyll $C_{40}H_{56}O_2$). The green and yellow pigments can be roughly separated by shaking up an alcoholic extract with benzene and allowing the liquids to settle; the alcohol then contains the yellow, the benzene floating above it the green pigments.

A solution of chlorophyll in alcohol or acetone exhibits marked red fluorescence, appearing green in transmitted and reddish-green in reflected light; moreover, it decomposes in strong light unless access of air is rigorously excluded, assuming a brownish colour, which contrasts sharply with the green of a solution kept in the dark. The chlorophyll in the leaf, however, shows only faint fluorescence and is not readily broken down by light. Spectroscopic examination of a chlorophyll-solution displays a strong absorption band in the red, a number of narrower and less distinct bands in the yellow and green, whilst much of the blue and violet is obliterated (Fig. 126); if the light is allowed to pass through leaves, the position of the absorption bands is somewhat shifted towards the violet end of the spectrum. The contrasts suggest that the chlorophyll is in a different state in the living plant and in the extracts. On the basis of other observations, it has been suggested that, in association with lipoids and carotenoids, the chlorophylls are linked with proteins, as chromo-proteins, in the chloroplasts. Carotin and xanthophyll only have absorption bands in the blue end of the spectrum.

It has already been noted that in the dark (p. 8), as well as in the absence of iron and magnesium (p. 207), no chlorophyll is formed. Cultivated Sea Kale and Celery clearly show the effect of growth in darkness. A suitable temperature is also necessary for chlorophyll-formation, the pale colour of many shoots that commence to grow early in spring being a result of its imperfect production.

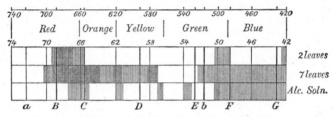

FIG. 126. Spectrum of chlorophyll (after Reinke, from Pfeffer) showing absorption by a chlorophyll-solution, and by two and seven leaves respectively.

The wave-lengths of light absorbed by chlorophyll are mainly used to provide the energy for the manufacture of carbohydrates from carbon dioxide and water. All are utilised, although there is evidence that the longer ones may play a bigger role. The building up of complicated compounds like carbohydrates from carbon dioxide and water is an endothermic reaction, which requires a large quantity of energy and, since the only source of this is light, it is comprehensible that photosynthesis cannot proceed unless the plant is illuminated. Only a small percentage of the total light-energy falling upon a leaf is used in photosynthesis; most is reflected or passes through the leaf.

FIG. 127. Starch-print. The leaf has been covered with a stencil-plate, exposed to sunlight, decolourised and placed in iodine solution.

The necessity for light is readily demonstrated in a plant that forms starch and has previously been kept in darkness, until a leaf gives no starch-reaction. If half a leaf of such a plant is covered with metal foil, starch will subsequently be formed only in the exposed half. Or, if a similar leaf be covered with a stencil plate (Appendix XVI) and illuminated for some time, treatment with iodine will give a dark letter on a light background (Fig. 127).

Starch is, however, not formed in photosynthesis,[1] but after it

---

[1] For further information on photosynthesis, see the books on the general physiology of plants cited on p. 193; also Ch. 30 of the book of Bonner, cited on p. 97; J. Franck and W. E. Loomis, *Photosynthesis in Plants*. Iowa State Coll. Press, 1950 (500 pp.); Society of Experimental Biology, Symposium No. 5, *CO_2-fixation and Photosynthesis*. Cambridge Univ. Press, 1951.

and independently of light. It is probably produced from a pre-existing simpler polysaccharide and a phosphoric sugar ester, both formed originally from sucrose. In many Monocotyledonous plants starch is rarely found in the leaves (except in the guard-cells of the stomata), sugars being here the temporary storage products. Thus, while starch-formation may often be taken as evidence of photosynthesis, its absence does not necessarily prove the contrary. Various sugars (p. 77) can always be detected in assimilating leaves and in most Dicotyledons the products of photosynthesis become converted into starch as they accumulate. Detached starch-free leaves of the Canadian Pondweed, placed in a 5 per cent. solution of grape sugar in the dark, form starch which shows how readily conversion is accomplished.

It has already been mentioned (p. 77) that the first *free* sugar produced in photosynthesis is the disaccharide sucrose and not a hexose as formerly supposed. A precursor of this is fructose di-phosphate, from which free fructose and, indirectly, glucose may be formed. Sucrose arises from fructose di-phosphate and glucose by a process known as transphosphatisation. It will be evident that the relatively complex sucrose can only be the end-product of a series of reactions, not all of which are yet fully understood; it is clear, however, that only some depend on a supply of light-energy (cf. below). The over-all process might be summarised by the equation:—

$$12CO_2 + 48H_2O = C_{12}H_{22}O_{11} + 37H_2O + 12O_2.$$

The energy necessary to raise carbon dioxide to the carbohydrate level is 112 calories per mole of that gas.

The equation shows that, during the formation of carbohydrates, a volume of oxygen equal to that of the carbon dioxide absorbed is liberated. The fact that this ratio (the assimilatory quotient) is unity affords evidence that carbohydrates only are produced in the process. It is by estimating the carbon dioxide absorbed or the oxygen evolved that photosynthesis is usually measured. The liberation of oxygen is readily demonstrated in water-plants (Fig. 128). If a bunch of Canadian Pondweed is exposed to bright light, with the cut ends beneath a completely submerged inverted funnel (f) covered by a test-tube (t) full of water, gas-bubbles will rise from the cut ends and collect in the test-tube. After some hours, when sufficient gas has accumulated, the glowing splinter test proves it to consist mainly of oxygen. It is instructive to perform a further experiment, using boiled water through which a stream of air deprived of its carbon dioxide by passing it over soda-lime, has subsequently been bubbled. In this experiment no gas is liberated, even in strong light. Aquatics thus depend on the dissolved carbon dioxide, as can likewise be shown by applying the iodine-test to leaves from the two experiments.

This method of experimentation is not applicable to terrestrial plants, whose gaseous exchange in photosynthesis is more difficult

to investigate and requires methods which cannot be described here. The above experiment can, however, be modified to give useful comparative data, helping to assess the influence of various factors on the rate of photosynthesis. For this purpose the cut end of the stem of a suitable water-plant, loosely tied to a long glass rod in an inverted position, is covered with a small hood, made of narrow-bore glass tubing drawn out into a fine point. Alternatively, the cut end can merely be covered with shellac varnish in which, after it has set, a small hole is pricked. With such an arrangement a stream of bubbles of equal size will escape from the aperture in sunlight, the number in a given time affording some measure of the rate at which photosynthesis is proceeding. In such experiments the rate of bubbling is allowed to become uniform, before counts are made.

FIG. 128. Apparatus to demonstrate evolution of oxygen in a water-plant. For description, see text.

In this way it is easily established that, up to certain limits, the rate increases with the light-intensity, the temperature of the water, and the concentration of available carbon dioxide. The last can be increased by adding small quantities of potassium bicarbonate, the carbon dioxide concentration being roughly proportional to the amount of dissolved bicarbonate. When any factor is at a minimum (e.g. semi-darkness, a temperature little above 0° C.), the rate of oxygen-evolution is very slow, no matter how suitable the other conditions may be. The minimal factor thus tends to limit the rate of photosynthesis, and its gradual increase, when others remain constant, will result in progressive acceleration of oxygen-evolution. At temperatures above 25°–30° C. some internal factor is affected, and the rate of evolution may decrease in successive observations. High light-intensities may also exert a retarding influence. In nature the rate of photosynthesis on a bright summer's day may be limited by the carbon dioxide supply and other circumstances, and the light-intensity could then be appreciably diminished without decreasing the rate of carbohydrate-formation.

Investigations of the course of photosynthesis in diverse plants by more exact methods (Fig. 128 *) show that, at higher light intensities (III, IV), the rise is at first proportional to increasing carbon dioxide concentration, but, above a certain value, the curve becomes progressively flatter as some other factor limits the rate; at no stage, however, will increase in amount of carbon dioxide fail to cause some further increase in the rate. In weakly il-luminated plants the rate is approximately proportional to the light-intensity, and increase of temperature has comparatively little effect. On the other hand, when neither light nor carbon dioxide is minimal, the rate is affected by increase of temperature in the same way as an enzyme-reaction, being doubled or trebled or more for every 10° C. rise. Since respiration is markedly acceler-

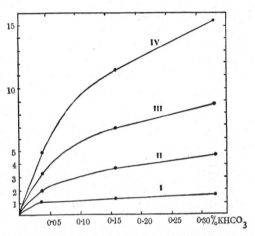

Fig. 128 *. Graphs showing rates of photosynthesis of the Moss *Fontinalis* at various carbon dioxide concentrations (supplied as KHCO₃) and light intensities (after Harder); I, 667; II, 2,000; III, 6,000; IV, 18,000 meter candles.

ated by rise of temperature (p. 240), a correction for it is necessary in all investigations of the effects of the latter on photosynthesis.

The experimental results referred to in the last two paragraphs have furnished some of the evidence for the conclusion that photo-synthesis occurs in a number of stages and comprises a photo-chemical one, as well as steps which are not dependent on light and constitute what are called protoplasmic or dark reactions. The fact that the first leaves of Runner Bean seedlings turn green some time before oxygen-evolution commences can be attributed to the slower development of such protoplasmic factors.

Recent experiments with isotopes have revealed that all the oxygen evolved comes from the water (containing O^{18}) used and none from the carbon dioxide. Absorption of carbon dioxide and oxygen-evolution are, therefore, distinct processes. It is now recognised that an essential step in photosynthesis is the reduction of carbon dioxide by the hydrogen of the water, although other substances may serve as hydrogen-donors. Thus, certain Sulphur Bacteria, which contain a green pigment (bacteriochlorophyll) very similar to chlorophyll, form carbohydrates from carbon dioxide and hydrogen sulphide (H_2S) and effect the reduction of a carbon dioxide complex by the transference of hydrogen from the sulphide, the sulphur accumulating as granules in the cells.

The first step in photosynthesis has been shown to be a combination of carbon dioxide with some substance in the cytoplasm. The carbon dioxide derivative thus produced is reduced by hydrogen liberated from the water, which is split in the photochemical stage. The product undergoes a long series of changes effected by enzymes, an early intermediate product being seemingly phospho-glyceric acid; later phospho-pyruvic acid and phosphoric sugar esters are produced and finally sucrose. Formation of the toxic formaldehyde (CH_2O) during the process was formerly assumed, but it is never found in significant amount in assimilating leaves.

The Sulphur Bacteria above mentioned, like all green plants, depend on the absorption of solar energy for the synthesis of carbohydrates. Diverse other, relatively simple, organisms, however, bring about synthesis of organic compounds with the help of energy liberated in internal exothermic chemical reactions, although the majority of colourless organisms do not possess this faculty. Good examples of such *chemosynthesis* are provided by the nitrifying Bacteria of soil (see p. 349). The thread-forming Iron Bacteria, living in ferrugineous waters, furnish other instances. These absorb ferrous salts from the water and oxidise them to the ferric state, the process often being accompanied by the precipitation of abundant reddish ferric hydroxide. In this way they acquire the energy to build up their bodies from inorganic substance only. Similarly, *Beggiatoa*, abundant in waters containing hydrogen sulphide, obtains energy for the synthesis of carbohydrates by the absorption and oxidation of this gas, sulphur, later oxidised to sulphate, being deposited within the cells of its colourless threads.

The production of soluble carbohydrates is only the first step in the formation of the organic substance of the green plant. Although a considerable fraction is built up into proteins and some may undergo conversion into fats, much usually remains in the form of carbohydrates, which are conducted away from the seat of formation to other parts. On bright days, however, leaves often exhibit an accumulation of transitory starch (p. 72), which disappears overnight, the transference being readily recognised by comparing the amounts of starch in a leaf removed at nightfall and in one picked early next morning. Detached leaves with their petioles in water do not lose their starch. The carbohydrates pass to storage organs or to centres of meristematic activity, where they form cellulose-walls and take part in protein-synthesis. In all living cells carbohydrates constitute a respiratory substrate (see Chapter XXI).

In the *synthesis of proteins* complex processes are involved, still incompletely understood. A first step is no doubt the reduction of nitrates to ammonium compounds, followed by incorporation of ammonia into keto- and other organic acids, with the formation of amino-acids (*e.g.* glycine, alanine, aspartic acid, glutamic acid), which are widespread in plants. Their molecules include both acid (COOH) and basic (NH₂) groups and some (*e.g.* cystine) contain sulphur. There is evidence that both nitrates and sulphates undergo reduction, the former to nitrites and then to ammonium salts From these and forerunners or derivatives of the sugars formed in photosynthesis the amino-acids are produced. The huge protein-molecules consist of chains of innumerable amino-acids. Polypeptides have been artificially synthesised from amino-acids. Most protein-synthesis probably takes place in leaves where the raw materials are available, but it is not always directly dependent on a supply of light-energy, since, given a good supply of carbohydrates, it can also take place in the dark. The nucleo-proteins also contain phosphorus.

Elaborated food-materials are conveyed from one part of a plant to another as soluble and readily diffusible substances, carbohydrates evidently mainly as sucrose, nitrogenous substances as amino-acids and amides (asparagine, glutamine), which are always produced when protein-reserves are utilised. Translocation takes place mainly through the phloem, although there may be slow diffusion of carbohydrates through elongated parenchymatous elements. When branches are ringed (p. 199), both carbohydrates and nitrogenous compounds accumulate in the intact tissues above the interruption. Sugars often occur in some quantity in the sieve-tubes, where also proteinaceous materials accumulate (p. 146); marked gradients in sugar concentration may exist between different parts of the stem. While the importance of sieve-tubes in the conduction of elaborated substances seems established, the mechanism remains uncertain, for translocation can occur at a much more rapid rate than can be accounted for by normal diffusion. Since its speed is affected by the vigour of respiration, it may depend on vital processes.

Green plants, as well as the colourless forms considered on p. 213A, are said to be *autotrophic* because they elaborate organic food from inorganic materials. Animals cannot do this and obtain their nutriment second-hand, either directly from the Vegetable Kingdom or indirectly (as in Carnivores) from other herbivorous animals; so that, if green plants were to disappear from the surface of the earth, almost the whole living universe would shortly perish.

There are plants, however, which are more or less dependent on elaborated food-substances and can only thrive when living or dead organic matter is available. Such plants, termed *heterotrophic*, comprise most of the Fungi and Bacteria, but also include a certain number of Flowering Plants in which the leaves are always of small size and usually devoid of chlorophyll. When part or all of the food is obtained from some other living organism the plant is known as a *parasite* and the organism on which it feeds as the *host*, whilst when the source of a plant's nourishment is non-living organic matter we speak of it as a *saprophyte*.

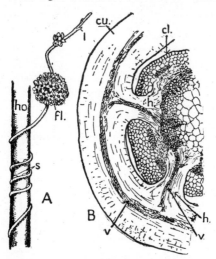

FIG. 129. Dodder (*Cuscuta*). A, small part of parasite, showing flowers (*fl.*), scale-leaves (*l.*) and haustoria (*s.*) attached to stem of host (*ho.*). B, *Cuscuta* (*cu.*)-stem cut longitudinally and host (Clover, *cl.*)-stem cut transversely, showing haustoria (*h.*) with vascular tissue (*v.*) joining that of host.

Among British Flowering Plants there are but few which are entirely parasitic, and none are very common; they include the Dodder, the Toothwort (see Fig. 131), and the Broomrapes.

As a typical instance we may select the Dodder, a close ally of Convolvulus, which is an annual parasitic on many different hosts (*e.g.* Clover, Furze, Heather, etc.). The thread-like stem of this plant entwines the host (Fig. 129, A). Some of the coils are distant and unattached, whilst others are close together and bear the suckers (*haustoria, s*) through which nourishment is absorbed. There would appear to be no leaves, but careful examination discloses a number of minute scales (*l*) separated by long internodes and, as in all true parasites, completely devoid of chlorophyll. The stems vary in colour between bright yellow and red, and thus the plant becomes conspicuous, even before the rosette-like bunches of pink flowers (Figs. 129, A, *fl.*, and 130) are formed. By the production of plentiful small seeds the risk of a host not being found is minimised, since one or other seed is very likely to germinate near a suitable plant.

The seedling is a simple thread containing a trace of chlorophyll, but showing no marked distinction into radicle, plumule, and cotyledons, *i.e.* the extreme reduction of the vegetative parts seen in the mature plant appears already in the seedling. The latter is, however, capable of a brief independent existence, and during this period the tip of the stem swings round in a circular manner and may thus happen to meet with a support; thereupon the root withers, so that the mature Dodder has no connection with the soil whatever. Failing the presence of a host the seedling soon dies away.

A striking feature of the anatomy of the Dodder is the feeble development of xylem, no doubt in relation to the reduction of the leaves. The *haustoria* arise from the stem (Fig. 129, B) as outgrowths (*h.*), which flatten out in contact with the surface of the host. The centre of the sucker grows out as a peg-like process, which penetrates the cortex and ultimately reaches the vascular tissue of the host, where it often expands considerably (Fig. 129, B, *h.*). At first this process consists of undifferentiated cells, but later those adjacent to the xylem become tracheids, whilst those in contact with the phloem develop as phloem-like elements. By the connection thus established between the conducting elements of host and parasite, the photosynthetic products and absorptive system of the former become available for the parasite.

The parasite, being relieved of those functions which necessitate elaboration of the vegetative structure, is enabled to utilise almost its entire energies for the purpose of reproduction. Simplification of structure, in every other direction but that which tends towards an increase in the output of seeds, is a marked characteristic of parasites. Even the ovules (cf. p. 445) and embryos are simpler in construction than those of most green plants, the material economised in this way presumably making possible a quantitative increase.

The Dodder is exceptional among British parasites, not only in being a climber and in having no roots in the mature condition, but also in being attached to the stem of its host. Nearly all other British plants of this kind are so-called *root-parasites*. They fix themselves by means of suckers to the roots of the attacked plant, as in the Toothwort (*Lathræa*) and the Broomrapes (*Orobanche*). The yellowish-white shoots of the former (Fig. 131) are usually found beneath the Hazel or the Wych Elm; they appear above ground in the early spring and flower about April. The overground part consists of an inflorescence of numerous purplish flowers, with

membranous leaves intermingled.   At a varying depth beneath the
surface of the soil one finds in the Toothwort a perennial stem which
is extensively branched, the upturned tips constituting the annual
aerial shoots.   The whole underground system bears numerous
decussate fleshy scales of a pink colour and richly branched adventitious roots which attach themselves to those of the host by flat
suckers.

FIG. 130. Photograph of a portion of a plant of the Gorse, covered with the
thread-like stems of the Dodder (*d*).   On these the numerous bunches of
flowers (*fl.*) can be seen.   [Photo. E. J. S.]

Owing to the connection of the Toothwort with the extensive
root-systems of its woody hosts and to the absence of the usual
transpiring surface, an excess of water readily collects within the
parasite.   This excess is exuded from hydathodes (p. 195) lining
the inner surfaces of the hollow fleshy scales borne on the underground stem, and at times the soil around the Toothwort appears
quite wet.   The hydathodes (Fig. 118, C, *h*) have the form of small
domes consisting of living cells, viz. a large basal cell (cf.
Fig. 118, B, *b.c.*) embedded in the epidermis, a short stalk-cell (*s.c.*),
and a head composed of two to four cells lying side by side (Fig. 118,
B, left-hand figure);   in the middle of the head there is a small
space between the cells, and above this the overlying cuticle is

pierced by a minute hole (*p.*) through which the water is secreted. Glandular hairs (Fig. 118, C, *g.h.*) of another type are present, which may take part in the secretion of water.

The species of Broomrape, the commonest of which is found on the roots of Clover, are close allies of the Toothwort and very similar in their overground organs. The seeds apparently germinate only when in contact with the roots of a suitable host. In

FIG. 131. Photograph showing three shoots of the Toothwort; each bears numerous flowers. [Photo. E. J. S.]

common with all other parasites, the Broomrapes exhibit a much reduced leaf-surface and numerous minute seeds dispersed by wind, but even so these plants are by no means frequent. The reduction of the vegetative as compared with the seed-producing part has gone much farther in some tropical parasites, in which the vegetative organs are represented by one much-branched haustorium traversing the tissues of the host (e.g. *Rafflesia*).

The Mistletoe is a somewhat exceptional type of parasite found growing on the branches of Apple, Hawthorn, etc. It possesses green leaves and is thus a *semi-parasite*. It sends peg-like suckers (whose growth in length keeps pace with the secondary thickening of the branch) deep down into the wood of the host. It differs from most other British plants, not only in its parasitic qualities, but also in growing aloft on the branches of trees. This kind of situation is, however, frequented by many non-parasitic plants of the Tropics (*e.g.* Orchids, p. 111).

The commonest saprophyte amongst British Flowering Plants is the Bird's-nest Orchid (*Neottia*) found growing in Beech-woods. This saprophyte (Fig. 132) blooms in late May, the plant emerging from the humus as an unbranched stem bearing a few scaly leaves (*l*) of moderate size and numerous flowers (*fl*), all of a brown colour, little or no chlorophyll being present. The erect shoots are borne on a subterranean mycorrhizal portion (*n*) (cf. p. 110), the numerous branches of which are interwoven so as to form a structure somewhat resembling a bird's nest; hence the common name. The saprophyte thus obtains its nourishment from the organic matter in the humus with the aid of the contained Fungus (Fig. 63, *m*).

Although parasites and saprophytes are rare amongst Flowering Plants, all Fungi and most Bacteria depend on these methods of nutrition and are often responsible for processes of decay (p. 335). An association with Fungi is, however, not confined to saprophytes like *Neottia*, but is seen in many other higher plants (*e.g.* the Conifers, the Beech, and most members of Ericaceæ), all of which grow where humus is plentiful.

In the trees the threads of the ectotrophic mycorrhiza (p. 110) completely invest many of the rootlets, although only penetrating into their surface-layers. They replace the root-hairs and, like other soil-inhabiting Fungi, break down the organic matter of the humus into soluble compounds which become available to the host. In *Neottia*, where the mycorrhiza is endotrophic (Fig. 63, *m*) and

FIG. 132. Complete plant of the Bird's-nest Orchid (*Neottia*) (about two-thirds natural size). *fl.*, flower; *l*, leaf; *n*, the underground nest-like portion.

undergoes digestion in the inner cortex, it is claimed that it can fix nitrogen (p. 350). Here, as in the Heather, the relation is obligatory, but in other instances the absence of fungal threads does not seem to impair the vigour of the plant. The Fungus no doubt obtains some nourishment from the host. The association seems to be one of controlled parasitism and under certain conditions the balance may be disturbed and the Fungus become harmful.[1]

An association between roots and Bacteria is met with in most Leguminosæ. On digging up a plant of the Bird's-foot Trefoil or a Vetch the roots are found to bear small swellings (Fig. 133, *t*), the so-called *root-nodules*, in which the Bacteria occur.

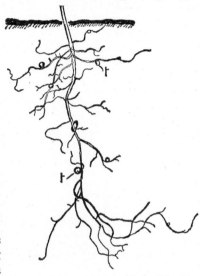

Even in the time of the Romans the inclusion of Leguminous plants in a rotation of crops was recognised as beneficial. Experience has shown that cultivation of Clovers, Sainfoin, Lucerne, etc., materially increases the nitrogen-content of the soil, especially if the crop is subsequently ploughed into the field (so-called green manuring). This phenomenon remained unexplained until it was discovered that the nodules contain certain nitrogen-fixing Bacteria (*Rhizobium*), which are present in every soil. Infection is brought about probably by means of the motile phase of the Bacteria

FIG. 133. Root-system of the Meadow Vetchling (*Lathyrus aphaca*), showing the root-nodules (*t*) (natural size). The level of the soil is indicated by a heavy line.

penetrating into some of the root-hairs, from which they pass into adjoining cells. These are stimulated to divide, so that an enlarging gall-like structure arises, which later becomes connected by a vascular strand to the central cylinder of the root. Within the nodule the Bacteria multiply rapidly, probably at the expense of carbohydrates provided by the Leguminous plant. Later they tend to assume swollen and deformed shapes (Fig. 227, p. 347) and simultaneously the cells harbouring them hypertrophy and show other symptoms of degeneration. Ultimately the nodules disintegrate from within outwards, but a few of the Bacteria persist unaltered and return to the soil. Part of the nitrogenous material (amino-acids, probably aspartic acid), formed during nitrogen-fixation, becomes available to the Leguminous plant, its removal being in fact necessary for the continued activity of the Bacteria.

[1] For further details, see M. C. Rayner, *Mycorrhiza*. Wheldon & Wesley, 1927 (246 pp.).

The importance of the presence of these nitrogen-fixing Bacteria is shown by the fact that Leguminous plants, grown from seed in soil which has been thoroughly sterilised by heating, fail to develop any nodules, and are just as dependent on a supply of soil-nitrates as other green plants. It appears that different strains of these Bacteria infect different Leguminous plants, and that normally those of a particular strain only attack other individuals

FIG. 134. Photograph of two plants of the Sundew (*Drosera*). On one of the leaves of the left-hand plant an insect (*ins.*) has been caught. *bl.*, leaf-blade; *infl.*, inflorescence; *p*, petiole. [Photo. E. J. S.]

of the same species. Similar nodules of a larger size occur on the roots of the Alder and the Bog Myrtle (*Myrica*).

Another special method of nutrition is that of the so-called *insectivorous plants*.[1] A common example is the Sundew (Fig. 134) which frequents boggy situations, such as damp moorlands and peaty heaths. The plant consists of a radical rosette of reddish leaves with relatively long petioles (*p.*), expanding into a blade (*bl.*) which is rounded or oval according to the species; from the centre of the rosette arise one or more upright inflorescences (*infl.*) with white flowers. The upper surfaces and the edges of all the leaf-blades are beset with numerous secretory tentacles having swollen ends which glisten owing to a sticky covering (see Fig. 134). These tentacles are supplied with a vascular bundle which extends into the enlarged tip. In the latter the bundle is enveloped by three distinct layers of cells, of which the innermost is thickened after

[1] See also C. Darwin, *Insectivorous Plants*. John Murray, 1908 (377 pp.).

the manner of an endodermis, while the two outer layers which contain the crimson pigment are those actually concerned in secretion; the superficial one has a palisade-like structure.

Insects attracted by the tentacles alight on the leaf and adhere to the secretion. Unless the insect be powerful enough to escape, the tentacles touching it begin to bend slowly towards the middle

FIG. 135. Photograph taken from above, showing the leaf-rosettes of a considerable number of plants of the Butterwort (*Pinguicula*). At the top left-hand corner is a specimen of the Cross-leaved Heath (*Erica tetralix*) and on the right, near the top, the trailing shoots of the Bog Pimpernel (*Anagallis tenella*).
[Photo. E. J. S.]

of the blade, and this is soon followed by a similar movement of the others.

In this way the insect's body is firmly held against the surface of the leaf, in fact it is often completely hidden from view by the incurved tentacles. At this stage digestive juices pass out from these structures and, attacking the insect's body, slowly convert its soft parts into a soluble form when they are absorbed by the tentacles. After a considerable lapse of time the latter resume their normal position and now the undigested hard portions of the insect alone remain. The Sundew is able to live without such insect-food, but under these circumstances it produces fewer flowers and seeds—in other words, its vigour is much diminished.

The Butterwort (Fig. 135) captures its prey in a somewhat similar manner. Here the upper surfaces of the yellowish radical leaves bear numerous sticky digestive glands (Fig. 136, *d*) composed of a basal cell, a short stalk-cell, and a usually eight-celled head.

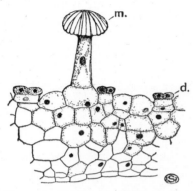

Similar glands occur also on the under-surface, but these are probably mainly concerned with the excretion of water. The digestive glands are accompanied by other long-stalked glands (*m.*), whose umbrella-like heads secrete the sticky mucilaginous matter to which the insects adhere.

A peculiar instance is afforded by the Bladderwort, a submerged water-plant bearing numerous little sack-like structures on its deeply divided leaves (Fig. 137, A, *bl.*). Each of these bladders has a narrow aperture (Fig. 137, A, *o*) surrounded by hairs and closed by a trap-door opening only inwards

FIG. 136. Transverse section through a small part of the leaf of the Butterwort (*Pinguicula*), showing the short digestive glands (*d.*) and a mucilage-secreting hair (*m.*).

(Fig. 137, B, *t*). The inner surface of the bladders bears four-armed hairs and absorbs the internal liquid. When the trap-door is shut this absorption leads to contraction of the bladder under tension. If a minute aquatic animal comes in contact with certain of the hairs around the aperture, the trap-door is released and water rushes in, carrying the organism with it. The imprisoned animals ultimately die, and the products of their decay are absorbed with the surrounding fluid so that a state of tension again arises. No digestive enzyme is known to be secreted by this plant.

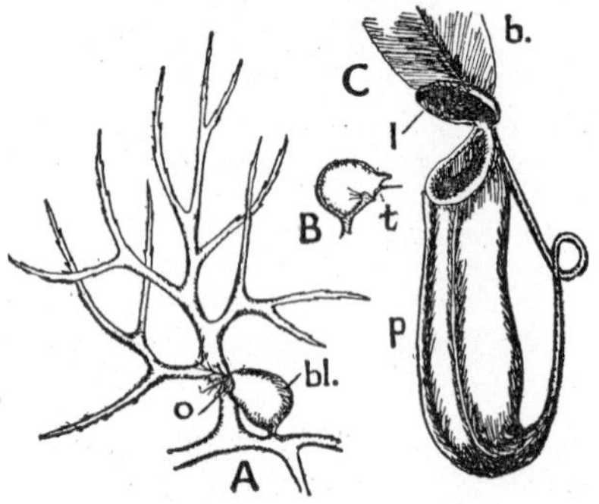

Mention should also be made of the well-known

FIG. 137. A, Single leaf of the Bladderwort (*Utricularia*) (about three times the natural size). B, Single bladder of the same cut through lengthwise (same scale as in A). *bl.*, bladder; *o*, aperture of bladder; *t*, lid of bladder. C, Single pitcher of the Pitcher-plant (*Nepenthes*) (somewhat reduced). *b*, leaf-like broadening of base of petiole; *l*, lid; *p*, pitcher.

Pitcher-plant (*Nepenthes*), in which the blade is modified to form the pitcher (Fig. 137, C, *p*), whilst a broadening (*b*) of the lower part of the petiole fulfils the usual functions of the lamina; the rigid lid (*l*) protects the contents from being flooded by rain. Numerous overlapping waxy flakes are secreted on the smooth inner surface of the pitcher, so that insects cannot obtain a foothold and slip into the liquid, which occupies the lower part; they are prevented from crawling out by the numerous downwardly directed scales upon the wall. Subsequently their bodies undergo digestion as a result of secretion from short-stalked glands. These are provided with a robust oval head of palisade-like cells and are situated beneath the overhanging scales in the lower part of the pitcher. The products are absorbed by the plant.

Most insectivorous plants frequent swampy localities, and it is probable that by their special method of nutrition they make up for the deficiency in nitrogenous salts which often obtains in such habitats.

Our study of the nutritive processes in autotrophic plants has shown that green leaves are the world's great factories, which build up complex from simple substances and store up the radiant energy of the sunlight in a form available for the maintenance of the plant's activities. More food is often elaborated than is necessary for immediate requirements and the surplus is stored up for a twofold purpose. For, such food-reserves not only further new growth by supplying materials to sprouting buds in the spring, but also enable the parent-plant to provide the necessary start in life for its offspring, whether these arise from seeds or from organs of vegetative propagation.

CHAPTER XX

FOOD-STORAGE AND VEGETATIVE REPRODUCTION

MANY plants are specially fitted for vegetative reproduction, namely, propagation by detachment of some part of the vegetative organs. One of the great advantages of the creeping habit is the

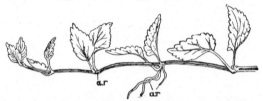

FIG. 138. Creeping shoot of the Yellow Dead-nettle (*Galeobdolon*) (about half natural size). The upright flowering axis from which this shoot arises is not shown. *a.r.*, adventitious roots, fully developed at one node, as rudiments at another.

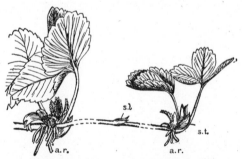

FIG. 139. Runner of the Strawberry (*Fragaria*, about half the natural size). One plant produced from a runner is seen on the left, a younger one on the right. The full length of the runner is by no means indicated. *a.r.*, adventitious roots; *s.l.*, scale-leaf; *st.*, stipule.

rapidity with which a considerable surface of the ground is covered (cf. p. 15). Tufts of adventitious roots are produced from some of the nodes of the prostrate shoots (e.g. *Lysimachia nummularia* and Ground Ivy, Fig. 7), and thus, if the older parts die away, the rooted branches become free as independent units. A similar propagation by horizontal creeping shoots, which arise from the base of the erect flowering stem and subsequently lose their connection with the main plant, is seen in the Yellow Deadnettle (Fig. 138).

Such creeping shoots often take the form of *runners*, as in the Cinquefoil (*Potentilla reptans*) and the Strawberry (Fig. 139). Towards the end of the flowering season numerous slender branches arise from the axils of the radical leaves of the Strawberry and radiate over the surface of the ground. These runners elongate with great rapidity, forming a few small scale-like leaves (*s.l.*) separated by long internodes; new plants are ultimately produced from the upturned tips of the runners, whilst the latter are continued by axillary branches, each arising from a leaf of a new rosette, giving a sympodial construction. Adventitious roots (*a.r.*) grow out from the base of the new plant and sooner or later the connecting portion of the runner decays away. The runner is distinguished by its considerable elongation, which serves to diminish competition with the parent.

A special method of vegetative reproduction by overground shoots is seen in the Bramble (Fig. 140), in which some of the woody stems arch over towards the ground and, on reaching the latter, exhibit a

FIG. 140. Rooting branch of the Bramble (*Rubus*) with numerous adventitious roots arising from the tip and showing one of the small leaves from which axillary shoots are produced (about two-thirds natural size).

swelling of their tips from which numerous adventitious roots are produced. From the axils of small leaves, which occur intermingled among the roots on the overground part, leafy shoots develop and produce a new Bramble-bush which after a few years becomes independent.

The *suckers* found in some fruit-trees (*e.g.* Damson), as well as in the Poplar and the Yarrow (Fig. 141), are axillary underground shoots which sooner or later come above the surface, when their tips give rise to new plants that may remain joined to the parent for some years. As a consequence of this prolonged attachment the daughter-plant is nourished by the parent until it becomes fully established; hence suckers are not swollen out with food-reserves like other subterranean organs of vegetative propagation,

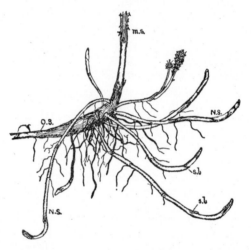

FIG. 141. Base of a plant of the Yarrow (*Achillea*), showing the remains of an old sucker (*o.s.*), whose upturned tip produced the main stem (*m.s.*), and numerous new suckers (*n.s.*) (about two-thirds natural size).   *s.l.*, scale-leaves.

to be subsequently considered, in which separation from the parent takes place before the daughter-plant is self-supporting. The underground portion of the sucker is white, but is readily distinguished from a root by the scale-leaves (*s.l.*) borne upon it. Here, too, the construction is sympodial, the main axis for any season being a lateral branch of that of the previous season (cf. Fig. 141).

Vegetative reproduction may be accomplished by adventitious shoots arising, usually endogenously, from roots, as in the Elm. It is this feature which renders the Bindweed, the Creeping Thistle (*Cirsium arvense*), and the Sheep's Sorrel (*Rumex acetosella*) such obnoxious weeds, and the Horse Radish so difficult to eradicate.

In many plants a portion of the stem is situated beneath the surface of the soil, such underground stems when they creep horizontally being termed *rhizomes*, whilst the short more or less erect structures seen in the Buttercup and Primrose are known as *root-stocks.* The Iris possesses a rhizome which is a thick branched horizontal stem bearing foliage leaves towards the tips and the remains of leaves attached to the leaf-scars on the older portions. The Solomon's Seal shows a further specialisation. Here the aerial flowering shoots will be found to arise vertically from a thick white rhizome (Fig. 142), situated at some depth in the soil and covered with ring-like remnants of reduced scale-leaves (*s*), as well as with adventitious roots (*a.r.*) which occur principally upon the under side. Examination of an entire plant in spring shows that

the ends of the main axis of the rhizome and its branches curve up to form the over-ground shoots (*a.s.*), whilst a bud, from the axil of the lowest scale-leaf on the latter, continues the horizontal growth of the sympodial sub-terranean system.

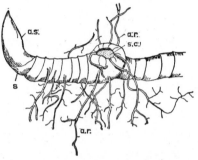

Some time after flowering the aerial shoots die away leaving on the upper surface of the rhizome a large round scar (*sc.*), the so-called "seal," marked by numerous dots which represent the broken ends of the vascular strands. In the autumn (the stage

FIG. 142. Rhizome of the Solomon's Seal (*Polygonatum*) in autumn (about half the natural size). *a.r.*, adventitious roots; *a.s.*, bud of next year's aerial shoot; *s*, scale-leaves on rhizome; *sc.*, scar of aerial shoot of past season. The portion of the rhizome to the right of this scar was formed a year earlier than the part to the left of it.

shown in the figure) the buds developed from the base of the aerial shoots have completed their horizontal growth, and their tips have now curved upwards, ready to grow above the soil in the following season. The rhizome persists for some time, so that several seals marking the annual flowering shoots may be found along its length, but sooner or later the older parts decay and as a consequence the branches become separate plants. Owing to food-reserves in the rhizome, the aerial shoots grow rapidly in the spring and the detached branches are well equipped for an independent existence.

The rhizome of the Solomon's Seal therefore serves not only as an organ of vegetative propagation, but also for food-storage, and thus constitutes the means of persistence for this perennial from year to year (cf. p. 12). Similar examples are furnished by the Lily of the Valley (*Convallaria*) and many Grasses, in which the terminal buds are encased in scales whose tips form a hard point, well suited to pierce the ground (seen also in the Sand

Sedge, *Carex arenaria*).   The slender underground stems of such
plants as the Woodruff (*Asperula*) serve mainly for extension and,
in common with many other rhizomatous plants, the Woodruff
exhibits a gregarious habit.   It is this gregarious habit that
accounts for the unisexual (cf. p. 449) patches of such plants as

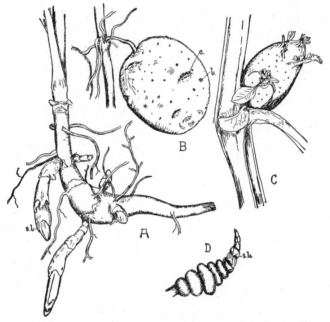

Fig. 143. Food-storage in tuberous stems (all figures about two-thirds natural
size).   A, Perennial Sunflower.   B, Potato (normal).   C, Potato-tuber formed
in axil of leaf of aerial shoot.   D, Chinese Artichoke (tuber only).   *e*, " eyes ";
l, lenticels; *s.l.*, scale-leaves.

the Nettle and Dog's Mercury, each patch being derived from one
individual which has spread vegetatively.

Vegetative reproduction is likewise combined with food-storage
in the Perennial Sunflower (*Helianthus perennis*, Fig. 143, A), the
Jerusalem Artichoke (*Helianthus tuberosus*), and the Chinese Artichoke (*Stachys tuberifera*, Fig. 143, D), in all of which a number
of axillary branches arise from scale-leaves on the underground
part of the stem, in the course of the summer, and grow more or
less horizontally through the soil.   These shoots bear scale-leaves
(*s.l.*) showing the same decussate arrangement as the foliage-leaves.
The food formed by the aerial shoot is in part stored up in the more
or less swollen tips of the subterranean branches, and, after the

plant has died down in the autumn, the latter become detached, giving rise to new and independent plants in the following spring; each of these thus really represents a lateral branch of the plant of the previous season. In the Chinese Artichoke (Fig. 143, D) the swollen tips exhibit a succession of swellings, each representing an internode, whilst in the Jerusalem Artichoke the several internodes form a large tuber of irregular shape. The abundant food-materials stored up in these organs render them valuable as vegetables.

The *tubers* of the Potato are formed in the same way, but differ in having a protective covering of cork (the peel), pierced by lenticels (Fig. 143, B, *l*). The "eyes" (*e*), which are best seen on young tubers, represent scale-leaves with axillary buds; sometimes the Potato is cut up into pieces, each including an "eye," which thus serve as the starting-point for as many new plants. Under exceptionally favourable conditions some of the axillary buds on the overground parts of the plant occasionally develop into similar tubers (Fig. 143, C) and here the true character of the scale-leaf and axillary bud is very obvious.

The *corm* of the Crocus is a special kind of root-stock formed by a swelling up of the base of the flowering stem. If we halve the lower part of a plant in April, as in Fig. 144, D, the new corm (*c. 1914*) is seen arising as a swollen structure enclosed within the sheathing bases of the lower leaves of the flowering shoot (*a.s.*), whilst below it is the corm (*c. 1913*) from which the latter has arisen. Later in the season, when the flowering shoot has withered, the new corm will be found to have increased greatly in size, the old one having shrivelled considerably, so that it is now the smaller of the two. In the autumn the corm has attained its full dimensions, is enveloped in the brown tunic constituted by the remains of the sheathing leaf-bases of last spring's shoot, whilst in their axils one or more buds (Fig. 144, B, *b*) have developed; beneath it is a dark mass, the remnant of the old corm (cf. Fig. 144, A and D, *c. 1912*).

The corm is thus a much-swollen stem-base ensheathed in scales and bearing one or more axillary buds, in each of which the young leaves and flower for next year's growth (Fig. 144, C) can be recognised. On removing the scales it will be found that each of them is attached around the whole circumference of the corm (Fig. 144, B, *sc.*), whilst at the top of the latter the scars left by the withered flowering stem and foliage leaves can be distinguished. In the following season the buds grow out to form the overground shoots and at the base of each of these the same sequence is repeated (Fig. 144, A and D). It will be realised that the corms

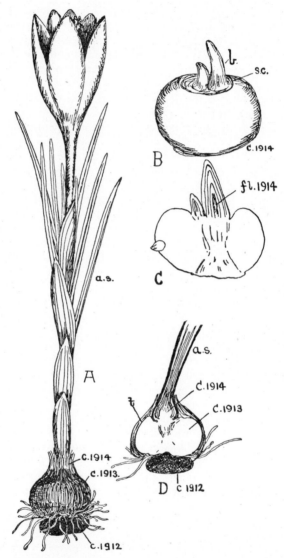

Fig. 144. Development and structure of the Crocus-corm. A, Spring condition. B, Winter condition, showing two buds which will produce flowering shoots in the subsequent season; one of the scales has been removed near the top of the corm, leaving a ring-shaped scar (*sc.*). C, Longitudinal section of the corm at the stage shown in B; all scales removed. D, Longitudinal section of base of corm and flowering shoot at stage shown in A. (All figures about natural size.) *a.s.*, aerial flowering shoot; *b.*, buds for next season's flowering shoots; *c. 1912, c. 1913, c. 1914*, corms of successive years; *fl. 1914*, flower which will unfold in 1914; *t*, tunic.

of any given year are lateral to those of the previous year, so that
the branching of the Crocus-plant is sympodial, each new segment
being terminated by a flower.   Inasmuch as the corms usually bear
several buds and each of these gives rise subsequently to a separate
daughter-corm, extensive vegetative reproduction is carried on.

The underground corm of the Cuckoo-pint is an abbreviated
and stout rhizome, in which the growths of previous years do not
die away so rapidly (Fig. 145).   In the autumn we find a well-
developed leaf-bud for next year's growth, the base of which is

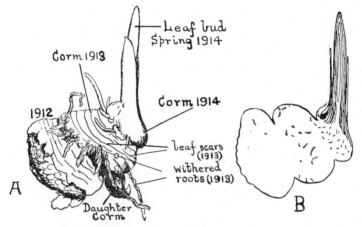

FIG. 145. Corm of the Cuckoo-pint (*Arum maculatum*) in autumn (natural size).
A, Entire.   B, In longitudinal section.

already prominently swollen to initiate the corm which will be
completed in the subsequent season (corm 1914 in Fig. 145, A),
whilst behind it are one or more corms of previous years (corm
1913, 1912) on which the ring-like leaf-scars and remains of roots
are a prominent feature.   The analogy to a fleshy rhizome, such
as that of the Solomon's Seal, is very clear, the construction again
being sympodial.   Corms are also found in the Bulbous Buttercup
(*Ranunculus bulbosus*).

Bulbs, such as those of the Tulip, Onion, or Narcissus, consist
of a number of fleshy scale-leaves (Fig. 146, A, *fl.sc.*) encircling
one another and the central bud (*f.a.*), the whole arising from a
flat disc-like stem (*st.*) and surrounded by a thin brown papery
investment (*i*) of one or more scales.   The detailed structure of
bulbs, however, differs considerably in various plants.   In a halved
Tulip-bulb we can recognise the central bud, comprising the future
flower and several young foliage-leaves, and just within the flattened

base the rudiments of numerous adventitious roots (*a.r.*) appearing
as small lines at right angles to the surface.   In the axils of one or
more of the fleshy scales will be found minute buds (*d.b.*), which
will give rise to the new bulbs for the following season's growth.
When the bulb begins to sprout, the adventitious roots exhibit a
rapid growth (Fig. 146, B, *a.r.*) and, after they have become well
established in the soil, the central bud elongates carrying up the
foliage-leaves and the terminal flower which soon expands.   This

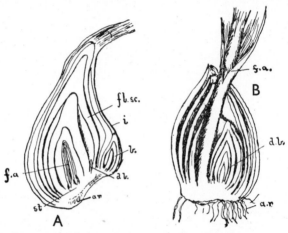

FIG. 146. Structure and development of bulb of Tulip (natural size).   A,
Winter condition in longitudinal section.   B, Spring condition in longitudinal
section, only the base of the flowering axis being shown.   *a.r.*, adventitious
roots; *b*, incompletely developed daughter-bulb; *d.b.*, bud which is giving
rise to a daughter-bulb; *f.a.*, flowering axis; *fl.sc.*, fleshy scales of bulb;
i, investment of dry scales; *st.*, flattened stem.

growth takes place at the expense of the food-substances stored
up in the bulb-scales which consequently commence to shrink (cf.
Fig. 146, B).
    After flowering, the green foliage-leaves, as in the Crocus and
Cuckoo-pint, persist for a considerable time; during this period
the food formed by them is passed down into the axillary buds
of the bulb, which now exhibit a rapid increase in size (Fig. 146,
B, *d.b.*).   The latter also receive any surplus food-material from
the main bulb.   When the overground shoot withers, we consequently find that the original bulb has been replaced by one or
more daughter-bulbs which have developed from the axillary buds
and are enclosed in the shrivelled papery remnants of the parent-
bulb.   Since the main axis of the latter is terminated by a flower,
the new Tulip-bulbs are axillary branches.   When there are

several daughter-bulbs, the supply of food is sometimes not sufficient for an adequate development of all, and some of them consequently appear as small structures adhering to the surface of the larger ones (Fig. 146, A, *b*). It will be realised that the

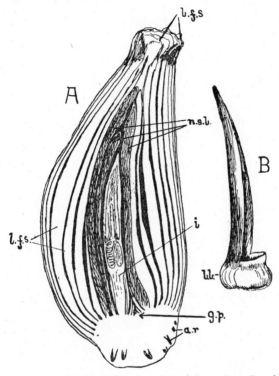

FIG. 147. Structure of bulb of *Narcissus* (somewhat enlarged). A, In longitudinal section. B, Single foliage-leaf from the latter, showing the sheathing leaf-base. *a.r.*, adventitious roots; *g.p.*, meristem of bulb (*i.e.* apex of stem); *i*, inflorescence; *l.b.*, leaf-base which enlarges to form a bulb-scale in the next season; *l.f.s.*, enlarged bases (scales) of leaves of previous seasons; *n.s.l.*, young foliage-leaves of current year, whose bases will form fleshy scales in the next season.

bulbs of the Tulip are really nothing more than huge buds in which most of the bud-scales are swollen with stores of food-material.

The bulbs of *Narcissus* (Fig. 147) or Snowdrop (*Galanthus*) are of a different type. The fleshy scales of the bulb (Fig. 147, A, *l.f.s.*) here consist mainly of the swollen bases of foliage-leaves of preceding seasons (of the last year only in the Snowdrop, of several years in the Narcissus). The foliage-leaves (*n.s.l.*) arise from the disc-like stem, while the flowering shoot (*i*) develops in the axil of one of them.   The terminal bud (*g.p.*) of the main axis is recognisable at its side and persists from year to year, producing each season two or more foliage-leaves and an axillary inflorescence, the whole enveloped in a membranous sheath; the bases of the leaves, as well as this sheath, swell up after flowering to form new fleshy scales for the next season's bulb.   Other buds may be formed in the axil of the outermost scale and give rise to daughter-bulbs, whereby multiplication is effected.   It will be noted that the growth of the Narcissus-bulb takes place in a monopodial manner, whilst that of the Tulip is sympodial.   The bulb of the Wild Hyacinth agrees with the Tulip in its sympodial construction, but with the Narcissus in consisting mainly of swollen bases of foliage-leaves.

Vegetative propagation is also seen in the formation of so-called *bulbils*, *i.e.* small buds which become readily detached and the leaves of which, as in bulbs, are filled with food-reserves.   In the British flora the best example is the Wild Onion, where the bulbils replace flowers.   The Lesser Celandine reproduces by bulbils which consist of an axillary bud bearing swollen adventitious roots.

Vegetative reproduction is widespread among Flowering Plants, and even more abundant among lower forms of plant-life in which, moreover, it often takes place with great rapidity.   As contrasted with seed-production, the advantage of vegetative propagation lies in its simplicity, no complex union of cells being necessary such as is involved in the formation of a seed (cf. p. 469).   Vegetative reproduction, however, usually fails to bring about a wide separation of the offspring, which develop side by side and may thus mutually harm one another by competition, although in propagation by runners or underground branches this disadvantage is diminished.

All the storage-organs considered in this chapter are found at a certain distance beneath the surface, the exact depth appearing to be relatively constant in the same soil for each kind of plant.   In plants arising from seed, these underground parts are at first situated near the surface, but they are gradually brought to the appropriate depth by the agency of so-called *contractile roots* (*e.g.* in the Cuckoo-pint and Hyacinth).   These are thick structures (Fig. 148, B and C) arising from the under side of rhizome, corm, or bulb, and penetrating downwards into the soil.   After their lower portions have become firmly anchored the upper parts (viz. those nearest the parent organ) shorten, their surface becoming markedly wrinkled. This is due to a change in form of the cortical cells which, while contracting longitudinally, expand laterally.   As a consequence the structure from which the roots arise is dragged down to a lower level.   Such contractile roots are produced each season until the

correct depth has been attained. Sometimes (*e.g.* the Crocus,
Fig. 148, B) the new individuals (*d.c.*) arise on the top of the old
ones (*m.c.*) and so come to lie higher in the soil; in these the level
is adjusted by contractile roots (*c.r.*) formed at the beginning of
each season on the daughter-individuals. Rhizomes maintain

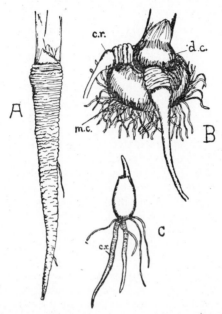

FIG. 148. Contractile roots (A and B, natural size; C, slightly enlarged). A,
Tap-root of Fennel (*Fœniculum*). B, Crocus-corm. *c.r.*, contractile root;
d.c., daughter-corm; *m.c.*, mother-corm. C, One-year-old bulb of Broad-
leaved Garlic (*Allium ursinum*) with contractile roots (*c.r.*).

their appropriate depth by changes in the direction of growth.
The so-called droppers of the Tulip likewise serve to adjust the
level of the daughter-bulbs.

Contraction is also exhibited by the swollen roots (p. 113) of
the Dandelion, Dock, Fennel (Fig. 148, A) and other members of
the Umbelliferæ. The new leaves of the radical rosette formed
above the old ones at the beginning of each season are thus pulled
down in close contact with the soil.

CHAPTER XXI

THE PHYSIOLOGY OF RESPIRATION[1]

THE life-processes of every living organism are always associated with a chemical break-down, the outward evidence of which is often intake of oxygen and emission of carbon dioxide. This respiration goes on at all times, but in green plants is masked during the daytime by the more active photosynthetic process in which the gaseous exchange is reversed. As a consequence the volume of oxygen evolved by the plant is less than that actually formed in photosynthesis, since part of it is used for respiration; similarly, the carbon dioxide produced in the latter process is not liberated, when the plant is exposed to light, owing to its being used for purposes of photosynthesis as soon as it is formed. Hence an evolution of carbon dioxide from a green plant can only be demonstrated in darkness.

It is probably for the most part carbohydrates that are broken down in the process of respiration and, taking grape sugar as an example, we can indicate the outcome of the very complex chain of chemical changes involved by the following equation:—

$$C_6H_{12}O_6 + 6O_2 = 6CO_2 + 6H_2O + 674 \text{ calories}$$

Grape   Oxygen.   Carbon   Water.
sugar.   dioxide.

The volume of carbon dioxide given out is therefore equal to that of the oxygen taken in, while water is also formed, the products being the same as those from which carbohydrates are built up during photosynthesis. The formation of water, very evident during breathing in Mammals, is difficult to demonstrate in plants owing to the invariable occurrence of transpiration.

That growth ceases when oxygen is lacking can be demonstrated by the experiment described on p. 9. The removal, during respiration, of a constituent of the air can be shown by placing germinating Peas in a flask which is closed with an air-tight rubber cork fitted

---

[1] For reference-books, see the general works on plant physiology cited on p. 193; also Ch. 15 of the work of Bonner cited on p. 97. E. Baldwin, *Dynamic Aspects of Biochemistry*, 2nd edit., Cambridge Univ. Press, 1952.

with a glass tube bent as in Fig. 149. Suspended in the flask by a cotton thread is a small bottle (b) containing a concentrated solution of caustic potash, whilst the free arm of the tube dips into a tumbler of water. Or a better method is to suspend the Peas in a small basket of wire-gauze and to cover the bottom of the flask with soda-lime. The carbon dioxide evolved by the Peas is removed through absorption by the potash or soda-lime, while the intake of oxygen reduces the pressure within the flask so that water rises in the tube (Fig. 149). To avoid the effect of changes of temperature the flask as a whole can be placed in a large vessel of water, maintained at a constant temperature. In control experiments, using dry Peas or Peas that have been killed by boiling, no rise of water will be observed.

Since every living cell must respire, there must be free access of oxygen to all parts, and this is effected by the continuous system of air-spaces opening to the exterior by the stomata (p. 152) and lenticels (p. 189). To illustrate the continuity of the whole intercellular space system of the plant and its connection with the stomatal apertures we use the apparatus already described on p. 199 (Fig. 122, B). Two similar

Fig. 149. Apparatus to demonstrate that germinating Peas give off carbon dioxide in the process of respiration. For description, see text.

leafy shoots of a plant in which the stomata are confined to the lower side of the leaf are selected. In the one the under surfaces, in the other the upper surfaces of the blades are vaselined, after which the shoots are attached to the free ends of the glass tubes (in the way shown in Fig. 122, B), so that the cut end of the former extends into the latter above the level of the surrounding rubber. Prior to doing this the long arm of each tube is partially filled with a column of water extending some 4 to 6 inches above the end of the stem. When the flask is cooled a stream of air-bubbles begins to arise from the cut end of the shoot in which the upper sides of the blades had been vaselined, and to ascend through the column of water in the long arm of the tube; this may go on for several hours as the flask becomes cooler. From the other stem, however, few or no bubbles arise.

The fact that the lenticels are apertures giving access to the intercellular system can be shown by placing woody twigs, in which the cut ends have been sealed with melted paraffin-wax, in warm water, when large bubbles of air will be seen to arise from the lenticels. If the stem of a plant is cut off just above the root and the latter immersed in hot water, bubbles of air will be given off from the cut surface for some little time, thus showing that the air-spaces of the root are continuous with those of the stem.

The quantity of carbon dioxide evolved can be determined by means of the apparatus shown in Fig. 150. This consists of a receptacle (C) containing the respiring material (*e.g.* germinating

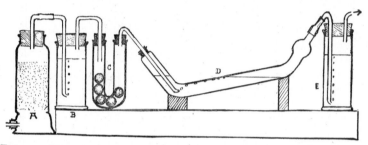

FIG. 150. Apparatus for determining the quantity of carbon dioxide produced in respiration. Description in the text. The arrow indicates the direction in which air is drawn through the apparatus.

Peas) and through which a slow current of air is drawn with the help of an aspirator or a filter-pump. Before reaching the respiring material the air passes through a jar (A) containing soda-lime, which renders it free from carbon dioxide; this is checked by bubbling the air through a jar (B) containing lime-water which should remain clear. After circulating over the material in (C) the air passes into an inclined Pettenkofer tube (D) containing a known volume of a standard baryta solution. The rate of bubbling should be such that the bubbles do not coalesce and the lime water in E should remain clear. The barium carbonate precipitated may be weighed, or the amount of carbon dioxide evolved in a given time by the respiring material may be determined by titration of the remaining alkali against standard hydrochloric acid.

The gaseous exchange in respiration can be investigated with the help of a respirometer, like that shown in Fig. 150 *. This is really a kind of retort (*r*), which is supported in a vertical position by a suitable clamp, its lower end being joined by pressure tubing (*t*) to a wide glass tube (*m*), open at both ends, so as to form a manometer. The stem is graduated to show the volume, when 2 c.c. of plant-material is introduced into the bulbous portion (*b*); the actual volumes, therefore, are those shown plus 2. The ground-glass stopper (*s*) at the top is channelled as in a dropping-bottle so that air can be excluded from, or admitted to, the interior of the retort by turning the stopper. After introducing the material, a 10 per cent. solution of caustic potash is poured into the mano-meter and its level adjusted to the 100 c.c. mark; the stopper is then closed. When the solution ceases to rise, the right-hand tube is raised until the level in the two parts of the manometer is the same. The level will now stand at the 80 c.c. mark, implying that one-fifth of the contained air (*i.e.* the oxygen) has been absorbed. The carbon dioxide given out has been absorbed by the potash.

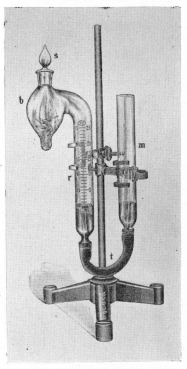

The equation on p. 236 shows that, when carbohydrates are respired, the ratio of carbon di-oxide evolved to oxygen absorbed, the *respiratory quotient*, will be one. When such material is used and a saturated solution of sodium chloride (in which carbon dioxide is scarcely soluble) substituted for the potash in the respirometer, there will be no alteration of level until pieces of potash are dis-solved in the solution to absorb the evolved carbon dioxide. Al-though carbohydrates customarily constitute the respired material, this is not always so. During the early germination of seeds

Fig. 150*. Ganong's respirometer. Description on p. 238.

containing a high proportion of fats, the respiratory quotient is about 0·7; if such seeds are placed in the respirometer, the level of the salt solution rises, since, owing to the lower proportion of oxygen in the fats as compared with sugars, more oxygen is absorbed than carbon dioxide produced. Conversely, where fats are formed from carbohydrates (p. 79), the respiratory quotient exceeds one. A small proportion of proteins are probably respired in all circum-stances, and especially in starved leaves. Certain Fungi (*Asper-gillus niger*), moreover, readily utilise peptones as a respiratory substrate; the quotient may then sink to 0·5. An unusual quotient is also shown by succulents and ripening fruits (p. 241, B).

16

Since respiration entails a breaking down of material, there will be a decrease in organic substance in the dark when photosynthesis cannot make good the loss.   Two sets of five Peas of about equal size are weighed separately and, after soaking, put to germinate, the one in the dark, the other in the light.   If, after a fortnight, the dry weight of each set of seedlings is compared with the weights of the original seeds,[1] those grown in the dark are found to have lost considerably in weight, while those in the light have gained.

If plants are to survive in natural habitats, the positive gain through photosynthesis must exceed the loss due to respiration. The light-intensity, at which these processes exactly balance one another, is called the *compensation point*.   It varies with the species and is usually high in sun plants.   Even so photosynthesis in these mostly exceeds respiration.   In deep shade or in poorly illuminated rooms, only plants with a low respiration rate can subsist, *e.g.* *Aspidistra*, with an exceptionally low compensation point.

Like other physiological functions (*e.g.* photosynthesis, p. 212) respiration proceeds slowly at lower temperatures, but steadily increases in intensity as the temperature rises.   To show this we add one or two drops of the indicator phenol-red to distilled water and shake up in a test-tube with a little tap-water.[2]   When a germinating Pea is introduced, the evolved carbon dioxide acts on the indicator and the time required for the solution to become yellow gives some measure of the respiratory rate; if the test-tube is immersed in a water-bath at a higher temperature, the colour change ensues more rapidly.   The rate usually increases 2·1–2·5 times for every rise of 10° C., but above 35° C. injurious effects affecting some stage of the respiratory process become apparent after a short time and increase in prominence as the temperature is further raised.   Light does not seem to have any direct effect on the rate of respiration.   Small amounts of organic poisons, as well as wounding, generally increase the rate, which is also affected by the amount of respirable sugar.

The intensity of respiration varies greatly in different stages of development.   Dormant structures containing little water, like dry seeds and the Lichens and Mosses found on tree-trunks, which remain alive even when apparently dry, respire very slowly.   On the other hand, during early germination and at the time of flowering the respiration-intensity may be high and much of the energy

---

[1] It would be better to compare with the *dry weight* of the original seeds. This can be approximately estimated by determining the dry weight in percentages of the original weight for a number of Peas, and working out the dry weight of those employed in the experiment by simple proportion.

[2] The tap water must be introduced in so small a quantity that on blowing through a tube into a similar sample, the indicator rapidly changes its colour.

liberated may even appear as heat. To show this a thermos flask is filled with germinating Peas or young flower-heads of Dandelion, which are packed round a thermometer bulb; the accumulating carbon dioxide, which would be harmful, is siphoned off by a bent tube, the shorter arm of which reaches to the bottom of the flask. The thermometer soon records a higher temperature than that in a control, containing cotton-wool or killed Peas, with an antiseptic added to prevent bacterial fermentation.

Since oxygen is essential for normal (*aerobic*) *respiration* its absence causes the arrest of most vital processes. Stoppage of growth is evident when seeds fail to germinate (p. 9) in such circumstances. Unlike most animals, plants are not immediately killed by absence of oxygen, but then carry on so-called *anaerobic respiration*, during which carbon dioxide is still evolved. This can be demonstrated with soaked seeds (*e.g.* Peas), from which the testa must be removed, since air may be included between it and the cotyledons. The seeds are passed under a test-tube filled with and inverted into a dish containing mercury, and float to the top. At first barely visible, they gradually come to lie freely in the accumulating gas, which will nearly fill the tube, provided enough seeds are used and the experiment lasts for about 24 hours. The gas can be shown to be carbon dioxide by introducing small pieces of potash.

During anaerobic respiration ethyl alcohol commonly accumulates in the tissues, though sometimes this is not so. Carbohydrates again furnish the usual substrate, so that the process can be illustrated by the over-all equation

$$C_6H_{12}O_6 = 2C_2H_5OH + 2CO_2 + 26 \text{ calories.}$$
$$\text{glucose} \quad \text{ethyl alcohol}$$

This is the same as that used to outline the process of alcoholic fermentation (p. 340). When the oxygen in the air surrounding a plant is reduced to 5 per cent. or less, the respiratory quotient increases and alcohol is formed, both anaerobic and aerobic respiration proceeding simultaneously. The enzyme-complex zymase, bringing about alcoholic fermentation in Yeast, is present in most, if not in all, tissues, and many of its individual enzymes have been found in higher plants. It is therefore probable that there is considerable similarity between the series of changes involved in most types of anaerobic respiration and in alcoholic fermentation.

The manifold reactions occurring during the last-named process, each activated by its own appropriate enzyme, cannot be discussed in detail. It must suffice to mention that hexoses are combined with a phosphate-radicle to form hexox-phosphates, which undergo splitting (glycolysis) into two molecules of triosephosphates. These, by a series of elaborate changes, give rise to phosphoglyceric and phosphopyruvic acids, and later to pyruvic acid ($CH_3.CO.COOH$), the first intermediate product which does not contain a phosphate group. An enzyme *carboxylase* then splits the pyruvic acid into acetaldehyde and carbon dioxide, thus

$$CH_3.CO.COOH = CH_3.CHO + CO_2$$
$$\text{pyruvic acid} \qquad \text{acetaldehyde}$$

and the acetaldehyde is reduced to ethyl alcohol by *alcohol dehydrase*. Acetaldehyde has been found in tissues respiring anaerobically.

It has long been held that, despite differences in final products, the early stages of aerobic are probably identical with those of anaerobic respiration and alcoholic fermentation. This view is supported by the apparent universal presence of the zymase-complex in living cells and the demonstration that outside the plant zymase-activity is not lessened by the presence of oxygen. Moreover, when material is returned to air, after exposure to anaerobic conditions, the respiration rate often exceeds the normal value, as would be expected if intermediate compounds of aerobic respiration had previously accumulated. Detailed studies show that much of the phosphorus in plants occurs as phosphoric esters and that pyruvic acid may be formed during aerobic respiration. Carboxylase is found in higher plant tissues, but the formation of pyruvic acid probably constitutes the stage of anaerobic respiration at which oxidation begins in the aerobic process. The following scheme outlines this conception of the relation between the two processes.

$$\text{Hexose} \xrightarrow[\text{zymase-complex}]{\text{action of}} \text{Intermediate Products} \begin{array}{c} \xrightarrow{\text{with } O_2} CO_2 + H_2O \\ \text{(pyruvic acid, etc. ?)} \\ \xrightarrow[\text{without } O_2]{} CO_2 + C_2H_5.OH \end{array}$$

Neither carbohydrates, nor the products of their breakdown, readily oxidise in air or oxygen, and the extremely rapid oxidations occurring in living organisms must be due to special catalysts. It is more than probable that some of the enzyme-systems effecting oxidations in plant-cells (p. 85) are concerned in aerobic respiration.

The first step in such oxidations is probably the transfer of hydrogen from one compound to another which undergoes reduction. Enzymes collectively termed *dehydrogenases* (*dehydrases*), effecting such changes, are widespread. They remove hydrogen from substances like aldehydes and acids formed by breakdown of sugars, either directly to atmospheric oxygen or more commonly to intermediate hydrogen carriers (*e.g.* pyridine nucleotides) which can be re-oxidised, either by reducing another intermediate product (cf. reduction of acetaldehyde to alcohol) or by an aerobic enzyme-system transferring hydrogen to atmospheric oxygen and producing the water formed in aerobic respiration.

The cytochrome system of animals and Yeast and the *catechol oxidase* system widespread in plants, are examples of aerobic systems. In the latter, which contains copper, hydrogen is taken up by an orthoquinone, and the oxidase then transfers it to oxygen giving water and reforming the quinone which can act again. A peroxide is also produced; hence the direct blueing of guaiacum by tissues containing catechol oxidase (p. 85).[1] Cytochrome C is a thermostable hydrogen carrier, composed of protein and an active iron-containing group. It is reversibly oxidised by *cytochrome oxidase* and so transfers hydrogen to atmospheric oxygen, with the formation of water.

Succulents (Crassulaceæ, Cactaceæ) exhibit striking anomalies in gaseous exchange. In darkness, although oxygen-absorption continues, liberation of carbon dioxide progressively diminishes and may even temporarily cease. During subsequent exposure to light, in air deprived of carbon dioxide, evolution of oxygen may nevertheless take place. The sap is rich in carboxylic (especially malic) acids, formed from carbohydrates mainly in the dark. In the light this process slows down, and the accumulated acid is decomposed with liberation of carbon dioxide, which is utilised in photosynthesis. The acids have been thought to be produced by incomplete oxidation of carbohydrate in the dark. Evidence has been obtained, however, suggesting an origin by direct interaction of carbon dioxide and intermediate products of respiration, since, if the quantity of carbon dioxide in the air is increased, this gas is absorbed in the dark simultaneously with oxygen. Formation of carboxylic acids by fixation of carbon dioxide occurs in animal tissues.

Most fleshy fruits contain similar acids (*e.g.* citric in lemons and oranges, tartaric in grapes) and the usual sweetening during ripening is due both to increased sugar-content and decrease of acid. The metabolic processes involved are possibly not unlike those of succulents, and, since cell-sap is usually acid, formation of organic acids, though on a smaller scale than in the examples just considered, is probably a general phenomenon. The complete oxidation of the products of glycolysis in aerobic respiration appears indeed to demand a cycle of changes involving at least ten organic acids.

The previous considerations show that very complex and diverse changes are concerned in the oxidative processes in plant-cells. The energy, that is rendered available, itself originally derived from solar sources during photosynthesis, is that which supplies the driving power of the plant's machinery, supporting not only life itself, but all the vital functions which are associated with it and which are usually arrested, when aerobic respiration is not taking place.

[1] These also contain a peroxidase which catalyses the oxidation of poly-phenols (incl. guaiacum). Another enzyme, *catalase*, breaks down peroxides with evolution of bubbles of gaseous oxygen, which are readily detected when a drop of hydrogen peroxide is applied to the cut surface of most plant tissues.

CHAPTER XXII

THE PHYSIOLOGY OF GROWTH

ONE way in which the energy of respiration is employed is in the process of growth, during which part of the food-material produced in the course of nutrition is used in building up new tissues. All growth comprises three distinct phases, viz. (i) the formation of new units by the division of the cells of the meristems (cf. pp. 6 and 52), (ii) the enlargement of the new cells (pp. 59, 99), and (iii) their differentiation to perform the various functions which they fulfil in the life of the plant. Of these the second is the only phase of growth visible externally and constitutes what is known as growth in popular parlance.

The restriction of growth to definite regions is a marked feature of contrast between the growth of plants and of higher animals. A further distinction is seen in the continual formation of new organs

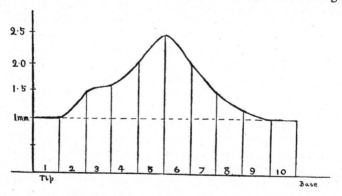

FIG. 151. Curve illustrating grand period of growth, constructed from radicle shown in Fig. 55, B. The tip and base of the radicle are indicated.

(leaves, branches, roots) from the meristems of plants, whereas in most animals the number of organs remains constant after the embryo-stage is over.

In roots elongation is restricted to a very short portion (p. 99), whilst in stems it is spread over a much greater length. If we adopt means to compare the rate of increase of different parts of the elongating zone we shall find that it is not uniform. This can be established for roots by repeating the experiment described on p. 98 (Fig. 55) and noting the exact amount of growth in length between each pair of marks. The intervals near the tip of the root will have elongated little, but, as we pass progressively farther from the apex, the intervals become wider and wider until they reach a maximum; beyond this they again exhibit a gradual decrease up to the mature zone, where no growth in length has taken place (see Fig. 55, B, p. 99).

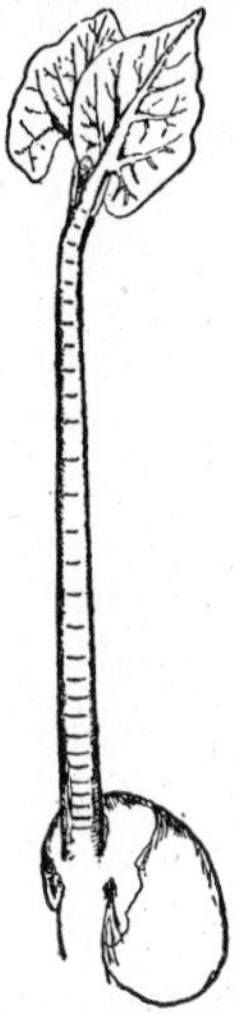

The result of this experiment can be more easily realised if a graph be constructed (Fig. 151) in which the abscissæ represent successive intervals, while the ordinates represent their respective lengths. The curve obtained by joining the ordinates rises to a summit and then again falls.

As we pass away from the tip of the root we come to older and older segments (*i.e.* intervals between two marks), and in the above experiment therefore we are comparing the amount of elongation in segments of different ages. This shows us that the cells of the newly formed segments elongate but slightly at first, but, as they get older, grow in length more rapidly until when they approach maturity their rate of elongation again decreases. This gradual rise and fall in the rate of elongation is spoken of as the *grand period of growth* and, since the cells in a given transverse plane exhibit the same rate of increase, the successively older segments epitomise the changes of the individual units.

FIG. 152. Experiment to demonstrate region of growth in plumule of Runner Bean (about two-thirds natural size). At the beginning of the experiment the marks were all at equal distances from one another.

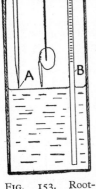

FIG. 153. Root-auxanometer (after Neilson Jones). For description, see p. 244.

A similar grand period is exhibited by growing stems. If we mark the entire plumule of a Runner Bean, it will show, after a day or two, the same gradual increase and decrease as we pass backwards from the tip, and also that elongation occurs over a much wider zone (Fig. 152).

The grand period is observable, not only in cells, but in the growth of entire plants (*e.g.* annuals) and in that of their individual organs. If the total lengths of shoots or leaf-areas are plotted against time, a sigmoid curve is always obtained. In developing shoots the nodes usually cease to grow soon after they are formed, the later elongation being restricted to the internodes, so that growth in length takes place in a number of separate regions, *i.e.* it becomes segmented. The ultimate length of the internodes is generally not equal, those near the base and the top of each season's growth being relatively short, whilst the intervening ones often show a progressive increase in length towards the middle. This is well seen in many herbaceous plants (*e.g.* Bedstraws, Woodruff), as well as in the shoots of many trees and shrubs (*e.g.* Apple, Poplar); the following are given as examples:—

LENGTHS OF SUCCESSIVE INTERNODES (IN MILLIMETRES) ALONG A ONE-YEAR'S SHOOT

Apple	.	1	2½	3	7	12	20	30	30	30	40	25	20	21	10	8	5	3
Laurel	.	4	7	16	16	18	21	20	13	3	...	...	...	...	...	...	...	...

Similarly, in some rhizomes (*e.g.* Solomon's Seal, *Iris*) an analogous rhythm is exhibited, which manifests itself mainly in a variation in the diameter of the internodes.

The simplest method of measuring the rate of growth of an entire organ is, of course, direct measurement, the observations being made at regular intervals. This is most easily applicable to roots which for this purpose may be grown down a glass tube over water. To magnify the growth of a root we use a glass jar fitted with a cork (Fig. 153) through which pass two glass rods, both of which can move freely through the cork; the one (A) tapers at its lower end, while the other (B) is square-ended and graduated. A germinating Bean is fixed to the end of a long pin (*p*) which is thrust through the cork until the tip of the radicle nearly touches the surface of the water in the jar. The rod B is then pushed downwards till the water-surface makes contact with the root-tip and the position of the water-surface read on the graduated scale. A is then adjusted so that its point also touches the water-surface. As the root grows it penetrates the water.

After some time the water-level is adjusted to the new position of the root-tip by raising the rod B. In this way repeated readings on the graduated scale of B can be made with reference to the index *c*. The level of the tip of A serves as a standard of reference. The amount of magnification given by these readings is determined by the ratio between the cross-sections of the rod B and of the jar.

To magnify the growth of a shoot we use an instrument known as a *growth-lever* (Fig. 154). It is composed of a light wooden lever (*l*), with two unequal arms, working on a metal pivot (*p*) (see the small inset in Fig. 154). A small strip of lead *w* is wrapped round the short arm of the lever, so as nearly to balance the weight of the long one. The pointed end of the lever works over a graduated arc, the divisions of which show the actual amount of movement of the short arm (Appendix XV). The growing tip of the plant is surrounded

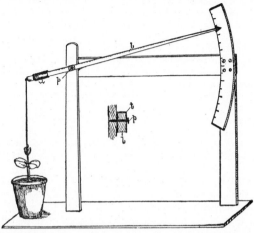

FIG. 154. Simple form of growth-lever. For description, see p. 244. The small figure in the middle explains the mode of attachment of the lever to the upright support.

with a small pad of cotton-wool, round which one end of a thread is then firmly tied, the other end being attached to the short arm of the lever in such a way

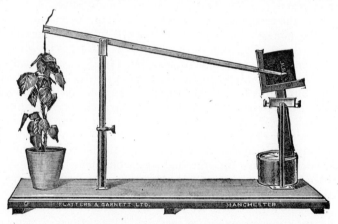

FIG. 155. Simple form of auxanometer. Description on p. 245.

that the pointer is at the top of the scale. As the plant grows the pointer will sink and thus the amount of elongation can be noted.

It is sometimes convenient to measure the hourly growth of a plant, and for this purpose we require an instrument known as an *auxanometer*. The type shown in Fig. 155 consists of a growth-lever, the long arm of which is pointed and just touches the blackened surface of a glass plate. The latter is held in a frame capable of movement in the plane of the lever. This movement is effected by hourly contact with the minute-hand of a clock whose position is such that the minute-hand after pushing aside the arm some little way ultimately loses contact with it, so that it swings back to its original position; this takes place automatically, owing to the glass plate being placed slightly to one side at the top of the arm.

To prepare the instrument for use, the glass plate is removed from its frame and covered with a uniform layer of soot by holding it over the smoky flame of burning camphor. The tip of the plant is attached as before to the short arm of the lever. Growth of the plant leads to a gradual fall of the pointer which traces out a downward line on the sooted surface. Every hour, however, the glass undergoes a lateral movement and the pointer scratches a horizontal line, the intervals between successive lines representing the magnified hourly growths.

The growth of plants over longer periods can best be estimated by determining the dry weight of a representative sample at successive intervals.

Both growth-lever and auxanometer make it possible to determine the conditions influencing growth of shoots. Thus both serve to establish that elongation is more rapid at night than during the day (provided the temperature remains approximately uniform). The marks made by the auxanometer will be farthest apart after midnight and nearest together after midday, whilst in between a perfect gradation connects the two extremes. There is thus a *daily period* in the growth of the plant, due to the alternation of light and darkness.

The increased rate of elongation in the dark is well seen in certain plants (*e.g.* seedlings, sprouting Potato-tubers, etc.), when grown in the total absence of light. Under these conditions, apart from the non-development of chlorophyll (cf. p. 8), they exhibit an exceptional elongation of the internodes (cf. p. 253), whilst the leaves remain of small dimensions (Fig. 156, A); such plants are said to be *etiolated*. Even dull light has a similar effect and many herbaceous forms (*e.g.* Willow-herbs) exhibit longer internodes in the shade of a woodland than when growing in the open. Similarly the herbs are often appreciably taller on the shady than on the sunny side of a hedge. This more rapid growth in darkness is of great advantage in nature, especially in shoots which commence their development underground (*e.g.* plumules and shoots of herbaceous perennials), since by virtue of this feature they reach the surface rapidly.

In plants whose leaves arise from underground stems the absence of light induces exceptional elongation of the petioles, a fact which is made use of in the commercial production of Celery, Rhubarb, and Sea Kale (*Crambe*). A further noteworthy effect of absence of light can be observed in certain rosette-plants (*e.g.* House-leeks) in which well-marked internodes are produced under these circumstances, so that the plant acquires quite a different habit.

Apart from its influence on the rate of growth, the intensity of the light also affects the development of plant-organs. For the formation of flower-buds a higher light-intensity is normally necessary than for mere vegetative growth, though some plants can develop a specialised type of flower in weak light (cf. p. 465). Most of the vegetative buds within the crown of trees which cast a deep shade fail to develop, whereas at the margin the majority of them give rise to branches; and we may even find that the crown is denser on the south than on the north aspect.

If the leaves of two plants of the same kind growing respectively in the sun and in the shade (*e.g.* Dog's Mercury, Enchanter's Night-shade) be compared, it will be found that the blades of the sun-form are smaller and thicker than those of the shade-form (Fig. 365). A similar difference will be found between the exposed and shaded leaves of the same plant (*e.g.* the Beech). There are also anatomical differences (see p. 522).

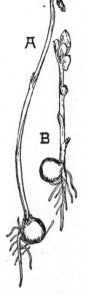

It is not, however, intensity of light alone that affects the manner of growth, but also its daily incidence. For instance, the so-called short-day plants, mostly natives of low latitudes (e.g. *Cosmos*), will only produce flowers if the length of daily illumination does not exceed twelve hours, whereas long-day plants, mostly natives of northern latitudes (e.g. *Rudbeckia*), are apt not to flower until the daily period of illumination exceeds twelve hours appreciably. Other species (*e.g.* Chickweed) are, however, apparently un-

FIG. 156. Seedlings of the Pea (about three-quarters natural size), normal (B) and etiol-ated (A). Both are of the same age.

affected by the daily period of light. The general phenomena of response to periodic illumination are referred to as *photoperiodism*.

Heat and cold exert a profound effect on growth, as on other functions (pp. 212, 240), the rate being slow at low temperatures and steadily increasing as the temperature rises, until it becomes injurious. The tendency for more rapid growth at night is, there-fore, usually counteracted by the lower temperature. Many observations out of doors show the effects of temperature on growth. Thus, some plants grow vigorously even in March (*e.g.* Dog's Mercury, Elm), whereas others only become active towards the end of April or early May (Ash, Beech, Horse Chestnut). While

Peas and Wheat germinate at temperatures near the freezing point, Maize and Vegetable Marrow will only do so at 10° C. or more. Some plants of warmer climates (*e.g.* Tsung Palm, *Trachycarpus excelsa*) exist in the open in South England, but not farther north, and many tropical plants can be cultivated in hothouses.

It is, however, not easy to separate temperature-effects from those due to light, and the problem is further complicated by photoperiodism. All these may limit northward and southward extension by preventing seed-production, which often requires higher temperatures and light-intensities than does vegetative growth. The time of flowering is markedly affected by temperature-changes and many plants (*e.g.* Lily of the Valley) will flower out of season if exposed to cool conditions followed by heat (forcing). Similarly Winter Wheat, which is usually sown so as to germinate in the autumn and flower the following year, can be caused to pass through its life-cycle in one season by using grain, which has been allowed to germinate slowly until the radicle appears and then stored for a few weeks at temperatures between 0° and 5° C. (*vernalisation*); the treatment affects the embryo only. Comparable results have been obtained with other plants. The onset of flowering, like sexual reproduction in simple plants, is favoured by conditions permitting of rapid photosynthesis, accompanied by a diminution in mineral supplies, so that the ratio of carbohydrates to nitrogen increases.

Apart from suitable light and temperature conditions, growth depends on adequate supplies of oxygen (p. 241), moisture and nutritive materials, including trace elements.

The rate of elongation (phase ii, p. 242) of most plant-organs is so slow that it is necessary to employ means to magnify it; and to this general statement there are but few exceptions. The filaments of Grass-stamens remain quite short until the pollen is ripe, when a very rapid elongation takes place, amounting, in Wheat, to nearly 2 mm. per minute. The shoots of some tropical Bamboos exhibit a similar, though somewhat less rapid, enlargement. The size attained by plants, although variable, is nevertheless approximately constant within certain wide limits; on the one hand are very minute forms (*e.g.* Duckweed, Whitlow-grass), on the other, tall-growing trees and annuals, such as the Sunflower.

The growing apex of a shoot does not move upwards in a straight line, but describes a slightly irregular course, somewhat spiral in its general character. This *circumnutation*, which is exhibited by stems and roots alike, is, however, generally not apparent unless magnified by using the apparatus shown in Fig. 157. This consists of a sheet of glass held horizontally beneath which is placed the plant to be observed. As the plant grows, the successive positions of the apex are marked from above by fixing pointed strips of gummed paper to the glass (see Fig. 157). A small rod *a* is fixed to one of the four supports, so that its tip is situated in alignment with the mature stem and about an inch from the growing apex. Each strip of gummed paper is always so affixed that its point forms a straight line with the tip of the rod *a* and the apex of the plant, a certain, though inconstant, magnification of the movement being thereby obtained.

Good material for observing circumnutation is furnished by the plumule of the Runner Bean (before its tip bends into a horizontal position), as well as by any uncurved tendril. This phenomenon is due to more rapid growth on one side of the apex, this zone continually shifting its position round the circumference. As a result the growing tip is not straight, but exhibits a slight, often scarcely recognisable curvature, in one direction or another.

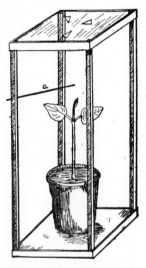

FIG. 157. Apparatus for the demonstration of circumnutation (see p. 248).

In plants the growth of one organ is often materially influenced by that of another, so that if the one is favoured or arrested, the other exhibits a reduction or promotion. We have already met with several instances of such *correlation*. Thus in certain etiolated plants the poor development of the leaves and the arrest of the lateral buds (p. 246) is associated with greater growth of the stem. If the terminal bud is removed from a normal shoot, laterals which would otherwise remain dormant begin to sprout (cf. p. 119); spur-shoots often elongate, when the apex of the main shoot is cut off. Similarly, after removing the tip of the tap-root in a Bean or Pea, one or more of the laterals bend downwards and take its place. In those forms, moreover, in which extensive vegetative propagation obtains, reproduction by seeds is generally rare, a correlation shown by many cultivated bulbous plants. There is evidence that soluble substances (hormones) produced in the various organs of the plant may stimulate or retard the development of others (cf. p. 253).

Pruning causes an artificial restriction of the shoot-system and aims sometimes merely at modifying the shape or size of a shrub or tree. More often its purpose is to encourage certain parts of the branch-system.   Thus the common practice of pruning fruit-trees to the outside buds aims at minimising mutual shading, and its success depends upon visualising the future development of the shoot-system.   Hard pruning may lead to undue vegetative growth, but continuous pruning (*i.e.* in summer, as well as in winter) is

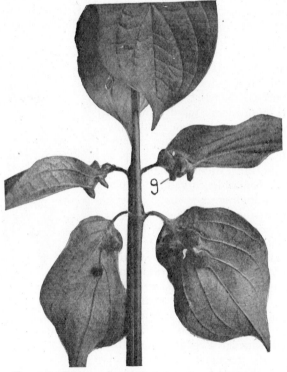

FIG. 158. Photograph of galls (*g.*) on leaves of Dogwood (*Cornus sanguinea*).   [Photo. E. J. S.]

often adopted as a means of restricting food-supply to the fruiting spurs.   By this means the crop of flowers, as in Roses, or fruits can be diminished, and a few large specimens in place of many small ones are obtained.

The effect of an injury to any woody axis is to cause the living cells, and especially those of the exposed cambium, to give rise to a large-celled, thin-walled tissue which at first forms a ring-shaped swelling, but often gradually becomes broader till the whole wounded surface is completely covered, the outermost cells usually becoming suberised.   The tissue thus formed is called a *callus*, and may subsequently produce adventitious shoots (*e.g.* pollarded trees) or adventitious roots as in cuttings (p. 108). Regions of injury in the parenchymatous tissues (*e.g.* of cortex or leaf) are commonly isolated from the healthy surrounding tissue by the formation of cork from a cambium produced by tangential divisions in the uninjured cells nearest the wound. In this way the attack of a parasitic Fungus is often localised.

A different stimulation to growth (hypertrophy) is sometimes consequent upon injury due to Insects or Fungus-pests which leads to the formation of so-called *galls* (Fig. 158, *g*). In Insect-galls the special growth results from the laying of an egg or eggs by the female beneath the epidermis and, in the same species of plant, different kinds of galls may be produced by different insects (*e.g.* Oak-apple gall, Cushion-gall, Fig. 159, C, Button-gall, Fig. 159, B, Bullet-gall, etc., all on the Oak). The abnormal growth known as the Witch's Broom is due to various fungal pests which lead to an exceptional branching of the attacked part, examples being commonly seen on the Cherry and Birch.

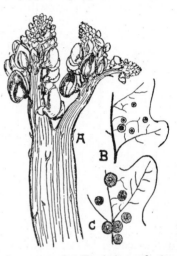

FIG. 159. A, Fasciation of the Runner Bean inflorescence. B, Button-gall of Oak. C, Cushion-gall of Oak. (All figures about two-thirds natural size.)

Little or no tissue differentiation exists in galls caused by Fungi (*e.g.* Finger and Toe disease, Fig. 217), and externally they commonly present an irregular and very variable form. Many animal galls offer a striking contrast in these respects, not only exhibiting a definite external structure (cf. Fig. 158), but, as in many of those produced by gall-flies, a complex internal differentiation due to enlargement and division of the probably chemically stimulated cells. In some the central region, where the larva of the gall-insect resides, consists of nutritive tissue composed of cells with dense cytoplasm, rich in protein material, and serving for the animal's nourishment. This region may be surrounded by a layer of sclerenchyma, whilst the outermost zone consists of parenchymatous tissue. The latter is usually well supplied with intercellular spaces, contains little or no chlorophyll, and is often traversed by vascular tissue.

Occasionally plants exhibit unusual forms of growth which are probably a result of exceptional physiological conditions. Such *monstrosities* find expression in various ways, most commonly in so-called *fasciations* which represent a combined development of the different branches of a shoot-system, so that the whole forms a flat structure (Fig. 159, A). A similar process leads to the production of the Cauliflower, a fasciation which is inherited. Double flowers seen in many cultivated plants furnish other examples of monstrosities.

Stimulation of growth as a result of wounding is made use of in the processes known as *budding* and *grafting*, which are much employed in Rose- and Fruit-culture. In budding (Fig. 160, A and B) a shield-shaped piece of the bark, extending in as far as the wood and bearing a bud (Fig. 160, A), is cut off from one plant and inserted beneath the flaps produced by making a T-shaped incision in the bark of the stock (Fig. 160, B). In grafting (Fig. 160, C–F) a portion of a twig is removed from the one plant (the *scion*) and its tapered lower end (Fig. 160, C and E) is pushed into a V-shaped slit in the wood (Fig. 160, D) or under the bark of the stock (Fig. 160, F), so that the wood and

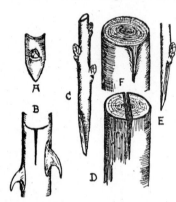

FIG. 160. Budding and grafting. A and B, Budding. *A*, bud; *B*, stock. C–F, Grafting. C–D, Cleft-grafting. E–F, Slip-grafting. *C* and *E*, scion; *D* and *F*, stock.

phloem of the latter are in contact with those of the scion. In both methods the cut surfaces are usually protected from infection and drying up by covering them with grafting wax. The cut surfaces of scion and stock become intimately associated owing to fusion of the intact cells, which is usually accompanied by some cell-division.

Grafting and budding are usually only possible between related types of plants. Those which can be associated successfully are termed *compatible*, but both compatible and incompatible strains of the same species may occur. These differences depend on such factors as relative growth-rates of stock and scion and the mechanical efficiency of the fusion. The general effect of the process of grafting in Fruit-trees is to bring about earlier and more abundant fruit-production, whilst the type of stock used may profoundly affect the ultimate size and habit of the mature tree. Grafting and budding are really special methods of propagating cuttings on another root-system and of perpetuating forms which are infertile or fail to come true from seed.

If the tip of a growing stem is removed, enlargement-growth ceases. Since growth is resumed, if the detached tip is immediately replaced, this cannot be due to wounding. Investigation has shown that complex organic substances, known as *hormones (auxins)*,[1] are constantly diffusing back in very small amounts from the growing tips. Though here without effect on cell-division, they render the walls in the zone of elongation plastic so that they readily stretch under turgor pressure. This causes separation of the cellulose-fibrils and permits of the intercalation of particles of wall-substance, bringing about permanent enlargement. Several different hormones, all producing similar effects, have been extracted from plants and animal urine, the best-known being auxins A and B and the chemically somewhat simpler hetero-auxin (β-indole acetic acid). A paste of very dilute hetero-auxin in lanoline is useful in experiments.

When the surface of a decapitated stem is smeared with it, growth continues. If the lower ends of cuttings are covered with the paste or briefly immersed in a very dilute solution of hetero-auxin, root-formation is greatly stimulated, a method employed in propagating plants of which cuttings cannot so readily be rooted (*e.g.* Pears). Auxins also form in growing leaves, hence the importance of using cuttings bearing young foliage. The auxins of root-apices, apparently identical with those of stems, retard elongation, but facilitate lateral cell-extension. The optimum concentration for the effect of auxin on growth differs for roots and stems and experiments with Cucumbers suggest that there is a critical concentration, beyond which the responses are reversed. This may explain many peculiarities of behaviour and differences in response to stimuli.

Auxins, probably owing to partial inactivation by light, exert a maximum effect in darkness, as shown by etiolated plants, which also exhibit arrest of lateral buds. In decapitated Bean-seedlings the usually dormant axillary buds of the cotyledons sprout, but they fail to grow if the cut surface is smeared with hetero-auxin paste. Auxins therefore also check the growth of lateral buds. Similarly, those in growing leaves arrest the outgrowth of their axillary buds. In trees nutritive causes probably determine which lateral buds shall develop, these being usually larger. When they start to grow, they produce hormones which, diffusing downwards, apparently check the other buds Auxins from unfolding leaves and opening buds initiate cambial activity in woody plants (cf. p. 185).

[1] For full details, see P. Boysen-Jensen, *Growth Hormones in Plants* (transl. by G. S. Avery and P. R. Burkholder). McGraw-Hill Book Co., 1936 (268 pp.); Society of Experimental Biology, Symposium No. 2, *Growth.* Cambridge Univ. Press, 1948.

17

CHAPTER XXIII

THE PHYSIOLOGY OF TROPIC MOVEMENTS

As a result of elongation during growth the positions of the growing tips are continually altering, *i.e.* they exhibit a forward movement which does not take place in a straight line (p. 248). The slight curvatures occurring during circumnutation ensue from internal causes and are not due to external influences or *stimuli*. One, however, frequently meets with other growth-movements leading to curvatures which can be definitely ascribed to outside agencies. The effect of these, when they do not act uniformly, is to produce a change, which ultimately results in a curvature in the zone of elongation. When the direction of the movement is determined by the direction of the external influence, we speak of the movement as a *tropic* one.[1]

Attention has been called to the influence of gravity in inducing the upright growth of the ordinary shoot (p. 15) and the downward growth of the main root (p. 106), the phenomenon being referred to as *geotropism*. The experiments already described sufficiently illustrate these general facts, and it need only be added that an organ which curves in the direction of the force due to gravity is said to be *positively*, whilst one which curves the opposite way is said to be *negatively*, geotropic.

It might be thought that the downward curvature of a horizontally placed root was due to its own weight, although the negative behaviour of the shoot makes this unlikely, as well as the absence of curvature in a dead root. Even when a certain amount of resistance has to be overcome, however, roots will nevertheless be found to curve downwards when placed horizontally. This may be shown by filling a shallow vessel with mercury and fixing seedlings to corks, wedged on to the edge of the vessel in such a way that their radicles lie horizontally on the surface of the mercury. The curving roots push their way into the latter, whereas others which have been killed remain horizontal.

---

[1] Consult the general works on plant physiology cited on p. 193. See also C. Darwin, *The Power of Movement in Plants*. Murray, 1880 (193 pp.).

So long as the shoot and root are situated with their axes parallel to the line of action of gravity, no curvature takes place, *i.e.* there is a condition of equilibrium. As soon, however, as either occupies any position other than the vertical, this state of equilibrium is upset and curvature sooner or later takes place until gravity again acts *equally on all sides*. The condition for a geotropic curvature in an ordinary shoot or root is therefore an unequal action of gravity.

If a seedling is placed horizontally in the dark and slowly rotated on its own axis, it will of course be exposed to such unequal influence; as a result of the rotation, however, all sides in succession will be subjected for an equal period of time to the stimulus and no curvature will result. In carrying

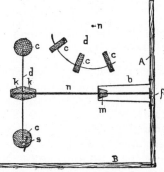

FIG. 161. Klinostat. (Reproduced by permission of Messrs A. Gallenkamp & Co., Ltd.)

FIG. 162. Diagram to explain construction of a simple centrifugal apparatus (modified from Osterhout). For description, see text. The upper figure shows a small part of *d* from the surface.

out this experiment control seedlings should be supported horizontally without rotation.

For such purposes we use an instrument known as a *klinostat* (Fig. 161), which consists of a clock-work mechanism giving a slow and sometimes adjustable rate of rotation to a disc to which either seedlings or plants in light pots can be attached. If seedlings are employed they should be protected from drying by means of a suitable cover.

A force similar in action to gravity, and moreover one with which we can more easily experiment, is centrifugal force. When attached to the edge of a wheel, which is rapidly rotated in the vertical plane, the root of a seedling assumes a position pointing outwards and the shoot one pointing inwards along a radius.   Thus, response is precisely like that due to gravity, as might be expected, if both influence growth by affecting the distribution of auxin.

A simple centrifugal apparatus (Fig. 162) consists of a circular tin disc d (6 to 8 inches in diameter) to which eight flat slices (c, about quarter of an inch thick) of cork are fitted firmly into slightly narrower slots, cut at equal intervals (c, c) into the margin of the disc.   The centre of the latter is attached with the help of two corks (k, k) to one end of a knitting-needle n, the other end of which is supported by a piece of tin (b), shaped as in the figure, and allowing free movement of the needle.   The tip of the latter revolves freely in the perforated tin plate f and is prevented from escaping from this lower bearing by the cork m through which it passes.   When the instrument rests on the base B the wheel d rotates in the vertical, when on A in the horizontal plane.

For use seedlings (s) with straight plumules and radicles (Appendix X) are pinned in any position to the right or left-hand side of each cork, all being on the same side in a given experiment.   Thereupon a spray of water is directed against the $unoccupied$ sides of the corks, so that the whole apparatus works like a water-wheel, the rapidity of rotation depending on the strength of the spray. If the wheel be made to revolve in the vertical plane, the result will be that the seedlings are exposed equally on all sides to the action of gravity and will consequently respond to the centrifugal force alone, assuming the position described above.

When the wheel is rotated horizontally the seedlings are exposed to the one-sided influence, both of gravity and centrifugal force, and will be found to take up a position with the radicles pointing outwards and downwards, and the plumules inwards and upwards; as the rapidity of rotation is increased, both radicles and plumules become more nearly horizontal.   The ultimate position of the two parts of the seedling is a resultant of the combined action of the horizontal centrifugal force and the vertical force due to gravity. Thus they come to lie at an angle which represents the position of equilibrium between these two forces.   Such experiments show that centrifugal force and gravity can have a combined effect upon the plant.

There are organs, such as creeping shoots and rhizomes, which, though responding negatively at certain times, are normally in a position of equilibrium when growing more or less horizontally. Such structures are said to be *diageotropic*.   If a rhizome is planted in an inclined position the growing zone curves until the apex again lies horizontally.   The lateral roots and the horizontal branches of trees also have a different position of equilibrium from that of the erect axes.   If the lateral roots of the first order are shifted from their customary position, the growing parts curve until they form the same angle with the horizontal as before (p. 106). The position occupied by laterals probably depends on some influence of the main axis, since removal of the latter causes one or more of the laterals to grow vertically (cf. p. 249) and this may be connected with auxin-concentration.

A given organ does not always show the same response to gravity in all stages of its development. Thus, in the Poppy (Fig. 163) the upper part of the flower stalk is positively geotropic before the flower opens (*a*), diageotropic during the process of

opening (*b*), and negatively geotropic when fruit-formation begins
(*c* and *d*). Similarly, many rhizomes
(*e.g.* the Solomon's Seal) are diageotropic, but their tips become
negatively geotropic prior to the
formation of the overground shoots.

If a seedling, in which plumule
and radicle have been marked in
the way described on p. 98, is
placed horizontally in a dark box
(cf. p. 106), it will be found that
the curvature after twenty-four
hours has in both regions taken
place approximately in the zone of
maximum elongation (Fig. 164, D).
Moreover, it will be noticed that
both the extreme tip and the older
part of each organ have remained
almost straight.

Various experiments suggest that
the root-tip [1] plays an important
role in geotropic response. The
growth-hormone (p. 253) produced
by the root-tip normally diffuses
evenly backwards, causing an equal
retardation in the rate of elongation.

FIG. 163. Flower-buds, flowers, and fruit of *Papaver*, showing the successive positions (*a–d*) of the flower-stalk in successive stages of development (about one-third natural size).

When, however, the root is placed horizontally, more auxin diffuses along the lower side, so that the lower elongates more slowly than the upper leading to a downward curvature. If the tip of a stimu-lated root be removed and replaced with an intervening layer of gelatine, the behaviour is similar to that of an uninjured root. If the tip of an unstimulated root is removed and replaced on the stump towards one side, a subsequent curvature in a direction towards the side bearing the tip is observed; this is due to more retarding

---

[1] In the root-tip and in the starch-sheath of some plants there occur large, readily movable starch-grains which have been thought by some botanists to be associated with graviperception.

auxin diffusing down the side which becomes concave. If cut root-tips, with the apex upwards, are allowed to rest on a block of gelatine or agar, the auxin gradually collects in the block. A small cube cut out of the latter can then be substituted for the root-tip in the above experiment, with identical results, showing that the living apex is requisite as a producer of the auxin.

Similar experiments can be performed with shoot-apices, but since the hormone here accelerates elongation, a negative curvature is produced when the stem is placed horizontally. Tips of growing

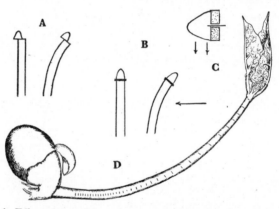

FIG. 164. A, Effect of excentric replacement of coleoptile-tip. B, Response of coleoptile to light (direction shown by arrow) when severed tip replaced with an intervening layer of gelatine. C, See p. 262. D, Demonstration of region of geotropic curvature in plumule of Runner Bean.

leaves behave similarly to stem-tips, and the coleoptile (p. 32) of Grass-seedlings is particularly suitable for these experiments.

Intercalary meristems marked by a soft region either towards the base or the apex of the internode occur in Grasses, Carnations, and members of the Labiatæ (cf. p. 54). They are an important means of enabling the stems to become erect if the shoot is laid prostrate by wind or rain. In fact, whereas in most plants, when the stem becomes horizontal, the older part remains prostrate and only the actually growing part becomes erect, the whole shoot in Grasses soon assumes an upright position under these circumstances. This is due to the fact that, when horizontal, the intercalary meristems are stimulated by auxin to more active growth on the under than on the upper side.

The ordinary erect shoot responds to one-sided light by curving more or less markedly towards the source of illumination (p. 14, Fig. 6, B), so that it exhibits *positive phototropism*. Aerial roots (*e.g.* Ivy, Fig. 61) and the tendrils of the Virginia Creeper and

Vine furnish the commonest instances of *negative phototropism*; a few subterranean roots (*e.g.* Mustard) are, however, also influenced negatively by one-sided light, although the majority of roots appear to be unaffected. Careful experiments have shown that the response is largely dependent on the intensity and duration of the illumination.

For exact experiments on phototropism it is best to employ a dark chamber of the type shown in Fig. 165. This is made light-tight and painted black inside to prevent reflection. A small slit is situated at one end of the box, while the opposite end is hinged and serves as a door for introducing and removing plants.

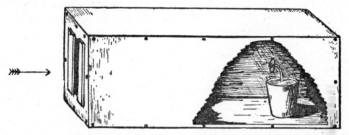

FIG. 165. Dark chamber for experiments on phototropism (see text). The arrow indicates the direction of the light.

In open spaces in nature light and gravity act together in producing the upright growth of the ordinary shoot, but at the edges of dense thickets and in hedges, where one-sided light comes into play, positive phototropism is more marked than negative geotropism, so that the shoots grow out towards the light. With the help of the dark chamber, it can be shown that the relative effect of the two influences varies in different plants; thus the shoots of some (*e.g.* Pea) assume an almost horizontal position, whilst others curve to a less extent (*e.g.* Cress, Runner Bean), showing that they are more strongly affected by gravity.

That erect shoots do not curve, when uniformly illuminated on all sides, is shown by everyday observation, as well as by the fact that no curvature takes place when a plant is rotated on a klinostat at right angles to the source of light, since each side is then in turn equally illuminated. If we mark the plumule of a seedling at equal intervals and then expose it to one-sided light in the dark chamber, it will be found that, as in geotropic curvatures, the bending ensues in the region of maximum elongation.

Another analogy between the two kinds of phenomena is furnished by plant-organs which respond to the influence of light by taking up a position more or less at right angles to its direction.

Such *diaphototropism* is most strikingly exhibited by ordinary dorsiventral foliage-leaves and is responsible for the definite position in relation to light, assumed by the blade during development, a feature which is specially noticeable in leaf-mosaics (cf. p 121). There are, however, leaves which are negatively geotropic and grow vertically (*e.g.* Iris).

A further similarity between phototropism and geotropism lies

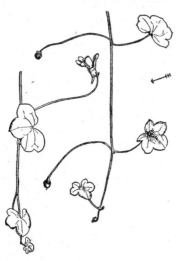

in the change of phototropic response exhibited by the flower-stalks of some plants. Thus, in the Ivy-leaved Toadflax (Fig. 166), very common on old walls, the flower-stalks bend towards the light (*i.e.* are positively phototropic), but during the development of the fruit they curve away from it (see right-hand figure); in this way the ripening fruits are carried in the direction of the wall, so that the seeds are often shed in its crevices.

The response to one-sided light is mostly not sharply localised, except in some Grass-coleoptiles, as can be demonstrated in seedlings of Canary-grass in which the plumular leaves have not yet burst through the coleoptile. The tips of some are covered with small caps (Fig. 167, *c*), each about half

FIG. 166. Change of phototropic response in the flower-stalks of the Ivy-leaved Toadflax (*Linaria cymbalaria*). The arrow marks the direction of the light.

an inch long and made by twisting silver paper round the point of a pin, whilst others (Fig. 167) are left uncovered. The whole pot is then placed in the dark chamber (Fig. 165). After about twenty-four hours the uncovered seedlings will have bent in the usual way towards the light, whilst the others have remained straight. The effect of light is therefore here confined to the upper part of the coleoptile, and, as in the geotropic curvature of roots, there is a conduction of hormone to the region in which bending takes place.

In phototropism, as in geotropism, diffusion of hormones is thus involved. As already noted (p. 253) the action of the hormone is retarded by light, while there is evidence that in unilateral light the rate of diffusion is diminished on the illuminated side. The shaded side therefore receives more hormone, which latter is also more effective, so that differential growth ensues. Even with an intervening layer of water or gelatine, replacement of the severed tip of a Grass-coleoptile which has been exposed to unilateral light, results in a subsequent response (see Fig. 164, B). The straightening of seedling-plumules (cf. p. 36) is probably due to similar causes.

An unequal distribution of moisture has been shown to produce a positive growth-curvature in roots (p. 107), a phenomenon known as *positive hydrotropism*. This behaviour can also be demonstrated by the following method (Fig. 168). A small wire sieve is

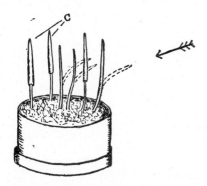

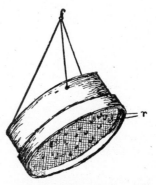

FIG. 167. Experiment to demonstrate the localisation of light-perception in young seedlings of the Canary-grass (*Phalaris*). The arrow shows the direction of the incident light. *c*, caps of silver paper. The positions occupied by the uncovered seedlings at the end of the experiment are indicated by dotted lines.

FIG. 168. Experiment to demonstrate hydrotropism in roots (see text). *r*, the curved radicles.

filled to the depth of about half an inch with damp sawdust in which Cress-seeds are sown, the whole being then covered with damp blotting-paper. After this the sieve is suspended in moderately moist air at an angle of about 45°, whilst a similar sieve is hung up horizontally. When the radicles of the Cress-seedlings emerge through the meshes of the sieve they will be found in the sloping one to curve through a right angle, so that they again reach the damp sawdust (Fig. 168, *r*). This is due to the vertically growing radicles, on entering the relatively dry air below the sieve, being nearer to the moist surface on one side than on the other, and hence the necessary conditions for a hydrotropic curvature are realised. On the other hand, in the horizontal sieve, no such curvature is observed, since all sides of the radicles are equally stimulated.

Negative hydrotropism is much rarer, but is seen in certain Fungi. In nature positive curvatures are chiefly shown in drier soils by the finer branches of the root-system, where they are of considerable value in carrying these rootlets into regions of greater moisture.

Other tropic movements, due to chemical stimuli (chemo-tropism, pp. 318, 468) or touch (haptotropism, p. 265) are described elsewhere. Here we may consider certain parallels among tropic curvatures, especially between geotropism and phototropism. In both there are organs which respond positively, others which respond negatively, and still others which place themselves at right angles to the directive stimulus. Further, the curvature always ensues in the zone of elongation, somewhere about the region of maximum growth in length, and is due to the convex side elongating more rapidly than the concave. Moreover, the region of perception is probably always separated from the region of curvature and consequently conduction must occur. This has been shown in both phenomena to be due to the same growth-hormones which under stimulation, diffuse unequally backwards. It has proved possible to interchange root-tips of Maize and coleoptile-tips on their respective stumps, the former accelerating the growth of the decapitated coleoptiles, the latter preventing that of the roots.

Since the degree of curvature induced in a coleoptile stump, when a tip or an agar block containing hormone is placed excentric-ally upon it in the dark (cf. Fig. 164, A), is determined by the con-centration of hormone, the resulting angle with the vertical affords a means of measuring that concentration. It has thus been possible to prove that redistribution of hormones takes place in stimulated coleoptile tips in both types of tropic movements. This has been done (cf. Fig. 164, C) by placing such tips from unilaterally stimu-lated material on agar blocks with a razor blade separating the sides that had faced towards and away from the stimulus. When the half-blocks, after a sufficient interval, are placed on coleoptile stumps in the dark, the difference in the resulting angle of curvature demonstrates the uneven distribution of hormones.

The same stimulus may produce a totally different effect in different organs (*e.g.* gravity causes roots to curve towards the earth, shoots to curve away), so that there is obviously no definite relation between the cause of the impression and the type of effect produced. Moreover, we have seen that in certain plants a given organ responds in a different way to the same external agency in various stages of its development, as in the flower-stalks of the Poppy and the Ivy-leaved Toadflax. Such changes in response emphasise the complexity of the phenomenon and suggest that differential move-ment of growth hormones is part only of an elaborate mechanism.

CHAPTER XXIX

THE PHYSIOLOGY OF PLANT MOVEMENTS
(continued)

CERTAIN tropic growth-curvatures which result from direct contact with a foreign body and are described as *haptotropic*, differ markedly from those discussed in the preceding chapter. The commonest examples of such curvatures are furnished by *tendrils* (cf. p. 17), whose morphological nature may first be considered.

Most such tendrils[1] are modified leaves or parts of leaves, as in many members of the Leguminosæ and *Cobæa scandens*, a common greenhouse climber. In the Leguminosæ one or more leaflets of the pinnate blade may be modified as tendrils, the consequent reduction of photosynthetic surface being often compensated by the enlargement of the stipules and the production of green wing-like expansions by the stems and petioles; all of these features are well illustrated by the Sweet-pea (Fig. 169, B). In *Lathyrus aphaca,* (Fig. 74, D) the whole blade is replaced by a single tendril, the large stipules taking over the normal work of the leaf. In seedlings of this plant the lower leaves not infrequently possess small blades with relatively small stipules, the latter becoming larger in the upper leaves as the blade becomes reduced.

In *Cobæa* the ultimate segments of the compound leaves are similarly replaced by tendrils, the tips of which are provided with a claw-like hook giving a firmer grasp on the support. In a few plants (e.g. *Clematis*, Canary Creeper) the leaf-blade remains unmodified, but the petiole acts like a tendril and entwines the support.

Branch-tendrils are relatively rare; instances are the tendrils of the Vine, the Virginia Creeper (*Ampelopsis*), and the Passion-flower. In the last-named plant the simple tendrils clearly arise in the axils of the leaves, so that their branch-nature is manifest. In the Vine and Virginia Creeper (Fig. 169, A) the branched tendrils arise at

---

[1] A considerable number of data on climbing plants will be found in C. Darwin, *The Movements and Habits of Climbing Plants*. J. Murray, 1905 (208 pp.).

each node, on the side of the stem opposite to that bearing a leaf. This is due to the fact that each segment of the stem ends in a tendril which is bent over to one side, the growth of the main axis being continued by the axillary bud between the tendril and the leaf situated opposite to it, so that the whole stem is a sympodium (cf. p. 118).

In the White Bryony (*Bryonia*, Fig. 9, p. 16) the exact nature of the simple tendrils is doubtful; each arises together with a short branch (Fig. 9, B, *br.*), and frequently an inflorescence as well,

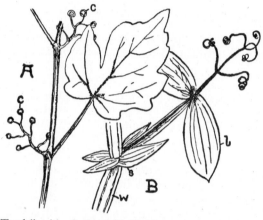

FIG. 169. Tendrils A, of the Self-climbing Virginia Creeper (*Ampelopsis Veitchii*), and B, of the Sweet-pea (*Lathyrus odoratus*) (natural size). *c*, attaching cushions; *l*, unmodified leaflets; *s*, stipule; *w*, winged stem.

from the axil of a foliage-leaf. Some regard the tendril as a modified first leaf of the short branch, whilst others look upon it as an accessory branch developed in the leaf-axil (p. 115). Such an accessory branch may represent part of an abbreviated branch-system which is precociously developed on the axillary bud and whose subtending leaf is suppressed.

The tendrils or their branches, when young, are almost straight and constitute flexible structures composed of soft turgid tissue. The growing tips show pronounced circumnutation (cf. p. 248), circling through a wide orbit in a comparatively short time, thus increasing the probability of their coming into contact with a support. If this occurs, the side of the tendril opposite to that touched is stimulated to grow more rapidly, whilst that in contact with the support continues to grow at the same rate as before. This brings about a curvature of the tip of the tendril (cf. Fig. 9, A) and, as a consequence, new parts of it come into touch with the support and thus receive a fresh stimulus; moreover, the resulting curvature is not confined to the part actually in contact, but also affects adjacent parts of the tendril. In this way more and more of the growing tip firmly grasps the support.

After this the part of the tendril between the parent-plant and the support gradually coils up into a close spiral and, since both ends of the tendril are fixed, the coils of this spiral of necessity exhibit a reversal at some point or other (Fig. 9, B). Hence an elastic spring-like connection is developed, so that the risk of the plant's being torn away by gusts of wind, etc., is diminished. Soon after its attachment the tissue of the tendril begins to thicken and lignify, so that it loses its soft flexible character. Tendrils which fail to reach a support wither away and sooner or later generally drop off. Where climbing is accomplished with the aid of sensitive petioles, the mechanism is similar, although the effect does not extend beyond the region of contact.

If the under surface of a White Bryony tendril is gently stroked for about a minute, a curvature almost immediately becomes apparent and, before long, is generally very pronounced. The changes leading to the curvature depend, not upon the actual contact, but upon rubbing against a foreign body. This is proved by placing tendrils in contact with a support and ensuring the absence of all vibration, when no curvature is observed. Tendrils are not stimulated by contact with fluid bodies, and impact of rain-drops is without effect. Contact presumably induces a greater concentration of auxin towards the convex side.

The negatively phototropic tendrils of the Self-climbing Virginia Creeper exhibit quite a different method of attachment. The tips of their branches swell up into little cushions (Fig. 169, A, c) which, on meeting a wall, cling to it by the production of an adhesive substance and then gradually flatten out to form sucker-like discs which adhere very tenaciously to the surface. In the ordinary Virginia Creeper and the Vine the tendrils mostly function in the usual way, but should their tips come into contact with a firm surface they develop similar cushions which subsequently form adhesive discs.

The mechanism for encircling the support in twiners (p. 17) is different and not due to contact. The young negatively geotropic shoots show strong circumnutation. As they grow taller, the upper internodes become inclined and growth of one flank is favoured. The nutation, combined with the gravitational responses, causes a circling movement and coiling around a support. Gravity is clearly concerned in producing the differential growth, since twiners only coil round approximately vertical supports and lose that power, when rotated on a klinostat. Furthermore, if a twiner is inverted, some of the last-formed coils untwine and commence to wind in the opposite direction (Fig. 170).

The direction of twining is usually constant for any given kind of stem-climber, taking place either from left to right (*i.e.* clockwise, as in the Hop, Fig. 10, Honeysuckle, and Black Bindweed) or from right to left (*i.e.* counter-clockwise, as in *Calystegia* and the

Runner Bean), but the Woody Nightshade (*Solanum dulcamara*) which is an occasional climber sometimes twines in one direction and sometimes in another. Among British plants the Honeysuckle (*Lonicera*) is the only woody twiner, but in the jungles of the Tropics larger forms known as lianes are abundant (cf. p. 185).

The curvature of the tentacles of the Sundew after an insect has been entrapped (cf. p. 221) is due to a contact stimulus, although a chemical influence may also be involved. Here we have a good example of transference of stimuli since, after the particular tentacles bearing the insect have curved inwards, other tentacles not in contact with it follow suit.

Movements due to contact-stimuli, but differing from those hitherto noticed in not depending upon unequal growth of the two sides of the curving organ, are seen in the stigma of *Mimulus glutinosus* and in the stamens of the common Barberry. In the

FIG. 170. Effect of inversion on the twining stem of the Runner Bean.

former the stigma consists of two flat spreading lobes (Fig. 171,A,*s*.) which, on being touched (*e.g.* by the tongue of a pollinating insect, cf. p. 460), close together in the way shown in Fig. 171, B. The six stamens of the Barberry-flower project outwards, so that their anthers are some distance from the stigma, but, when the bases of the filaments are touched as by an insect, the stamens thus stimulated spring up into a vertical position, thereby covering the insect with a shower of pollen. In both of these plants the movement is due to sudden decrease of turgidity in certain cells.

Many leaves exhibit so-called *sleep-movements*. In these the petiole takes up different positions in darkness and in light, the

swollen leaf-base, or *pulvinus* (Fig. 172, *p.*), being the region of
movement.   Movement is facilitated by a flattening of the vascular

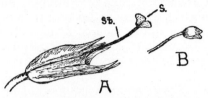

FIG. 171. Response of the stigma of *Mimulus glutinosus* to contact-stimuli.
A, Normal position.   B, With the two lobes of the stigma closed together,
       after a stimulus has been received.   *s.*, stigma; *st.*, style.

tissue in a plane at right angles to the direction of curvature (Fig.
172, *Pu.*), the necessary rigidity being attained by a greater development of the cortex, which consists of large, turgid, thin-walled

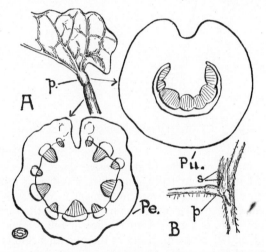

FIG. 172. A, Pulvinus of Runner Bean (*Phaseolus*) and diagrams of transverse
sections of the pulvinus (*Pu.*) and the petiole (*Pe.*).   B, Pulvinus of Sensitive
       Plant (*Mimosa pudica*).   *p.*, pulvinus; *s.*, stipules.

parenchyma-cells.   The fall of the leaf at dusk is accompanied
by a decrease in the turgidity of the cortical cells on the lower side
of the pulvinus, whilst at the same time some of their watery sap
escapes into the intercellular spaces.   This is due to a change in the
permeability of the protoplasm and, as a result of the infiltration
of the intercellular spaces, the whole pulvinus acquires a more
transparent, deeper green appearance.   At dawn the cells of the

pulvinus become turgid and the leaf assumes the day-position. A rhythmic production of auxin in the pulvinus has been demonstrated.

A common example of sleep-movements is furnished by the Wood Sorrel in which the leaflets droop down at night (Fig. 173). Such movements can also be induced by the influence of contact. Thus, if the leaflets of the Wood Sorrel be repeatedly flicked with the finger, they will after some time assume the night position (Fig. 173, N). Other kinds of Wood Sorrel which are cultivated in conservatories display these changes much more rapidly. The

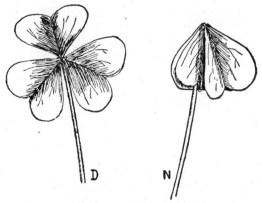

FIG. 173. Leaves of the Wood Sorrel (*Oxalis acetosella*) (natural size). D, day-position. N, night-position.

most striking instance is that of the familiar Sensitive Plant (*Mimosa pudica*), a member of the Leguminosæ. Here not only do the leaflets fold together in pairs, but with a sufficient stimulus the whole leaf performs a downward movement. Moreover, after this has happened other adjacent leaves may undergo the same change, so that here there is a rapid transference of the original stimulus. A very sudden fall in the turgidity of the pulvinus results when the leaf is touched or injured. All these organs sooner or later recover their normal position, after the effect of the stimulus has passed away. Sleep-movements are also well seen in the Dutch Clover (where the leaflets move upwards and lie face to face at night) and other members of the Leguminosæ (cf. Fig. 174). An advantage of the assumption of a more or less vertical position by the leaflets at night may be the smaller surface from which radiation can take place, so that relatively little dew is deposited. Sleep-movements of leaves are seen much more commonly in tropical plants than in our own flora.

Many flowers close at night, as for example the Tulip, the White

Water-lily, and the Wood Anemone, and these changes are analogous to the sleep-movements just discussed. Similarly, the flower-heads of many members of the Compositæ close up at certain times, most commonly on the approach of night (*e.g.* Daisy), but sometimes at midday, as in *Tragopogon*, whence the popular name for this plant "John-go-to-bed-at-noon." Night-flowering plants (*e.g.* Evening Primrose, Tobacco, cf. p. 464) have their flowers closed during the daytime, but open them at night. In the Carrot it is the whole inflorescence that hangs down at night. By means of all such floral movements stamens and stigma are protected at times when the pollinating insects are not flying.

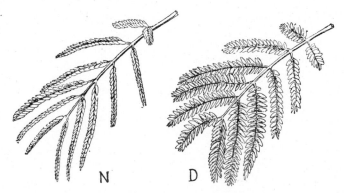

FIG. 174. Day- (D) and night- (N) positions of the leaflets of the bipinnate leaf of *Acacia lophantha* (natural size).

The external causes of sleep-movements and of these diurnal changes on the part of flowers are very complex, but since they generally follow on the daily alternation of light and darkness, associated with which is a change of temperature, these are no doubt the two stimuli especially concerned; other factors, partly rhythmic responses, are also involved, as is obvious in *Tragopogon*. That change of temperature can sometimes be a prime cause of these movements is shown by the Tulip, whose flowers open out widely in a warm room. Most movements of floral organs are accompanied by growth-changes and hormones are no doubt involved.

In the movements described on the last three pages, the response exhibited is independent of the direction of the stimulus, and such are usually termed *nastic* movements. The response therefore contrasts with the directional one seen in tropic movements. But there are some plant-movements (*e.g.* those of certain tendrils) which cannot easily be allocated to one or other of these categories.

All the movements of plant-organs discussed in this and the

18

preceding chapter take place only when other external conditions are suitable, the most important of these being an adequate temperature. At low temperatures the movements are either not exhibited at all or are performed very slowly. In the absence of the necessary amount of oxygen for respiration they usually cease (cf. p. 241), and the same result is obtained if the atmosphere around the plant contains small quantities of anæsthetics (*e.g.* chloroform). Unless, however, these arresting influences operate for a considerable period, their paralysing effect is only temporary.

The effect of a stimulus depends on its quantity, *i.e.* its intensity multiplied by the interval of time during which it acts. Weak stimulation, if sufficiently prolonged and continuous, has the same effect as a stronger stimulus of shorter duration. If intermittent stimuli are applied, there may be a summation of their effects, resulting in response, providing the intervals between successive stimuli are sufficiently short. The fact that a small amount of stimulation has no effect, if interrupted for an appreciable time, is an important safeguard against unnecessary response in nature.

If, however, a stimulus has acted for a certain minimum time (*presentation time*), a subsequent response will occur, even if the stimulus cease to act, as is specially obvious in geotropic and phototropic reactions. Thus, if a seedling is placed horizontally with the lower side marked with Indian ink and, after half an hour, is fixed on a klinostat so that gravity now acts equally on all sides in succession, a curvature of the radicle towards the marked side is nevertheless observed after some little time. A similar result would be obtained with a plumule exposed, for the same period, to one-sided action of gravity or light, and fixed on the klinostat before a bending movement is apparent. These experiments demonstrate that a period (*reaction time*) elapses between the reception of the impression and the occurrence of the curvature and further that, when once a sufficient stimulus has been received, it cannot be obliterated by subsequent exposure to uniform conditions. Similarly, if a tendril is stroked for a short time and then left untouched, curvature nevertheless ensues.

Plants, in common with animals, thus possess a certain power of movement, though of a more limited character. All growing organs are able to bend and thus to adjust their position in relation to external influences, and such movements may be exhibited even by mature organs. The next chapter will show, moreover, that many simple Algæ swim freely from place to place. Movements of ripe fruits and other reproductive structures are, however, merely due to differences in shrinkage or expansion of dead cells.

CHAPTER XXV

SIMPLE PLANTS

PLANTS exhibit a great variety of external form, but nevertheless can be assembled in groups having many features, both of structure and life-history, in common. Very many vegetable organisms are, however, far simpler in every way than the highly complex Flowering Plant. For example, whole groups of lower plants lack true roots and possess no vascular system. A specialised conducting tissue consisting of xylem and phloem is only encountered in the Flowering Plants (Angiosperms), in the Gymnosperms (*e.g.* Conifers), and in the Ferns and their allies (Horsetails, Clubmosses, etc.), whilst it is lacking in Mosses, Liverworts, Fungi, and Seaweeds.

The Vegetable Kingdom can therefore be conveniently divided into vascular and non-vascular plants.[1] This difference may perhaps be related to the fact that a considerable percentage of the latter flourish in wet or damp habitats, for it is only amongst some of the larger and definitely terrestrial Mosses that anything simulating the vascular tissues of higher plants is developed. Many non-vascular plants possess a type of body called a *thallus* which exhibits no definite stem and leaves, and is often a mere flattened cellular expansion (Figs. 187, 188). The further classification of the Vegetable Kingdom (cf. p. 609) is based mainly on the methods of reproduction and the structure of the reproductive organs.

A considerable number of the simplest types of plants are unicellular, and such minute organisms, by their abundance, often cause the green colouration of small stagnant pools. Some of the plants commonly responsible for this phenomenon belong to the genus *Chlamydomonas*, one of the most striking characteristics of which is the power of movement from place to place, usually associated with animals.

Each individual consists of a spherical or oval cell, about one-fiftieth of a millimetre in diameter. The cell is bounded by a thin

---

[1] Since many so-called vascular plants possess no true vessels, these terms are apt to be misleading, but long use justifies their retention.

wall which is often produced into a slight colourless papilla at the front end (Fig. 175, A, *h*), *i.e.* that which is foremost during movement. There is commonly a single large *chloroplast* (*c*), having the shape of a deep cup with a very thick base and with the opening directed forwards. Within the thickened part is embedded

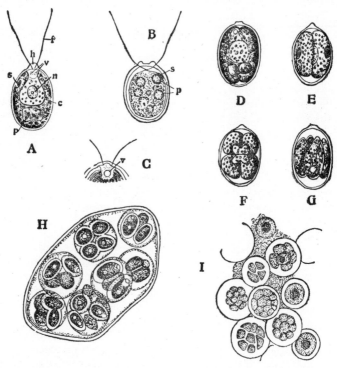

FIG. 175. Structure of individuals and asexual reproduction of *Chlamydomonas*. A, Individual of *C. angulosa*. B, ditto of *C. sphagnicola*. C, front end of a cell greatly magnified. D–G, stages in the asexual propagation of *C. angulosa*. H, I, *Palmelloid* stages of two different species. *c*, chloroplast; *f*, flagellum; *h*, anterior papilla; *n*, nucleus; *p*, pyrenoid; *s*, eye-spot; *v*, contractile vacuole. (A, D–G, after Dill; B and I, after Fritsch; H, after Goroschankin.)

a *pyrenoid* (cf. p. 43), surrounded by a sheath of small starch-grains (Fig. 175, A, *p*), but after active photosynthesis starch may also be found stored in other parts of the chloroplast. Adjacent to the rim of the latter lies a small red speck or streak of modified cytoplasm known as the *eye-spot* (*stigma*) (Fig. 175, A, B, *s*), which is concerned with the perception of light intensity (cf. below). A single nucleus (*n*) lies in front of the pyrenoid suspended by cytoplasmic strands within the cavity of the chloroplast.

If a stationary individual be observed under the high power of the microscope, a pair of small highly refractive vacuoles will be recognised in the clear cytoplasm at the front end (Fig. 175, A, C, *v*); when these are watched closely they will be seen, alternately, to enlarge gradually and then suddenly to collapse. Similar *contractile vacuoles* occur in many unicellular plants, as well as among the lower animals, and they probably serve to get rid of excess water and waste products.

The movement of the *Chlamydomonas*-individuals is accomplished by means of two delicate thread-like outgrowths, the *flagella* (Fig. 175, A, *f*), which lie in a plane at right angles to that of the two contractile vacuoles (Fig. 175, C) and arise close together from the front end. They are more readily seen after adding a drop of iodine, which has the effect of killing the organisms without much change, and not only brings out the flagella, but also makes the nucleus more distinct. The flagella are whip-like prolongations of the cytoplasm which, by their rapid backward strokes, pull the plant through the water, the movement being accompanied by a rapid rotation of the organism upon its axis. In returning to the front position, the flagella are not stretched out, and thus do not counteract the effect of the back stroke, the movements being thus comparable to those of the arms in swimming. The rate of travel of these organisms is rapid relative to their size. Thus, a *Chlamydomonas* occupies a mere fraction of a second in traversing a distance equal to its own length, whilst for a liner this evolution requires several seconds.

The direction of movement is influenced by various external stimuli, such as light, distribution of chemical substances, etc. If some water containing *Chlamydomonas* be placed in a glass bottle covered, except for a small aperture on one side, with black paper, after exposure to illumination for some hours, the organisms will be found to concentrate in a dense cluster at the spot where the beam of light penetrates. If, however, the latter is very intense, the plants swim away from the illuminated region. The influence of the direction and intensity of the light on such movements is spoken of as *phototaxis*. This is an example of so-called *tactic movements* in which the whole organism moves from place to place in a direction determined by an external stimulus. Like the movements of the cytoplasm within the cells of higher plants (cf. p. 40), the movement of these unicellular organisms can be temporarily arrested by slight traces of anæsthetics.

Chlamydomonas, with the help of its chloroplast, is able to manufacture food from simple inorganic substances like any other green plant, and consequently the cell grows. After attaining a certain size it comes to rest, draws in its flagella, and begins to form *daughter-individuals* (Fig. 175, D–G). The protoplast contracts slightly away from the wall and, after nuclear division has taken place, gradually constricts into two equal portions (E), each containing half the nucleus, chloroplast, etc. The resulting segments may divide again (F, G), and these even for a third time, the successive divisions taking place in planes at right-angles to one another. Each segment develops a cell-wall and two flagella, and thus 2, 4, or 8 new individuals are constituted which, apart from size, resemble the parent in every respect.

This process of *asexual reproduction* is completed by the rupture or dissolution of the membrane of the parent-cell, with consequent liberation of the daughter-individuals. Since, under favourable circumstances, the succession of events just described recurs about every twenty-four hours, one individual would in the course of a week give rise to 2,097,152! Hence the often rapid appearance of such organisms in huge numbers in small bodies of water. The protoplasm of the parent is entirely incorporated in the bodies of its offspring, the dead cell-membrane alone remaining behind; thus, death from senile decay does not occur.

Under certain undetermined conditions the daughter-individuals fail to produce flagella and remain at rest within the parent cell-membrane, which gradually becomes mucilaginous (Fig. 175, H, I). The daughter-individuals assimilate and grow and sooner or later divide again, their membranes in their turn becoming mucilaginous. This may be repeated indefinitely until large gelatinous masses, enclosing numerous cells and constituting so-called *palmelloid stages* (Fig. 175, I), are produced. In the temporary adoption of this sedentary mode of life, *Chlamydomonas* and similar organisms exhibit a more marked resemblance to the majority of plants. On the return of favourable conditions, the individual cells acquire flagella and, escaping from the enveloping mucilage, resume the motile condition.

For a long time multiplication may be purely asexual, but sooner or later—usually when growth is checked—another method of reproduction sets in. This too is accompanied by division, but the resulting segments are more numerous, 16 or even 32 being formed; these are liberated as *sexual cells* or *gametes* (Fig. 176, A), which only differ from ordinary individuals in being considerably smaller and usually naked (*i.e.* devoid of a cell-wall). They move for a short time, but soon meet in pairs, and thereafter a gradual fusion (Fig. 176, B) of the two protoplasts and of their nuclei takes place to form a single cell. This (*zygote*) moves for a longer or shorter period with the aid of its four flagella and then comes to rest.   The flagella are withdrawn, the protoplast assumes a spherical shape and secretes a thick stratified membrane, and copious reddish oil appears in the cytoplasm. This body (Fig. 176, C, D), known as a *zygospore*, sinks to the bottom and enters upon a resting condition.

The process of reproduction just described is known as a sexual

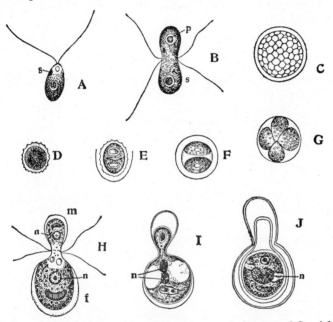

FIG. 176. Sexual reproduction of *Chlamydomonas*. A, Gamete of *C. reinhardi*. B, Stage in fusion; and C, zygospore of same.   D, Zygospore of *C. ehrenbergii*; and E–G, its germination.   H, Sexual fusion in *C. braunii*.   I, J, Later stages of same.   *f*, macrogamete; *m*, microgamete; *n*, nucleus; *p*, pyrenoid; *s*, eye-spot.   (All after Goroschankin.)

one since, as in all such processes, the fusing together of two distinct cells is involved.   Although the gametes are often of the same shape and size, there are usually two kinds (strains) which are formed from distinct parent-cells and differ in the secretions they discharge into the water.   Only gametes of different strains are attracted to each other and fuse to form zygotes.   In a few species (e.g. *Chlamydomonas braunii*) the gametes differ also in size. Some, produced by few divisions of an individual, are large (macro-gametes, Fig. 176, H, *f*), relatively sluggish in their movements, and soon come to rest (although the flagella persist), whilst others, formed by numerous divisions in the parent-cells, are small and quick-moving microgametes (Fig. 176, H, *m*). The zygote is produced by one of the latter approaching a passive macrogamete and fusing with it (Fig. 176, H–J).

This kind of sexual union between morphologically distinct gametes is described as *anisogamous*, in contrast to the *isogamous* fusion of similar gametes, found in the majority of species of *Chlamydomonas*. Since in higher forms of plants, where the differentiation between the gametes is more extreme, the female are motionless and the male alone motile, the state of affairs obtaining in *C. braunii* can be regarded as a simple phase of differentiation of sex.[1]

Prolonged desiccation and extremes of temperature leave the thick-walled zygospores unharmed, even when the pool dries up. Wind may then carry them away, or dispersal may be effected by the mud adhering to the feet of wading birds. If the zygospores are moistened, their colour sooner or later changes to green, owing to the absorption of the reddish oil, and the contents divide successively into a small number of parts (Fig. 176, E–G) which are liberated as new organisms by the bursting of the thick membrane. It is in this way that *Chlamydomonas* and similar forms reach, and develop in, almost any suitable piece of water.

The genus *Carteria*, which is not infrequent in fresh water, differs essentially from *Chlamydomonas* only in possessing four flagella (Fig. 177, G). In *Hæmatococcus* another motile unicellular form, commonly found in small pools, the protoplast is separated from the firm bounding membrane by wide transparent mucilage forming the inner part of the thick wall and traversed by several, usually branched, thread-like prolongations of the protoplast (Fig. 177, A, C). There is an ill-defined chloroplast (*c*) in the peripheral cytoplasm, containing 2–8 scattered pyrenoids (*p*), an eye-spot near the front end, and numerous irregularly distributed contractile vacuoles. Even more abundant in small ponds are species of *Euglena* (Fig. 177, E) and *Trachelomonas* (F), with a single thick flagellum. They have no wall and the protoplast commonly alters its shape continuously, although in some *Euglenas* (Fig. 177, D) it is rigid; in *Trachelomonas* (Fig. 177, F) each individual lives within a firm, smooth or spiny case. The cells have a large nucleus (*n*), several chloroplasts (*c*) and large grains of reserve-food (*r*).

The cells of *Hæmatococcus* often contain a red pigment which is specially conspicuous in the resting-stages (Fig. 177, B), formed after withdrawal of flagella. Similar cysts are produced by *Euglena*.

---

[1] *C. braunii* is peculiar in having gametes provided with a cell-membrane (Fig. 176, H), a feature also seen in a few other unicellular plants, although in all other members of the Vegetable Kingdom the sexual cells are naked.

If these occur in quantity they may lend a deep red colour to the water or mud. The reproduction of *Hæmatococcus* is similar to that of *Chlamydomonas*. *Euglena* multiplies by longitudinal division into two.

Chlamydomonas, *Hæmatococcus*, and *Euglena* are representatives of different classes of simple green plants, which swim about like

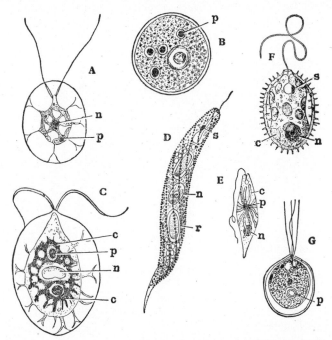

FIG. 177. A, *Hæmatococcus* (*Sphaerella*) *pluvialis*, motile individual (after Schmidle). B and C, H. *droebakensis* (after Wollenweber); B, Resting cell. D, *Euglena spirogyra* (after Lemmermann). E, *E. viridis* (after Schiller). F, *Trachelomonas hispida* (after Stein). G, *Carteria* (after Takeda). *c*, chloroplast; *n*, nucleus; *p*, pyrenoid; *r*, food-reserve; *s*, eye-spot.

animals during the greater part of their life, and most of which are inhabitants of fresh-water. In their mode of nutrition, however, they are altogether plant-like, and there is no justification for placing them in the Animal Kingdom.

There are many different kinds of *Chlamydomonas*, all of which possess two flagella, a pair of contractile vacuoles, a relatively thin cell-wall, and an oval or spherical form. These are the so-called *generic characters*, while the species differ among themselves in respect to such features as the form of the chloroplast, the presence or absence of pyrenoids, etc. (cf. Fig. 175, A, B). The genus

Hæmatococcus differs in the thick wall traversed by cytoplasmic processes. Generic and specific characters cannot be defined, since the degree of difference that justifies the placing of an organism in a separate genus is a matter of judgment and depends on a competent knowledge of the group concerned.

In other genera the unicellular individuals are combined in different ways to form *colonies*. Such is *Eudorina* (Fig. 178, A), which is often to be found among the slimy growth covering submerged parts of higher aquatics. The colony commonly consists of 32 globular cells arranged in five tiers in the peripheral

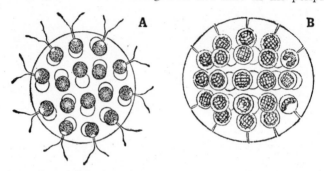

Fig. 178. *Eudorina elegans.* A, Vegetative colony; the flagella are seen on ten of the individuals. B, A colony showing asexual reproduction, the daughter-colonies in various stages of development. (A, after West; B, after Hartmann.)

portion of a spherical or oval mass of mucilage. Each individual cell is almost identical in structure with a *Chlamydomonas*-plant, the two flagella projecting well beyond the mucilage-investment, and often being easily recognisable where they traverse the latter (Fig. 178). By their united action the colony moves through the water, with one pole foremost, meanwhile rotating rapidly on its axis. Reproduction is usually effected by the subdivision of each of the constituent cells to form as many small *daughter-colonies* (Fig. 178, B), which are subsequently liberated by the breaking down of the mucilage-investment of the parent. Not uncommonly associated with *Eudorina* are the plate-like colonies of *Gonium* (Fig. 180, D).

The spherical colonies of *Volvox* are far more elaborate. Since they are composed of several thousand cells, they are of quite appreciable dimensions (usually about the size of a pin's head) and readily visible to the naked eye (Fig. 179, A, B). The constituent cells (Fig. 179, C, D) often show more resemblance to *Hæmatococcus* than to *Chlamydomonas*, since they have thick mucilaginous walls (*m*) traversed by protoplasmic processes, which are broad and correspond in adjacent individuals. Movement is effected, as in *Eudorina*, but flagella are lacking from a few large cells (Fig. 179, A, *d*) located in the part of the colony directed backwards during movement. It is these large cells alone that divide to form daughter-colonies, the latter being at first liberated

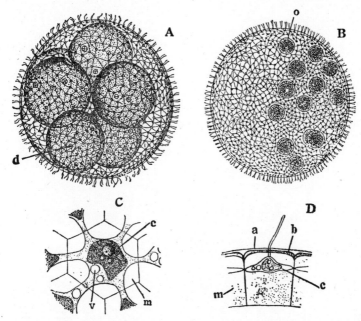

FIG. 179. Structure of *Volvox*. A, B, *V. aureus*. A, Colony enclosing five daughter-colonies, the latter already exhibiting the large cells (*d*) from which another generation will be developed. B, Female colony with mature oospores (*o*). C, Surface-view; and D, section of single cells of *V. globator*. *a, b,* external layers of wall; *c,* chloroplast; *m,* mucilage of cell-wall; *v,* contractile vacuole. (A, B, after Klein; C, D, after Meyer.)

into the hollow interior of the parent (Fig. 179, A), where they grow until set free by its rupture.

Volvox thus affords a simple example of the setting apart of certain cells for special purposes; most are purely vegetative and perish with the death of the parent, whilst a few are destined to undergo division and persist as daughter-colonies. This is in marked contrast with *Eudorina*, where every cell is generally capable of performing *all* the life-functions (nutrition, growth, reproduction, etc.). The specialisation exhibited by *Volvox* brings with it the death of the greater part of the colony, a feature which is generally associated with division of labour. *Eudorina* and

Volvox also exhibit an advanced type of sexual reproduction, analogous to the oogamy described on p. 306 (cf. Fig. 179, B).

A large proportion of the simple unicellular and colonial green plants are, however, non-motile throughout the vegetative phase

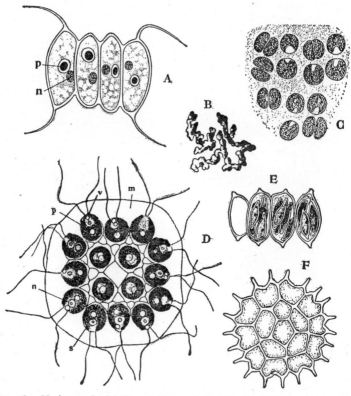

FIG. 180. Various colonial Green Algæ. A and E, *Scenedesmus quadricauda*; in E, the individuals are producing daughter-colonies. B, C, *Tetraspora*; B, a colony approximately natural size; C, a small part, much enlarged. D, *Gonium pectorale*. F, *Pediastrum*. *m*, mucilage; *n*, nucleus; *p*, pyrenoid; *s*, eye-spot; *v*, contractile vacuole. (A, after G. M. Smith; B, after West; C, after Reinke; D, after Hartmann; E, after Senn.)

of their life-history, and only exhibit movement, if at all, in connection with reproduction. They thus recall the palmelloid stages of *Chlamydomonas*, to which some, indeed, show considerable resemblance, *e.g.* the bright green gelatinous masses of *Tetraspora* (Fig. 180, B), commonly found in spring in small ponds, and containing numerous cells arranged in groups of four (Fig. 180, C).

As examples of motionless unicellular plants, the growths

which appear abundantly as green powdery coverings on tree-trunks, palings, etc. and which include *Pleurococcus*, may be studied. Under the microscope the green powder is seen to consist of small groups of 2, 4, or rarely more, cells, intermingled with which are more or less numerous rounded individuals (Fig. 181, A), all representing different stages of these plants. Each cell has a moderately thick wall, and contains a single nucleus and a lobed chloroplast (Fig. 181, B). The isolated cells constitute the adult form, and sooner or later divide, commonly by two successive walls at right angles to one another, to form four-celled packets. Each daughter-cell is thus the quadrant of a sphere, but with subsequent growth it rounds off and separates from its neighbours. This process of vegetative propagation is, when conditions are favourable, repeated at frequent intervals, and in this way the plants rapidly cover large areas.[1]

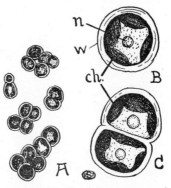

FIG. 181. *Pleurococcus*, etc. A, Group of cells, under the low power. B, Single cells and C, pair of cells, under the high power. *ch.*, chloroplast; *n*, nucleus; *w*, cell-wall.

The ordinary cells of these Algæ possess a remarkable power of withstanding drought, almost comparable to zygospores such as those of *Chlamydomonas* and other simple forms in which the vegetative cells are extremely susceptible to adverse conditions. Terrestrial Algæ like these can survive and, when circumstances allow, even multiply in the exposed dry habitats which they frequent, and their specialisation for these habitats is evidenced by their usual inability to survive prolonged submergence. Although retaining their normal green appearance throughout the year, their activities are more or less completely arrested during prolonged periods of drought, when the only source of moisture is inadequate dew.

Many of the motionless colonial green forms are common in fresh-water pools where they occur entangled among the filaments of the pond-scums or in the slimy growth on the surface of larger water-plants. As examples we may mention the four- or eight-celled colonies of *Scenedesmus* (Fig. 180, A) and the characteristic

[1] Intermingled with cells like those shown in Fig. 181, A are other spherical cells of about the same size, which differ in possessing a central lobed chloroplast with a prominent pyrenoid. These belong to the terrestrial Alga *Trebouxia* (*Cystococcus*), which plays a part in the formation of many Lichens (p. 342 and Fig. 224, B).

disc-like plates of *Pediastrum*, in which particularly the marginal cells are often of very distinctive form (Fig. 180, F). In both, the ordinary course of reproduction consists in the division of the contents of each cell to form a new colony (cf. Fig. 180, E).

Forms like *Scenedesmus, Pediastrum, Eudorina*, etc., together with many of the unicellular Diatoms and Desmids to be mentioned later (pp. 294, 296), commonly float in considerable numbers in the surface-layers of lakes, rivers, etc. (Fig. 182) and such a *plankton*, composed of Diatoms and other Algæ, is abundant in most seas.

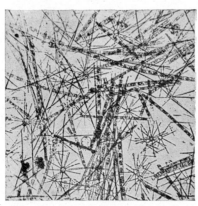

FIG. 182. Photograph of freshwater Diatom-Plankton; the two principal forms present are the filamentous *Melosira*, and the star-shaped colonies of *Asterionella* (from Wesenberg-Lund).

The microscopic plants form the food for many aquatic animals and probably provide essential vitamins. They may at times occur in such prodigious quantity as to lend a visible colouration to the water, a phenomenon especially seen in fresh water and spoken of as "waterbloom"; for this the Blue-green Algæ (p. 293) are most frequently responsible. The plankton usually differs markedly in character in the different seasons and is most abundant in spring and early summer.

The Vegetable Kingdom taken as a whole comprises sedentary organisms, and consequently the capacity for free movement has come to be regarded as an essentially animal characteristic. But the motile habit has been seen to occur in quite a considerable number of unicellular and colonial aquatic plants, and is by no means confined to them, being observable also among higher forms (*e.g.* Mosses, Liverworts, Ferns, etc.), although here restricted to the male reproductive cells. The power of movement cannot therefore serve as an invariable distinction between the two Kingdoms.

Nevertheless the Vegetable Kingdom may be described as essentially sedentary, and the Animal Kingdom as essentially motile. This distinction may be related to the necessity for animals to move from place to place in search of food, whilst plants, depending as they do almost solely on simple chemical compounds, can best obtain these by being stationary. It will, for instance, be clear that, for the terrestrial plant, the intimate contact which is necessary between root and soil is totally inconsistent with a motile habit. Another distinction between higher plants and animals is the possession by the latter of highly developed sense-organs. This too can probably be related to the motile habit, with the concomitant necessity for rapid response to the ever-changing conditions of the environment. It is significant that in animals like the Hydrazoon *Obelia*, which have a motile and sedentary phase in their life-history, the more specialised organs of sense occur in the former.

Contractile vacuoles and eye-spots are found alike in many lowly plants and animals, and cannot be said to be characteristic of either. In fact, the only satisfactory criterion as to the inclusion of an organism in the one Kingdom or the other is the method of nutrition. Plants absorb their food in liquid or gaseous form, and, with the exception of those lacking chlorophyll, build up their bodies from simple inorganic compounds; animals feed on complex organic substances, and take up a large part of their food in the solid state.

The most important distinction between the two Kingdoms thus depends on the presence or absence of chlorophyll. There are many organisms, however, which, as comparative study shows, possess the characteristics of plants, but which are colourless saprophytes (p. 315). Some green plants can even ingest solid food. Just as it is amongst the simple unicellular plants and animals that we find the closest resemblances, so too it is the complex organisms of the highest groups, as exemplified by Flowering Plants and Mammals, that exhibit the greatest distinction and portray the salient plant and animal characters in the most marked degree.

CHAPTER XXVI

SEAWEEDS AND OTHER ALGÆ

THE organisms considered in the last chapter belong to a group of simple plants termed *Algæ*,[1] which also include Seaweeds and many fresh-water species. The Algæ, with very few exceptions, possess chlorophyll and their nutrition is like that of other green plants. They are distinguished mainly by the relatively simple construction of their body, which varies from a single cell to a multicellular thallus of some complexity, and by the essentially unicellular character of their reproductive organs.

The simplest type of multicellular plant-body is a filament or row of cylindrical cells, all nearly identical, both in structure and function. Examples are furnished by *Ulothrix* (Fig. 194, A), *Spirogyra*, and *Œdogonium*, genera whose species commonly occur as floating tangled masses in ponds and stagnant ditches, although some are found in flowing water. Every cell is generally capable of division, but in *Œdogonium* this is restricted to occasional cells, recognisable by the presence, at one end, of a succession of fine rings (known as caps), formed singly at each division (Fig. 195, C, H).

The habit of the plant becomes slightly more complex when the filaments are branched, as in *Cladophora* (Fig. 183, A, B) and *Ectocarpus* (Fig. 197, B, C). Species of the latter commonly occur as brown tufts or tresses attached to diverse substrata in the rock-pools on the seashore, whilst those of the former, though also found in similar situations, are common in well-aerated fresh-water. Each branch of a *Cladophora* (Fig. 183, B) terminates in an elongated apical cell, with specially dense contents. These cells constitute *growing points*, by whose enlargement and division the branches gradually lengthen, the segments cut off from them not uncommonly undergoing no further division. Branching originates by the outgrowth from the upper ends of the cells, just beneath the septa, of small protrusions which are cut off to form the apical cells of the new branches (Fig. 183, B); the degree of branching varies greatly in the different species and even in different individuals.

[1] For reference-books, see p. 314.

The lower cells of the main *Cladophora*-filament put out thread-like organs of attachment (rhizoids), which have scanty contents, and

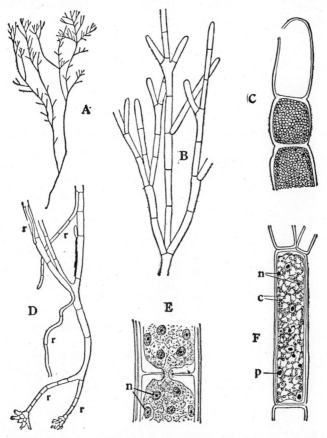

FIG. 183. *Cladophora.*   A, Small part of a plant of *C. glomerata* (natural size, after West). B, The same, enlarged (after Migula). C, Apex of a branch with three zoosporangia, the top one having liberated its contents through the aperture seen on one side (after Oltmanns). D, Base of plant, showing the attaching rhizoids (*r.*) (after Brand). E, Small part of a cell showing the manner of ingrowth of the septum (cf. p. 60) separating two daughter-cells (after Strasburger). F, Single cell stained to show nuclei (*n.*), pyrenoids (*p.*), and the net-like chloroplast (*c.*) (after Wettstein).

are often branched (Fig. 183, D, *r*).   In the young stages of most filamentous Algæ the basal cells are specially modified for attachment (Fig. 195, G), but in *Spirogyra, Œdogonium,* and *Ulothrix* the filaments usually break off and become free-floating as they grow older, except in species which inhabit flowing water.   The

19

lobes of the attaching cells grow into all the irregularities of the substratum, to which they cling after the manner of a sucker, adhesion being often increased by the secretion of a cementing substance. The great efficiency of the attaching cells is very evident in those species of *Cladophora* which grow on wave-beaten rocks or in rapidly flowing streams.

The frequent restriction of the power of division to the terminal cells of *Cladophora* marks a considerable step in division of labour as compared with *Ulothrix*. This is also seen in the formation of reproductive units, which are almost confined to the cells of the lateral branches (cf. p. 301). Further specialisation is seen in *Draparnaldia* (Fig. 184), which is not uncommon in slowly flowing water. Here the main axes, which serve almost solely for support, consist of large cells with small chloroplasts, whilst photosynthesis and reproduction are relegated to the densely branched laterals.

FIG. 184. Photograph of part of a plant of the Green Alga *Draparnaldia*, seen under the low power of the microscope.
[Photo. E. J. S.]

Division of labour is also well marked in *Ectocarpus*, where the thallus usually exhibits a differentiation into upright and prostrate portions (Fig. 197, B), both of which are branched and filamentous, the latter acting as the organ of attachment. The ends of the branches often consist of almost colourless tapering cells.

A very unusual type of thallus is that of *Vaucheria*, the species of which form rather coarse dark green wefts on damp soil or in fresh or salt water. The branched filaments, though of considerable width and length, lack septa (Fig. 196, A), and might as a consequence be regarded as consisting of single cells. Since, however, each contains numerous nuclei (Fig. 196, D, *n.*), it is better compared with a multicellular organism where too the cytoplasm exhibits continuity (cf. p. 59), but where mechanical support is afforded by the walls separating the uninucleate portions. The filaments of *Vaucheria* depend for their rigidity entirely upon turgor, and very readily collapse after injury.

At low tide on rocky shores one often sees thin crinkled slimy

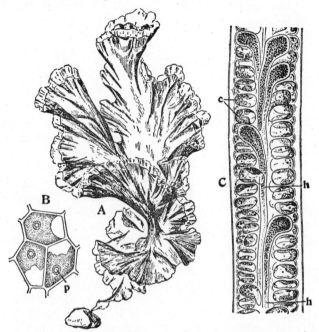

FIG. 185. *Ulva lactuca*. A, Habit. B, A few cells in surface-view. C, Section of thallus. *c*, chloroplast; *h*, attaching rhizoids; *p*, pyrenoid. (B, after Schimper; the rest after Thuret.)

sheets of a vivid green colour which are the Alga *Ulva* (the Sea Lettuce) (Fig. 185, A). The large thallus consists of two super-posed layers of cells of a uniform character throughout (Fig. 185, C) except where they grow out into rhizoids (*h*) which form the attaching base. Very young plants of *Ulva* begin as a simple un-branched filament, whose cells, however, soon undergo division in several directions to produce the flat thallus.

The genera hitherto mentioned (except *Ectocarpus*) belong to the Green Algæ (*Chlorophyceæ*), the majority of which inhabit fresh-water. Most Seaweeds, however, are brown or red owing to the presence of special pigments in the chloroplasts masking the chloro-phyll. The colouring matters are readily extracted with water from dead specimens, which then assume a green colour. Diverse functions have been attributed to these pigments.

Many Brown Seaweeds (*Phæophyceæ*), of which *Ectocarpus* (Fig. 197, B) has already furnished a relatively simple example, are far bulkier than any Algæ yet noticed, and evince marked division of labour. Thus *Laminaria*, which occurs near low-tide level, has a thallus consisting of three distinct regions (Fig. 189 *): viz. a richly branched holdfast, by which the Alga is anchored to rocks, a long cylindrical stalk which may be a yard long and reach an inch in diameter, and an even longer blade. The latter either takes the form of a broad ribbon (*L. saccharina*) or of a deeply divided frond like the palm of a hand (*L. digitata*, Fig. 189 *). Whilst the stalk and attaching organ are perennial, the blade is renewed, usually in the spring of each year, by means of a small-celled meristem situated at the top of the stalk; the new frond therefore appears at the base of the old one, which eventually becomes detached by the action of the waves. The holdfast is composed of numerous cells with thick gelatinous walls, and develops additional branches suggestive of prop-roots in each growing season, whilst simultaneously the stalk slowly increases in thickness.[1] A related form, *Chorda*, has whip-like hollow thalli, up to 8 yards long.

The Seaweed *Macrocystis*, which is a close ally of *Laminaria* and particularly common in the Southern Hemisphere, attains to enormous dimensions and may measure as much as 60 yards from end to end.

The commonest Brown Alga is the Bladder Wrack (*Fucus vesiculosus*, Fig. 187, B), which is found on rocks between tide-levels, so that it is uncovered for several hours at a time (Fig. 186). An entire plant often attains a length of from one and a half to three feet, and exhibits three regions similar to those of *Laminaria*, but the stalk is short and the frond repeatedly forked (Fig. 187). Such forked branching is common among the simpler plants and is termed *dichotomy*; it results from a halving of the apical cell. Each portion of the thallus possesses an obvious midrib (*m.*), which is thicker and more pronounced in the older parts where it gradually passes over into the stalk. The latter is indeed nothing else than the persistent midrib of the first-formed part of the thallus. The holdfast is a sucker-like disc composed of many cells.

In a slit-like pocket at the tip of each branch of the frond is an apical cell, the segments of which divide to form the tissue of the

---

[1] This Alga may occasionally develop on rock-fragments that are too small to anchor the adult, in consequence of which the thalli and attached rocks get carried out to sea. This may sometimes take place on a considerable scale.

FIG. 186. Photograph of *Fucus vesiculosus* on rocks between tide-levels.
[Photo. E. J. S.]

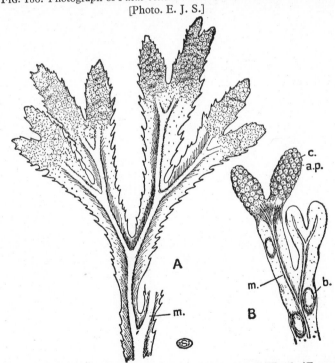

FIG. 187. *Fucus.* A, Part of a thallus of the Serrated Wrack (*F. serratus*). B, Ditto of the Bladder Wrack (*F. vesiculosus*); fertile apices are evident in both. *ap.*, aperture of conceptacle (*c.*); *b.*, air-bladder; *m.*, midrib of thallus.

thallus. The paired air-bladders (Fig. 187, B, *b*.), which appear as occasional large swellings on either side of the midrib, and to which the specific name is due, increase the buoyancy of the plant when submerged and may also, like the air-canals of aquatic Flowering Plants, serve for purposes of respiration.

Scattered irregularly over the whole surface of the frond are slightly protruding dots marking the positions of small spherical cavities (*conceptacles*) in the thallus. These are lined with hairs which mostly project as a minute tuft through the tiny aperture leading to the exterior. Usually some of the branches of the frond have swollen ends (Fig. 187) provided with much more conspicuous (fertile) conceptacles (*c*.) enclosing the sexual organs (cf. p. 310).

The Serrated Wrack (*Fucus serratus*, Fig. 187, A), which is equally common at rather lower levels on rocky shores, has toothed fronds without air-bladders and less swollen fertile tips. Related Seaweeds, which cannot withstand exposure, grow submerged below low-tide level. This is so in *Halidrys*, with almost cylindrical fronds, provided with characteristic pod-like air-bladders.

In a transverse section through a *Fucus*-frond (Fig. 200, B) the surface is occupied by a columnar photosynthetic layer (*a*), followed by a few layers (*cortex*) of larger cells (*s*.) with highly refractive contents, which are presumably stored photosynthetic products. Most of the section (*m*.) consists of cells with very thick mucilaginous walls, so that the protoplasts are widely separated. The cells of this medulla are elongate and connected by occasional anastomoses, but most run longitudinally and appear oval in the section. They probably fulfil both conducting and mechanical functions. The older midribs show a much firmer structure, since the cortical cells are protruded into numerous, rather thick-walled threads (hyphæ), which mainly pursue a longitudinal course through the medullary mucilage within which they are densely crowded; in old thick midribs the cortex also shows secondary meristematic activity.

The fronds of *Halidrys* have a comparable, but much firmer structure (Fig. 189), without the striking production of mucilage seen in *Fucus*. The photosynthetic surface-layer (*a*) is followed by a broad cortex (*c*), surrounding a compact medulla (*m*), composed of elongate cells. The special structure seen in *Fucus*, and others of its allies (e.g. *Pelvetia*) living between tide-levels, is probably related to the need to conserve moisture during the diurnal exposure to desiccation.

The outermost cell-layer in these Seaweeds shows frequent tangential divisions, though these are much more marked in *Halidrys*

(Fig. 189, *a*). This leads to progressive formation of new cortical layers, while the innermost cortical elements are transformed into medullary cells, so that the same cells may successively perform different functions. Although the tissue-differentiation is broadly comparable to that found in other groups, the mode of increase in thickness is peculiar to these Seaweeds.

A cross-section of the stalk or frond of *Laminaria* shows an analogous structure, rendered more complex by abundant production of hyphæ. Many of the elongate elements of cortex and

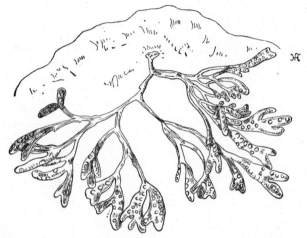

FIG. 188. Plant of *Pelvetia canaliculata*, about natural size, showing the basal attaching disc and the prominent fertile conceptacles.

medulla here show sieve-like areas on the septa, which are specially prominent in *Macrocystis* where they are strikingly like sieve-plates and even show callose-deposits.

Clothing the rocks, which for the greater part of the season are only reached by spray, one finds the Seaweed *Pelvetia*, which, though closely allied to *Fucus*, is much smaller, and in which the swollen fertile ends are a particularly conspicuous feature (Fig. 188). The structure of the thallus shows no important differences, but the branches of the frond are much narrower and channelled on their upper surface, features which aid in the retention of moisture; moreover, the thallus is thus mainly illuminated by oblique light, so that the heating effect of the sun, and therefore transpiration, is presumably diminished during the hot hours of the day. The principal differences exhibited by *Pelvetia* can therefore be related to the special conditions of its habitat (cf. p. 556).

On rocky shores the Brown Algæ *Pelvetia*, *Fucus*, and *Laminaria*

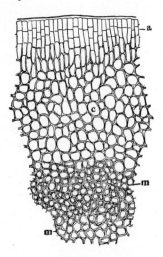

FIG. 189. Part of transverse section of young frond of *Halidrys*. *a*, meristematic surface layer; *c*, cortex; *m*, medulla.

often form three zones at successively lower levels, occurring in the order named. Certain of these Seaweeds continue to live unattached, as, for example, some species of *Sargassum*, huge stretches of which characterise the Sargasso Sea in the Mid-Atlantic. Dwarfed forms of *Fucus* and *Pelvetia* are abundant in the vegetation of certain salt-marshes where they live with the base of the thallus embedded in the soil.

Most of the Red Algæ (*Rhodophyceæ*) are smaller plants often favouring weakly illuminated habitats, so that they either grow at considerable depths below low-tide level or in shady rock-pools. In many the thallus is a branched thread (e.g. *Polysiphonia, Ceramium,* Fig. 190, C), whilst in others it is flattened (*Chondrus,* Fig. 190, A). In the former

the larger branches usually consist of several rows of cells, whilst in the latter a number of distinct tissue-regions can often be distinguished. A red alga, often abundant in rock-pools, is *Corallina* (Fig. 190, B), whose branched thallus is composed of numerous segments loosely jointed to one another, and densely encrusted with carbonate, of lime, giving it a pinkish-white colour. Similar *calcareous Algæ*, often of larger dimensions, are common in tropical seas, where they frequently play an important part in the production of coral-reefs, and comparable forms are known in the past to have contributed largely to the formation of certain limestone rocks. Most Red Algæ

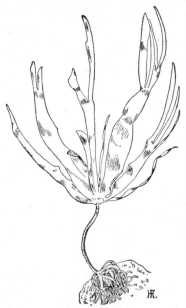

FIG. 189 *. Young plant of *Laminaria digitata*, about one-fifth natural size.

exhibit apical growth and, in many of them, the protoplasts of adjacent cells are linked by broad protoplasmic connections, which traverse the often thick mucilaginous walls.

There is still another large group of Algæ (*Cyanophyceæ*) named after the prevailing blue-green colour. These, though relatively rare in the sea, are common in fresh-water, and often particularly characteristic of damp terrestrial habitats, such as rocks exposed to a constant trickle. Their great adaptability to varied conditions is also shown by their playing the leading rôle alike in the vegetation of hot springs and in the frigid lakes of the

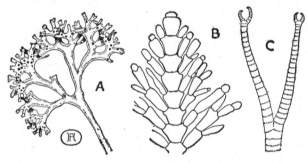

FIG. 190. Rhodophyceæ.   A, *Chondrus crispus*, with tetraspores.   B, *Corallina*.
C, *Ceramium*.   (B and C enlarged.)

Antarctic continent. The Blue-green Algæ are either colonial (*Glœocapsa*, Fig. 191, B), or filamentous (*Oscillatoria; Lyngbya*, Fig. 191, G; *Nostoc*, Fig. 191, C, D). The colourless central region of each cell lacks a true nucleus, although nucleo-proteins are present, and the pigments are diffused through the peripheral cytoplasm. The cells or filaments are often contained in large numbers in mucilaginous envelopes (e.g. *Glœocapsa*, *Nostoc*), to which and to the absence of vacuoles may be probably attributed the capacity of many species to survive considerable periods of drought.

Common members of the group are: *Glœocapsa* forming extensive gelatinous coverings on damp substrata (Fig. 191, B); *Oscillatoria* and *Lyngbya*, whose undifferentiated and unbranched filaments of discoid cells (Fig. 191, G) occur as sheets or bundles in fresh-water pools, on moist stonework, etc.; *Tolypothrix*, a branched filamentous form, usually aquatic (Fig. 191, E); and *Nostoc*, some species of which are terrestrial. The species of *Nostoc* have the form of variously shaped gelatinous clumps (Fig. 191, C) in which are embedded numerous tortuous chains (D) of rounded cells, interrupted here and there by slightly larger colourless ones (*heterocysts*, seen also in *Tolypothrix*, Fig. 191, E, *h.*) of uncertain

function.   The Cyanophyceæ often play a very important part in
nature as the first plants to colonise bare ground.

In every habitat where other Algæ occur there can usually

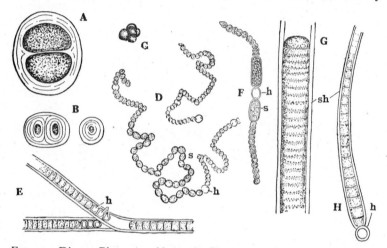

Fig. 191. Diverse Blue-green Algæ. A, *Chroococcus.* B, *Glœocapsa.* C, D,
Nostoc; C, colony shown natural size; D, parts of two threads. E, *Tolypothrix.*
F, *Anabæna* (with spore, *s*). G, *Lyngbya.* H, *Rivularia.* *h.,* heterocysts;
sh., sheath.

be found unicellular forms known as *Diatoms* (Fig. 192) which
possess quite special characteristics of their own.   The individuals
are either unattached, and then often endowed with a power of
fairly rapid movement, or else fixed to the surface of larger Algæ
and other aquatics.   The Diatoms are brown or greenish in colour.
Each plant is provided with a cell-wall richly impregnated with
silica, and usually bearing a symmetrical and often highly elaborate
pattern of sculptured markings (Fig. 192).   With the death of the
organisms the practically unaltered siliceous shells sink, so that,
where Diatoms are plentiful, deposits of almost pure silica slowly
accumulate at the bottom of the water.   Instances are afforded by
the extensive beds of "diatomaceous earth" found at Dolgelly in
Wales, at Bilin in Bohemia, and elsewhere, some being of marine,
others of fresh-water origin.   Such deposits are utilised commercially in the preparation of dentifrices, as insulating material, and,
owing to the very small size of the individual particles, for filtration.
Marine plankton at times consists almost entirely of Diatoms, and
is an important source of food for fishes.

Although several groups of Algæ are designated according to
the prevailing colour of their plastids, they are characterised by

many more important features, and especially by the nature of their reproductive processes (see next chapter). The *chloroplasts*, in general, assume the most complex forms among the Green Algæ, where there is often but a single one in each cell, a condition already noticed in *Chlamydomonas* and its allies (cf. p. 272). Moreover, the chloroplasts of the Green Algæ commonly possess one or more pyrenoids and, during active photosynthesis, starch is formed as a reserve-product, first around the pyrenoids, and then in the general substance of the plastid. Whilst most of the colonial (e.g. *Scenedesmus*) and less differentiated filamentous forms (e.g. *Ulothrix*) have a relatively simple undivided chloroplast, greater complexity is met with in many of the more highly organised Green Algæ.

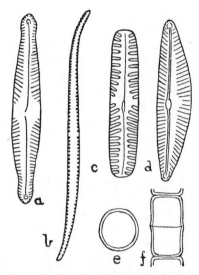

The band-shaped chloroplast of *Ulothrix* has the form of a complete or incomplete cylinder (Fig. 194, A, B), occupying the lining layer of cytoplasm within the thin cell-wall; it contains one or more pyrenoids. In *Cladophora* and *Œdogonium*, on the other hand, the cylindrical chloroplast is a perforated network with numerous scattered pyrenoids.

FIG. 192. Various Diatoms (only the siliceous walls are shown). *a* and *c*, *Navicula; b, Nitzschia; d, Cymbella; e*, end-view, and *f*, side-view of cells of the colonial *Melosira*.

In *Œdogonium* (Fig. 195, A) the meshes are elongated and more or less parallel to one another, whilst in *Cladophora* (Fig. 183, F) the network is irregular and ill-defined. Other peculiarities of the cell-structure of *Cladophora* are the numerous small nuclei (Fig. 183, F, *n*), that are recognisable after careful staining, on the inner side of the chloroplast, and the thick stratified wall to which this Alga owes its coarse texture; the former feature is in marked contrast to the single nucleus found in the cells of *Ulothrix* and especially obvious in *Œdogonium* (Fig. 195, A, *n*).

The non-septate threads of *Vaucheria* possess numerous discoid chloroplasts which are lodged in the lining layer of cytoplasm and lack pyrenoids (Fig. 196, D, *c*); this Alga also contrasts with other Chlorophyceæ in producing no starch, the excess food being stored as oil.

The most elaborate types of chloroplasts are found in *Spirogyra* and its allies, which belong to a group of the Green Algæ known as the *Conjugales*, practically confined to fresh-water. Some of these are filamentous like *Spirogyra* (Fig. 27), whose spiral chloroplasts,

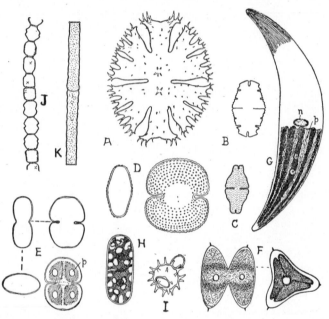

FIG. 193. Diverse Desmids. A, *Micrasterias*. B and C, *Euastrum*. D and E, *Cosmarium* (in E the top left-hand figure shows the cell in side-view; the lower left-hand figure the cell in end-view). F, *Staurastrum* (the right-hand figure shows the end-view) (after Ostenfeld). G, *Closterium*. H, *Cylindrocystis*. I, zygospore of *Cosmarium meneghinii* (after West). J, *Desmidium* (filamentous). K, *Pleurotænium*. The cell-contents are shown only in E–H. *n*, nucleus; *p*, pyrenoids.

one or more to each cell, have already been described (p. 42), and *Zygnema* (Fig. 201, F), where the cells contain two star-shaped chloroplasts with a conspicuous pyrenoid (*p*.) at the centre of each. A large number of the Conjugales are, however, unicellular forms, named *Desmids* (Fig. 193), which resemble *Spirogyra* and *Zygnema* in their methods of reproduction, but often have even more elaborate chloroplasts.

The Desmid-cell usually exhibits two symmetrical halves, each containing one or two chloroplasts, and not uncommonly separated by a median constriction, where the single nucleus is situated (e.g.

Cosmarium, Fig. 193, D, E). The wall is often richly sculptured or provided with spinous outgrowths (Fig. 193, A, D). In *Closterium* (Fig. 193, G), species of which are very frequent, each half of the, usually semilunar, cell is occupied by a chloroplast consisting of a central rod which contains a row of pyrenoids (*p.*) and bears a number of radiating longitudinal plates; the latter appear as dark green streaks when the cell is viewed from the surface. The small vacuoles, commonly seen at either end of the cell, enclose minute crystals of gypsum exhibiting Brownian movement and are peculiar to this genus. Similar elaborate chloroplasts occur in *Cosmarium* (Fig. 193, E) and *Micrasterias* (A). The pigments in Brown and Red Algæ are usually lodged in discoid plastids.

The extreme variety of the chloroplasts amongst the Algæ is in striking contrast with their comparative uniformity amongst Flowering Plants. It may be remarked, however, that the chloroplast of the simple Alga is as much the photosynthetic organ as is the leaf in the higher plant, where, too, a great diversity of shape in an apparently uniform habitat is found.

The Algæ afford an excellent illustration of the fact that *division of labour* is associated with increased complexity of structure. In many filamentous Green Algæ all the cells, except that serving for attachment, may be alike in form and play an equal part in growth and division (e.g. *Ulothrix, Spirogyra*). At the other extreme the large Brown Algæ not only exhibit a relegation of attachment, growth, and reproduction to definite parts of the thallus, but the units of which the latter is built up also show a certain specialisation into conducting, photosynthetic and meristematic elements.

It is probable that the complex type of cell arose from a much simpler one, and that similarly the multicellular organism had its origin in the unicellular, as is usually the case in the course of the individual development. High efficiency for particular conditions of life demand complexity of structure which, however, like all specialisation tends to diminish the adaptability of the organism and to reduce its capacity to meet changed conditions. It is in harmony with this that only a small part (viz. the relatively unspecialised reproductive cells) of highly specialised organisms persists from one generation to the next, whereas in a simple organism the whole may survive in the bodies of its offspring. Herein the more highly differentiated forms exhibit a provision whereby the next generation is temporarily relieved of the trammels of the specialisation of its parents, and thus probably becomes better fitted to meet the extremely varied conditions to which the different individuals are subjected during their development.

Many Algæ are to be found in quantity only at certain seasons of the year.   The freshwater flora usually shows a marked *periodicity*, the successive phases varying both in the nature and abundance of the species present.   It is most luxurious in spring and early summer (cf. p. 282).   Similarly, in our latitudes, the Seaweed flora generally shows the greatest diversity and largest number of individuals at these same periods, while many species (*e.g.* of Red Seaweeds) will be sought in vain in other seasons.   This periodicity is conditioned by a multiplicity of factors, among which temperature, illumination and supply of mineral nutriment are most important. The amounts of mineral salts (nitrates, phosphates, etc.) diminish rapidly during the vernal outburst, and subsequent depletion of one or other arrests further growth and may even cause disappearance of certain species.   Decay of the previous season's vegetation during autumn and winter, as well as adventitious supplies from drainage, gradually replenish the stock of nutriment which is thus available to be exploited by the new growth developing as light and temperature increase in spring.   Many of the larger Brown Seaweeds, however, persist for several seasons and are found in quantity all the year round, and this is true also of some of the freshwater *Cladophoras*.

Extensive algal growth may be harmful.   Algæ in reservoirs may lend a disagreeable odour or taste to the water and cause blockages of the filters, necessitating frequent cleansing.   Similarly, Seaweeds settling on ocean-going vessels may cause appreciable reduction of speed and require frequent cleaning of the hulls. Since salts of copper and certain other heavy metals are extremely poisonous, algal growth can often be retarded by adding suitable amounts to the water or by incorporating them in anti-fouling paints.

Algæ are, however, also important as a source of food and vitamins (cf. p. 282) for aquatic animals (including fish) who find shelter and suitable breeding grounds amid the often dense growths. Their nutritive value for man is small, although *Laminaria* and its allies have sometimes furnished food for maritime peoples, especially in the Far East, and Carrageen (Fig. 190, A) is a valuable invalid diet. The large iodine-content of Seaweed-ash is no longer commercially exploited, but the use of *Fucus* as fodder and manure in coastal districts is beneficial because of the high potassium-content.   The large Phaeophyceæ are, however, chiefly important commercially because of the extraction from them of alginic acid, used in the manufacture of cosmetics, textiles, adhesives, etc.   The valuable culture-medium agar-agar, obtained from mucilages of Rhodophyceæ and formerly almost entirely imported from Japan, is now prepared from various Red Algæ, in Britain from *Chondrus crispus* (Fig. 190, A) and the related *Gigartina*.

CHAPTER XXVII

REPRODUCTION OF THE ALGÆ

JUST as the vegetative structure of the Algæ shows progressive stages in complexity, so also do the processes of reproduction, although specialisation in the one respect does not always go hand in hand with specialisation in the other. Thus *Cladophora*, with its markedly differentiated vegetative system, shows simple reproductive processes, similar to those of *Ulothrix*.

At times of active growth *Ulothrix* reproduces vegetatively by the mere breaking or *fragmentation* of its filaments into short lengths which develop into new threads. Not infrequently, however, a more specialised mode of multiplication obtains, which is spoken of as *asexual reproduction* owing to its general resemblance to the sexual method except for the absence of fusion. Both the sexual and asexual reproductive cells are motile, although the ordinary *Ulothrix*-filament is without any power of movement.

Asexual reproduction may take place in some or all of the cells of a filament. At its commencement, the protoplasts round off slightly and thereupon usually divide, along successive planes at right angles to one another, into 2, 4, or even 8 separate parts, the number depending upon the size of the cell (Fig. 194, C). The products of division (*sp*), each of which has a chloroplast and pyrenoid of its own, are liberated through a small round hole formed in the side-wall, but remain enveloped for a few seconds in a thin bladder of mucilage (Fig. 194, C). Meanwhile each portion has developed four flagella, two contractile vacuoles, and an eye-spot, so that in all essential respects it resembles a naked *Carteria*.

The oval motile elements thus formed are the asexual reproductive cells or *zoospores* (Fig. 194, D), which can swim after the manner of a *Chlamydomonas* for several hours, and thus travel some distance away from the parent filament. During most of this time they seek out well-lighted regions of the water, but ultimately they tend to move towards darker spots, where they usually come to rest on the surface of stones. The zoospore flattens out against the substratum and the flagella are withdrawn (Fig. 194, E, F); a cell-

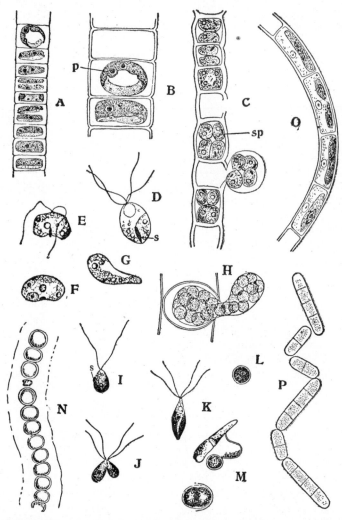

Fig. 194. A–N, Structure and reproduction of *Ulothrix*. A, B, Parts of
threads to show structure of chloroplast, etc. C, Thread showing stages in
the development of zoospores (*sp*). D, Zoospore. E, The same coming to
rest. F, G, Stages in its germination. H, Liberation of gametes. I, Gamete.
J, Fusion of gametes. K, The resulting zygote. L, Zygospore. M, Two
germination stages. N, Formation of resting spores. O, P, *Hormidium*.
O, Vegetative thread. P. Fragmentation. *p*, pyrenoid; *s*, eye-spot. (A, B, N,
after Fritsch; D–G, after Gross; H, after West; the rest after Klebs.)

wall is secreted (Fig. 194 F) and then, by gradual elongation and division, there is produced a new filament (Fig. 194, G), which soon breaks away from its attachment and becomes free-floating. Such asexual reproduction is obviously very prolific.

The *gametes* are formed and liberated in exactly the same way as the zoospores, except that 16 or even 32 may be formed in a cell (Fig. 194, H). The isogamous sexual cells (I), which differ from the zoospores only in their small size and in having but two flagella, behave just as in *Chlamydomonas*, those from different filaments fusing together in pairs (J) to form a quadriflagellate zygote (K) which, soon after, comes to rest and secretes a thick wall (L.) The resulting zygospore remains in a dormant condition during the hot season, and may be dispersed in the same way as in *Chlamydomonas* (cf. p. 276). On germination, the contents divide usually into four parts, each of which gives rise to a new thread (Fig. 194, M). During the greater part of its life-history *Ulothrix* is thus sedentary, but motility is associated with reproduction. A form is then assumed resembling that of the unicellular organisms which are motile throughout their existence.

At certain times the cells of the ordinary *Ulothrix*-threads, after thickening their walls and becoming laden with food-reserves, often fall apart and form as many separate resting spores (Fig. 194, N).

The reproductive cells of *Cladophora* are essentially similar to those of *Ulothrix*, but in several species the zoospores and gametes are produced in distinct plants and both are, moreover, formed in large numbers (Fig. 183, C); the cells developing them are usually restricted to the finer branches. During periods that are unfavourable to vegetative growth (*e.g.* the cold months of the winter), many of the finer branches are shed and the remaining cells become laden with food-reserves and develop thicker walls.

Most multicellular Algæ resemble *Ulothrix* and *Cladophora* in the restriction of motility to the reproductive phase, which, however, exhibits a varying degree of specialisation. Vegetative propagation by *fragmentation* (*i.e.* cell-separation without preparatory division) is common, as in *Spirogyra*. In *Hormidium*, an alga common on damp soil, this is the customary method of propagation during a great part of the year (Fig. 194, P). The thick-walled threads of *Cladophora* just mentioned often fragment in a similar manner, before renewed growth takes place. Formation of new individuals by cell-division is the commonest form of reproduction in Desmids and Diatoms, whilst the filamentous members of the Blue-green Algæ propagate abundantly by mere fragmentation. In such massive forms as *Fucus*, the same end is attained by the detachment of small adventitious branches of the thallus, which are often formed

20

in bunches from the midrib and stalk, and are especially characteristic of the unattached species of this genus which occur on salt-
marshes (p. 292).

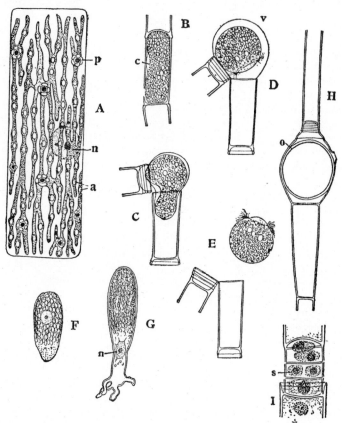

FIG. 195. *Œdogonium.* A, Single cell, highly magnified (after Schmitz),
showing the net-like chloroplast with starch-grains (*a*), pyrenoids (*p*), and
the single nucleus (*n*). B–G, *Œdogonium concatenatum* (after Hirn). B–D,
Stages in formation of zoospores. E, Liberation of ditto. F and G, Germination of zoospores (in G the characteristic attaching cell is seen). H, *O. lautum-
niarium* (after West), showing an oogonium (*o*), with caps. I, *O. Boscii* (after
Hirn), antheridia, with young spermatozoids. *c*, front end of future zoospore;
n, nucleus; *s*, spermatozoid; *v*, vesicle.

Many Green Algæ reproduce asexually by means of *zoospores*,
but these often possess a more elaborate structure than those
of *Ulothrix*. For example, in *Œdogonium*, where they are produced singly from the ordinary cells, they are much larger and
bear a ring of flagella a little way behind the colourless front end

(Fig. 195, E). If filaments of this Alga are grown in water indoors, zoospores are usually formed within a few hours, and their development and liberation can be observed more readily than in other fresh-water Algæ.

The protoplast contracts slightly away from the wall, and a colourless area, marking the future front end of the zoospore, arises on one side (Fig. 195, B); the nucleus moves towards this side of the cell (cf. p. 40). Around the edge of the colourless area the numerous short flagella sprout out, appearing as fine lines. Thereupon the wall breaks across, near one end of the cell, and the shorter piece hinges back to form an aperture through which the contents slowly glide (C). When liberated the almost spherical zoospore is surrounded by a thin bladder of extruded mucilage (D), but it almost immediately commences to move away (E) with the help of its flagella. Sooner or later the zoospore becomes

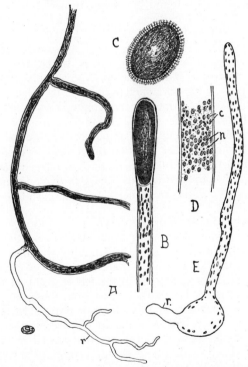

FIG. 196. *Vaucheria.* A, Portion of a plant showing the branched non-septate thallus and the colourless rhizoid-like attaching organ (*r.*). B, Zoosporangium. C, Zoospore. D, Small part of thallus, showing the numerous chloroplasts (*c*), and nuclei (*n*). E, Germinated zoospore. (C after Oltmanns; rest original.)

attached to some submerged object by its colourless front end
(Fig. 195, F), and the flagella are withdrawn; then a cell-wall is
secreted and division takes place to form a new filament, whilst the
end in contact with the substratum grows out into the branched
holdfast (Fig. 195, G).

In *Vaucheria*, zoospore-production involves swelling of the tips
of the branches, which become cut off by a wall to form a *zoosporangium* (Fig. 196, B). Within this the contents round off and
the numerous nuclei take up a peripheral position. A pair of
flagella arise opposite each nucleus, and the large multi-flagellate
oval zoospore (Fig. 196, C) escapes into the water by the breaking
down of the tip of the thread. After a short period of movement
a thin wall is formed and the two ends lengthen into tubes, of
which one frequently penetrates the soil or mud and becomes a
colourless attaching organ (Fig. 196, E, *r.*).

Zoospores are also found in various Brown Algæ, *e.g.* in *Ectocarpus*, *Chorda*, and *Laminaria*. In the first-named they develop
in sporangia of two kinds, each borne laterally on a branch of
the filament (Fig. 197, B). The one kind (unilocular, Fig. 197,
B and H, *u*) produces several zoospores which are liberated by
rupture of the apex. The other kind (plurilocular, Fig. 197, B,
C, *p*) are divided by horizontal and vertical walls, each of the
numerous small compartments producing one zoospore. In *Laminaria* and *Chorda* dense patches of unilocular sporangia, interspersed with protective unicellular outgrowths (paraphyses) (Fig.
198, A, B) occur as darker areas on the fronds. The pear-shaped
zoospores (Fig. 197, D; Fig. 198, C) have two flagella, one directed
forwards and the other backwards during movement, and these are
attached to one side adjacent to the chloroplast (*c*) and the prominent
eye-spot (*s*).

The production of zoospores serves as a rapid means of multiplication and dispersal at times when vegetative activity is at its
height, but this method lacks the stimulus which sexual fusion
appears to provide. There are quite a number of Algæ in which
a *sexual process* is unknown, as in the whole group of the Cyanophyceæ and in many Desmids. Apart from these, however, most
Algæ reproduce sexually at some time or other. In many fresh-
water Algæ sexual fusion results, as in *Ulothrix*, in the production
of resistant spores and, in contrast to the asexual method, is frequently associated with the onset of conditions adverse to the
plant's growth.

The fusing gametes are outwardly alike in *Ulothrix* and *Cladophora*, as well as in many species of *Chlamydomanas*, but not in
C. braunii. The dissimilarity in size and behaviour of the sexual

cells seen in this species (cf. p. 275) is paralleled, or even more emphasised, in the higher Algæ.   A relatively simple instance is afforded by *Ectocarpus*, where the gametes are produced in elongate

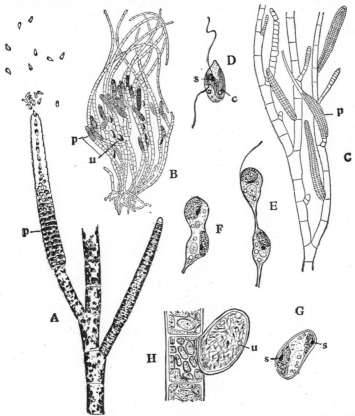

FIG. 197. Structure and reproduction of *Ectocarpus*. A, Small part of a thread showing a gametangium (*p*) liberating gametes. B, Diploid plant showing creeping and erect threads, the latter bearing unilocular (*u*) and plurilocular (*p*) sporangia. C, Branched haploid filament with several gametangia (*p*). D, Zoospore: *c*, chloroplast; *s*, eye-spot. E, F, Stages in fusion of gametes. G, Zygote, with two chloroplasts and two eye-spots (*s*). H, Small part of thread with a unilocular sporangium (*u*). (A, after Thuret; B, after Setchell and Gardner; C, after Migula; D and H, after Reinke; E–G, after Berthold.)

gametangia (Fig. 197, A, C), similar in position and form to the plurilocular sporangia above described and only to be distinguished by the behaviour of the contents.   Each compartment forms a single gamete (Fig. 197, A).   These sexual cells are smaller, but otherwise resemble the zoospores.   Despite their structural uniformity, some gametes are relatively sluggish, and, after a brief period of movement, become attached to any suitable substratum by a disc-like expansion at the end of their forward flagellum, whilst others move actively and for a much longer time. The latter ultimately collect in groups around the others and, sooner

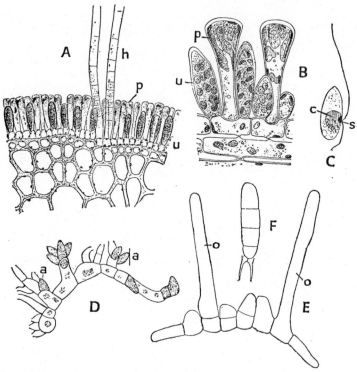

FIG. 198. Reproduction of Laminariaceæ. A, Section of series of unilocular sporangia of *Chorda*, and B, small part enlarged (both after Reinke). C, Zoospore (after Sauvageau). D, Male, and E, female gametophytes (after Printz and Sauvageau). F, Germling from fertilised ovum. *a*, antheridia; *c*, chloroplast; *h*, hair; *o*, oogonium; *p*, paraphyses; *s*, eye-spot; *u*, unilocular sporangia.

or later, an active gamete fuses with a resting one (Fig. 197, E and F). There is thus a marked difference in behaviour between the two fusing cells, but the differentiation into active males and passive females is here purely physiological.

The distinction between the two sexes is much more marked in genera like *Œdogonium*, *Vaucheria*, and *Fucus*, where one sexual cell (the female or *egg*) is large, motionless, and provided with plentiful food-material, whilst the other (the male or *spermatozoid*) is small, actively motile, and possessed of very scanty cytoplasm. The two kinds of gametes are usually formed in special sexual organs differentiated from ordinary vegetative cells; that producing the egg (*ovum*) is termed the *oogonium*, whilst that forming the spermatozoids is known as the *antheridium*.

In *Œdogonium* the oogonia are spherical or oval cells which develop from cap-cells (p. 284) and occur either singly or in short chains (Fig. 195, H, *o*). At one point the wall of the oogonium develops a small papilla by the breaking down of whose tip an aperture for the entry of the male cells is created (Fig. 199, C); in some species of *Œdogonium*, however, opening is effected by a complete transverse split in the wall. The single egg, formed by the contracted protoplast of the *oogonium*, develops a small colourless area, adjacent to the aperture, known as the *receptive spot* (Fig. 199, C, *r*), and at this point a quantity of mucilage is extruded shortly before fertilisation.

The antheridia are small and tabular, being formed by repeated transverse division of cells of the filament (Fig. 195, I). Each antheridium produces two spermatozoids (*s*) which are diminutive, yellowish-green replicas of the zoospores, liberated in the same manner.

Spermatozoids are attracted to the oogonia, probably by some chemical substance[1] in the extruded mucilage, and, passing through the aperture, penetrate into the egg, the cytoplasm and nucleus of the one thereupon fusing with those of the other. Neither sexual cell can develop independently.

It is customary to speak of such sexual union as *fertilisation*. The effects of the fusion are probably always essential to further development, and the stimulus provided is doubtless both chemical and physical in character. This view is supported by the fact that eggs of Sea-urchins have been induced to develop into embryos by mere immersion in suitable solutions, whilst those of the Frog have been caused to undergo the first stages of development by mere pricking. Moreover, in plants, fertilisation sometimes stimulates other cells near the egg to develop into embryos (cf. p. 473).

The fertilised eggs, or *oospores*, of *Œdogonium* develop thick protective walls and fatty pigmented contents and, as the filaments containing them die away, sink to the bottom of the water. Here they pass through a prolonged resting period, and, should the pond dry up, may be dispersed by the wind. In germination they

---

[1] The influence exerted by chemical substances on the direction of movement of motile elements is spoken of as *chemotaxis*, and the positive chemotaxis evident in sexual union is only one of many examples of such chemical stimulation (cf. p. 318).

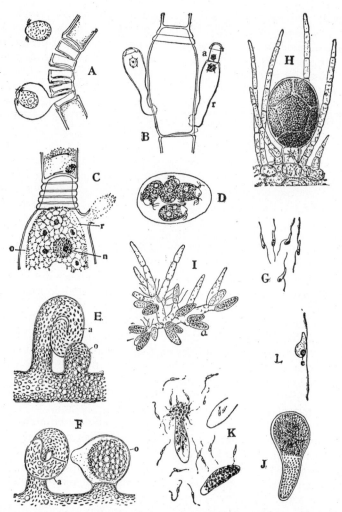

Fig. 199. Oogamous sexual reproduction among the Algæ. A–D, *Œdo-gonium*. A, Part of thread of *O. braunii*, showing liberation of special zoospores that form the dwarf-males. B, Oogonium of *O. concatenatum*, with two dwarf-males. C, Apical part of oogonium of *O. boscii* showing the receptive spot (*r*). D, Germinating zygote showing the four zoospores. E–G, *Vaucheria sessilis*. E, Young oogonium (*o*) and antheridium (*a*). F, The same almost mature. G, Spermatozoids. H–L, *Fucus*. H, Oogonium, with surrounding hairs. I, Branched hair bearing numerous antheridia (*a*). J, Young plant. K, Liberation of spermatozoids. L, Spermatozoid. *a*, antheridium; *n*, nucleus; *r* (in B), rhizoid of dwarf-male. (A, B, after Hirn; C, after Klebahn; D, after Juranyi; E, F, after Oltmanns; G, after Woronin; H–K, after Thuret; L, after Guignard.)

usually give rise to three or four zoospores (Fig. 199, D), which are set free by the bursting of the thick membrane.

The sexual organs are arranged in various ways in the different species of *Œdogonium*, male and female sometimes occurring in the same filament (monœcious forms), sometimes in different filaments (diœcious forms); in the latter the male plants often consist of only a few cells (*dwarf males*, Fig. 199, B), and arise from special smaller zoospores (Fig. 199, A) which become attached to the female plant, on or near an oogonium.

It will be evident that *Œdogonium* exhibits considerable specialisation in its methods of multiplication, and not the least conspicuous feature is the division of labour manifest in the *oogamous sexual reproduction*. Owing to its stationary character, the egg can possess the greater bulk which a more adequate provision of food-material for the benefit of the next generation necessarily entails (cf. p. 306). Since the spermatozoids contribute nothing to this food-supply, they can be correspondingly smaller, and therefore, without additional strain on the organism, produced in larger numbers, whereby the chance of fertilisation occurring is greatly increased. The probability of fusion between the two gametes is, moreover, doubled by one of them remaining stationary. The greater certainty of sexual union admits of a corresponding decrease in the production of eggs, which will afford as many off-spring as would a larger number of motile female gametes. These remarks apply with equal force to all plants in which oogamy occurs.

The oogonia and antheridia of *Vaucheria* are produced near one another as outgrowths (Fig. 199, E) of the main filament or of short lateral branches, from which in either case they become cut off by a septum (Fig. 199, F). Their relative positions are very diverse, but the adjacent sexual organs usually mature almost simultaneously, so that self-fertilisation is probably the rule. The more or less oval oogonium (*o*) develops a protrusion on one side, whose tip becomes mucilaginous, and breaks down to form the aperture through which the male cell enters. The mature egg possesses a pronounced receptive spot and contains only a single large nucleus.

The antheridium is a coiled tube (Fig. 199, F, *a*) and gives rise to numerous minute pear-shaped spermatozoids with two laterally attached flagella (Fig. 199, G); they are liberated by breaking open of the tip of the antheridium. The attraction of the spermatozoid towards the egg is probably again connected with the extrusion of mucilaginous matter by the latter. After fusion, the oospore becomes enveloped by a thick wall and accumulates large stores of oil; it then enters on the usual resting period, which is ultimately terminated by the direct development of a new plant.

Apart from vegetative propagation which is unusual, *Fucus* exhibits only sexual reproduction, the antheridia and oogonia being developed in the large *fertile conceptacles* occupying the swollen tips of the thallus (Fig. 187). In some species (e.g. *F. spiralis*) the two kinds of sexual organs occur in the same conceptacle, but in *F. vesiculosus* and *F. serratus* there are distinct male and female plants. The globular cavities of the conceptacles (Fig. 200, A) are separated from the interior of the thallus by a wall (*w*) composed

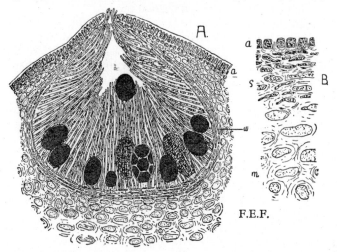

FIG. 200. The Bladder Wrack (*Fucus vesiculosus*). A, Vertical section through a fertile conceptacle, containing oogonia in different stages of development. B, Small part of a transverse section through the thallus, more highly magnified. *a.*, photosynthetic layer; *m.*, medulla; *s.*, storage cells; *w.*, wall of conceptacle.

of several layers of flattened cells, from whose inner surface arise numerous multicellular hairs bending towards, and some often protruding from, the small aperture; in the fertile conceptacles the sexual organs are interspersed among various hairs (Fig. 200, A).

The oval oogonia possess a thick transparent several-layered membrane, and are seated on a unicellular stalk which arises directly from the wall of the conceptacle (Fig. 199, H; 200, A). At maturity the contents are divided into eight uninucleate eggs, containing abundant chloroplasts and separated by delicate walls. The antheridia are oval cells, which likewise possess relatively thick walls and occupy the ends of most of the short lower segments of richly branched hairs (Fig. 199, I).[1] In each are formed

---

[1] These antheridial hairs are best examined by teasing out the contents of a male conceptacle in a drop of water.

numerous minute biflagellate spermatozoids (Fig. 199, L), containing a well-marked nucleus, but only traces of a chloroplast. The mature antheridia have a yellowish colour, which they impart to the entire conceptacle, and by this means, in the diœcious species, the male plants can be distinguished.

When the sexual cells are ripe, the outermost layer of the antheridium or oogonium breaks open and sets free the contents enclosed in the inner layers. The extrusion of the sexual packets from the opening takes place commonly at fortnightly intervals and is probably largely due to expansion of mucilage secreted by the hairs, and turgor-changes in the conceptacle wall. The packets are exposed at low water and, when the sea returns, it dissolves the membranes still enveloping the sexual cells (Fig. 199, K), and the ova, which have now assumed a spherical form, become fertilised by the actively moving spermatozoids. The oospore secretes a thin membrane and immediately, without a resting period, develops into a new *Fucus*-thallus. The young plant is at first spherical, but at an early stage produces the basal holdfast (Fig. 199, J) and acquires a strap-shaped form, and this is soon followed by branching.

In *Pelvetia*, where both sexual organs occur in the same conceptacle, the oogonium has an exceptionally thick wall and produces only two eggs. These remain after liberation enclosed in their thick envelopes, within which fertilisation and early development take place.

Fucus and *Pelvetia* differ from other oogamous Algæ in having oogonia with several eggs which are fertilised outside the plant. In relation to the former feature it should be noted that *Pelvetia* has only two eggs and *Halidrys* even only one, though the nucleus of the oogonium always divides into eight parts, six or seven of the nuclei subsequently aborting. Fertilisation takes place outside the plant in all Phæophyceæ, where, as in all Seaweeds, the zygote never becomes a thick-walled spore.

The Conjugales (cf. p. 296) owe their name to a very special type of sexual reproduction (*conjugation*), in which neither gamete is free-swimming. In the filamentous forms, such as *Spirogyra* and *Zygnema*, two threads come in contact with one another, and their opposing cells develop finger-like protrusions, which, as they lengthen, push the threads apart (Fig. 201, B); after this the separating wall breaks down, so that an open tube (the conjugation canal, Fig. 201, *c.c.*) is established. In *Spirogyra* and many species of *Zygnema* the development of processes always commences a little sooner on the one filament than on the other, and a similar difference is observed with respect to the contraction of the protoplasts which now ensues. The cells of the filament that first put out processes act as males, since their contents commence to glide over, through the conjugation canals, into the opposite cells (Fig. 201, B, *b*), with whose passive (female) protoplasts they fuse.

In some species of *Zygnema* (e.g. *Z. pectinatum*), however, the events leading up to conjugation take place simultaneously in the two filaments, and the fusing protoplasts contract to the middle of the conjugation canal; in such forms there is no outward

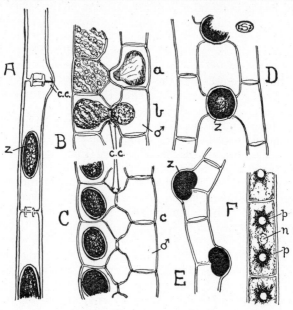

FIG. 201. Sexual reproduction in various Conjugales. A, *Spirogyra weberi*, showing lateral conjugation (after Petit). B and C, *Spirogyra bellis*. B, Successive stages (*a* and *b*) in conjugation; C, completed conjugation. D, Ladder-like, and E, lateral conjugation in *Zygnema pectinatum*. F, Small part of filament of same. *c.c.*, conjugation canal; *n*, nucleus; *p*, pyrenoid; *z*, zygospore; ♂ = male cells

differentiation of sex, the gametes being isogamous as in *Ulothrix* (Fig. 201, D).   But even in *Spirogyra* the gametes are essentially distinguished only by their behaviour.

In some species, both of *Spirogyra* and *Zygnema*, sexual union may take place between adjacent cells of the same filament (Fig. 201, A and E), the conjugation canals (*c.c.*) forming loop-like connections between their contiguous ends.   Here the threads must be regarded as including cells of both sexes, the zygospores as before being formed either in the conjugation canal or in one of the two cells.   The fact that both methods of conjugation may occur simultaneously in the same weft of *Spirogyra* or *Zygnema* indicates that sexual differentiation must arise at a late stage within the filaments.

The zygospores (Fig. 201, *z*) always secrete a thick several-layered wall and pass through a prolonged resting period, during which they may be distributed in the normal manner (see p. 276). When they germinate, the membrane bursts, the contents growing out to produce a new filament, one end of which may form an attaching cell.

Among the Desmids, where sexual reproduction is rare, fusion takes place between the liberated protoplasts of two individuals, which usually become enveloped in mucilage. The empty halves of their cell-walls are often recognisable near the resulting zygospores (Fig. 193, I), which frequently have elaborately sculptured membranes. In some of the Diatoms a sexual process of an analogous type is encountered.

The Red Algæ possess only motionless reproductive cells, and the male cells drift passively to the female organ which is produced into a long-receptive process (trichogyne). After fertilisation the female organ puts forth a number of filaments, the ends of these threads giving rise to special asexual reproductive cells known as *carpospores*. The dense clusters thus produced are often conspicuous as minute patches of a darker colour. The ordinary asexual cells, so-called *tetraspores* (Fig. 190, A) are produced in fours in small usually spherical sporangia on other plants.

The examples of reproductive processes among the Algæ might be multiplied considerably, but sufficient have been described to show the diversity of methods by which the same end, namely, the multiplication and perpetuation of the species, is attained. It is the result rather than the means which must be regarded as the more important biological phenomenon, indeed in the less specialised Algæ several different means of attaining this end may occur. With all the variety in reproductive methods, the outcome is a cell, or cells, each capable of giving rise to a new plant.

The product of sexual fusion is often a comparatively large spore well supplied with food-material for the next generation. It is, however, not difficult to recognise the importance of other (asexual) methods of multiplication by spores which, being unprovided with either food-reserves or resistant walls, can be formed rapidly and in large numbers, thus giving great facility of responding to favourable conditions.

During nuclear division it has been seen (p. 56) that definite chromosomes, whose number is constant in all the vegetative cells of a plant, become recognisable. When two gametes fuse the resulting nucleus contains twice the normal number of chromosomes, *i.e.* is diploid.   Sooner or later, however, division of a special type occurs (reduction division, see p. 590) during which entire chromosomes pass to the daughter nuclei so that the original (haploid) condition is again restored.   In many of the simpler Algæ (*Ulothrix*, *Œdogonium*) in which the zygote divides to form zoospores (Fig. 199, D), or other asexual cells, the first nuclear division is the reduction division and restores the haploid number; the zygote is therefore the only diploid phase in the life-cycle.   In some species of *Cladophora*, however, the zygote grows direct into a diploid asexual plant, reproducing by zoospores only, identical externally with the haploid gamete-bearing plant.   Here the asexual and sexual phases alternate.

In *Ectocarpus* the diploid asexual and the haploid sexual individuals are likewise usually similar.   It is in the unilocular sporangium (Fig. 197, H) of the diploid individual that reduction in chromosome number occurs so that the resulting swarmers are haploid, whilst the zoospores from the plurilocular sporangia remain diploid and serve to propagate the diploid plant.

The haploid zoospores give rise to sexual individuals, but these too can often propagate indefinitely by means of gametes which germinate without fusion, thus behaving like haploid zoospores. The zygote, on the other hand, grows into the diploid plant.   In northern latitudes diploid individuals propagating solely by asexual means occur, a phenomenon paralleled in some Flowering Plants. Alternation of two generations also occurs in most Red Algæ in which tetraspores and carpospores are formed on distinct though otherwise similar plants.   In all these alternations the change from the diploid to the haploid number of chromosomes occurs when the zoospores (or tetraspores) are formed.

Markedly dissimilar generations are found in *Laminaria* and its allies, in which the large diploid thallus reproduces only by haploid zoospores, which give rise to minute haploid *Ectocarpus*-like filaments producing either antheridia (Fig. 198, D) or oogonia (Fig. 198, E).   The spermatozoids fuse with the ova and the zygote develops at once into the asexual plant.   This type of alternation is of special interest because it closely parallels the condition in Mosses and Ferns (cf. p. 368).

[For a more detailed treatment of the Algæ, see F. E. Fritsch, *The Structure and Reproduction of the Algæ*, 2 vols., Cambridge University Press, 1935 and 1945, a comprehensive account of algal morphology; and G. M. Smith *et al.*, *Manual of Phycology* Chronica Botanica, 1951 (375 pp.).   A useful reference work is: H. B. Ward and G. C. Whipple, *Freshwater Biology*, Wiley & Sons, New York, 1918 (1111 pp.).   For taxonomic works, see p. 579.]

CHAPTER XXVIII

THE STRUCTURE AND REPRODUCTION
OF THE FUNGI

THE *Thallophyta*, the first class of the Vegetable Kingdom, include not only the chlorophyll-containing Algæ, but also the Fungi [1] which contain no chlorophyll. These are, consequently, like the colourless saprophytes and parasites among higher plants, dependent upon organic material elaborated by other organisms.

A considerable number derive all their nourishment from other *living* plants or animals, such *parasites*, exemplified by the Smut of Wheat, the Gooseberry Mildew, Potato Blight, and the Fungi attacking insects and their larvæ, often seriously harming their hosts. Numerous Fungi, however, live upon decaying organic matter (*e.g.* many Moulds and Toadstools), and these *saprophytes* play an important part in nature in connection with processes of decay and the circulation of nutritive materials.

Fungi show many peculiarities, both in vegetative structure and the nature of their reproductive processes. The plant-body is of a peculiar type, consisting generally of a loose weft, the *mycelium* (Fig. 204, *a*), composed of very delicate branched threads or *hyphæ*, which may or may not be septate (Fig. 208, *a*). The narrow diameter of the hyphæ facilitates their penetration either into the interior of a host (parasites), or between the particles of decaying organic material (saprophytes). The hyphæ, moreover, secrete at their tips various enzymes (cf. p. 83), which bring about solution of the obstructing cell-walls and also convert the organic material into a readily assimilated form, a single species of Fungus producing a number of different enzymes, according to the substratum upon which it occurs. The extreme simplicity of the vegetative structure may well be compared with that of parasitic Flowering Plants, some of which have a plant-body so reduced that it resembles a mycelium (cf. p. 217).

In some Fungi the wall of the hyphæ consists of cellulose, but much more commonly of a complex nitrogenous compound

---

[1] For reference-books, see p. 334.

similar to the chitin found in animals, together with other substances such as pectose, callose, etc.   Embedded in the lining layer of cytoplasm in the lower forms are numerous minute nuclei, but in the septate hyphæ of the higher types there are only one or two in each cell; neither plastids nor starch-grains are ever present, but there are often small oil-drops and sometimes crystalline albuminous bodies.   The central vacuole is prominently developed. Food is customarily stored, especially in reproductive cells, as the polysaccharide *glycogen*, which assumes a brown colour with iodine, while mannitol is frequently found in the mycelium.   In coloured hyphæ, such as occur in species of *Peziza*, etc., the pigment is either located in the cell-wall or in granules.

The Fungi are classed in three main groups—Phycomycetes, Ascomycetes, and Basidiomycetes—each of which has many characteristic features.   The *Phycomycetes*, which are not specialised to so marked an extent as the other two groups, include forms which usually show a well-marked sexual process, and which, in this and other respects, somewhat resemble the alga *Vaucheria*.   The hyphæ, for example, contain numerous nuclei, and often only exhibit transverse walls in relation to the formation of reproductive bodies. The group includes many common parasites, such as *Cystopus* (the White Rust of Cruciferæ, Fig. 202, A), *Pythium debaryanum* (the cause of the "damping off" of seedlings, Fig. 203, B), *Phytophthora infestans* (the Potato Blight), *Empusa* (responsible for a disease of house-flies), as well as the saprophytes *Mucor* (the black Mould appearing on jam, bread, etc.), *Saprolegnia* and *Achlya* (the last two frequent on decaying water-plants).

Cystopus, a species of which often attacks the Shepherd's Purse, furnishes a typical example, whose life-history can easily be studied. The parts affected by the Fungus are swollen and distorted (Fig. 202, A), and exhibit a white surface.   Such enlargement, or *hypertrophy*, is a frequent symptom of fungal attack, and is an outcome of the abnormal development of the diseased tissue, whose cells undergo increase in size with, or without, division.   A longitudinal section through such a swelling (best stained with eosin) shows the hyphæ within the intercellular spaces and middle lamellæ of the host.   Here and there larger hyphæ (Fig. 202, B, *h*) bearing small club-shaped branchlets (the *haustoria*, *S.*), and belonging to *Peronospora parasitica*, commonly associated with *Cystopus*, are recognisable.   *Cystopus* has smaller, rounded haustoria which, like those of *Peronospora*, penetrate the host's cells and absorb elaborated food.

Near the surface of the stem the hyphæ are more densely packed, and their almost parallel branches form a pile-like felt (the *hymenium*, Fig. 202, C) which ruptures the overlying epidermis and causes the

white appearance above mentioned. The slightly swollen ends of
the hyphæ of the hymenium exhibit various stages of constriction,

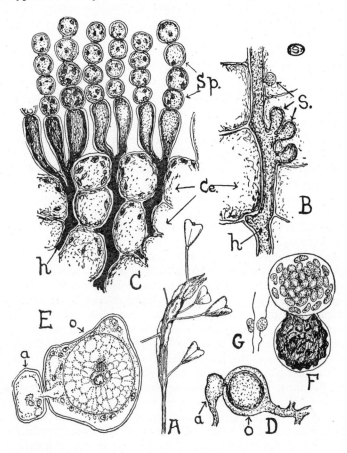

FIG. 202. The White Rust of Cruciferæ (*Cystopus candidus*). A, Diseased
inflorescence of Shepherd's Purse, showing the white patches where the
conidia of the Fungus are being formed. B, Hypha (*h*) of *Peronospora*, with
haustoria (*S.*), in a longitudinal section, between the cells (*Ce.*) of the host.
C, Transverse section near surface of host, showing hyphæ (*h*) and conidia
(*Sp.*). D, Antheridium (*a*) and oogonium (*o*) (after De Bary). E, The
same in section at the time of fertilisation (after Stevens). F, Germination of
oospore (after De Bary). G, Zoospores (after De Bary). All, except B, of
Cystopus. (Figs. A–C, original.)

resulting in the gradual formation of chains of spherical structures
called *conidia* (*Sp.*), the oldest of which is farthest away from the
point of origin. The mucilaginous septa between them shrink and

appear as short stalks which break down in moist air, after which wind carries away the conidia, often to considerable distances.

When rain or heavy dew cause a sufficient accumulation of moisture, the contents of the conidia divide into several parts, which are liberated as minute colourless *zoospores* (Fig. 202, G), swimming by means of a pair of flagella. Many doubtless perish before reaching a suitable host, but should they encounter seedlings of a Cruciferous plant, they come to rest on the surface, secrete a membrane, and elongate into a short hypha which penetrates into the interior by way of a stoma. The stimulus directing the movement of the zoospore towards the host-plant is probably a chemotactic one (p. 307), whilst the growth of the hypha into the interior affords an example of positive chemotropism. For some weeks the hyphæ of the Fungus branch and spread through the tissues of the host, until a sufficiently large haustorial system has been created to supply the materials for reproduction. In dry weather the conidia grow out directly into a hypha.

Sexual reproductive organs are usually produced towards the end of the host's flowering period (*i.e.* when the supply of nutriment probably becomes deficient), and arise in the interior of the infected regions. They consist of spherical *oogonia* (Fig. 202, D, *o*), generally situated at the ends of the same hyphæ as bear the club-shaped *antheridia* (*a*) at a slightly lower level. Both are multi-nucleate and, during development, undergo differentiation of their protoplasmic contents into a denser central and a less dense peripheral region (Fig. 202, E); the former constitutes the egg in the oogonium and the male gamete in the antheridium, while the outer region plays no part in sexual fusion.

The antheridium becomes applied to the female organ and puts out a slender tube which, piercing the oogonial wall, penetrates through the peripheral cytoplasm up to the egg (Fig. 202, D, E). The tip of the tube thereupon opens and the male gamete passes through it to fertilise the ovum, the process involving nuclear and cytoplasmic fusion in the usual way. The product becomes invested by a thick dark-coloured wall. After the decay of the host the *oospores*, which constitute the resting-stage in the life-history, may remain dormant in the soil for a considerable period. When conditions suitable for germination occur, the contents divide to form numerous zoospores (Fig. 202, F) which, after rupture of the thick wall, infect seedlings in the way already described.

Potato Blight and *Pythium debaryanum* have life-histories very similar to that of *Cystopus*, except that in them the conidia more commonly germinate direct into a new plant without form-ing zoospores. The mycelium extends widely within the host,

and the asexual reproductive organs alone appear on its surface.
In the Potato Blight the oval or elliptical conidia are formed
singly at the ends of branched hyphæ, which emerge through
the stomata of the diseased leaves (Fig. 203, A). If blown on
to the leaves of another Potato-plant, the conidia grow out direct

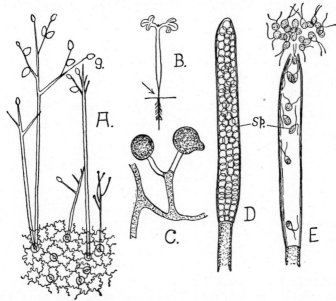

FIG. 203. Asexual reproduction in various Oomycetes. A, Small part of
epidermis of Potato-leaf, infected with Blight (*Phytophthora infestans*), showing
branched hyphæ bearing conidia (*g.*) emerging from the stomata. B, Seedling
of Cress which is " damping off," due to an attack of *Pythium debaryanum*;
where the hypocotyl is giving way is indicated by an arrow. C, Hypha with
sporangia of the same. D, Young, and E older, sporangia of *Saprolegnia*,
showing numerous zoospores (*Sp.*). (A, after Strasburger; B, after Miyake;
C, after Hesse; D and E, after Thuret.)

into an infecting hypha; whilst, if they fall on the ground, they
can, in the presence of moisture, produce zoospores, as in *Cystopus*.
The first signs of disease are discoloured spots exhibiting a dark
central region surrounded by successive zones of greyish and
pale green tissue, which rapidly become brown or even blackish;
closer inspection discloses the white tufts of hyphæ bearing
the conidia, especially on the lower surface of the infected leaf.
Infection of the tubers may be a result of downward spread of the
hyphæ from the overground parts or by direct infection from
conidia washed down by rain. Hence early removal of diseased
shoots is advisable.

An attack of *Pythium* results in a rapid softening of the hypocotyls of the diseased seedlings (Fig. 203, B), which soon give way here and collapse. The rounded conidia, which are borne on simple or forked hyphæ (Fig. 203, C), usually give rise to zoospores without becoming detached, so that the disease rapidly spreads from one seedling to another. The sexual reproduction of *Pythium* and *Phytophthora* is practically identical with that of *Cystopus*.

Owing to the ease with which the Fungi just considered produce zoospores, which of course require a film of moisture in which to swim, spells of damp, warm weather are particularly favourable to their spread and development. Indeed, the damping-off of seedlings through attacks of *Pythium* only occurs in conditions of excessive humidity due to overwatering or over-crowding.

In the aquatic Phycomycetes reproduction by zoospores is the rule. *Saprolegnia ferox*, which usually accompanies the Bacteria causing Salmon Disease, forms wefts on the gills and causes asphyxiation. Other aquatic Fungi often attack fish in aquaria. The biflagellate zoospores are produced in large numbers in tubular sporangia (Fig. 203, D, E), whilst the only essential difference in the sexual reproduction of this genus lies in the development of several, or even many, eggs in each oogonium. In many of the species, moreover, the eggs develop into oospores without fertilisation (so-called apogamy), although functionless antheridia may be formed.

In contrasting the Fungi hitherto described with the Algæ, one of the most striking peculiarities, apart from the absence of chlorophyll, is the non-motile character of the male gamete. This feature may be related to the fact that the Fungi as a whole are a terrestrial group, living under conditions (*e.g.* in the interior of a host-plant) in which the necessary moisture for the movement of spermatozoids is not available.

The saprophytes among Phycomycetes are well exemplified by *Mucor*, which thrives on all kinds of decaying substrata (especially horse manure), upon which its mycelium forms a white weft (Fig. 204, *a*). Numerous absorptive branches penetrate downwards into the source of nourishment, and sooner or later conspicuous, dark brown or black, spherical *sporangia* (*sp.*) appear at the ends of relatively thick upright hyphæ, which in some species are branched. An ally of *Mucor* (*Rhizopus stolonifer*), that occurs very commonly on stale bread and horse dung, spreads very rapidly by hyphæ resembling minute strawberry runners, at the end of each of which a tuft of absorptive threads and sporangia is produced.

The wall of each sporangium (Fig. 204, *b*) is beset with numerous minute needles of oxalate of lime, whilst the swollen end of the hypha below projects into the cavity as a central column (*Co.*); between this and the wall are many small thick-walled spores embedded in a mucilaginous substance. The latter swells, in the presence of moisture, and thus contributes to the bursting of the

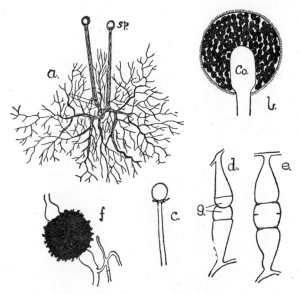

FIG. 204. *Mucor*. *a*, Mycelium, slightly magnified, showing two of the long-stalked sporangia (*sp.*); *b*, Sporangium, much enlarged, in optical section, showing the numerous spores and the central column (*Co.*); *c*, Dehisced sporangium in which only the column and a small part of the wall remains; *d* and *e*, Conjugation of gametes (*g.*); *f*, Mature zygospore. (*a, b* and *f*, after Brefeld; *c*, after Sachs; *d* and *e*, after De Bary.)

sporangium. It is also responsible for the adhesive nature of the spores, which are so widely disseminated by the wind that they are almost ubiquitous. They are extremely resistant, and are capable of remaining dormant for many years. On germination they grow direct into a new plant without the production of zoospores.

Sexual reproduction in most species only takes place between two mycelia belonging to physiologically distinct strains, not distinguishable outwardly (*heterothallism*). The gametes are produced within swollen club-shaped branches whose end-portions become separated off by cross-walls (Fig. 204, *d*, *g*.). Two perfectly similar branches meet by their tips, one being derived from each of the two plants (Fig. 204, *d*), and the intervening membrane breaks down (*e*), whereupon the protoplasts and nuclei fuse. The multinucleate product, deriving nutriment from the respective mycelia, subsequently slowly enlarges to form a black spherical zygospore (Fig. 204, *f*). The latter on germination produces a short hypha terminating in a sporangium, containing spores of both strains.

In certain allies of *Mucor*, sexual fusion occurs between gametes

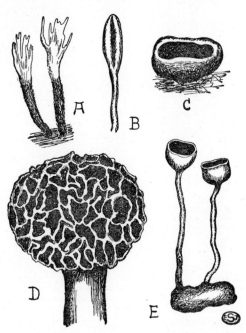

FIG. 205. Fruit-bodies of various Ascomycetes. A, *Xylaria hypoxylon* (Stag's Horn Fungus). B, *Geoglossum*. C, *Peziza* (Cup-fungus). D, *Morchella* (Morel). E, *Sclerotinia*, showing apothecia arising from sclerotium.

from the same mycelium (homothallic). This is so in *Sporodinia*, sometimes found on fruit-bodies of Toadstools and forming its sporangia on forked hyphæ. *Empusa* spreads by means of conidia, abstricted from hyphæ which often project in numbers from diseased flies. These three members of the Phycomycetes are classed among the *Zygomycetes*, which are characterised by reproducing by motionless spores and by an isogamous sexual process, whereas the oogamous forms previously considered are grouped as *Oomycetes*. They are also distinguished by the ease with which they form zoospores. The Zygomycetes are clearly more markedly adapted to terrestrial conditions.

The second main group of Fungi, the *Ascomycetes*, are characterised by their method of spore-formation and by the usual absence of a true sexual process. Common parasites belonging to this group are the Mildews (Erysiphaceæ), the Ergot of Rye (*Claviceps purpurea*, Fig. 207, A), and the Vegetable Caterpillar (*Cordyceps*); but there are numerous saprophytes, such as the ubiquitous Blue Mould (*Penicillium*), the Cup-fungi (species of *Peziza*, Fig. 205, C), the Stag's Horn Fungus (*Xylaria*, Fig. 205, A), the Morel

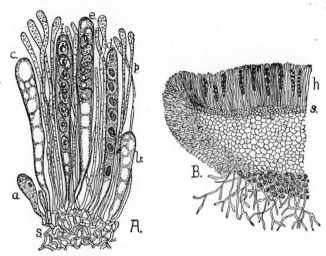

Fig. 206. *Peziza vesiculosa*. B, Section of half an apothecium (diagrammatic), and A, Small part of the hymenium enlarged, showing asci in progressive stages of development (*a–f*). *h.*, hymenium; *p.*, barren hyphæ of same; *s.*, small-celled subhymenium. (After Goebel.)

(*Morchella*, Fig. 205, D), and *Nectria*, which causes the bright red pustules common on decaying branches and sticks.

A general idea of the Ascomycetes can be obtained from an examination of *Peziza*. The septate mycelium of this Fungus is perennial and ramifies in the decaying substratum (*e.g.* dead trunks and branches, soil rich in humus), its presence only becoming apparent in autumn, when conspicuous, and often brightly coloured, cup-shaped fruit-bodies (*apothecia*, Fig. 205, C) are produced at the surface. In a vertical section through one of these (Fig. 206, B) the hyphæ are seen to be so densely compacted as to produce a *false tissue*, the elements of which are quite irregularly arranged, except for those lining the inner surface of the cup. These form a palisade-like layer (the *hymenium*, *h.*) composed of numerous elongated sporangia or asci (Fig. 206, A, *a–f*), interspersed with

slender hair-like ends of barren hyphæ (*p.*).   The mature asci, which
contain eight ellipsoidal *ascospores* (*e*, *f*), develop a high osmotic
potential and on contact with moist air, burst by the detachment of
an apical lid.   Mere breathing on a ripe fruit-body will cause the
explosive discharge of numerous asci, thus liberating a cloud of spores.

The ascus is typical of the Ascomycetes as a whole, and constitutes one of their chief characteristics.   For, by contrast with

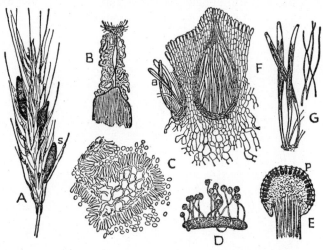

FIG. 207. Ergot of Rye (*Claviceps purpurea*).   A, Head of Rye, with a number
of black sclerotia (*s.*).   B, Longitudinal section of ovary of Rye-flower,
showing the dense hyphæ forming the sclerotium in the lower part, and the
looser mass of hyphæ producing conidia in the upper.   C, A small part of the
latter in section, highly magnified, showing the budding off of conidia.   D,
Germinating sclerotium.   E, Vertical section through one of the swellings
arising from the latter, showing numerous perithecia (*p.*).   F, Part of same,
highly magnified, to show perithecia with asci (*a.*).   G, Three asci and (on the
right) four of the thread-like ascospores.   (A and D, after Wettstein; the
remainder after Tulasne.)

the Basidiomycetes (cf. p. 328), the spores are produced *within* the
mother-cell, whilst in contradistinction to the Phycomycetes they
are nearly always only eight in number.   The asci, as in *Peziza*,
are frequently grouped together in compact and large fruit-bodies,
the hymenium either covering a great part of the exposed surface
(as in *Morchella*, Fig. 205, D, and *Geoglossum*, Fig. 205, B) or being
completely enveloped within sterile hyphæ, as in Truffles (*Tuber*),
whose fruit-bodies are, moreover, subterranean.

Ergot (*Claviceps*) infests the ovaries of Rye, Oats, and other
Grasses, becoming very conspicuous at the time of harvest, as
a result of the gradual replacement of the grains by a black banana-

shaped mass (about half an inch long) of closely interwoven hyphæ (Fig. 207, A, s.). This constitutes a resting-stage of the Fungus, and is so hard that the term *sclerotium* [1] is applied to it. In transverse section all the hyphæ, and especially those at the periphery, are seen to have very thick walls, whilst the more central ones, forming the lighter-coloured region, are laden with food-reserves. The sclerotia drop off in the autumn and remain dormant in the soil until the following spring. Then they send up one or more stalked swellings (Fig. 207, D), in which are embedded numerous flask-shaped cavities (*perithecia*, Fig. 207, E, *p*.) communicating with the exterior by small pores (Fig. 207, F). Each perithecium is lined with a hymenium similar to that of *Peziza*, but the ascospores developed within the asci are here thread-like (Fig. 207, G), so that they are readily distributed by the wind. If caught by the stigma of a Grass-flower the spores germinate and the hypha grows down through the style into the ovary, thus bringing about a fresh infection.

By slow degrees the contents of the ovary are replaced by a dense hyphal mass with deep surface furrows (Fig. 207, B, upper part). From the ends of the superficial hyphæ large numbers of minute oval conidia are budded off (Fig. 207, C), and at the same time the surface secretes a sugary liquid. This attracts insects, to whose bodies the conidia adhere, and so a rapid spread of the disease from flower to flower is brought about. Later in the summer the production of conidia ceases and the outer hyphæ blacken, whereby the resting sclerotium is formed.

The bright red pustules of *Nectria* and the branched sclerotia of *Xylaria* (Fig. 205, A) harbour similar flask-shaped perithecia and, at a younger stage, form conidia on their surface.

In some Ascomycetes reproduction by conidia is far more frequent than the formation of asci, as, for instance, in the two common Moulds *Penicillium* (Fig. 208, *a*, *b*) and *Eurotium* (= *Aspergillus*, Fig. 208, *f*). Here the conidia are budded off in chains from the terminal branchlets of erect hyphæ which, in *Eurotium* (Fig. 208, *f*), are strongly swollen at their apices. Both Fungi also occasionally produce spherical ascus-fruits (Fig. 208, *d*), which arise from special sexual organs (Fig. 208, *c*), although it is doubtful whether any actual fusion of cell-contents occurs.

In the White Mildews (*Erysiphaceæ*) [2] formation of conidia

---

[1] Similar sclerotia occur, as resting-stages, in the life-cycle of several other Ascomycetes, e.g. *Sclerotinia* (Fig. 205, E), a close ally of *Peziza*, whose cup-shaped apothecia arise from the sclerotia.

[2] The Mildews are the cause of many familiar diseases of cultivated plants, as instances of which may be mentioned the Gooseberry Mildew (*Sphærotheca mors-uvæ*), the Rose Mildew (*S. pannosa*), *Erysiphe polygoni* (on Field Peas and

is again relatively common. The mycelium in these parasites develops externally, on the surface of the leaf (Fig. 209, *b*), the haustoria alone penetrating into the epidermal cells. The mildewed appearance is usually due to the extensive production of chains of conidia from the ends of unbranched upright hyphæ (Fig. 209, *c*), such chains being very striking in the Mildew

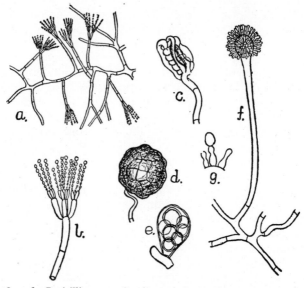

FIG. 208. *a–b, Penicillium. a,* Small part of mycelium with conidiophores; *b,* One of the latter enlarged. *c–g, Eurotium (Aspergillus). c,* Very early stage of fruit-formation, showing the coiled hypha (female organ) from which the asci arise; *d,* Mature fruit; *e,* An ascus from the interior of the same; *f,* Conidiophore; *g,* Small part of apex of same, showing the way in which the conidia are budded off. (*a* and *b,* after Brefeld; the remainder after De Bary.)

commonly found on Forget-me-not leaves (due to a species of *Oidium*). Later in the season many of these Fungi develop numerous small dark specks (Fig. 209, *a*), the ascus-fruits, on the greyish-white mycelium. Under the microscope they are seen to be almost spherical structures, provided with very diverse hair-like appendages and without an aperture (Fig. 209, *b*). The hard black wall ruptures irregularly, exposing one or more small asci (Fig. 209, *e*).

Cucumber), and *E. graminis* (on Wheat). Many so-called Mildews do not, however, belong to the Ascomycetes, but are Phycomycetes, whose richly branched conidia-bearing hyphæ give a whitish appearance to the leaves; such are the Cabbage Mildew (*Peronospora parasitica*) and Grape Mildew (*Plasmopara viticola*).

In the Hop Mildew (*Sphaerotheca castagnei*) it has been established that the fruit arises from club-shaped *sexual organs* of

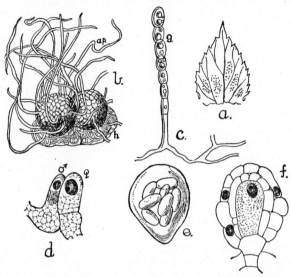

FIG. 209. The Hop Mildew (*Sphaerotheca castagnei*). *a*, Part of the leaf of the Hop, with the ascus-fruits; *b*, Small part of the surface, greatly magnified, showing the superficial hyphæ (*h*.) and two ascus-fruits, each with numerous long appendages (*ap*.); *c*, Production of a chain of conidia (*g*.); *d*, Sex organs in apposition; *e*, Ascus; *f*, Young fruit. (*a*, after Wettstein; *b*, *c* and *e*, after Tulasne; *d* and *f*, after Harper.)

unequal size, the larger functioning as the female (Fig. 209, *d*). Their tips become closely adpressed, but, owing to the great difficulty of establishing such facts, there exists a marked difference of opinion as to whether or not there is a nuclear fusion like that described for the Phycomycetes. The same doubt attaches to many instances of sexual fusion that have been investigated in the Ascomycetes. Since, however, the asco-genous hyphæ are known to arise from differentiated

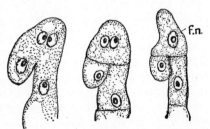

FIG. 210. Ascus-formation in *Pyronema confluens*, slightly diagrammatic (based on Harper). *F.n.*, fusion-nucleus in cell from which ascus will arise.

organs (*ascogonia*) in certain species developing each type of ascus-fruit encountered in this group, the view is generally held that all its members are to be regarded as being descended from Fungi which exhibited a sexual process, now often functionless. In fact, in most Ascomycetes no traces of sexual organs are to be found.

As a result of nuclear division in the cells of certain hyphæ which, when ascogonia are present, arise as branching outgrowths from them, a binucleate condition is realised. The binucleate cell is commonly the penultimate cell of a crozier-shaped hypha and the first step in the development of an ascus consists in the fusion of the nuclei (Fig. 210). This is regarded by some as giving the same stimulus as a sexual fusion. The single nucleus thus produced undergoes successive division into eight, whereupon membranes are formed independently around each nucleus and the adjacent cytoplasm, so that eight ascospores are cut out; a small portion of the cytoplasm remains, however, which is not incorporated in the latter. These stages in the formation of the asci are to be found in the subhymenium.

The *Basidiomycetes* are altogether devoid of sexual organs. They are likewise characterised by a special mode of spore-formation in which a definite number of spores (usually 4) is constricted off from the mother-cell. This large group includes many saprophytes, familiar examples being the Mushroom (*Psalliota*, Fig. 213), various Toadstools (e.g. *Coprinus*, *Boletus*), Puff-balls (*Lycoperdon*, Fig. 216, B), etc. The mycorrhizal Fungi of higher plants mostly belong to this group. The Smuts (Ustilagineæ) and Rusts (Uredineæ) are peculiar members of Basidiomycetes.

The *Rusts* are of special importance as being the cause of many serious diseases of crops, and of these the Rust of Wheat (*Puccinia graminis*) is, unfortunately, all too common. Like many other Uredineæ, it possesses a very complicated life-history, whose phases occur on two different hosts. In summer the parasite attacks the leaves and stems of various Grasses, and betrays its presence by the development of orange-coloured streaks upon them. These are due to clusters of unicellular thick-walled spores (summer- or *uredo-spores*) of an orange colour, beset with numerous minute spines; each spore arises at the end of a projecting hypha (Fig. 211, B, *u*). After detachment they may be blown by the wind on to another appropriate Grass, whereupon hyphæ grow out through special thin areas of the wall (Fig. 211, F), to start a fresh generation of the Rust. In this way the disease rapidly spreads during the summer months.

Towards autumn special winter- or *teleuto-spores* are produced, and these remain dormant in the soil until the following spring. The formation of teleutospores is evidenced by a darkening of the streaks on the Grass-leaves. These are now caused by clusters of bicellular spores (Fig. 211, D), again borne singly at the ends of projecting hyphæ, and provided with a thick dark brown membrane (Fig. 211, B, *t*) which has a thin germinal pore in each cell.

With the advent of spring both cells of the teleutospore put out

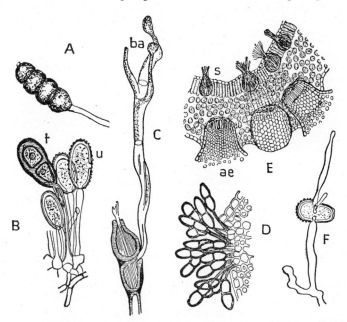

FIG. 211. A, Teleutospore of *Phragmidium*. B–F, Rust of Wheat (*Puccinia graminis*). B, Group of uredospores (*u.*) and one teleutospore (*t.*). C, Germinating teleutospore (only the hypha growing from one of the two cells is shown at its full length), with developing basidiospores (*ba.*). D, Group of teleutospores, seen in section of leaf of Wheat. E, Section of Barberry-leaf, showing æcidia (*ae.*) in two stages of development, and spermogonia (*s.*). F, Germinating uredospore. (B, D and F, after De Bary; C, after Tulasne; E, after Sachs.)

a short hypha composed of four cells (Fig. 211, C), each of which gives rise to a process bearing a small spherical spore (*basidio-spore, ba.*). The latter is only capable of further development if carried by the wind to a plant of the Wild Barberry (*Berberis vulgaris*). In that event a mycelium is produced within the new host, and the presence of the disease is soon manifested by the appearance, usually on the under-surface of the leaf, of groups of small orange-coloured cups (the cluster-cups or *æcidia*, Fig. 212). The minute specks, recognisable on the upper surface of the leaf, are caused by small flask-shaped cavities (*spermogonia*, Fig. 211, E, *s.*)

containing hyphæ from the ends of which small reproductive cells (*spermatia*) are abstricted, together with a sweet liquid.

In a vertical section (Fig. 211, E) the hyphæ of the æcidium (*æ.*) form a compact bounding wall, whilst from the dense inter-woven mass at the base arises a palisade-like hymenial layer whose hyphæ bud off rows of orange-coloured *æcidiospores*, separated by flat sterile cells. The spores, if carried by the wind to Wheat or other Grasses, give rise to a new uredo-form.

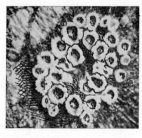

While the mycelium bearing spermogonia has uninucleate cells, those composing the æcidia, including the æcidiospores, are binucleate. In some Rusts a single basidiospore can produce a mycelium forming æcidiospores, but this is not the rule. Many are hetero-thallic or, more correctly, self-incompat-ible, two of each four basidiospores being of one or other strain. The binucleate condition arises by fusions between the hyphæ of two compatible strains growing on the same leaf, or through the transference of spermatia by wind or insects to a mycelium of opposite strain. Certain projecting hyphæ are believed to be receptive organs. The uredo- and teleuto-forms have binucleate cells, but fusion occurs in the maturing teleutospores.

FIG. 212. Group of cluster-cups (æcidia) on leaf of *Ranunculus* (magnified about 5 times).

The existence of the Fungus on different host-plants, at different stages of its life-cycle, is paralleled among animal parasites (*e.g.* Malarial Parasite, Tapeworm), and affords one means for the extermination of the disease, viz. by the eradication of one host. Wheat Rust may, however, appear in successive years, even where the Barberry does not grow (*e.g.* Australia), which is probably due to survival of uredospores through the winter, or persistence of the Fungus in the tissues of winter-green Grasses. In some Rusts there is no uredospore phase (e.g. *Puccinia anemones* on the Wood Anemone), whilst in others (e.g. *Puccinia malvacearum* on the Hollyhock) only teleutospores are known. Another common Rust is *Phragmidium bulbosum*, causing purple spots on the leaves of the Blackberry. This has 3- or 4-celled teleutospores (Fig. 211, A).

Some Rusts exhibit very extreme specialisation in relation to definite host plants, possessing strains which, though morphologi-cally identical, only develop on one particular species (biologic strains). Others, however, can attack a variety of related hosts, and, in the continuance of a disease of cultivated crops, wild plants may often play an important part in bridging the interval of a rotation.

The Smuts (*Ustilagineæ*) are characterised by the sooty black mass of spores which are formed by the breaking up of the hyphæ into unicellular portions with a thick pigmented wall. They occur extensively as diseases of various Cereals (*e.g.* Oats, Wheat, Maize), infesting either the leaves (Fig. 216, G) or the ovaries.

The common Mushroom (*Psalliota campestris*) affords an

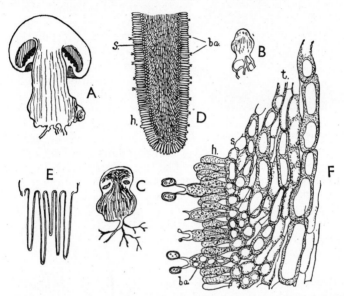

Fig. 213. The common Mushroom (*Psalliota campestris*). B, C and A, Successive stages in the development of the fructification (in A the annulus is distinct, but yet unruptured). E, Transverse section through small part of cap, showing gills. D, One of the latter enlarged. F, Surface of a gill, in section, highly magnified. *ba.*, basidium; *h.*, hymenium; *s.*, subhymenium; *t.*, large cells of middle of gill. (After Sachs.)

example of the more typical Basidiomycetes. The mycelium, which inhabits soil rich in humus, and is present in considerable amount in so-called Mushroom spawn, is composed of binucleate cells. The hyphæ, as in many other Basidiomycetes, tend to be interwoven in bundles, so that the mycelium appears thicker and coarser than in other Fungi. The overground edible portion is the reproductive body which first appears on the mycelium as a knob-like swelling (Fig. 213, B) composed of densely interwoven hyphæ, but later, as it gradually enlarges, broadens out at the top (Fig. 213, C, A). In the mature condition it consists of a stalk and an umbrella-shaped cap (cf. also Fig. 215, A, *cp.*), with a large number of radiating plates or gills (*g*) on the under surface, which bear the *hymenium*. A little way below the cap the stalk is surrounded by a membranous ring of broken tissue (the *annulus, a*) which,

FIG. 214. The Bracket Fungus (*Poly-porus squamosus*).   [Photo. E. J. S.]

before the expansion of the cap, extended continuously from the edge of the latter to the stalk, thus constituting a protection for the developing gills (Fig. 213, A).

In a vertical section through the cap (Fig. 213, A, E) the middle of each gill (D, F) is seen to consist of longitudinally arranged hyphæ. These are composed of rather large cells (*t.*), and diverge at their ends to form a round-celled sub-hymenium (*s.*) and the superficial palisade-like hymenium (*h.*). The latter comprises two kinds of club-shaped hyphal terminations: some, the *basidia* (*ba.*), bear at their apex two, or four, short processes, each of which bears a *basidiospore* placed excentrically, whilst the others are purely sterile. This method of spore-formation is that characteristic of Basidiomycetes generally, four being the usual number produced. The colour of the spores varies considerably in different species.

The enormous production of spores in this and other similar Fungi can be gauged by placing the mature caps, with the gills downwards, on a sheet of white paper, when, after a short time, the outline of each gill will be marked by the spores which have been shed. It has been estimated that a moderate-

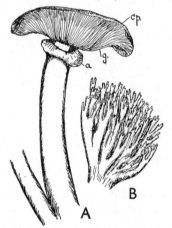

FIG. 215. A, Toadstool (*Armillaria*), slightly reduced. B, *Clavaria. a.*, annulus; *cp.*, cap; *g.*, gills.

sized specimen will produce some 1,800,000,000 spores, and other allied species form spores in even greater profusion.

In the genus *Boletus*, whose fruit-body has the same general form as that of the Mushroom, the under side of the cap presents the structure of a honeycomb, consisting of a multitude of vertical tubes, the inner surfaces of which are lined with hymenium (Fig. 216, E).

A similar construction is seen in the Bracket Fungus (*Polyporus squamosus*, Fig. 214), whose thick tough fruit-bodies are commonly found on decaying tree-trunks, to which they are attached along one side of the cap (Fig. 220). Some of the related Fungi (e.g. *Dædalea quercina*) have woody fructifications which may persist for several years, whilst others are dangerous parasites of forest trees (e.g. *Armillaria mellea*, Fig. 219). In *Hydnum* (Fig. 216, F) the

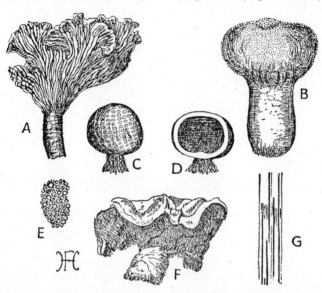

FIG. 216. Various Basidiomycetes. A, *Cantharellus*. B, *Lycoperdon*. C, D, *Scleroderma vulgare* (C, entire; D, in vertical section, showing the wall and the dark mass of contained spores). E, Surface-view of small part of hymenium of *Boletus*. F, *Hydnum repandum*. G, *Ustilago longissima* (on leaf of *Glyceria aquatica*).

hymenium covers the numerous pointed projections arising from the under side of the cap.

Other kinds of fruit-bodies found in this class are: the purple encrusting ones of the Fungus (*Stereum purpureum*) causing Silver-leaf disease of the Plum; the rounded fruits of *Scleroderma* (Fig. 216, C, D) which, like those of the Puff-balls (*Lycoperdon*, Fig. 216, B), are filled at maturity with a powdery mass of spores, liberated by irregular rupture in the former and through an apical aperture in the latter; and the richly branched fruit-bodies of the Coral-Fungus (*Clavaria*, Fig. 215, B), which bear hymenium over their entire surface.

The young basidium is binucleate, but these nuclei fuse prior to the production of basidiospores. The binucleate condition

334

FIG. 217. *Pleurotus ostreatus.*   FIG. 218. *Amanitopsis vaginata.*
FIG. 219. *Armillaria mellea.*   FIG. 220. *Polystictis versicolor.*
[All after photos by Mr. E. M. Cutting, M.A.]

usually arises, long before the formation of fruit-bodies, through the fusion of two hyphæ belonging to mycelia of different strains, which are compatible and, only when fusion has occurred, are fertile fruit-bodies produced (cf. Rusts, p. 330). Some species are, however, self-compatible. In the binucleate cells the two nuclei always divide simultaneously, and in many Basidiomycetes this is associated with the formation of loops between adjacent cells, known as clamp-connections.

In all the Fungi studied nuclear fusion takes place at a certain stage of the life-cycle. It may occur in connection with an obvious sexual process (Phycomycetes), but in many Ascomycetes and all Basidiomycetes it happens in the young ascus or basidium. The two fusing nuclei are often descendants, through a long series of divisions, of pairs of nuclei that became associated much earlier (diploidisation). As in other plants (cf. p. 314), nuclear fusion necessitates a reduction division to restore the haploid chromosome-number; this ensues in the young ascus and basidium and in the zygotes of Phycomycetes.

Brief reference should be made to the Slime Fungi (*Myxomycetes*) whose affinities are obscure. They show certain similarities to Protozoa, but the reproductive processes resemble those of lower plants. They are most evident in damp weather, when the large naked protoplasmic masses (*plasmodia*), constituting the vegetative phase, creep out from the crevices of decaying tree stumps, humus, or other substrata. Small, often rounded sporangia, containing numerous spores, are formed, especially in the autumn, and are sometimes very conspicuous owing to their brilliant colouration (*e.g.* the yellow-coloured Flowers of Tan, common on tanner's bark). The group also includes some parasites, one of the most noteworthy (*Plasmodiophora brassicæ*) being that responsible for the disease known as "Finger and Toe" in Cabbages, etc. (Fig. 221).

Included among Phycomycetes are parasitic unicellular forms (Chytridiales), infesting Algæ and small animals, while a few (e.g. *Synchytrium endobioticum*, the cause of Wart Disease of Potatoes) are responsible for virulent diseases of higher plants. Propagation takes place by zoospores. The Chytrids attacking plankton Algæ play some part in their diminution after a period of abundance.

[For more detailed treatment of the Fungi, see H. C. I. Gwynne-Vaughan and B. F. Barnes, *The Structure and Development of the Fungi*, 2nd edit., Cambridge University Press, 1937 (449 pp.); H. M. Fitzpatrick, *The Lower Fungi (Phycomycetes)*, McGraw Hill-Book Co., 1930 (331 pp.); E. A. Gaumann, *Comparative Morphology of Fungi* (transl. by C. W. Dodge), McGraw-Hill Book Co., 1928 (701 pp.); E. A. Bessey, *Morphology and Taxonomy of Fungi*, Blakiston Co., Philadelphia, 1950 (791 pp.). For taxonomic works, see p. 579.]

CHAPTER XXIX

PHYSIOLOGY OF FUNGI, LICHENS

MANY of the Fungi play a very important rôle in the economy of nature. The *saprophytes*, in association with Bacteria, are largely responsible for the decomposition of organic remains, and without them the whole surface of the earth would become buried under the bodies of plants and animals. Through their agency the material locked up in the raw humus of the soil is transformed into simpler chemical compounds, and rendered available for the use of higher plants. A striking instance of this function is afforded by those Fungi, responsible for the decomposition of humus, and intimately associated as a *mycorrhiza* with the underground organs of Flowering Plants (cf. p. 218). The extensive woody strands, often called "boot-laces", formed by the bundles of hyphæ of the Honey Fungus (*Armillaria mellea*), are the means by which this parasite (p. 333) accomplishes its devastating spread through the soil from tree to tree. The decay initiated by saprophytes is commonly detrimental to man's interests, as in the "dry rot" of timber due to *Merulius lacrymans* (Basidiomycetes) and the almost ubiquitous Moulds which readily develop upon articles of food. *Cladosporium herbarum*, which discolours meat in cold-storage, is exceptional in growing slowly at low temperatures.

The parasitic species [1] often seriously damage cultivated plants. Sometimes the host is ultimately killed, as in the Silver-leaf disease of Plum-trees, but more commonly (Mildews, Rusts) the diseased plant lives on as an unhealthy individual supporting the parasite. Most Fungi are strictly saprophytic or parasitic (obligate parasites), but some (facultative) parasites continue to grow as saprophytes after the host has died (e.g. *Pythium debaryanum*). So-called wound-parasites, which obtain access at points of injury, have a brief saprophytic phase; an example is afforded by the species of *Nectria* causing Coral-spot disease of various trees. Few Fungi are pathological in man, although they are the cause of certain skin-diseases (Ringworm, *Favus*).

---

[1] For a detailed treatment, see F. T. Brooks, *Plant Diseases*, Oxford Univ. Press, 2nd edit., 1953 (430 pp.); E. J. Butler and S. G. Jones, *Plant Pathology*, Thacker Spink & Co., 1949 (xii + 979 pp.); L. E. Hawker, *Physiology of Fungi*, Univ. of London Press, 1950 (360 pp.).

Often special conditions, such as excess of moisture (e.g. *Pythium*), the general state of health of the host, or accidental injuries to the latter, may be instrumental in bringing about the attacks of parasitic Fungi. Epidemics of such widespread diseases as the Potato Blight and the Gooseberry Mildew have, for instance, been associated with particularly damp warm seasons. The small spores of Fungi are often widely disseminated by wind and infection by this means is particularly effective within a limited area. Infection from a distance is generally to be attributed to transport of a disease in plants or plant-fragments, through human or other agency, hence the importance of inspection and control of imported horticultural produce.

Germination of spores or conidia usually takes place on the host's surface, often on the leaves, and requires the presence of moisture. Although the developing hyphæ commonly pass into the interior through stomata or lenticels, some (*e.g.* those of the basidiospores of *Puccinia graminis*) penetrate the cuticle. In them the mucilaginous and sometimes swollen tip of the germinal thread adheres to the surface and puts forth a very fine hypha, which bores its way through the cuticle. A contact-stimulus is believed to be involved.

As already noted (p. 330) a species of Rust Fungus may include a number of specialised strains, some of which are able to attack only one particular host. This is also true of Mildews. Similarly, there are often differences between various races of a cultivated plant as regards *susceptibility* to a certain disease; thus, some varieties of Potato and Wheat are immune to Blight and Rust respectively and would be grown in regions in which these pests are prevalent. Their properties of immunity have been combined with other essential properties to produce immune hybrids (cf. p. 589). Immunity no doubt depends on diverse causes, among which thickness of cuticle, thickness and chemical composition of internal walls, and production by the host of substances detrimental to the growth of the Fungus may be mentioned. The ravages of a disease sometimes decrease in intensity after some years, the host presumably becoming adapted to the presence of the parasite; thus, the Rust *Puccinia malvacearum* played great havoc with Hollyhocks when first introduced into Europe about 1870, but now, though still commonly attacked, they do not appear to suffer appreciably.

For successful *control of fungal diseases* a knowledge of the life-history of the parasite is essential. The treatment varies according as it attacks the overground (*e.g.* Potato Blight, p. 319) or underground organs of the host. Diseases of the latter, exemplified by the pernicious Wart Disease of Potatoes (p. 335) and by Finger and Toe (p. 335), which causes irregular swellings upon the root-systems of Turnips, Cabbages, etc. (Fig. 221), are far more difficult to eradicate than those which develop overground, although in the treatment of Finger and Toe application of unslaked lime to the soil is often successful.   They are, however, frequently counteracted most easily by growing only such crops in the infected soil, for several seasons in succession, as are not attacked by the particular parasite.   A remedy commonly employed against Fungi infesting the overground parts is spraying with a *fungicide* which, though deleterious to the parasite, leaves the host practically unharmed. Bordeaux mixture, consisting of a solution of copper sulphate and slaked lime, is one of the most popular.   For many diseases no adequate remedy has yet been found, and the only advisable procedure, in the event of an outbreak is, to remove and burn all infected parts, so as to prevent the spread of the parasite.

Not all Fungi, however, are to be deplored as causes of decay or disease.   Some afford greatly prized articles of diet (*e.g.* Mushrooms, Truffles, Morels, etc.), although their actual food-value is probably small.   Most British Basidiomycetes are innocuous, but

FIG. 221. *Sisymbrium officinale* and Brussels Sprouts attacked by "Finger and Toe" (*Plasmodiophora brassicæ*). [Photo. E. J. S.]

certain species, in part very widely distributed, harbour deadly poisons (alkaloids, etc.); such Fungi are by no means always highly coloured.   Examples are the Fly Toadstool (*Amanita muscaria*) and the Death Cap (*Amanita phalloides*).   An edible Fungus, extensively cultivated in the Far East and used as a condiment, is the so-called Vegetable Caterpillar (*Cordyceps*), where a sclerotium (p. 325) completely replaces the internal organs of the larva.   Certain fungal products are of great medicinal value, as for example the Ergot (*Claviceps*), the sclerotium of which contains a nitrogen base having the property of causing muscular contraction (cf. also p. 339).

Saprophytic Fungi and various facultative parasites grow readily in artificial media, and such *cultures* (cf. p. 347) are of great service in studying reproduction and conditions of life. Although unable to effect the primary synthesis of organic carbon-compounds, Fungi often thrive in media containing, apart from carbohydrates (glucose or sucrose), only certain inorganic salts, but some require an organic nitrogen-source (*e.g.* asparagin, etc.). Obligate parasites are unable to grow in artificial cultures.

Many Fungi form specific organic compounds, which accumulate in the medium, their nature and amount varying with its composition and the conditions of growth. Among such substances are various dyes. Certain species of *Aspergillus* and *Mucor* produce appreciable quantities of carboxylic *acids* (citric, oxalic, etc.). There is evidence that, as in some higher plants (p. 241, B), these acids are synthesised from glucose and carbon dioxide.

Of outstanding importance for human welfare are the *antibiotic substances* formed by various Moulds. Among the most important is penicillin, now produced on a commercial scale from *Penicillium notatum* and invaluable in the treatment of pneumonia, diphtheria, diverse skin-diseases, etc. Penicillin destroys many pathogenic Bacteria, although, if correctly used, harmless to human beings. Another example, streptomycin, derived from *Streptomyces griseus*, a soil-inhabiting Fungus, is a powerful antibiotic, effective against the tuberculosis-Bacillus, which is not destroyed by penicillin.

The production of most alcoholic beverages is due to the activity of Yeasts (*Saccharomyces*), special members of the Ascomycetes. The Yeast-plant (Fig. 222) consists of oval cells, which are either isolated (A) or cohere in groups (C). The thin-walled cells contain a large central vacuole (Fig. 222, B, E, *va*), and, in contact with the latter at one point, the nucleus (*n*), which becomes apparent on staining the living cells with a dilute aqueous solution of methylene blue. The Yeast-cells often contain large glycogen-vacuoles, as well as small bodies (*v*), stained deeply by methylene blue, and known as volutin-granules, which appear to constitute another kind of reserve.

When a cell has reached a certain size, it gives rise to a small outgrowth (Fig. 222, B) which slowly enlarges and assumes the form of the parent, from which it becomes separated by gradual constriction; if this process of *budding* takes place rapidly, the cells do not immediately separate, and thus groups (Fig. 222, C) are formed. A resting-stage also occurs, as when Yeast is grown on the surface of a raw Potato; under these circumstances the cell-contents undergo division, usually into two or four parts, each with a thick wall (Fig. 222, D). In many Yeasts eight such ascospores

(I) are formed and the ascus producing them arises as a result of the conjugation (F–H) of two cells.

Many different species of Yeast ferment sugars, splitting them into alcohols (mainly ethyl alcohol) and carbon dioxide. Only certain sugars are directly fermented, but the cells often contain diastase, invertase, etc. which readily change other carbohydrates into a fermentable form. As noted in the reference to alcoholic fermentation on p. 241, it shows great resemblance to anærobic respiration, but in the former the sugars broken down are outside

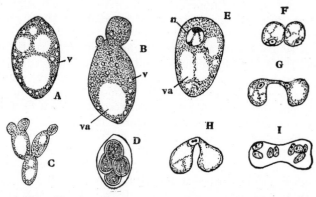

Fig. 222. Yeast (*Saccharomyces*). A–C, Various individuals, showing general form and multiplication by budding. D, Individual containing ascospores. E, Cell with nucleus (*n*). F–I, Conjugation of two cells to form an ascus with 8 ascospores; *v*, volutin granules; *va*, vacuole. (A–D, after Wettstein; E–I, after Guilliermond.)

the organism, so that no loss of weight is involved. Yeast can carry on normal (ærobic) respiration, and a little oxygen is favourable to active fermentation. It can build up its substance from sugars and simple inorganic salts only. In this it resembles many other Fungi, but the extreme rapidity of its growth, when alcoholic fermentation is proceeding, is doubtless due to the acceleration of protein-elaboration with the help of the energy transferred during the breakdown of sugars.

Much of the dry weight usually consists of proteins, rendering Yeasts of considerable food-value. They are rich in certain vitamins of the B group. So-called "Food Yeast" (*Torulopsis utilis*), which grows readily on molasses, ammonium salts and phosphates and has an agreeable taste, has been reared on a large scale and used to supplement food-supplies at times of shortage.

The alcohol in beer, wine, etc. is formed by Yeasts, while the carbon dioxide simultaneously evolved (p. 241) is compressed into cylinders and sold as a by-product. In the manufacture of Beer, malt (*i.e.* germinated Barley),[1] treated with hot water, supplies part of the sugar, various other sugars being used according to local practice. After addition of hops to provide the peculiar flavour, the "wort" is fermented in vats. The success of brewing depends largely on employing pure races of Yeast and the use of suitable temperatures at the different stages of the process.

Other Fungi, besides Yeasts, can ferment sugars. If spores of *Mucor* are placed in a sugary liquid, they reproduce by budding and cause alcoholic fermentation (so-called *Mucor*-yeast). Another manifestation of energy liberated by fungal activity is the luminescence of the hyphæ of *Armillaria mellea* (Fig. 219) and certain other Fungi.

The instances already noted in which a parasitic Fungus may do comparatively little harm to the host, are but a step removed from those in which the balance, between the Fungus and the organism with which it is associated, is so perfect that both are mutually benefited. Such a condition is found in the *Lichens*,[2] whose body is composed of algal cells embedded in a weft of fungal hyphæ. Lichens, with but few exceptions, are subaerial, being commonly found on peaty soils, rocks, tree-trunks, old walls, etc. In conjunction with various Algæ and Mosses, Lichens play an exceedingly important part in the primary colonisation of rock surfaces and of other ground laid bare of vegetation, being conspicuous, for instance, among the early vegetation of burnt heaths. The black-coloured blotches, which are such a familiar sight on the pebbles of a shingle-beach, are due to various Lichens (e.g. *Rhizocarpon confervoides*, Fig. 223, C), which are here the first colonisers.

The shape of the thallus is very diverse, and, as a general rule, almost entirely determined by the Fungus. The growths commonly appear as flat, lobed, encrusting expanses which are often almost circular (e.g. *Parmelia, Xanthoria*, Fig. 223, D). Other frequent types are those exhibiting repeated branching (Fig. 223, B); in such the segments may be upright (*e.g.* Iceland Moss, *Cetraria islandica*, Fig. 225) or hanging (e.g. *Usnea*, Fig. 223, A). The thallus is sometimes highly gelatinous, so that it is much more conspicuous in wet than in dry weather (e.g. *Collema*).

The Algæ found within the thalli of Lichens are similar to forms

---

[1] If all the starch in the malt is allowed to undergo conversion into sugar, and the fermented product is distilled, whisky results; brandy is similarly obtained by distilling the alcohol from fermented grape-juice. The Japanese *saké* is obtained by the fermentation of rice.

[2] For a more detailed account of Lichens, see A. Lorraine Smith, *Lichens*, Cambridge Bot. Handbooks, 1921 (464 pp.); and F. Tobler, *Die Flechten*, G. Fischer, Jena, 1934 (84 pp.), the latter the most recent account of their biology and reproduction. For taxonomic works, see p. 579.

which grow independently in terrestrial habitats; examples are
afforded by the unicellular green *Trebouxia* (p. 281, Fig. 224, B, in
Cladonia) and the filamentous blue-green *Nostoc* (found in *Peltigera*).
The Fungi concerned are, on the other hand, unable to lead an
independent existence in nature, and are only normally capable

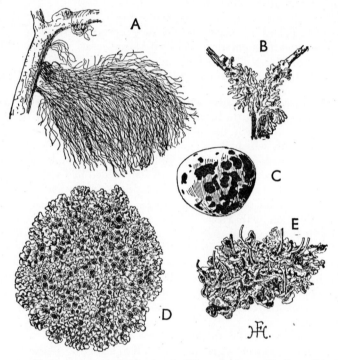

FIG. 223. Various common Lichens. A, *Usnea barbata*. B, *Parmelia phy-
sodes*, on twig. C, *Rhizocarpon confervoides*, on pebble. D, *Xanthoria
parietina* (showing numerous apothecia). E, *Cladonia* sp., showing the
upgrowths on which the apothecia are borne.

of growth when associated with one particular Alga. Different
physiological races of the same species of Alga may, however, be
coupled with several different Fungi to form as many distinct
Lichens, but each Fungus has only one algal associate. It has
even proved possible to produce a Lichen artificially by sowing
the spores of its fungal constituent among the appropriate algal
cells. The vast majority of Lichen Fungi belong to the Ascomycetes, as shown by their fructifications, which closely resemble
small rather flattened *Peziza*-cups (Fig. 223, D). In *Cladonia*
(Fig. 223, E), where the thallus itself is often inconspicuous, the

reddish apothecia are borne on the edges of variously shaped
upgrowths.

Since the hyphæ at the two surfaces of the thallus are usually
densely compacted and thick-walled (Fig. 224, C), the Alga (*al*)
embedded in the interior is well protected during times of drought.
As a general rule, moreover, tufts or isolated hyphæ project from

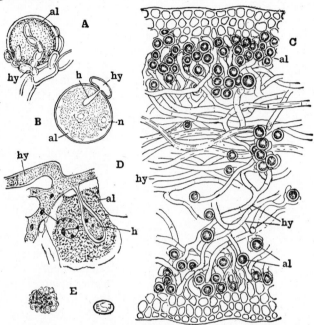

FIG. 224. A, An algal cell from the Lichen *Cladonia*, illustrating the intimate
relation between it and the fungal hyphæ.   B and D, Penetration of haustoria
(*h*) into algal cells; the alga in B is *Trebouxia*.   C, Section through the thallus,
of the Lichen *Xanthoria parietina*.   E, Soredium of same.   *al*, algal cells; *hy*,
fungal hyphæ; *n*, nucleus.   (A after Bornet; B after Geitler; D after Frye;
the rest original).

the underside into the substratum, absorbing moisture which is
held there by capillarity, and thus the algal cells are kept supplied
during dry periods.   In Lichens growing on rocks, the penetration
of these hyphæ is facilitated by the secretion of solvents, and it is
to this property that such Lichens owe their important rôle in the
disintegration and colonisation of bare rock-surfaces.   Most of the
internal hyphæ are loosely arranged (Fig. 224, C, *hy*), facilitating
inward diffusion of carbon dioxide.   The algal cells may occupy
definite zones (e.g. *Xanthoria parietina*, Fig. 224, C) or may be
distributed throughout the thallus (e.g. *Collema*).

Whilst the Alga is thus protected and supplied with moisture, the Fungus no doubt absorbs photosynthetic products from the algal cells which, though appearing healthy and often even multiplying vigorously, rarely contain reserve food.   Some of the finer hyphæ establish intimate contact with the algal cells (Fig. 224, A), commonly forming haustoria (Fig. 224, B, D, *h*) which penetrate into the protoplast.   This may cause destruction of some cells, but, under normal conditions, the parasitic effect is controlled.   The partnership, however, often borders closely on parasitism.

The association between Alga and Fungus is paralleled by the

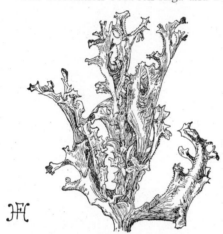

so-called "green cells" found in several aquatic animals (fresh-water Sponges, *Chlorohydra*); these are due to unicellular Algæ (*Chlorella*).   In such partnerships the relations resemble those in Lichens, and this condition of equilibrium leading to mutual benefit is, in both, spoken of as *symbiosis*.   Algæ commonly inhabit the intercellular spaces of certain higher plants (Duckweed,

FIG. 225. Iceland Moss (*Cetraria islandica*), part of a large specimen, about natural size.

the Liverwort *Anthoceros*), but here they appear to be mere "space-parasites" obtaining protection.

The ordinary cup-like fructifications of Lichens originate from the Fungus, and the resulting ascospores reproduce the latter only, so that germination of the spores must take place in the neighbourhood of the approprate Alga, if a fresh Lichen is to be formed.   But multiplication involving the dual organism is the rule; small parts of the thallus, or algal cells surrounded by interlacing hyphæ, become detached, and when this takes place on a large scale the surface of the thallus acquires a powdery appearance.   The individual granules (so-called *soredia*, Fig. 224, E), being distributed by the wind, afford a rapid means of propagation of the dual organism.

The bright colours of many Lichens are due to pigments, remarkable for their "fast" character and employed in dyeing.   The well-known chemical indicator litmus is obtained from species of *Roccella*.   Iceland Moss (*Cetraria islandica*, Fig. 225), which forms a slimy fluid when boiled with water, is used as an invalid food.

CHAPTER XXX

BACTERIA AND VIRUSES

THE *Bacteria*[1] constitute a highly important group of mainly unicellular plants of uncertain relationships. The majority are colourless and of extremely small size. The larger ones are not more than 1/100th mm. in length and about one-tenth as wide, whilst the globular forms average 1/1000th mm. in diameter. Some are so minute as to be almost, if not quite, invisible under the highest powers of ordinary microscopes. They occur in almost every possible situation, and live under the most varied conditions. They are not killed by cold, some surviving for many months at the temperature of liquid air. Whilst most die if heated to about 50° C., a few (*thermophilic Bacteria*) live in fermenting hay and manure heaps which, owing to their activity, may attain a temperature of 70° C.[2] Bacteria are also abundant in the waters of hot springs.

Bacteria are rod-shaped (*Bacillus*, Fig. 226, *d*, *f*, *Bacterium*), spherical (*Micrococcus*), or curved (*Spirillum*, Fig. 226, *k*). The rod-shaped individuals may be joined end to end to form long filaments (Fig. 226, *d*), whilst the *Coccus*-forms may occur in chains (*Streptococcus*, Fig. 226, *b*), in cubical packets (*Sarcina*), or in irregular masses (*Staphylococcus*, Fig. 226, *a*). The individuals may exhibit movement by means of flagella, which are visible only after careful staining, or may merely exhibit Brownian movement in correspondence with their minute dimensions. In the elongated forms the flagella are either situated in tufts at the two ends (*Spirillum*, Fig. 226, *k*), or else arise all over the body (*Bacillus*, Fig. 226, *e*, *f*), but there are some genera possessing only one or two flagella restricted to one end of the cell (*Pseudomonas*, Fig. 226, *l*).

Investigation of the structure of these minute cells presents great difficulties and has led to diverse interpretations. Plastids are absent. Much of the protein is combined with nucleic acids as nucleoproteins. Under the electron microscope and after special

[1] See W. W. C. Topley and G. S. Wilson, *Principles of Bacteriology and Immunity*, Arnold, 1929 (1645 pp.); R. J. Dubos, *The Bacterial Cell*, Harvard Univ. Press, 1949 (460 pp.); M. Stephenson, *Bacterial Metabolism*, Longmans, Green & Co., 1949 (398 pp.); W. J. Dowson, *Manual of Bacterial Plant Diseases*, Black, 1949 (183 pp.).
[2] Hence the employment of manure for hot-beds, etc.

treatment it has been possible to recognise 1–6 minute bodies which have been regarded as consisting of nuclear material. There is a firm wall of unknown nature, which is seen when cells are plasmolysed. The cytoplasm commonly contains glycogen (p. 316), as well as volutin (p. 338) and fat globules.

Multiplication of the cells by *division*, under normal circumstances, ensues with great rapidity, often taking place once every hour, or even more frequently. In some of the elongated forms the daughter-individuals are separated off by a mere constriction

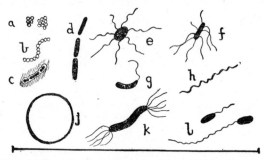

FIG. 226. Various Bacteria (magnified about 1000 times). *a, Staphylococcus aureus; b, Streptococcus pyogenes; c, Pneumococcus; d, Bacillus anthracis; e, B. typhosus; f, B. tetani; g, Microspora comma; h, Spirillum* of relapsing fever (possibly Protozoal); *k, Spirillum rubrum; l, Pseudomonas* spp. *j* represents a blood corpuscle on the same scale, and the line below, the width of a fine human hair, or about half the thickness of a sheet of newspaper. (*a–h*, from Muir and Ritchie; *k–l*, after Engler and Prantl.)

(e.g. *Bacterium* spp.), whilst in others the cell is subdivided by a transverse septum which subsequently splits down the middle. In certain Bacteria inhabiting water or other fluids, the daughter-cells become surrounded by wide mucilage-envelopes and unite to form an, often iridescent, surface-pellicle.

Bacteria survive unfavourable conditions by the formation of resting *spores*, produced within the cells by a localised concentration of the greater part of the protoplasm, which then stains differently from the peripheral portion. The central region eventually becomes surrounded by a thick wall, and at maturity the remainder of the cell is often empty (Fig. 227, *b, c*). The spores are frequently located in special parts of the cell, giving the spore-forming individuals a characteristic appearance, as in *Bacillus tetani*, where they occupy a dilation of one end (Fig. 227, *a*). In certain forms (e.g. *Bacillus amylobacter*) more than one spore may be developed by each individual. Bacterial spores are often very resistant to extremes of temperature and can indeed sometimes (e.g. *Bacillus subtilis*) withstand prolonged boiling.

Most Bacteria lead a free life in water, earth, etc., many being highly beneficial in promoting decay and maintaining the circulation of nitrogen and carbon dioxide in nature. The Bacteria (e.g. *Bacillus subtilis*) occurring in the rumen of sheep and cattle and forming part of the intestinal flora of other animals, including man, afford a remarkable instance of symbiosis. They are responsible for the production of the cobalt-containing vitamin B 12, which is essential for all higher animals and without which they die of anæmia. A few Bacteria, however, are extremely harmful parasites in higher plants and animals, these *pathogenic forms* causing such diseases as typhoid, cholera, plague, etc. Whilst some Bacteria (e.g. *Bacillus subtilis*), in common with Fungi, require a supply of oxygen (aerobic species), others (e.g. *B. tetani*, responsible for lock-jaw), will grow in the almost complete absence of oxygen (anaerobic species).

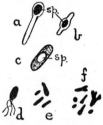

FIG. 227. *a–c*, Spore-formation in Bacteria. *a*, *Bacillus tetani*; *b*, *Bacillus* of malignant œdema; *c*, *Bacillus œdamitis*. *d–f*, Nitrogen-fixing Bacteria. *d*, *Azotobacter*; *e*, *Clostridium pasteurianum* sp.; *f*, *Rhizobium*. (After Engler and Prantl, and Ellis.)

The identification of the pathogenic forms, in particular, is very important. Their small dimensions, however, usually makes it impossible to recognise species of Bacteria by microscopic examination alone, and resource is therefore had to their various reactions when grown in cultures. These are made up with gelatine or agar (p. 298), including a nutritive medium like extract of meat, decoctions of fruit, etc. In such cultures, at temperatures suitable for the species, multiplication is very rapid and the mass of offspring from a single organism is soon visible to the naked eye. In making cultures [1] all the vessels and instruments employed are scrupulously cleaned and freed from live Bacteria (*sterilised*) either by exposing them to superheated steam in an autoclave or by washing with strong disinfectants, since even small quantities of dust are full of bacterial spores.

The various kinds of Bacteria present in any material can be isolated by mixing a little of it thoroughly with a quantity of one of the above-mentioned media, liquefied by moderate warming. The individual Bacteria become widely separated and are immobilised when the medium sets on cooling. As they multiply, each individual gives rise to a small, but visible, group (colony), which can be transferred to another culture. In this way growths derived from single organisms (clones) and consisting of one species only

---

[1] Similar cultural methods are used for the study of Fungi and Algæ.

(*pure cultures*) are obtained. They afford the means for studying such features as the form, the mode of growth, the formation of pigment (usually outside the cells) and other chemical substances, etc. on which specific identification is based.

A very valuable staining technique is that known as the *Gram-reaction*. This consists essentially in staining with a basic triphenyl-amine dye, like crystal violet, followed by iodine solution or picric-acid as a mordant. After washing with water or alcohol, some Bacteria (gram-positive) remain fully stained, others (gram-negative) become decolourised. The contrast is associated with some marked difference in cellular organisation, since it serves to separate forms distinguished by their toxic properties, their resist-ance to antibiotics and other inhibitors, the degree of permeability of the cell-wall, and various other features.

Some Bacteria are obligate parasites (*e.g.* the *Micrococcus* which causes spotted fever) and cannot live apart from their host, whilst others are facultative parasites (e.g. *Bacillus tetani*) and can live either in earth, etc., or in the body of a Mammal. Each parasitic species can generally use only one or two species of Mammal as hosts; children, for example, do not have distemper, and dogs and cats do not have measles and chicken-pox. Similarly, *Bacillus caroto-vorus* causes "soft rot" of Carrot, but does not attack Parsnips.

The evil effects of parasitic Bacteria result from the production of *toxins* which are proteins and among the most poisonous chemical substances known. The invasion is resisted by the infected animal, partly with the help of the leucocytes of the blood which devour the Bacteria, and partly by producing chemical substances which neutralise the toxins. The power of the body to make a successful resistance is much improved by practice, and one attack of an infectious disease often enables a person to destroy that particular bacillus at once if it obtains access a second time. Inhibitors, like penicillin and the sulphonamides, are often highly efficacious in arresting a bacterial attack. If grown in concentrations of such substances insufficient to kill them, Bacteria can, however, be trained to endure increasing strengths, which may ultimately much exceed the concentration that would originally have been lethal.

Many Bacteria obtain energy [1] by bringing about processes of *fermentation*. Thus the Vinegar Bacteria convert alcohol into acetic acid,[2] whilst the lactic acid Bacteria cause the souring of milk, changing the milk sugar (lactose) into lactic acid. Other examples

---

[1] Sometimes part of this energy is dissipated as heat (cf. p. 345) or light (*e.g.* the phosphorescence of bad meat).

[2] In the commercial production of vinegar either wine or spirit is used as the raw material, and to these vinegar is added in order to introduce the necessary Bacteria.

of bacterial activity are the production of butyric acid, the chief cause of the rancidity of bad butter, and the putrefaction of meat due to the decomposition of proteins. Fermentation is often due to several organisms. Each type of cheese, for instance, is the product of a definite bacterial and Fungus flora, whilst in the manufacture of ginger-beer a Yeast (p. 339) and certain Bacteria are used.

The decomposition of the cellulose in dead leaves, etc., whereby undue accumulation is prevented, and the carbon again enters into circulation as carbon dioxide, is largely due to Bacteria and certain Fungi. The former are likewise responsible for the processes of decay involved in the "retting" of fibres (Flax, Hemp, Jute), and the conversion of sewage.

The nitrates of the soil, upon which plants depend as their source of nitrogen, are extensively leached owing to their ready solubility, but the supply is continually being reinforced by the action of Bacteria. The decay of plant and animal bodies, which is likewise due to bacterial agency, results in the formation of numerous simpler substances, one of the most important of which is ammonia. This combines with calcium carbonate to form ammonium carbonate which is oxidised to a nitrite by the so-called Nitrite-Bacteria (*Nitrosomonas*). The nitrites in their turn are converted into nitrates by the Nitrate-Bacteria (*Nitrobacter*), and thus the ammonia liberated in decay again becomes available to living plants.

By means of the energy obtained in these oxidative processes, these *nitrifying Bacteria* are able to build up their bodies from inorganic sources (chemosynthesis, cf. p. 213, A). In cultures they can only be reared in the absence of organic matter, but in nature its presence in the soil seems even to be beneficial. They do not flourish in acid soils or in such as contain much free ammonia. This probably explains their scarcity in many soils which are rich in acid humus (*e.g.* moorlands) or poor in lime. Where there is extensive decay of organic matter, as in the guano-fields of Chile, so large a quantity of nitrates may be formed that they accumulate as an efflorescence on the surface of the soil. This is the mode of origin of Chile saltpetre (potassium nitrate).

The beneficial action of these organisms is in nature counteracted by the decomposition of nitrates, with evolution of nitrogen by *Bacterium denitrificans*, etc., a process termed *denitrification*. Other Bacteria, however, can fix free nitrogen with the formation of organic nitrogen-compounds, although the steps in the process are still imperfectly understood. The most important of the *nitrogen-fixing Bacteria* is *Azotobacter* (Fig. 227, *d*) which, like the nitrifying Bacteria, is an aerobic form. It obtains its energy by the break-

23

down of carbohydrates, with the formation of a considerable amount of carbon dioxide, the amount of nitrogen fixed being proportional to the quantity of organic matter decomposed. Another nitrogen-fixing form is *Clostridium pasteurianum* (Fig. 227, *e*), which is anaerobic, the principal product of its activity, apart from nitrogenous compounds, being butyric acid. *Azotobacter* and *Clostridium* are largely responsible for the gradual increase in the nitrogen-content of unmanured grassland. An important rôle in

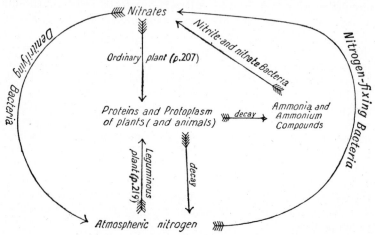

nitrogen-fixation is played by the Bacteria in the root-nodules of Leguminous plants (see p. 219). The capacity to fix nitrogen is not, however, confined to Bacteria, but is possessed also by certain aquatic and soil-inhabiting Cyanophyceæ (e.g. *Anabæna*, Fig. 191, F), as well as probably by some Fungi.

The diverse processes involved in the circulation of nitrogen in nature, which are epitomised above, are of supreme importance. The various organisms concerned evidently work sufficiently well in unison to maintain a balance.[1]

The so-called *Thread-Bacteria* (*Beggiatoa*, *Leptothrix*, etc.) in some respects show more resemblance to the Blue-green Algæ than to the Bacteria proper and are of uncertain affinity. Their rôle in effecting diverse chemical changes in nature is described on p. 213, A.

An important group of plant diseases is caused by what are known as *viruses*. Their presence is usually betrayed by characteristic symptoms, which may manifest themselves as a stunting of

---

[1] For further details, see S. A. Waksman, *Principles of Soil Microbiology.* Ballière, Tindall & Cox, 2nd edit., 1931 (894 pp.).

the plant (*e.g.* in Raspberries), as a mottling of the foliage commonly termed mosaic (*e.g.* in Tobacco), or by the occurrence of spots, patches or rings of discolouration in the leaves. Sometimes the leaves present a puckered or crinkled appearance, while in the virus-disease of Sugar Beet known as "Sugar-Beet Yellows" the whole leaf may look chlorotic. The so-called "Broken Tulip", with mottled flowers, is another expression of virus-infection. It may be added that, in many instances, the symptoms of virus diseases are similar to those produced by nutritional deficiencies.

Viruses are not confined to plants. They cause several widespread diseases of man and animals, as for example mumps, influenza, yellow fever, and foot-and-mouth disease. They appear to be able to exist only in living cells, since no one has yet succeeded in cultivating them apart from such cells, in artificial media.

All viruses appear chemically to be of the nature of nucleo-proteins. Most are elongated in shape, although a few seem to be more or less spherical. The largest are but little smaller than some Bacteria, while the smallest approach in size the molecules of some proteins. In Potato virus the particles may be 100 millimicrons [1] in diameter, whilst in the Tomato virus they are less than 25 millimicrons so that they will pass through the finest filters. Such minute forms can only be detected with the electron micro-scope. Whether they are living or not is not certainly known, but in either event their presence must stimulate the infected cells to produce more of the virus, after the manner of an autocatalytic reaction. Recent evidence indicates that some virus particles are crystalline in nature and that they possess very high molecular weights, of the order of millions.

Most viruses are not transmitted by the seeds of infected plants, although there are some exceptions, notably among those affecting Leguminosæ (Broad Beans, Peas), and that causing the mosaic disease of Lettuce. The usual agents of transmission (vectors) in this country are Aphides. Thus, all the common Potato viruses and many that attack other plants are conveyed by the Green Fly *Myzus persicæ*. The reason for usually planting "seed Potatoes" from Scotland is largely because Green Flies are often absent so far north or only appear late in the season, so that any virus-infection of the leaves has not had time to spread to the tubers before the haulms are removed. As a consequence Potato-plants are relatively free from the two chief virus-diseases "leaf-roll" and "virus Y" that, between them, can reduce the yields by from 50–90 per cent.

The Aphid vectors sometimes become effective as transmitting agents only after they have fed for a day or two on diseased plants

[1] A millimicron is a millionth of a millimetre ($\mu\mu$).

(*e.g.* leaf-roll), but with other viruses the insect can become infective immediately. The period during which they are infective may be brief or they may remain capable of transmitting the disease throughout their life. Such variables necessarily influence the rate of spread. It should be added that some strains of plants serve as carriers. Although they are infected, they show few or no external symptoms of the disease and constitute centres for its spread. Examples are afforded by the Strawberry "Huxley" and the variety of *Dahlia* known as the "Bishop of Llandaff."

An interesting feature of virus diseases is that various types may give rise to similar symptoms and that, when two such are present in the host at the same time, there may be no obvious deleterious effects, although either of them alone would be accompanied by symptoms of disease. Multiplication of the virus particles often leads to the death of the infected cells.[1]

It would seem that the *bacteriophages*, which destroy Bacteria, are of the nature of virus diseases. According to electron microscope photographs they appear to be rounded structures bearing a tail-like appendage.

[1] For further details, see K. M. Smith, *Plant Viruses*, Methuen, 1935 (107 pp.); F. C. Bawden, *Plant Viruses and Virus Diseases*, Chonica Botanica, 3rd edit., 1947 (336 pp.).

CHAPTER XXXI

LIVERWORTS AND MOSSES

THE plants so far considered agree in possessing relatively simple sexual organs, consisting of more or less modified single cells, whose contents, with or without division, give rise to the gametes. The sexual organs, moreover, are often, except in such forms as *Fucus* and *Pelvetia*, distributed over the entire thallus. On the other hand, in Liverworts (Hepaticæ) and Mosses (Musci), which are grouped as *Bryophyta*,[1] the sexual organs are not only much more elaborate, but are commonly restricted to definite portions of the plant-body. The latter also usually exhibits greater cellular differentiation, which may be related to the fact that the majority of the Bryophyta are terrestrial plants and not aquatic like most Algæ.

The majority of Liverworts are damp-loving plants, many of them growing in situations that are covered with moisture in the wetter seasons of the year (*e.g* along the sides of water-courses), whilst some few are even truly aquatic. Many Mosses, on the other hand, can flourish in habitats that are comparatively dry for a great part of the year, extreme examples being furnished by the Hair Moss (*Polytrichum juniperinum*), found on dry heaths, and the Wall Moss (*Tortula muralis*, Fig. 232, D), common on old walls, rocks, etc.

The body of the Liverwort in its simplest form is a small flat green ribbon-like structure, often repeatedly forked, and growing in close contact with the substratum (e.g. *Metzgeria*, Fig. 228, D, and *Marchantia*, Fig. 228, A). At the base of the notch situated at the tip of each lobe of the thallus lies an apical cell or meristem. The middle part of each lobe is generally somewhat thickened like a *midrib* (Fig. 228), and projects to a more or less marked extent on the lower side of the thallus. Water and nutrient salts are absorbed by numerous fine thin-walled unicellular hairs (*rhizoids*, Fig. 228, A; Fig. 235, A, *r*), which grow out into the soil from the lower surface, often mainly from the region of the midrib; these rhizoids also function as organs of attachment.

---

[1] For reference-books, see p. 368.

The under side of the thallus, in many Liverworts, also bears one or more rows of flat overlapping *ventral scales* (Fig. 228, E, *v.s.*), which are one cell thick, and not uncommonly purplish in colour. Some (e.g. *Marchantia* and its allies) exhibit, in the axils of these scales, a second type of rhizoid, characterised by possessing a wall with numerous peg-like internal thickenings (Fig. 231, A, B). The capillary channels, between the dense weft of rhizoids and the

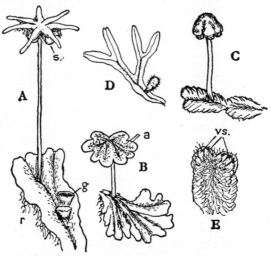

FIG. 228. Thalloid Liverworts. A, *Marchantia*, showing archegoniophore with sporogonia (*s.*), gemma-cups (*g.*), and rhizoids (*r.*). B, Same, with antheridiophore (*a.*). C, *Reboulia*, with archegoniophore. D, *Metzgeria furcata* (under surface). E, Under side of *Preissia*, showing ventral scales (*v.s.*).

overlapping scales, are no doubt of importance in the conduction of water and for its retention during periods of drought.

The Liverworts, however, also include *leafy types* which somewhat resemble Mosses in habit, and, in general, grow in rather drier situations than do the simple thalloid forms; the leaves, unlike those of Mosses, are usually lobed (Fig. 229, A), and sometimes even deeply divided. Two of the commonest genera of foliose Liverworts are *Lophocolea* and *Cephalozia*. Here there is a prostrate stem, bearing on either flank a row of frequently overlapping, sessile, two-lobed leaves (Fig. 229, A) and, on the under side, a row of scales with tufts of rhizoids arising from their base. In some foliose forms the two lobes of the leaves are folded together (e.g. *Scapania*, Fig. 234), and the lower lobe may be modified as a water-receptacle. *Frullania*, a common epiphyte on tree-trunks, affords an extreme example, in which this lobe is developed as a

small, helmet-shaped pitcher (Fig. 230).   These Liverworts, belong
to the Jungermanniales which also include *Pellia* and *Metzgeria*.
In them growth is effected by the division of a single apical cell,
whereas in Marchantiales there is a marginal meristem.

The thallus of most Liverworts exhibits little anatomical
differentiation.   In *Pellia*, for example, all the cells, apart from their

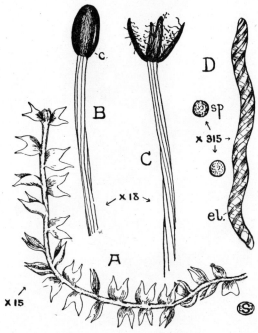

FIG. 229. A Leafy Liverwort (*Cephalozia bicuspidata*).   A, Portion of a plant.
B, Sporogonium showing capsule (*c.*) before dehiscence.   C, The same with
   dehiscent capsule, showing elaters.   D, Elaters (*el.*) and spores (*sp.*).

elongated form in the region of the midrib, are similar in shape,
and most of them contain the numerous small discoid chloroplasts
which are typical of Bryophyta (Fig. 235, A).   An equally simple
structure is displayed by most of the foliose forms, the leaves being
invariably only one cell thick, and with rare exceptions (e.g.
Diplophyllum), devoid of a midrib.   In *Marchantia* and some of
its allies, however, the upper part of the thallus, which is always
the principal photosynthetic region, shows considerable complexity
(Fig. 231, A).   It is subdivided into a large number of very
shallow polygonal chambers, each of which is roofed over by an
epidermis, and communicates with the exterior through a central

barrel-shaped pore (*p.*).   From the floor of each chamber arise
numerous short filaments of green cells (*a.*), which form the
photosynthetic system of the thallus.   The whole of the lower
portion of the latter consists of large colourless cells, serving in
the main for the storage of food-reserves, and in part showing
reticulate thickenings.   On the surface of the thallus the photo-

FIG. 230. Photomicrograph of a small portion of the epiphytic Liverwort
Frullania tamarisci, showing the pitcher-like lower lobes of the leaves.
[Photo. E. J. S.]

synthetic chambers appear to the naked eye as a number of small
diamond-shaped areas, each with a minute central dot corresponding to the pore.

In the Mosses there is a definite stem usually bearing three or
more rows of alternate sessile leaves.   The plants either have a
prostrate habit (e.g. *Hypnum*, Fig. 232, C), like that of most leafy
Liverworts, or grow erect, as in the Hair Mosses (*Polytrichum*,
Fig. 232, A, *Funaria*, etc.).   The lower part of the stem, which is
buried in the soil, forms a kind of rhizome bearing numerous
rhizoids, and sometimes small scales as well.   The rhizoids, which
may also develop from the part of the stem just above the soil, are

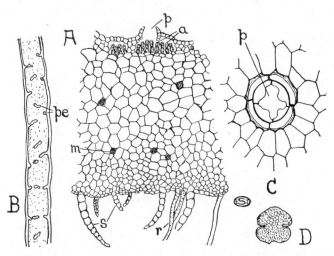

FIG. 231. Structure of *Marchantia*. A, Small part of a transverse section through the thallus. B, Part of a peg-rhizoid, much enlarged, showing the thickenings (*pe.*). C, Surface-view, showing a single pore. D, Gemma, seen from the surface. *a.*, photosynthetic filaments; *m.*, mucilage-cell; *p.*, pores; *r.*, rhizoid; *s.*, ventral scales.

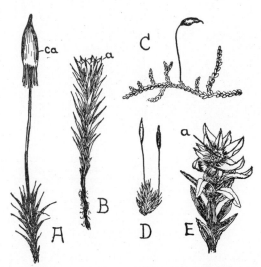

FIG. 232. Various Mosses. A, Plant of *Polytrichum,* bearing a sporogonium whose capsule is covered by the calyptra (*ca.*). B, Male plant of the same, showing the antheridial head (*a.*). C, *Hypnum,* with sporogonium. D, *Tortula muralis.* E, Male plant of *Mnium,* with antheridial head (*a.*).

outgrowths of the superficial cells, but differ from those of Liverworts in being multicellular and branched; they usually have brown
membranes, and are divided by oblique septa, just behind which the
branches originate.

The leaves of Mosses are never lobed, are attached to the stem
by a broad cushion-like base, and usually, except in the region of

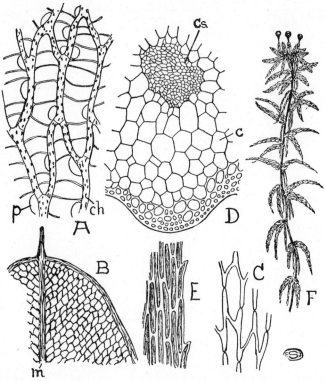

FIG. 233. Structure of Mosses. A, Portion of a leaf of the Bog-moss (*Sphagnum*), showing cells with chloroplasts (*ch.*) and the large empty cells with
their thickenings and pores (*p.*). B, Leaf-apex of *Mnium*, with the midrib
(*m.*). C, Leaf-cells of *Hypnum*, from the surface, showing thickened walls
and pits. D, Transverse section of the stem of *Mnium hornum* (after Bastit),
showing conducting strand (*Cs.*) and storage-cells (*c*). E, Leaf-cells of
Hylocomium, from the surface. F, Habit of *Sphagnum* (after Schimper),
showing three sporogonia.

the midrib, consist of a single layer of cells (Fig. 233, B). The
midrib (*m.*) is generally well differentiated, and its presence forms
a point of contrast with most leafy Liverworts. The branches of
the stem arise from below the leaves, and, in some of the erect forms,

are produced in such large numbers from the base that the plants exhibit a densely tufted habit (e.g. *Tortula*, Fig. 232, D).   Many of the Bog-mosses (*Sphagnum*) are likewise richly branched.   The peculiar habit of these Mosses is partly due to the fact that some of the branches elongate considerably, and hang down alongside the main stem (Fig. 233, F).   The branching of many prostrate Mosses takes place in a pinnate manner (e.g. *Hypnum*, Fig. 232, C).   Growth of the stem and its branches is effected by means of three-sided apical cells, similar to those of *Equisetum* (cf. p. 51).

Mosses show a greater degree of anatomical complexity than Liverworts, as is well shown by the almost invariable presence in the stem of a distinct *conducting strand*, consisting of small, thin-walled, much elongated cells (Fig. 233, D, *Cs.*); in some of the larger Mosses (e.g. *Polytrichum*) these cells may be of two kinds, perhaps serving respectively for the conduction of water and elaborated food-materials.   In Mosses generally conduction of water by capillarity between the leaves and contiguous shoots is also important.   The outer tissues of the stem, as seen in transverse section, consist, except in Mosses occupying damp habitats, of cells with strongly thickened walls which are often reddish-brown in colour (Fig. 233, D).   Between this peripheral mechanical cylinder and the central conducting strand are larger cells (*c.*) with thinner walls, which seem to function mainly for food-storage.

The cells composing the leaves may be spindle-shaped (as in many species of *Hypnum*, Fig. 233, C), or almost isodiametric (e.g. *Funaria* and *Mnium*, Fig. 233, B), whilst those of the midrib (*m.*), when present, are elongated; the cells at the margin are often produced into teeth, and not uncommonly strongly thickened.   The remaining cells may also be somewhat thick-walled, when they frequently bear well-marked pits (e.g. *Hypnum*, Fig. 233, C).   In a few Mosses the photosynthetic surface is increased by outgrowths from the stem (e.g. *Thuidium*) or by longitudinal lamellæ, running parallel to the midrib (e.g. *Catharinea undulata*, an abundant Moss in many woods).

The leaves of Bog-mosses (*Sphagnum*) are peculiar in being composed of two kinds of cells (Fig. 233, A).   The green photo-synthetic cells (*ch.*) are of narrow form, and are arranged as a reticulum whose meshes are occupied by large spirally thickened transparent cells which are dead and empty.   The latter communi-cate with the exterior by means of one or more holes (*p.*) in their walls (cf. the velamen of epiphytic Orchids, p. 111, and *Leucobryum*, p. 523).   These large colourless cells readily fill with water, and it is owing to this that so much liquid can be squeezed out of a handful of Bog-moss.   Similarly, dry *Sphagnum* can suck up a great deal of moisture, hence its employment as an absorbent in surgery, or for molasses in the manufacture of Molassine Meal. In the dry condition, the air in the dead cells obscures the green colour of the living ones, and causes the whole plant to appear whitish.

Both Liverworts and Mosses propagate abundantly by vegetative means. In most foliose Liverworts, and some few Mosses, the plant forms special bodies called *gemmæ*, which consist of a varying number of cells and are often of characteristic shape. In *Marchantia* (Fig. 231, D) they are formed in special cup-like outgrowths on the upper surface of the thallus (Fig. 228, A, *g.*), but in the leafy Liverworts they are usually budded off from the tips of the shoots (Fig. 234). An abundant production of gemmæ is likewise seen in the Moss *Aulacomnion androgynum*, where they arise in a spherical cluster at the top of the stem.

FIG. 234. *Scapania nemorosa*, a Leafy Liverwort, showing gemmæ (*g*) at apex of stem; the same are shown on an enlarged scale at the side.

The ordinary Moss or Liverwort plant, however, also reproduces by sexual means, the *sexual organs* developing especially in the early spring. Their general character, in the Liverworts, will be gathered from an examination of *Pellia*. The male organs are found in the region of the midrib, and are visible to the naked eye as a number of dark pimples, each of which, in a vertical section (Fig. 235, A), is seen to correspond to a single more or less spherical *antheridium*. The latter (Fig. 235, B) is borne on a very short stalk, and almost fills a flask-shaped cavity in the thallus which communicates with the exterior by a narrow pore.

The antheridium is a multicellular structure with a wall (Fig. 235, B, *w.*) of a single layer of cells containing chloroplasts and, at maturity, encloses numerous small, colourless, closely packed *spermatozoid mother-cells*, each producing a single spermatozoid (Fig. 235, D). Through vigorous absorption of water the apex of the antheridium is ruptured, and the expanding mucilaginous mass of mother-cells is discharged into the surrounding moisture. Here occurs the final liberation of the *spermatozoids*, each of which possesses a spirally coiled body (formed mainly from the nucleus

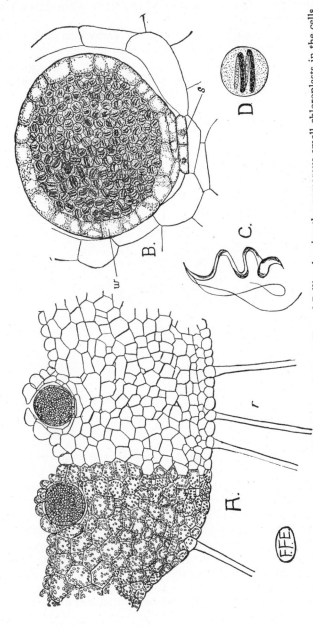

FIG. 235. A, Part of a transverse section through the thallus of *Pellia*, showing the numerous small chloroplasts in the cells (only indicated in part of the figure), the rhizoids (*r.*), and two antheridia within their respective cavities, that on the right showing the aperture to the exterior. B, A single antheridium, much enlarged, showing the short stalk (*s.*), the wall (*w.*), and the numerous mother-cells in which the spermatozoids are seen in course of development. C, A single spermatozoid. D, A spermatozoid mother-cell enlarged, with the contained spermatozoid. (C, after Guignard, the rest original.)

of the mother-cell), bearing two long flagella at the slightly tapering front end (Fig. 235, C).

A rather exceptional grouping of the antheridia obtains in *Marchantia*, where the stalked thallus-lobe, in which the male organs are sunk, is raised above the general surface (Fig. 228, B). Amongst the leafy forms the antheridia are situated, either singly or in groups, in the axils of the leaves.

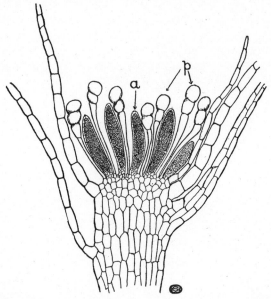

FIG. 236. Vertical section through the antheridial head of the Moss *Funaria*, showing the antheridia (*a.*) and interspersed sterile hairs (*p.*).

The antheridia of Mosses show essentially the same structure as those of Liverworts, except that they are elongated and possess a broader stalk (Fig. 236, *a.*). They occur in groups, interspersed with multicellular sterile hairs (*p.*), at the top of the stem or its branches. Each antheridial group is surrounded by a number of spreading protective leaves (*involucre*), which are not infrequently arranged to form a kind of cup, and usually differ in shape and size, and sometimes also in colour, from the ordinary leaves. The male plants of Mosses are thus easily recognised (Fig. 232, B, E). The spermatozoids are like those of Liverworts, and are liberated in the same way, the mass of mother-cells often being ejected to some slight distance.

The female organs, or *archegonia*, which are essentially similar in the two groups, differ markedly from those of Thallophyta. They are flask-shaped structures (Fig. 237, B), composed of a lower swollen part, or *venter* (*v.*), and a long neck (*n.*), which, in Mosses, is often twisted. The neck is a tube consisting of a single layer of elongated cells arranged in five or six longitudinal rows and surrounding a narrow canal. The latter is occupied by a row of naked *neck-canal cells* which ultimately become mucilaginous, and, in swelling, push apart four lid-cells which, till then, close the upper end of the neck-canal. The venter possesses a wall (one-layered in Liverworts, Fig. 237, B, two-layered in Mosses), enclosing

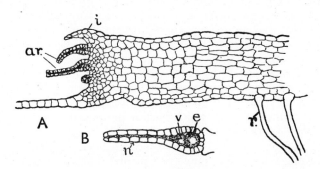

FIG. 237. A, Longitudinal section through the apex of the thallus of *Pellia*, showing a group of archegonia (*ar.*) and the involucre (*i.*). *r.*, rhizoid. B, Single archegonium of *Marchantia*, on a larger scale. *e.*, egg; *n.*, neck; *v.*, ventral canal cell.

a large naked *ovum* (*e.*), with a small *ventral canal cell* (*v.*) at the base of the neck. The venter is borne on a short stalk which is rather more massive in Mosses than in Liverworts.

In Mosses, where they are interspersed with sterile hairs, and in most leafy Liverworts, the archegonia occur in groups at the top of the stem or its branches. They are enveloped by a number of "*involucral*" leaves which generally differ in size, and sometimes also in shape and colour, from the ordinary leaves; in most Mosses, however, such archegonial groups are scarcely distinguishable from the ordinary leaf-buds. In some leafy Liverworts (e.g. *Lophocolea*) the leaves of the involucre are fused together, almost to their tips, to form a cup.

In some of the thalloid Liverworts (e.g. *Pellia*) the archegonia are found at the front end of the thallus, where they occupy depressions roofed over by a scale-like involucre (Fig. 237, A, *i.*). In others (e.g. *Marchantia*, Fig. 228, A) and *Reboulia* (Fig. 228, C) they are situated on special upgrowths which are divided into 4–10 lobes or branches; the archegonia form groups on the lower surface, between the lobes, each group being enclosed between a pair of involucral scales.

The diverse forms of involucre surrounding the archegonia not only protect them from desiccation, but form capillary chambers tending to retain water. This facilitates the movement of the sperms in fertilisation, which only takes place when the plant is covered with a film of moisture. In forms like *Marchantia*, the stalk bearing the lobed archegonial disc does not lengthen till after fertilisation, so that the necks of the archegonia remain in close contact with the water-film on the upper surface of the thallus. In the same way the branches bearing the archegonial groups of Mosses are at first usually short and adjacent to the soil, so that they are readily covered with moisture.

After escaping from the antheridia, the spermatozoids, swimming in the surface films of moisture, are chemotactically attracted to the open necks of the archegonia by substances (cane-sugar in Mosses) contained in the mucilage formed by the breaking down of the canal cells. The spermatozoid passes down the neck-canal and enters the egg, after which nuclear fusion occurs and a diploid condition (p. 314) is established.

The fertilised ovum or zygote secretes a cell-wall and, without any resting-stage, grows into a new plant. This, however, in both groups differs fundamentally from the parent, especially in being parasitic upon the latter, and at maturity constitutes an organism (the *sporogonium*, Fig. 232, A; Fig. 238, A) that is almost solely concerned in the production and dispersal of spores. This simplicity of structure can possibly be related to the parasitic habit, thus affording an interesting analogy to parasitic Flowering Plants. As the embryo enlarges, the venter of the archegonium stretches and grows into a protective covering, the *calyptra*, which can often be recognised around the young sporogonium (Fig. 238, B, *c*;` and Fig. 239, I, *c.*).

In Liverworts the dividing ovum first forms a spherical mass of cells which later elongates and gradually becomes differentiated into three regions. The end adjacent to the thallus penetrates into the underlying tissue as a cone-shaped sucker, the *foot* (Fig. 238, B, *f.*). This consists of parenchymatous cells, and serves to absorb and transfer food to the developing sporogonium. The opposite end swells into a usually spherical *capsule* (*ca.*) with a wall of one or more layers enclosing a mass (the *archesporium*) of spore-forming cells. Up to a certain stage all the latter are alike, but the archesporium in most Liverworts ultimately differentiates into two kinds of cells, which at first are often arranged in radiating series. One type is rounded, and, since each of these cells divides to form four spores (Fig. 238, C, *sp.*), they are known as *spore mother-cells*. The first division in the spore mother-cell is the reduction division (p. 314). The other cells are elongated and

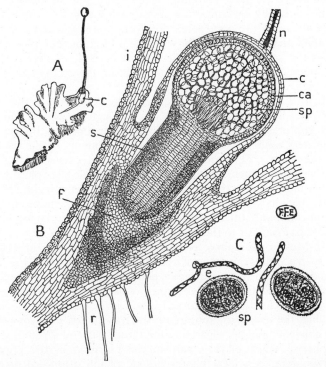

Fig. 238. The sporogonium of *Pellia*. A, Small part of a thallus, showing a mature sporogonium, with the ruptured calyptra (*c.*) at the base (after Leunis). B, Longitudinal section through an almost mature sporogonium, still enclosed within the calyptra (*c.*); the elaters are shown as dark lines among the much larger spores. *ca.*, wall of capsule; *f.*, foot; *i.*, involucre; *n.*, neck of archegonium; *r.*, rhizoid; *s.*, seta; *sp.*, spore. C, A group of spores (*sp.*) and elaters (*e.*).

at first thin-walled, when they assist in the translocation of food-materials to the developing spores, but subsequently they acquire spiral thickening bands, and form so-called *elaters* (Fig. 238, C, *e.*; see also Fig. 229, D).

The region between capsule and foot, consisting of small cells, often densely crowded with starch-grains, constitutes the *seta* or *stalk* (Fig. 238, B, *s.*), which always remains short until the spores are ripe. In *Pellia* and most leafy Liverworts the stalk then elongates rapidly, owing to great increase in cell-size resulting from

24

conversion of the starch into sugars and accompanying intake of water, and bursts through the calyptra, which can be recognised as a torn sheath around its base (Fig. 238, A, c). The capsule is thus raised above the damp soil into the less humid air, where dispersal of the spores by air-currents is more readily attained. Where, as in *Marchantia*, the archegonia are borne on a special receptacle, the stalk of the latter elongates after fertilisation (cf. above), and serves the same purpose as the seta of other Liverworts, whilst the sporogonium retains the short stalk of the embryonic phase (Fig. 228, A, C).

In *Pellia* and most leafy Liverworts the capsule-wall splits into four petal-like valves (Fig. 229, C), although in *Marchantia* the apex ruptures irregularly. Owing to their unequal thickening, the elaters tend to coil and bend as the contents of the capsule become drier. This movement is, however, prevented by the tightly packed contents until rupture of the capsule takes place, when the tensions set up in the elaters are manifested in a wriggling movement which loosens the mass of spores and flicks them into the air. Not uncommonly tufts of elaters remain adhering to the top of the stalk (e.g. *Pellia*) or to the valves (Fig. 229, C).

In Mosses the embryo elongates considerably at an early stage, and soon acquires the shape of a rod tapering at either end (Fig. 239, H and I). The lower extremity penetrates into the tissue of the Moss-stem and forms the absorptive *foot* (*f.*), which is, however, much less clearly distinguished than in Liverworts. Soon, a swelling, the *apophysis*, appears on the rod-shaped embryo, a little way above its middle, separating the future seta and capsule. The apophysis, which plays a part in the nutrition of the growing sporogonium, is a local photosynthetic region composed of cells rich in chloroplasts and provided with abundant intercellular spaces (Fig. 239, A, *ap.*). The epidermis here contains *stomata* (Fig. 239, F) like those of higher plants, except that in many Mosses the septa between the guard-cells break down at maturity, so that the latter form an oval canal surrounding the pore (Fig. 239, G).

The upper part of the embryo enlarges progressively, during the subsequent development, to form the capsule, so that at maturity the latter is usually far more prominent than the apophysis, which, though it mostly remains recognisable, does not grow much after its first formation (cf. Fig. 239, A). The mature capsule is here also raised aloft by a considerable elongation of the slender *stalk* (Fig. 232), and again this causes rupture of the calyptra. In Mosses, however, this takes place in such a way that the upper part of the calyptra is carried up on the capsule as a hood (Fig. 232, A, *ca.*). When this is removed, the apex of the capsule is seen to

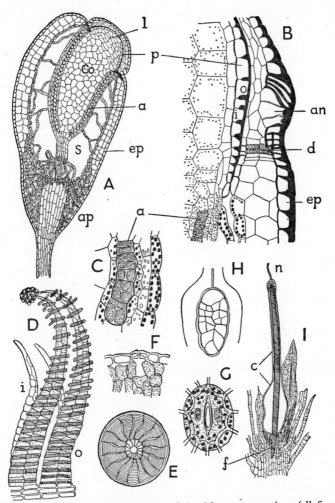

FIG. 239. Structure and development of the Moss-sporogonium (all figures, except F, represent *Funaria hygrometrica*). A, Longitudinal section through young capsule, apophysis (*ap.*), and the top of the stalk. B, Part of the capsule in the region of the lid, much enlarged. C, Small part of archesporium and spore sack, enlarged. D, Two pairs of peristome-teeth (inner and outer). E, Aperture of dehisced capsule, showing arrangement of peristome-teeth. F, Section of small part of apophysis of *Bryum argenteum*, showing stoma. G, Single stoma, in surface-view. H and I, Stages in development of the sporogonium. *a.*, archesporium; *an.*, annulus; *c.*, calyptra; *Co.*, columella; *d.*, diaphragm; *ep.*, epidermis; *f.*, foot; *i.*, inner peristome tooth; *l.*, lid; *n.*, neck of archegonium; *o.*, outer peristome tooth; *p.*, peristome-layer; *S.*, air-space. (D, after Ruhland; E, after Braithwaite; F and G, after Haberlandt; the remainder after Sachs.)

be separated from the rest by a slight constriction, and it is this part that becomes detached as a *lid* and allows of dispersal of the spores.

The internal structure is best studied in a longitudinal section of a nearly ripe capsule (Fig. 239, A). Here the axis is occupied by a rather broad column of thin-walled parenchyma (the *columella, Co.*) passing below into the tissue of the apophysis (*ap.*) and above into that of the lid (*l.*). Surrounding the columella are two concentric cylinders of cells, separated by the granular *archesporium* (*a.*), each mother-cell of which, as in Liverworts, divides to form four spores (Fig. 239, C). Between the spore-sack so formed and the capsule-wall is a conspicuous air-space (*S.*) bridged by occasional fine threads of green cells; in a few Mosses (e.g. *Polytrichum*) a similar air-space separates the spore-sack from the columella. The capsule is protected by a thick-walled epidermis (*ep.*) beneath which are several layers of cells containing chloroplasts. The features just described are equally recognisable in a transverse section through the middle of the capsule.

Just below the constriction (Fig. 239, A and B) marking the commencement of the *lid*, a diaphragm (*d.*) composed of thickened cells, and having the form of a circular ledge perforated by the central thin-walled tissue, stretches inwards from the epidermis (*ep.*) of the capsule. Arising from the inner edge of this diaphragm is a dome-shaped layer of cells (the *peristome, p.*) characterised by marked thickening of the outer tangential walls (*o.*) and of the adjoining portions of the horizontal walls, although the radial (*i.e.* vertical) walls remain thin. At the lower edge of the lid the thick-walled epidermis is interrupted by one or two rings of larger thin-walled cells which constitute the so-called *annulus* (*an.*). Dehiscence eventually takes place along this line, as a result of the differential shrinkage between the annulus and the adjacent cells; soon after the lid is blown away. The epidermal cells above the annulus are usually markedly flattened, and form the lower edge of the lid (Fig. 239, B).

At maturity all the thin-walled tissues of the capsule shrivel, leaving, apart from the spores, only the epidermis, the diaphragm, and the thickened walls of the peristome. Each of the rows of cells forming the latter necessarily tapers from base to apex, and, as a result of the breaking down of the thin radial (*i.e.* vertical) walls between some or all of the rows, a number of separate plate-like *peristome-teeth* (Fig. 239, D), attached below to the edge of the diaphragm, are formed. Sometimes both inner and outer tangential walls of the peristome are thickened, when a double set of teeth (*o.* and *i.*) of course arises as the thin portions of the horizontal walls shrivel. The peristome varies greatly in different Mosses, and, together with the characters of the leaves, constitutes one of the chief means for distinguishing the different genera and species.

The peristome-teeth are extremely sensitive to changes in the moisture-content of the air, curling outwards when the latter is dry, and inwards when it is damp. This is due to differential expansion or contraction on the two sides of each tooth depending on the unequal distribution of thickening. In dry weather, therefore, the powdery mass of spores inside the capsule is readily dispersed, whilst in wet weather the dome is reconstituted (Fig. 239, E), and the aperture, left by the shedding of the lid, covered in. The actual dispersal, in which the elasticity of the seta plays a considerable part, is effected by a catapult-mechanism similar to that of some fruits (cf. p. 480).

In *Sphagnum* (Fig. 233, F) the stalkless sporogonium is raised after fertilisation on a naked prolongation of the stem (false stalk), the foot being embedded in its top. The columella is replaced by gas upon which the contracting wall exerts pressure, so that the lid, covering the dome-shaped archesporium, is shot off explosively.

The spores ultimately give rise to a new Liverwort or Moss, but the adult plant is not produced directly on germination. This is especially obvious in Mosses, where the spores usually develop into a branched multicellular filamentous structure, the *protonema*, which exists partly above and partly below ground (Fig. 240, C). The overground portion appears as a green weft on the surface of the soil, and its cells contain numerous discoid chloroplasts (Fig. 240, D), whilst the underground portion closely resembles the rhizoids of the ordinary Moss (Fig. 240, C, *r.*). In fact, the latter readily grow out into protonema, if exposed to the light, and can thus bring about the development of new plants. Vegetative multiplication of the protonema, by the detachment of branches or of small terminal groups of cells (Fig. 240, C, *g.*), is often prolific, and may set in at a comparatively early stage.

Sooner or later some of the short lateral branches of the protonema become pear-shaped and undergo segmentation by three oblique walls to cut out the characteristic tetrahedral apical cell of the stem of the adult Moss (Fig. 240, A, *b.*). By its continued divisions a small mass of cells is formed from which leaves soon arise, and it is not long before the new Moss attains recognisable dimensions. This formation of Moss-plants takes place at many points on the protonema, and, as the latter usually dies away soon after, the individuals become independent. A protonema readily develops from most parts of the adult Moss, in fact, whenever vegetative propagation from fragments of the plant occurs (cf. p. 358), a protonema is first formed, and from this the new plants arise secondarily.

The protonema of the foliose Liverworts is similar in appearance to that of Mosses, but in most of the thalloid species the early stages are not sharply marked off from the adult.

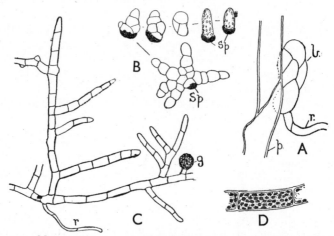

FIG. 240. Moss-protonema. A, Development of young *Funaria*-plant (*b*) from the protonema (*p.*) (after Campbell). B, Stages in germination of spores, and C, Protonema of *Dicranella heteromella* (after Servettaz). *g.*, gemma on protonema; *r.*, rhizoids; *sp.*, spore-membrane. D, Single cell of overground part of protonema.

The life-history of the Bryophyta thus includes two distinct phases: the one, concerned in the production of the sexual organs, is usually highly specialised morphologically and self-supporting, whilst the other, concerned solely with the production of asexual spores, is always dependent, and relies for its sustenance, either entirely (most Liverworts) or partly (Mosses), upon food obtained from its host. These two phases normally alternate with one another and arise from one another, and an analogous alternation is encountered in all the higher groups of plants. For convenience of designation the diploid spore-producing phase is spoken of as the *sporophyte*, and the haploid sexual phase as the *gametophyte*.

[For a more detailed treatment of Bryophyta, see F. Cavers, "The Inter-relationships of the Bryophyta," *New Phytologist*, vols. 9–10, 1910–11; and F. Verdoorn *et al.*, *Manual of Bryology*, The Hague, 1932 (486 pp.); G. M. Smith, *Cryptogamic Botany*, vol. 2, McGraw-Hill Book Co., 1938 (380 pp.). For taxonomic works, see p. 579.]

The plants described in this chapter contrast markedly with those to be considered in the ensuing ones, amongst other features in lacking roots and highly differentiated conducting tissues.

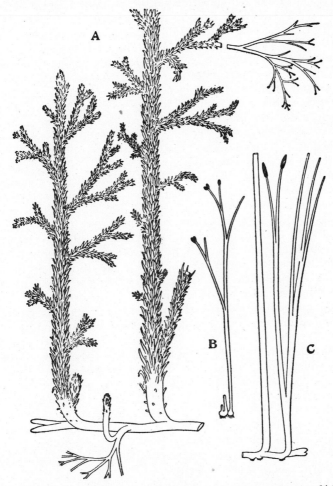

FIG. 240*. Reconstruction of Psilophytales. A, *Asteroxylon mackiei*. B, *Hornea lignieri*. C, *Rhynia major*. Reproductive regions black (after Kidston and Lang).

Special interest therefore attaches to an extinct vascular group, the *Psilophytales*, several members of which possess a very simple organisation, in some respects more like that of an alga or liverwort. This group lived during the Devonian period, and remains of it have been found preserved as fossils in various parts of the world. It is probable that it flourished in peaty swamps. It is perhaps remotely related to the Psilotales (*Psilotum* and *Tmesipteris*), a family of Pteridophyta scantily represented in the Southern Hemisphere.

The best-known members of the Psilophytales [1] (Fig. 240 *) are small plants referred to the Middle Devonian genera *Rhynia* (C), *Hornea* (B), and *Asteroxylon* (A). The first two possessed a horizontal rhizomatous portion which doubtless traversed the peaty soil and bore no roots; from it arose erect *leafless* branches which forked and reached a height of 6 to 18 inches. The third genus *Asteroxylon* (Fig. 240 *, A) bore tufts of root-like branches on the rhizomes and also differed in the fact that the main stem produced forked lateral branches; moreover, the overground parts were clothed with numerous small leaves so that the plant must have resembled a modern Clubmoss (p. 390).

All three genera possessed a cuticularised epidermis containing scattered stomata of much the usual type. The stems were traversed by a single central conducting strand, the xylem consisting of tracheids with only annular or spiral thickenings and being surrounded by a tissue of larger thin-walled elements that probably functioned as phloem. The broad cortex was supplied with intercellular spaces and more especially in the rhizomatous region, was distinguished by the frequent occurrence of fungal hyphæ, suggesting a mycorrhizal mode of nutrition. In *Asteroxylon*, as the name implies, the woody strand was ribbed and commonly appeared four-lobed in transverse section. Its leaves contained no vascular tissue.

The plants reproduced by means of spores, apparently all of one type, which were formed in terminal sporangia (shown black in Fig. 240 *), not very sharply demarcated from the vegetative part below. Those of *Rhynia* (Fig. 240 *, C) were cylindrical and tapering but in *Hornea* (Fig. 240 *, B) they were sometimes bilobed, while the spore-mass in this genus surrounded a central column of sterile tissue so that the sporangia resembled the capsules of some Liverwort-sporogonia. In *Asteroxylon* the sporangia seem to have terminated special leafless laterals.

The Lower Devonian fossil *Psilophyton* is a still older member of this group which was probably even represented in Silurian rocks. The lack of differentiation is very striking. It must be emphasised, however, that, contemporaneously with these simple Devonian Pteridophyta, there have been found fossil stems, broadly comparable to those of Gymnosperms which indicate that land plants had already reached an advanced stage of evolution at that period.

[1] For further details, see the works cited on p. 386.

CHAPTER XXXII

FERNS (FILICALES)

THE Bryophyta, though exhibiting a marked advance in organisation as compared with the Thallophyta, differ from the remaining flowerless plants, or *Pteridophyta*, in lacking roots and specialised conducting tissue. In the Pteridophyta the gametophyte is usually thalloid and short-lived, whilst the sporophyte is far more conspicuous and more permanent, and is quite independent of the gametophyte except in its earliest stages. In the sexual process and the general structure of the sexual organs, however, there is considerable resemblance between the two classes. Pteridophyta, like Bryophyta, possess motile male cells, and thus depend on the presence of liquid water at the time of fertilisation. The former generally grow in moist habitats, although quite a considerable number tolerate relatively dry conditions. Included in the Pteridophyta are the Ferns (Filicales), the Horsetails (Equisetales), and the Clubmosses (Lycopodiales), as well as the Psilophytales (p. 368A).

In many common Ferns [1] the stem is relatively insignificant in comparison with the conspicuous, usually deeply divided, pinnate fronds. The Tree Ferns of subtropical regions, however, have well-marked trunks. The stem is either a rhizome (as in the Bracken, *Pteridium aquilinum*, Fig. 241, B), or compact and more or less erect (*e.g.* Royal Fern, *Osmunda regalis*). It rarely shows branching, though this occurs at intervals where the rhizome is elongated (*e.g.* Bracken). In the prostrate types the leaves usually arise in rows on either side of the underground stem, and are separated by well-marked internodes (Fig. 241, B). In short-stemmed species, however, whether the root-stock be erect or inclined (*e.g.* Male Fern, *Dryopteris filix-mas*), the leaves are densely crowded, and show an obvious spiral arrangement. Adhering bases of the leaves, which persist after lamina and petiole have died away, may add appreciably to the stem's apparent thickness. All the *roots* of the adult Fern are adventitious (Fig. 241, B); they usually arise in the neighbourhood of the leaf-bases, and are generally black in colour and forked.

---

[1] For reference-books, see p. 385.

The young *leaf* is commonly more or less densely clothed with brown scaly hairs or *ramenta*, many of which are shed as the blade unfolds; they usually persist, however, upon the petioles (Fig. 242, A, *r.*) and on the leaf-bases. As the leaf-rudiment produced behind the growing point gradually develops, the axis of the lamina becomes coiled after the manner of a watch-spring, and, in compound leaves,

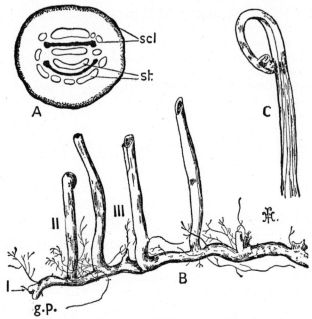

FIG. 241. The Bracken (*Pteridium aquilinum*). A, Diagram of transverse section of rhizome. *scl.*, sclerenchyma; *st.*, steles. B, Rhizome showing apex with growing point (*g.p.*), successively older leaves (I, II, III), and the bases of leaves of former seasons. C, Young frond.

the individual portions become inrolled in a similar way (*circinate vernation*) (Fig. 241, C). Each segment of the blade grows by means of an apical cell, which thus occupies a protected position within the spiral formed by the maturer parts. These features are readily observed in a young Bracken-frond, as it emerges from the soil, and the prolonged growth of its tip is evidenced by the retention of the coiled character in the uppermost portion, long after the older basal portion is fully expanded. The development of Fern-leaves is usually very slow, the rudiment being produced and undergoing gradual enlargement for two or more years before the frond appears above the surface (cf. Fig. 241, B, I, II, III).

Not all Fern-leaves are as deeply compound as in the Bracken or

Lady Fern (*Athyrium filix-fœmina*). Those of the Polypody (*Polypodium vulgare*, Fig. 242, B) and Hard Fern (*Blechnum spicant*, Fig. 248), for instance, are simply pinnate, whilst those of the Hart's Tongue Fern (*Phyllitis scolopendrium*, Fig. 242, A) are undivided. The venation is exceedingly characteristic, the midribs of the leaves or pinnæ, as the case may be, bearing numerous forked lateral veins which are often not connected by cross-branches (Fig. 246, A, B).

A general idea of the more characteristic features in the internal *structure of the stem* can be gathered from a study of the Bracken rhizome. In transverse section (Fig. 241, A) this is seen to be traversed by two rings of vascular strands or *steles* (*st.*). Separating the rings are two bands of dark brown sclerenchyma (*scl.*), and the same tissue also forms a layer beneath the epidermis; its elements (Fig. 244, *Scl.*) differ from the fibres of higher plants in being short and relatively thin-walled. The remaining ground tissue is parenchymatous, and contains an abundance of starch.

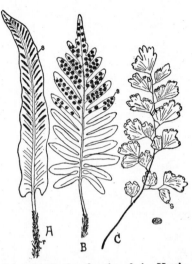

FIG. 242. Entire fronds of A, Hart's Tongue Fern (*Phyllitis scolopendrium*); B, Polypody (*Polypodium vulgare*); and C, Maidenhair Fern (*Adiantum*). *r.*, ramenta; *s.*, sori. (All three considerably reduced.)

The vascular strands are concentric (Fig. 243), with the component tissues more or less symmetrically arranged. The term stele is customarily applied to these concentric strands of Ferns, but this does not necessarily imply that they are comparable to the entire vascular cylinder of a higher plant. Each stele is bounded by an endodermis (*En.*), with dark brown membranes, and a pericycle (*P.*), composed of rather larger thin-walled cells. Next follow one or two layers of much smaller cells, constituting the so-called phloem-parenchyma (*P.p.*). Immediately within is a conspicuous zone consisting chiefly of large, empty-looking, thin-walled elements, the sieve-tubes (*S.*), which are often absent towards the ends of the strands, and which are separated from the central xylem by a zone of small-celled wood-parenchyma (*X.p.*). The bulk of the xylem consists of large tracheids (*Xy.*), but near the ends and towards the centre of the strand, small elements, representing the protoxylem (*P.xy.*), can usually be

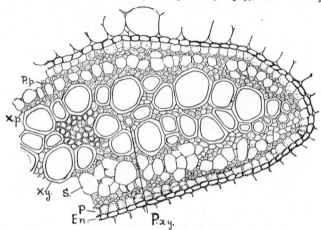

FIG. 243. Part of a stele from the rhizome of the Bracken (*Pteridium aquilinum*), in transverse section. *En.*, endodermis; *P.*, pericycle; *P.p.*, phloem-parenchyma; *P.xy.*, protoxylem; *S.*, sieve-tube; *X.p.*, xylem-parenchyma; *Xy.*, xylem.

recognised. There is generally a small central mass of wood-parenchyma.

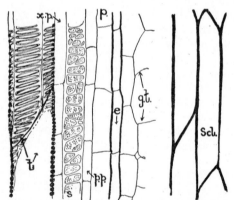

FIG. 244. On the left, part of a radial longitudinal section through one of the steles of the Bracken-rhizome. *e.*, endodermis; *g.t.*, ground tissue; *p.*, pericycle; *p.p.*, phloem-parenchyma; *s.*, sieve-tube; *t.*, tracheid of the metaxylem; *x.p.*, xylem-parenchyma. On the right, a little of the sclerenchyma (*Scl.*) in longitudinal section.

In longitudinal sections, cut so as to pass radially through a stele (Fig. 244), the *sieve-tubes* appear as elongated structures with tapering ends, and bearing the sieve areas on their sloping radial faces. Under the high power these sieve areas exhibit a rather irregular thickening of shining bars (*s.*), with intervening darker zones exhibiting a fine dotting and bearing a number of highly refractive adhering granules. The longitudinal walls of the meta-xylem *tracheids* (*t.*) exhibit several rows of closely arranged oblong bordered pits, producing an exceedingly characteristic type of

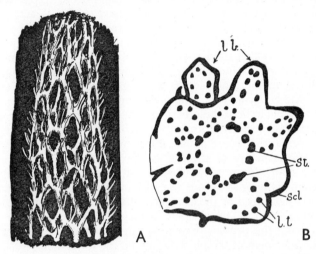

FIG. 245. *Dryopteris filix-mas.* A, Skeleton of vascular system showing the cylindrical network of steles, with numerous leaf-trace strands arising from the edges of the "leaf-gaps" (original). B, Transverse section of the rhizome (after De Bary). *l.b.*, leaf-bases; *l.t.*, leaf-trace strands; *Scl.*, sclerenchyma; *St.*, stem-steles.

scalariform thickening, whilst the protoxylem tracheids are spirally thickened in the usual way.

The number of steles varies, though structure and arrangement of xylem and phloem remain essentially the same. The seedling stem always possesses a single strand, but in many Ferns the mature structure is more complex, although some (*e.g.* the tropical *Gleichenia*) permanently retain a single large stele (*protostele*). Some Tree Ferns have an elaborate system of several concentric stelar cylinders. On the other hand, *Dryopteris* has but a single ring (*dictyostele*, Fig. 245, B, *St.*). In such Ferns, as the plant grows older, the protostele is first replaced by a cylindrical *solenostele* with central medulla and phloem on either side of the xylem, and this later becomes perforated by outward passage of vascular tissue into the large leaves.

These relations between the vascular system of stem and leaf are easily recognised in *Dryopteris* when the rhizome has been allowed to rot, so that all but the hard vascular tissues have disintegrated. In the resulting skeleton (Fig. 245, A) the steles form a cylindrical network, in which each mesh or *leaf-gap* corresponds in position to the attachment of a leaf. The latter is supplied by the numerous fine strands passing through the cortex from the margin of the mesh. These *leaf-traces* can be recognised, in a transverse section of the rhizome (Fig. 245, B), as arcs of small strands (*l.t.*) occupying the lobes that represent the leaf-bases (*l.b.*). In *Pteridium* a series of transverse sections, cut in the region of the node, shows that the leaf-base is supplied by several strands passing off from the outer ring. The gap thereby created is filled by steles from the inner series, which pass out, through a break in the sclerenchyma-ring, and also supply strands to the petiole. The petiole in both these Ferns is thus traversed by a large number of strands, normally forming an arch, but in certain genera (e.g. *Gleichenia*) the leaf-stalk, like the stem, contains but a single stele.

The structure of the *leaf* conforms to the dorsiventral type. Since many Ferns grow in shady situations, the epidermis often contains chloroplasts, and the palisade tissue is not uncommonly poorly developed or the mesophyll may even be spongy throughout (cf. Fig. 250). The ultimate branches of the concentric strands traversing the petioles become collateral within the pinnæ, owing to development of the phloem only on the lower side.

The *roots* of most Ferns are diarch, and owe their frequent wiry character to the development of an exceedingly thick-walled sclerenchymatous cortex, but otherwise do not differ appreciably from those of other plants. The tetrahedral apical cell, by whose divisions the tissues of stem and root are formed, has already been described on p. 51.

The Fern-plant sooner or later commences to produce spores. These are developed within small, stalked, usually brown-coloured *sporangia*, almost invariably borne on the under-surfaces of the fronds. Most commonly they are arranged in numerous separate groups, or *sori*, each usually comprising a considerable number of sporangia arising from a slight central swelling of the leaf-tissue, known as the *placenta* (Fig. 250, *pl.*).

Such sori are well seen in the Common Polypody (*Polypodium vulgare*, Fig. 242, B, *s.*), where they appear as small circular brown patches situated over the lateral veins of the pinnæ. A similar arrangement obtains in *Dryopteris* (Fig. 246, B), but here each sorus is protected by a kidney-shaped outgrowth (*indusium, In.*) of the placenta, which withers when the sporangia are mature. In the Maidenhair Fern (*Adiantum*, Fig. 242, C, *s.*) and the Wall

Rue (*Asplenium ruta-muraria*) the sori are near the edges of the pinnules; in the latter they are covered by indusia having the form of flaps attached along the edge facing the margin (Fig. 246, C). In *Pteridium* (D), where the sporangia form a continuous fringe all round the margin of the pinnule, the incurved edge of the latter functions as an indusium.

A peculiar type of sorus is found in the Filmy Ferns (Hymenophyllaceæ), which are so called because of their delicate fronds,

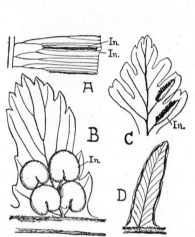

FIG. 246. Sori of various Ferns. A, Hart's Tongue Fern (*Phyllitis*). B, Male Fern (*Dryopteris*). C, *Asplenium*. D, Bracken (*Pteridium*). *In.*, indusium.

FIG. 247. On the left part of a Filmy Fern (*Hymenophyllum tunbridgense*), bearing sori (*s.*). The two smaller figures on the right show a sorus, entire and in longitudinal section respectively. *i.*, indusium; *s.*, sorus.

consisting of but a single layer of cells. Though mainly encountered in the Tropics, they are represented in Britain by one or two species (e.g. *Hymenophyllum tunbridgense*, Fig. 247) occurring in damp caves and other humid situations in rocky districts. Here the sporangia arise in sequence from above downwards on rod-like placentæ (*s.*) projecting from the leaf-margin, and each sorus is enveloped at its base in a cup-shaped indusium.

In most Ferns there is only one kind of frond which fulfils the ordinary functions of a leaf, as well as those connected with spore-production. In a few species, however, there is division of labour, as in the Hard Fern (Fig. 248). Here some of the leaves, spreading out near the surface of the ground, have broad pinnæ and are

FIG. 248. The Hard Fern (*Blechnum spicant*), showing foliage-leaves and sporophylls. [Photo. E. J. S.]

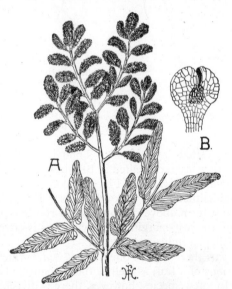

FIG. 249. A, Small part of a frond of the Royal Fern (*Osmunda regalis*), showing sterile pinnules (below) and fertile pinnules (above). (About half natural size.) (Original.) B, Single sporangium (after Luersen).

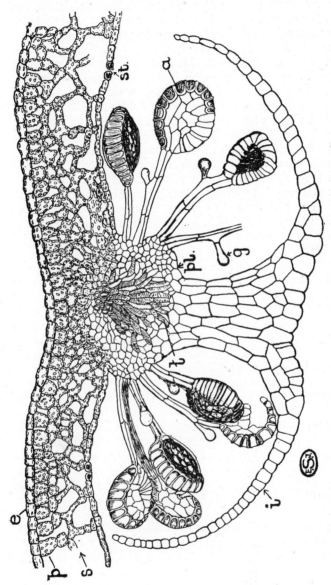

FIG. 250. Transverse section of a pinna, passing through a sorus, of the Male Fern (*Dryopteris filix-mas*), showing the indusium (*i.*), the placenta (*pl.*), and sporangia in various positions and stages of development. *a.*, annulus; *e.*, epidermis; *g.*, gland on sporangial stalk; *p.*, palisade tissue; *s.*, spongy tissue; *st.*, stoma; *t.*, tracheids.

purely vegetative, whilst others, which assume an erect position, have narrow pinnæ and are almost entirely concerned in the production of sporangia. Such fertile leaves are called *sporophylls*.

A less marked specialisation is seen in *Osmunda regalis*, where the lower part of the huge frond is sterile, whilst the upper pinnules, bearing the sporangia on both sides, exhibit practically no lamina (Fig. 249, A). In this connection it may be noted that in some tropical Ferns (e.g. *Platycerium*), which grow aloft on the branches of trees (a habit commonly seen in the Polypody in this country, Fig. 360), the lowest leaves are modified to form an oblique bracket by which humus is retained. A greater contrast between leaves and sporophylls is met with in other groups of Pteridophyta.

In transverse sections through a fertile pinnule of *Dryopteris filix-mas* (Fig. 250), the bulging placenta (*pl.*) on the under side is seen to be supplied by tracheids (*t.*) from the overlying vascular bundle. The indusium (*i.*) appears as an umbrella-shaped outgrowth, one layer of cells thick, arising from the top of the placenta. On the sides of the latter are borne numerous sporangia in various stages of development.

A mature *sporangium* (cf. also Fig. 251, B) consists of a stalk of usually three rows of elongated cells, terminated by a biconvex *capsule* which is more or less oval in side-view, and encloses the spores within a wall of a single layer of cells. The cells of the wall fit firmly together, and most of them are thin-walled and very flat, appearing more or less polygonal in surface-view, but tabular in optical section. The edge of the capsule, however, is occupied by a single row of specially differentiated cells. The greater part of this band, from the base of the capsule on one side to half-way down the other edge, is composed of cells which have all but their outer walls thickened, and which constitute the *annulus* (*a.* in Fig. 250 and *an.* in Fig. 251, B). The remainder, forming the so-called *stomium*, are much broader and thin-walled throughout (Fig. 251, B, *s.*), and it is here that the mature capsule ruptures.

Each sporangium arises as a papillate outgrowth from a single surface cell of the placenta, which is cut off by a cross-wall, and undergoes division by three oblique septa to produce a tetrahedral apical cell (Fig. 251, C, I, II). The three rows of segments, primarily cut off parallel to the three flat faces of the latter (III), elongate and become the stalk. Next, walls are formed parallel to all four faces of the apical cell (IV), and give rise to the one-layered capsule-wall (Fig. 251, D and E, *w.*), an inner nutritive layer, or *tapetum* (*t.*), and a central cell, the *archesporium* (*a.*). The last-named divides to form the *spore mother-cells*, each of which gives rise to four spores, the first of the two divisions in each

mother-cell being a reduction division. The development of the
spores takes place at the expense of the food-materials contained
in the granular thin-walled cells of the tapetum, which thus dis-
organises before the sporangium matures.

The four nuclei, produced in the spore mother-cell, usually
become grouped so as to form a tetrahedral figure. Each, together

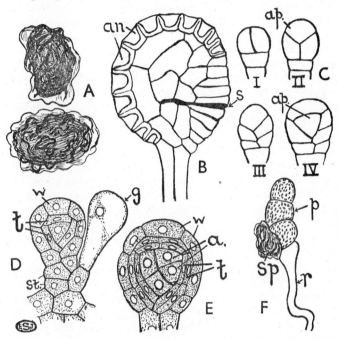

Fig. 251. *Dryopteris filix-mas.* A, Mature spores, greatly magnified. B,
A single sporangium, showing the annulus (*an.*) and stomium (*s.*). C, Early
stages (I–IV) in the development of the sporangium (after Müller). D and E,
Successively later stages. *a.*, archesporium; *ap.*, apical cell; *g.*, gland;
St., cells of stalk; *t.*, tapetum; *w.*, wall. F, Germinating spore (*sp.*). *p.*,
beginning of prothallus; *r.*, rhizoid.

with part of the cytoplasm, becomes surrounded by a separate
wall, the whole of the contents of the mother-cell being thus used
up to form four spores. Their faces of contact are more or less
flattened and triangular, while the outer walls are convex, so that
each spore, at its inception, has the form of a tetrahedron with a
rounded base (cf. Fig. 263, D). Often, however, the spores round
off after the mother-cell membrane has broken down.

With the ripening of the sorus the indusium dries and shrivels,
exposing the sporangia, which likewise begin to lose moisture.

As evaporation proceeds, the thin outer walls of the annulus cells commence to bulge inwards (cf. Figs. 250 and 251, B), owing to the gradual reduction in the volume of their sap. The marked thickening of the walls, transverse to the annulus as a whole, resists lateral shrinkage and thus restricts contraction to the longitudinal direction. Hence an increasing tension is set up in the annulus, which eventually leads to rupture of the capsule-wall along the plane of greatest weakness, viz. the junction between the transversely extended cells of the stomium (Fig. 251, B). On the release of the tension, the annulus, carrying with it a great part of the capsule-wall and many of the contained spores, bends back until evaporation is sufficient to overcome the force of adhesion between the water in the cells of the annulus and the wall. When this separation takes place, the annulus flies back and the spores are shot out as from a sling; they are further dispersed by air-currents, and may thus be carried to a considerable distance. Rupture of the ripe sporangia can be observed under the microscope by adding glycerine.

The sporangia of the Bracken, and many other British Ferns, agree in all essential respects with those of the Male Fern. In the Royal Fern (*Osmunda regalis*), however, the sporangia are short-stalked and pear-shaped. Dehiscence takes place by a vertical split starting from a group of thick-walled cells, a little below the summit of the sporangium, and extending over the top of the latter and some way down the opposite face (Fig. 249, B).

The spores of most Ferns retain their capacity for germination for some time. In their thick walls three layers can often be distinguished, of which the outermost, usually dark-coloured and opaque (Fig. 251, A), is cuticularised, and constitutes the principal protective covering, whilst the innermost is thin and elastic. In germination (Fig. 251, F) the outer coats (*Sp.*) are burst, and the innermost is stretched to form a long, colourless, tubular outgrowth, which becomes separated off from the main body of the spore by a transverse wall, and penetrates the soil as the first *rhizoid* (*r.*) of the future plant. The remainder of the spore-contents, enveloped by the innermost layer of the wall, lengthen into a short horizontal filament (*p.*) whose few cells contain chloroplasts. Within the terminal cell two intersecting walls soon arise, and the apical cell thus formed cuts off segments on either side, so that the filament widens into a flat plate.

As the front margin broadens, two or more of its cells become meristematic (Fig. 252, *g.p.*) and development proceeds rapidly; at the same time horizontal divisions in the middle region of the plate form the *cushion*, which is several cells thick. The green thalloid plant thus established is known as a *prothallus*, and when mature is usually heart-shaped, sometimes attaining a diameter of over a centimetre (Fig. 252). All the cells are alike and contain chloroplasts. From the under side, especially in the region of the cushion, scattered superficial cells grow out as colourless

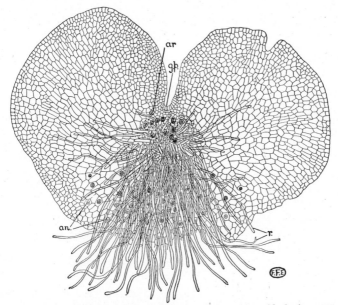

FIG. 252. Fern-prothallus, from the under surface (magnified about twenty times). A considerable number of antheridia (*an.*) are seen, on the older part, and the projecting necks of twelve archegonia (*ar.*), in the region of the cushion, from which also numerous rhizoids (*r.*) arise. *g.p.*, meristem.

rhizoids (*r.*), which serve for anchorage and the absorption of moisture.

When the prothalli grow densely crowded, they often remain more or less filamentous, a condition which is normal for most of the Filmy Ferns.

The prothallus is the Fern-plant (*gametophyte*) that bears the sexual organs. These are of the same general type as in Bryophyta, and are produced by the outgrowth of single cells, situated on the lower surface. Both kinds usually occur on the same prothallus (Fig. 252). The *antheridia* (*an.*), found mainly on the thinner marginal wings and the less robust prothalli, are almost spherical structures (Fig. 253, *g.*) with a small number of relatively large spermatozoid mother-cells (*s.*). The enveloping wall (*w.*) is peculiar in being composed only of two superposed ring-shaped cells surmounted by a dome-shaped cap-cell (Fig. 253, *e*). The spermatozoids (Fig. 253, *d*), which are developed in the same way as in the Bryophyta (cf. p. 358), have a spirally coiled, spindle-shaped body bearing numerous flagella near the pointed end. Dehiscence of the antheridium, by the breaking away or rupture of the cap-cell (Fig. 253, *e* and *f*), takes place in wet weather, and

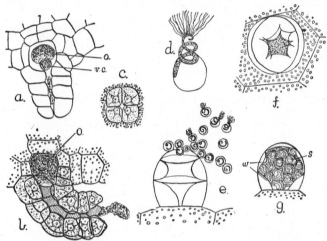

FIG. 253. *a–c*, Archegonia, *e–g*, Antheridia, and *d*, Single spermatozoid of the Fern.   *a*, Immature, and *b*, mature, archegonium in longitudinal section; *c*, Neck in surface-view.   *o.*, egg; *v.c.*, ventral canal cell.   *g*, Almost mature antheridium in optical section, showing the wall (*w.*) and the spermatozoid mother-cells (*s.*);   *e*, Dehiscing antheridium with the escaping spermatozoids; *f*, Dehisced antheridium from above.   (*a*, after Goebel; the remainder after Kny.)

the liberated spermatozoids swim in the film of water retained by capillarity between the lower surface of the prothallus and the soil.

The *archegonia* are restricted to the region of the cushion, in which they are partially embedded, the necks alone projecting (Fig. 252, *ar.*; Fig. 253, *a* and *b*). The necks are all curved towards the pointed end of the prothallus, and differ from those of a Bryophyte archegonium in being short and composed of only four longitudinal rows of cells (Fig. 253, *c*), whilst there is but a single canal cell. The venter, containing the egg (*o.*) and the ventral canal cell (*v.c.*), appears as a mere cavity in the tissue of the prothallus. At maturity (Fig. 253, *b*) the four cells at the top of the neck are forced apart by a mucilage containing malic acid, formed during the disorganisation of the canal cells, and an open passage is thus left leading down to the egg. It is apparently the malic acid that attracts the spermatozoids to the archegonia.

After fertilisation the ovum becomes enveloped by a thin membrane, and divides by three successive walls into octants of a sphere (Fig. 254, A). Their further segmentation leads to the differentiation of four apical cells, which are situated one in each quadrant, and which respectively give rise to the root, the

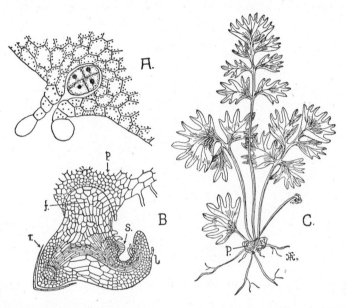

FIG. 254. Embryology of the Fern. A, Longitudinal section through an archegonium, showing the octant-stage in the division of the fertilised egg (after Sadebeck). B, Young embryo escaping from the prothallus (*p.*) (after Hofmeister). *f.*, foot; *l.*, first leaf; *r.*, first root; *s.*, stem. C, Young plant, with the remains of the prothallus (*p.*) at the base, four unfolded leaves of increasing complexity, and one leaf not yet unfolded (original).

stem, the first leaf, and the "foot" of the *embryo*. The *foot* develops as a large parenchymatous sucker which becomes firmly lodged in the tissue of the cushion, from whose cells it absorbs nourishment for the young Fern (Fig. 254, B, *f*).

By this means rapid growth of the root (Fig. 254, B, *r*.) takes place, and it soon pierces the prothallus and penetrates into the soil. Simultaneously the first leaf (*l*.), carrying with it the still rudimentary stem (*s*.), emerges on the lower side, and, arching up through the notch at the front end of the heart-shaped prothallus, exposes its green blade to the light. The stem now grows more vigorously, giving rise to adventitious roots which replace the short-lived primary root, and it is not long before further leaves develop (Fig. 254, C). The latter, however, show but a very gradual increase in complexity, from the first, often almost undivided leaf, to the normal compound foliage of the adult Fern, which is frequently only attained after the lapse of several years. Production of sporangia is generally deferred till this stage is reached.

The young Fern, like the sporophyte of Liverworts and Mosses, is thus for a time dependent for nourishment on the prothallus.

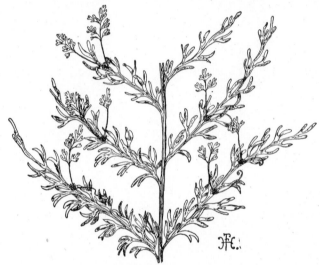

FIG. 255. Small part of a frond of *Asplenium bulbiferum,* showing the vegetative production of new plants (about half natural size).

But, as soon as the root has become established in the soil and the first leaf has spread out its lamina to the light, this dependence ceases and, soon after, the prothallus withers away (cf. Fig. 254, C). As compared with Bryophyta, the relative importance of the two phases in the life-history is therefore reversed. The free-living sporophyte usually attains large dimensions and exhibits a complexity of structure which is barely approached by the perennial gametophytes of some few Mosses. On the other hand, the sexual generation is as a general rule short-lived, though in a few Ferns (e.g. *Osmunda*) it persists for some years. Normally the two generations alternate regularly with one another, but occasional abnormalities are encountered.

Thus, in certain Ferns the prothalli may arise by direct budding from the leaves or sporangia, without the formation of spores (*apospory*), a condition that has been experimentally induced in a variety of the Lady Fern by pinning detached segments of the fronds on damp sand. Sometimes the sporophyte develops vegetatively from the prothallus without the intervention of sexual organs (*apogamy*). Vegetative multiplication is not infrequent, new plants arising from buds formed on the surface of the fronds, as in the commonly cultivated *Asplenium bulbiferum* (Fig. 255).

In the normal life-cycle, of Bryophyta and Pteridophyta alike, the spore is the starting-point of the sexual, and the fertilised egg of the asexual, generation. The spore mother-cells, with few exceptions, give rise to four spores, after undergoing two successive nuclear divisions. The first of these involves the passage of entire chromosomes to the two poles of the dividing nucleus, as a result of which their number is halved. The two successive divisions produce four haploid spores. The diploid number is restored by sexual fusion. The sexual generation is thus haploid and the asexual diploid. The alternation in Ferns and other Pteridophyta is similar to that exhibited by *Laminaria* (p. 314).

Fossil evidence suggests that the Ferns are a very ancient group and that they were already a marked constituent of the earth's vegetation as far back as the Devonian epoch, some four hundred million years ago. Remains, known as *Archæopteris* and attributable to this group, are widespread in Upper Devonian rocks. In the Carboniferous epoch the forests contained tree-like Ferns, whose stems (known as *Psaronius*), with a complex stelar structure, are frequently preserved. They occurred in various parts of the world and perhaps represented a stock, of which the tropical and subtropical Marattiaceæ are the sole living survivors. Other ferns, found in rocks of Carboniferous age, are shown by their anatomical structure to be related to the modern *Osmunda*.

Although it is probable that Ferns abounded in the Carboniferous vegetation, the possession by Pteridosperms (p. 402) of quite similar fronds leaves it open as to what proportion of the numerous impressions of such leaves belonged to the one or other group. The Carboniferous Ferns often showed forking of the fronds, sometimes in two planes, and some exhibited axillary branching. In general these ancient Ferns seem to have been more robust and woody than most of their modern relatives, but this is perhaps merely due to the better preservation of such types.

[For further details on Ferns, see F. O. Bower, *Primitive Land Plants*, Macmillan & Co., 1935 (658 pp.), a good brief account; a much more extensive treatment by the same author is: *The Ferns*, 3 vols., Cambridge Botan. Handbooks, Cambridge Univ. Press, 1923–28. For taxonomic works, see p. 578.]

CHAPTER XXXIII

HORSETAILS (EQUISETALES) AND CLUBMOSSES (LYCOPODIALES)

THE Ferns (*Filicales*) alone of the existing groups of Pteridophyta are widely represented at the present day. Not only are they almost ubiquitous in their distribution, but they comprise a large number of families and genera. The Bracken in North Temperate zones, and *Gleichenia* in the Tropics, illustrate, moreover, the important rôle played by Ferns in many types of vegetation.

The Horsetails (*Equisetales*) and Clubmosses (*Lycopodiales*),[1] on the other hand, which, like the Ferns, have been traced back in the fossil state to very early periods of the earth's history, are now only represented by a few very distinct genera. These groups flourished vigorously, however, at the period when the Coal Measures were laid down; then they comprised woody plants which, in great part, attained to the dimensions of trees (Fig. 259). These features have been lost by the living forms of the present day, which are mostly small perennials. It is, indeed, probably correct to regard the remote past as the age of trees and the present rather as that of herbs (see p. 19).

By contrast with Ferns the leaves of Horsetails and Clubmosses are remarkably small and simple in form, so that the habit of the plant is here determined mainly by the character and extent of branching of the stem (Fig. 256, A and C; Fig. 262, A). The Horsetails (*Equisetum*) are switch-plants (Fig. 256, A and C and p. 504) whose green, longitudinally furrowed stems bear whorls of brownish scale-leaves fused to form a toothed sheath (*s.l.*) around each node. The branches are likewise whorled (Fig. 256, C), and, since they arise relatively late, have to pierce their way through

---

[1] For a more extensive treatment, see F. O. Bower, *Primitive Land Plants*, Macmillan & Co., 1935 (658 pp.). For fossil Pteridophyta consult D. H. Scott, *Studies in Fossil Botany*, 2 vols., A. & C. Black, 3rd. edit., 1923, a general anatomical and morphological account; and A. C. Seward, *Fossil Plants*, 4 vols., Cambridge Univ. Press, 1898–1919, a comprehensive taxonomic account of fossil plants.

the bases of the fused leaves.   The erect shoots are the upturned
ends of the branches of underground rhizomes (Fig. 256, A), which
bear similar whorls of scale-leaves, as well as numerous adventitious
roots, at each node.   The rhizome of the Field Horsetail (*Equisetum*

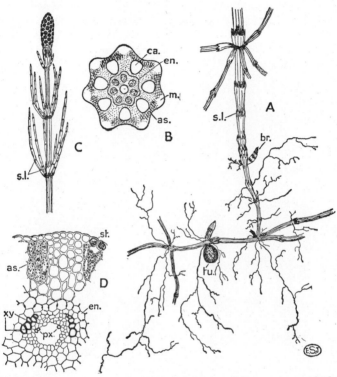

FIG. 256. *Equisetum*.   A, Lower part of aerial shoot of *E. arvense*, attached to
the rhizome; *br.*, branch; *s.l.*, scale-leaves forming whorl at node; *tu.*,
tuber.   B, Diagram of transverse section of stem of same; *as.*, photosynthetic
tissue; *ca.*, air-canal in cortex; *en.*, endodermis surrounding the seven
vascular bundles; *m.*, mechanical tissue.   C, *E. palustre*, upright fertile shoot
with terminal cone.   D, Portion of a transverse section of a stem of same
showing the photosynthetic tissue (*as.*), the endodermis (*en.*), a stoma (*st.*),
the protoxylem-canal with protoxylem elements (*px.*) at its margin and the
metaxylem (*xy.*).

arvense) bears easily detached tubers (Fig. 256, A, *tu.*) which are
formed from modified branches and are a prolific means of vegetative
reproduction.   In the ancient Horsetails (*Calamites*) of the Palæozoic,
the leaves were larger (cf. Fig. 257, B) and, like the branches, were
whorled.

The *anatomy* of the stem (Fig. 256, B, D) superficially resembles that of a Dicotyledon in the arrangement of the vascular tissues and shows groups of photosynthetic tissue (*as.*) opposite the shallow furrows in which the stomata (*st.*) are situated.   There is always great reduction of the xylem and a conspicuous system of air-canals in the cortex and pith (Fig. 256, B, D).   These aquatic characteristics (cf. p. 544) are to be expected in partially submerged

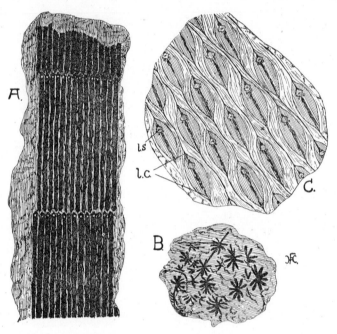

FIG. 257. Common forms of preservation of the fossil Horsetails and Club-mosses. A, Pith-cast of *Calamites*. B, *Annularia sphenophylloides*, the foliage of *Calamites*. C, Small part of the surface of the stem of a *Lepidodendron*, showing the characteristic leaf-cushions (*l.c.*); *l.s.*, leaf-scar.

species like *Equisetum fluviatile* and *E. palustre*, but the fact that others (e.g. *E. arvense*), growing in relatively dry situations, show similar features may imply that the genus has an aquatic ancestry.   Indeed, there is evidence that the Palæozoic *Calamites*, with stems of similar structure, though possessed of extensive secondary thickening, lived in swamps.   Their remains are commonly found as pith-casts (Fig. 257, A).

The sporangia of Horsetails are borne on little mushroom-shaped *sporophylls* (Fig. 258, B), differing widely from the ordinary leaves, and grouped in whorls at the ends of the stems to form *cones* or *strobili* (Fig. 256, C; Fig. 258, A).   These usually terminate the ordinary vegetative shoots, though in the Field Horsetail (*E. arvense*) they are found in spring on special shoots distinguished by their brown colour and the absence of branches. Each peltate sporophyll is perpendicular to the main axis, and bears on the inner face of its hexagonal lamina a ring of 5 to 10 sporangia encircling the stalk (Fig. 258, B).   In the young cone the heads of the sporophylls fit closely together, thus forming a compact protection for the sporangia; but as the latter mature the sporophylls separate, through elongation of the axis, and permit escape of the green spores.   The individual sporangia are rather larger than those of Ferns, and have a several-layered wall. Many of the fossil Horsetails possessed cones of more elaborate structure.

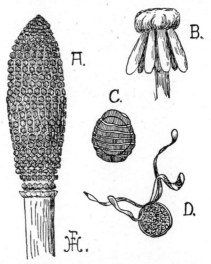

At maturity the outermost coat of each spore consists of four extremely hygroscopic spiral strips (Fig. 258, C, D) which only remain attached at one point.   Groups of spores consequently tend to be entangled when the contents of a sporangium

FIG. 258. A, Entire cone, and B, Single sporophyll of *Equisetum telmateia* (original). C and D, Mature spores, showing the splitting of the outer coat. (C, after Sachs; D, after Dodel-Port.)

are scattered by the wind, and this may be of importance, since the archegonia and antheridia are usually produced on distinct *prothalli*. The spores are, however, all alike, the sex of the resulting prothalli depending on the conditions of nutrition, those poorly nourished becoming male, whilst those well nourished become female.   Both kinds are more or less richly branched, but the male are much smaller than the female.   The sexual organs borne upon them do not differ markedly from those of Ferns.   It may be noted that, when Fern prothalli grow densely crowded, they often bear antheridia only, although unisexuality is here the exception rather than the rule.

The present-day Clubmosses are represented mainly by the genera *Lycopodium* (Fig. 261, A) and *Selaginella* (Fig. 262).   The Quillwort (*Isoëtes lacustris*, Fig. 260), which occurs submerged in mountain tarns, is a peculiar member of this group, many of whose features recall those of the fossil Clubmosses (*Lepidodendron*, Fig. 259). Fragments of the stems of *Lepidodendron* with, or often without, the leaves are very common in the Coal Measures and are readily identified by their characteristic markings (Fig. 257, C).

FIG. 259. Restoration of various fossil Clubmosses (*Lepidodendron* and *Sigillaria*). (After Grand Eury.)

FIG. 260. The Quillwort (*Isoëtes lacustris*), somewhat reduced.

The small spirally arranged leaves of *Lycopodium* densely clothe the stems, which are either erect, as in the Fir Clubmoss (*L. selago*), or prostrate, except for the cone-bearing shoots, as in *L. clavatum* (Fig. 261, A). The stems, as well as the occasional adventitious roots, exhibit forked branching, and never contain more than a single rather root-like stele,[1] whose detailed structure is often somewhat complex. The sessile leaves are attached by a broad cushion-

---

[1] A single stele was likewise found in *Lepidodendron* where, however, it became enveloped by a broad zone of secondary wood and phloem.

like base, and are traversed by but a single median vein (Fig. 261, B); the same obtained in *Lepidodendron*, the persistent leaf-cushions (Fig. 257, C, *l.c.*) affording the distinctive markings above referred to. The British species of *Lycopodium* are found in moist upland pasture, except for *L. inundatum*, which occurs in lowland bogs.

The *sporophylls* (Fig. 261, B) are similar to the foliage-leaves,

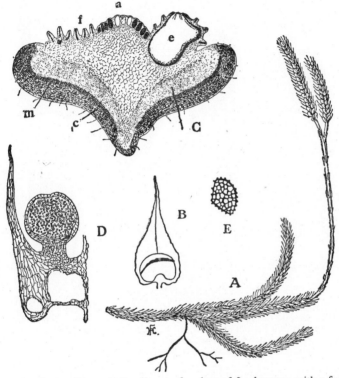

FIG. 261. *Lycopodium.* A, Small part of a plant of *L. clavatum*, with a fertile shoot bearing two cones. B, Single sporophyll of same, with a dehiscent sporangium. C, Prothallus of same in section, much enlarged, showing antheridia (*a*), archegonia (*f*), and a developing embryo (*e*). *c.*, cortex; *m.*, mycorrhizal layer. D, Longitudinal section of sporophyll with sporangium. E, Spore. (B, after Strasburger; C, after Bruchman; the rest original.)

and are commonly in whorls; they are readily recognised by the single large, somewhat kidney-shaped, sporangium which each bears on its upper surface. In most species the sporophylls are aggregated in cones, as in *Equisetum*, although in *L. selago*, for example, the reproductive region is not clearly marked, zones of sporophylls usually alternating with vegetative leaves. Another peculiarity of this species is the development of large *bulbils* in the axils of the uppermost leaves; these structures, which serve for vegetative reproduction, must not be mistaken for sporophylls.

The *cones*, when present, occupy the ends of erect branches, which are of the ordinary type, except in *L. clavatum* (Fig. 261, A); here they bear minute leaves, at rather wide intervals, contrasting

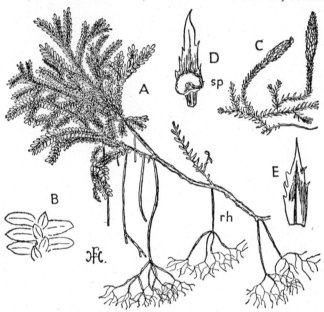

FIG. 262. A and B, *Selaginella martensii* (original).   A, Part of a plant showing the leafy shoots, the rhizophores (*rh.*), and the roots arising from their ends. B, Small part of a branch enlarged, to show the two kinds of leaves.   C, Plant of *S. selaginoides* (after Wettstein), showing two cones.   D, Sporophyll, and E, foliage-leaf of *S. selaginoides* (after Hieronymus).   *sp.*, sporangium.

markedly with the densely arranged sporophylls of the cone.   Each sporangium contains numerous spores (Fig. 261, D) which, after being shed, give rise to peculiar fleshy *prothalli* (Fig. 261, C).   In most species these grow underground as saprophytes, obtaining their food with the aid of a mycorrhiza (*m.*) from the humus in which they are embedded, but despite this fact they show rather more anatomical differentiation than is usual in prothalli.   Some species exhibit a slight development of green leafy lobes at the surface. Archegonia (*f*) and antheridia (*a*) are borne on the same prothallus (Fig. 261, C).

Although *Selaginella* is represented in Britain only by *S. selaginoides* (Fig. 262, C), which is found in similar habitats to those frequented by our species of *Lycopodium*, several members of the genus are commonly cultivated. The general habit is like that of *Lycopodium*, but in most species the leaves are arranged in four rows, two comprised of small leaves situated on the upper side of the stem, and two of large leaves towards the lower side (Fig. 262, A and B); at each node there is one large and one small leaf. The British *S. selaginoides*, in which the habit is erect, possesses leaves that are all alike (Fig. 262, C).

In many *Selaginellas* the method of rooting is peculiar, the roots arising from special leafless branches known as *rhizophores* (Fig. 262, A, *rh*.). These are formed in pairs at the points of forking of the stems, but usually only one member of each pair develops. This grows downwards, generally forking repeatedly, and, on reaching the soil, roots originate from the swollen tips of the ultimate branches.

The stem is traversed by one or few steles,[1] essentially like those of Ferns, except that each is surrounded by an air-space, which is bridged either by strands of cortical cells, or by radially elongated endodermal cells. The roots and rhizophores are peculiar in exhibiting but a single protoxylem group.

The *cones*, again situated at the ends of usually erect branches (Fig. 262, C), exhibit four rows of sporophylls, all of the same size and shape, and each with an axillary sporangium borne on a short stalk (Fig. 262, D, *sp.*; Fig. 263, A, E). The sporangia are of two kinds: the one kind (microsporangia), generally found towards the apex of the cone, are filled with numerous small *microspores* (Fig. 263, A, *mi*.); the other kind (megasporangia) each contain only four large *megaspores* (Fig. 263, A, *mg*.). These features are readily observed in longitudinal sections through the cones, which also show the presence of a small outgrowth (the *ligule*, Fig. 263, *l*.) from the upper surface of each sporophyll, between its upturned tip and the sporangium. Such ligules, though most conspicuous on the sporophylls, occur also on all the vegetative leaves, but their function is obscure. A ligule is not met with in the genus *Lycopodium*, but occurs in *Isoëtes* and appears to have been characteristic of most of the extinct representatives of the group, which also possessed two kinds of spores.

The young sporangia of *Selaginella* have a several-layered wall, enclosing a large number of spore mother-cells, and, up to this stage, all are alike. In the microsporangia each mother-cell gives rise to four small spores, but in the megasporangia only one develops further, enlarging rapidly at the expense of the others, and dividing to form the single tetrad (Fig. 263, A). An American species

---

[1] One in *S. selaginoides*, three in *S. kraussiana*.

(*S. rupestris*) exhibits an even greater reduction, since occasionally only one of the four megaspores reaches maturity, and, in this and certain other species, they are retained within the sporangium until after the fertilisation of the archegonia produced in the resulting prothalli. Both kinds of sporangia dehisce by a wide slit, the spores ordinarily maturing their prothalli on the ground.

The contents of the microspore divide to form a few-celled,

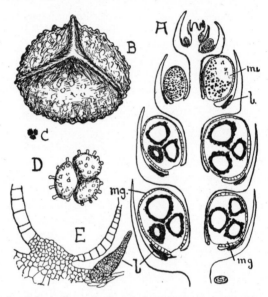

FIG. 263. *Selaginella umbrosa*. A, Longitudinal section through part of a cone, showing microsporangia (*mi.*) above and megasporangia (*mg.*) below. E, Small part of megasporangium enlarged to show the stalk and wall. *l.*, ligule. B, Single megaspore enlarged. C, Tetrad of microspores on the same scale of magnification as B. D, Tetrad of microspores enlarged.

exceedingly reduced *male prothallus*, developing neither chloroplasts nor rhizoids, and consisting in the main of a small number of spermatozoid mother-cells (Fig. 264, *f*). The resulting biflagellate spermatozoids (Fig. 264, *d*) are liberated, during wet weather, by the rupture of the coats of the microspores.

The *female prothallus* begins to develop within the megaspore long before the latter is shed, and, like the male, exhibits considerable reduction and usually remains colourless. The early stages of its formation are characterised by repeated division of the megaspore-nucleus, separating walls only arising much later. When ready for fertilisation the prothallus consists of a small-celled tissue, situated opposite the apex of the tetrahedral spore and exposed by the rupture of its coats (Fig. 264, *a* and *b, p.*), while the bulk of the spore-contents, still enclosed in the megaspore-wall, are occupied by large cells laden with food-material (*f.*).   The few

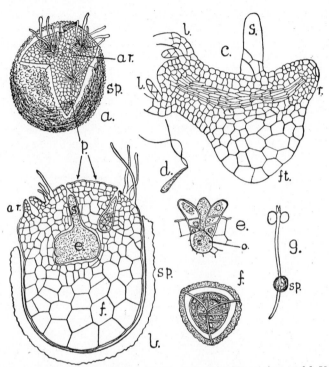

FIG. 264. *Selaginella*, prothallia and embryology. *a*, Front view, and *b*, Vertical section of mature megaspore with female prothallus; *c*, Older embryo; *d*, Spermatozoid; *e*, Archegonium in longitudinal section; *f*, Microspore with contained male prothallus; *g*, Young plant still attached to the megaspore (*sp.*). *ar.*, archegonia; *e.*, embryo (in *b*); *f.*, large-celled nutritive tissue (in *b*); *ft.*, foot (in *c*); *l.*, leaves of embryo; *o.*, egg (in *e*); *p*, prothallus; *r.*, radicle; *S.*, suspensor; *Sp.*, coat of megaspore. (*a, e* and *g*, after Bruchman; *d*, after Belajeff; remainder after Pfeffer.)

archegonia, which have very short, scarcely projecting necks (Fig. 264, *e*), are embedded in the small-celled apical region (Fig. 264, *a,b, ar.*).

The fertilised egg divides transversely, the inner (lower) half giving rise to the *embryo* proper. The outer (upper) half, forming the so-called *suspensor* (Fig. 264, *b* and *c, S.*), divides a few times and elongates considerably, so that the developing embryo is pushed down into the large-celled nutritive tissue (*f.*) below. The suspensor is a structure characteristic of the higher seed-plants, but in other essential respects the embryology resembles that of Ferns. Absorption of the stored food takes place by means of a sucker or foot (Fig. 264, *c*, *ft.*), but the young plant acquires independence at an early stage (Fig. 264, *g*).

Regarded as a whole, the Pteridophyta exhibit a great variety of vegetative structure, and considerable specialisation in their reproductive processes. They offer a marked contrast to the Bryophyta in the relative importance of the spore-producing phase, which is an independent plant highly adapted to a terrestrial existence. Associated with the last-named feature we see the differentiation of specialised conducting tissue and of true roots. There is, moreover, a marked tendency towards division of labour, on the one hand between vegetative and reproductive leaves, on the other between the prothalli. In the Ferns all the latter are alike and bear both kinds of sexual organs, although there are occasional exceptions when the conditions of nutrition are abnormal (cf. p. 389). This tendency manifests itself in the definite uni-sexual prothalli of the Horsetails, which, however, like the Ferns, have only one kind of spore, *i.e.* are *homosporous*. *Lycopodium* resembles the Ferns in these respects, but in *Selaginella* and *Isoëtes*, not only are the prothalli unisexual, but they are produced from two kinds of spores, *i.e.* these genera are *heterosporous*.

Heterospory involves the risk of the two sexes of prothalli not germinating in sufficiently close proximity to one another. Certain advantages similar to those obtained by oogamy (cf. p. 309), obviously accrue, *e.g.* the provision by the mother-plant of an abundant store of food for the development of the new sporophyte. These reserves are laid down in the megaspore before it is shed, and, as a consequence, the resulting prothallus can dispense with rhizoids and a photosynthetic mechanism. Moreover, the embryo acquires additional protection during the early stages of its development from the coats of the megaspore, within which the greater part of the prothallus remains enclosed (cf. Fig. 264, *b*.). A further step would obviously be the retention of the megaspore within the sporangium until after fertilisation and during the development of the embryo, and this is the rule in the Spermaphyta. The microspores, requiring no appreciable amount of food-reserves, and being consequently of small dimensions, can be produced in large numbers. This affords an increased power of dispersal whereby the association of the two prothalli is rendered more probable.

CHAPTER XXXIV

CYCADS AND EXTINCT SEED-BEARING PLANTS

A GROUP may now be considered which, although portraying many of the characteristics of Flowering Plants, nevertheless shows several features reminiscent of Ferns. These are the *Cycads*,[1] which have a wide distribution in the tropical regions of America, South Africa, Eastern Asia, and Australia, though most of the genera have a very restricted range (cf. Fig. 416). Fossil records show the group to be a very ancient one that played a particularly important part during the Mesozoic period, the present-day representatives appearing merely as relics. The Sago-palm (*Cycas revoluta*) is in most respects typical of the living forms.

Most Cycads (Fig. 265) have the appearance of Palms or Tree Ferns, the often huge pinnate leaves forming a crown at the top of the partly subterranean and tuberous, or overground and columnar, stems which may attain a height of sixty feet. The trunk is rarely branched, and, in the older portion, its entire surface is covered with an armour formed by the large persistent bases of the leaves of previous seasons. Fresh leaves are produced at intervals, the outer ones of each crop being modified to form protective bud-scales. In some of the genera the unfolding leaves exhibit a spiral inrolling of the pinnæ (e.g. *Cycas*, Fig. 266), or of the midrib, similar to that characteristic of Ferns. Other resemblances to this group are to be found in the forked veining of the blades (Fig. 267, E) and in the structure of the petiole. The numerous vascular strands of the latter have the protoxylem embedded within the metaxylem, a feature especially characteristic of Ferns (cf. p. 372 and Fig. 243, *P.xy.*), whereas in the vast majority of the Seed Plants the protoxylem of the stem is immediately adjacent to the pith (cf. p. 136).

Cycads often attain a great age and their stems exhibit secondary thickening like that of woody Dicotyledons. The pith is very large, and, in the Sago-palm, contains the stores of starch which are one of the sources of the sago of commerce.

[1] For reference-books, see p. 425.

The *sporophylls* are of two kinds, microsporophylls and mega-sporophylls, and are arranged in distinct male and female cones, borne on separate individuals.   The *microsporophylls* are thick

FIG. 265. Young plant of *Cycas circinalis*.   [Photo. E. J. S.]
FIG. 266. Young leaf of *Cycas*, showing spiral inrolling of the pinnæ.
[Photo. E. J. S.]

scales which are spirally arranged (Fig. 267, A), and bear, on their under-surface, numerous sporangia (Fig. 267, D), often collected together in small groups; they dehisce by a wide split.   The *megasporophylls* are usually of a similar nature, although they produce only two megasporangia, often placed one on either side of the stalk-like lower part (Fig. 268, B); the megasporangia are of a peculiar type and are known as *ovules*.   In *Cycas*, however, the megasporophylls resemble the foliage-leaves, although relatively small, hairy, and brown in colour, and often bear more than two ovules (Fig. 268, A).   The female plant of *Cycas* can be com-pared with such a Fern as *Blechnum* (cf. p. 375), since in both the sporangia occur on fronds which are but little modified.   An examination of the megasporophylls of different Cycads shows all stages in the reduction of the lamina to a condition in which the leaf-like character is almost entirely obscured (e.g. *Encephalartos*, Fig. 268, B).

The *ovules* (*megasporangia*) (Fig. 268, C and D) are of considerable size, but contain only a single large megaspore (*p.*) within the several-layered parenchymatous wall or *nucellus* (*n.*). The delicate texture of the latter can be related to the presence of a thick protective covering (*o.* and *i.*). This integument completely envelops the nucellus, and is indeed fused with it except at its

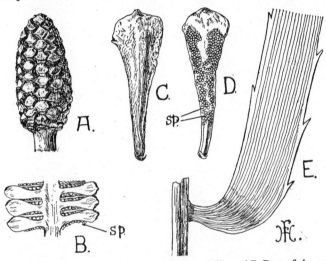

FIG. 267. A, Entire male cone of *Bowenia spectabilis*, and B, Part of the same in longitudinal section, showing the microsporangia (*sp.*) on the lower surfaces of the sporophylls. C, Upper, and D, Lower surface of a microsporophyll of *Cycas. sp.*, microsporangia. E, Part of a pinna of the leaf of *Encephalartos* to show the veining.

extreme apex. In this region the integument is pierced by a narrow canal, the *micropyle* (*mi.*), leading down to the *pollen chamber* (*p.c.*), which is a conical cavity formed by the breaking down of cells in the tip of the nucellus. The ovule is supplied by two vascular strands from the sporophyll. These fork at its base to form two systems of branches, extending almost to the extreme tip: those of the outer series (*o.b.*) traverse the peripheral layers of the integument, whilst those of the inner (*i.b.*) run close to the line of junction of the latter and the nucellus.

The wind- or insect-borne microspores (*pollen grains*) are drawn into the pollen chamber by the drying up and contraction of the mucilaginous fluid (formed by the disintegrating cells of the nucellus) which exudes from the micropyle at the time of pollination. Within the pollen chamber germination ensues (Fig. 268, C, and 269, C), and a short branching sucker-like pollen tube (*p.t.*) grows into the adjacent tissue of the nucellus.[1] Subsequently two *spermatozoids*, each with a spiral band of flagella [2] (Fig. 269, B, *s.*), are developed within the main body of the micro-

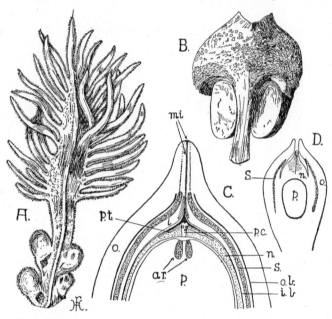

FIG. 268. A, Megasporophyll of *Cycas revoluta* with four ovules (about half natural size). B, Mature megasporophyll of *Encephalartos hildenbrandtii*, bearing two seeds (about half natural size). D, Diagram of longitudinal section of ovule of *Bowenia spectabilis*, and C, Front end of same enlarged. *ar.*, archegonia; *i.*, inner fleshy layer of integument; *i.b.*, vascular bundle of inner series; *mi.*, micropyle; *n.*, nucellus; *o.*, outer fleshy layer of integument; *o.b.*, bundle of outer series; *p.*, female prothallus within megaspore; *p.c.*, pollen chamber; *p.t.*, pollen tube; *s.*, stony layer of integument. (A and B, original; C and D, after Kershaw.)

spore. In the meantime the large megaspore has become filled with a uniform tissue, the *female prothallus* (Figs. 268, C, and 269, C, *p.*) which produces a, commonly small, number of archegonia (*ar.*), with very minute necks (*n.*) and large eggs (*o.*), at the end adjacent to the micropyle.

The nucellar tissue between the pollen chamber and the female

---

[1] The sequence of events in the germination of the microspores of Cycads is very similar to that in Conifers (cf. p. 421).

[2] Apart from the Cycads, the Maiden-hair Tree (*Ginkgo biloba*) is the only seed-plant which has flagellate, free-swimming sperms.

prothallus breaks down (Fig. 269, C), with the formation of a slimy fluid in which the liberated spermatozoids (*s.*) swim to the archegonia (*o.*), and in this way fertilisation is accomplished. The nucleus of the fertilised egg divides repeatedly to form numerous nuclei which, at least in the lower part of the oospore, become separated by cell-walls. It is this region alone that gives rise to

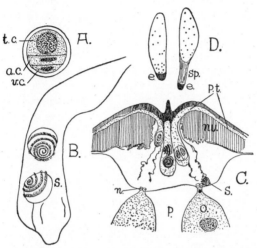

Fig. 269. A, Germinating microscope of *Cycas*, showing vegetative cell (*v.c.*), antheridial cell (*a.c.*), and tube cell (*t.c.*). B, Pollen tube with the two spermatozoids (*s.*). C, Diagram of longitudinal section through apex of nucellus (*nu.*) and female prothallus (*p.*) of *Dioon edule*, showing pollen tubes (*p.t.*) and pollen grains in various stages of development, spermatozoids (*s.*), and archegonia with eggs (*o.*) and necks (*n.*). D, Two proembryos of *Dioon edule*, the left-hand one younger than the right-hand one; the dotted part is the fertilised ovum. *e.*, embryo; *Sp.*, suspensor. (A and B, after Ikeno; C and D, from Chamberlain.)

the embryo (Fig. 269, D, *e.*), whilst the remainder serves for nutrition.

In each ovule only one *embryo* ultimately develops, its growth taking place at the expense of the surrounding prothallus, into the centre of which it is carried by the marked elongation of a suspensor (Fig. 269, D, *sp.*). Upon reaching a certain stage, however, in which two cotyledons, plumule, and radicle can be distinguished, the embryo becomes dormant, the residue of the female prothallus around forming a nutritive tissue, the *endosperm*. The whole is enveloped by the thick integument, now differentiated into three layers, which can even be recognised in an immature form in the young ovule. These layers comprise an inner (Fig. 268, C, *i.*), and a much thicker outer (*o.*), flesh, with an intervening very hard stony layer (*s.*). This product of megasporangium, female pro-thallus, and embryo is a plum-like *seed*, many times the size of the original ovule.

The Cycads obviously show many superficial resemblances to Ferns, but these are even more pronounced in another group of plants (*Pteridosperms*) which, like the *Calamites* and *Lepidodendrons* of the Coal Measures, are known only as fossils. The members of this group, though closely resembling the Ferns in habit, show analogies with Cycads in their anatomy, their mode of reproduction, and especially in the possession of seeds.

A complete knowledge of such fossil plants [1] is only acquired gradually and as a result of prolonged research. At first the separate fragments of stem, root, leaves, etc., are studied as un-related structures, but subsequently patient toil pieces them together till a more or less complete picture of the whole is obtained. The external appearance of a fossil plant is best appreciated from casts or impressions preserved in consolidated mud, sand, etc. Not . infrequently, however, the tissues have been impregnated with silica, calcium carbonate, etc., so that the internal structure is recognisable. From such petrified portions thin slices, comparable to those prepared from a living plant, can be obtained.

Lyginopteris oldhamia, one of the commonest of the Coal Measure fossils, has been pieced together until it is known with a degree of completeness only shared by a few living plants. *Lygino-pteris* was probably a woody scrambler, with relatively slender stems and large compound Fern-like leaves (Fig. 270), the whole surface being beset with spines and large glandular hairs. The leaves were separated by long internodes and produced occasional axillary branches, whilst the stem was attached to the soil by a number of adventitious roots arising near its base. The micro-sporangia and megasporangia (ovules) were borne on the ultimate ramifications of the ordinary foliage-leaves (cf. Fig. 272).

The *stem* underwent considerable secondary thickening. In transverse sections (Fig. 271) the parenchymatous pith, which included patches of sclerotic tissue, is seen to have been surrounded by five or more groups of primary wood (*X.*), some of which occurred in pairs; in each such strand of primary xylem the protoxylem occupied a more or less central position. Beyond was a prominent zone of secondary wood (*Sec.*), with wide parenchy-matous rays, through which the leaf-trace bundles emerged (*Bs.*). The delicate cells of the cambium and phloem, external to the

---

[1] See the works of D. H. Scott and A. C. Seward, cited on p. 386. A valuable presentation of the successive floras of the past will be found in A. C. Seward, *Plant Life through the Ages*. Cambridge Univ. Press, 1931 (601 pp.).

wood, are rarely well preserved. A layer of cork-like tissue (*periderm*) was usually developed in the pericyclic region, whilst

FIG. 270. The foliage of *Lyginopteris oldhamia* (formerly known as *Sphenopteris hœninghausii*). (From a drawing, after Potonié, lent by Prof. F. W. Oliver, F.R.S.)

the thin-walled inner cortex contained numerous secretory cells. A sharp contrast is afforded by the outer cortex, with its system of radial sclerenchymatous plates (*S.*), anastomosing at frequent intervals and giving mechanical support to the stem. In surface sections these appear as a network in which the meshes are lozenge-shaped, hence their irregular spacing as seen in transverse sections.

Each *leaf* was supplied by one of the primary xylem strands which, as it passed outwards, became associated with phloem and, on entering the pericycle, divided into two. The double bundle (Fig. 271, *Bs.*) traversed several internodes before bending out into the leaf, whose detailed structure was much like that of many of

FIG. 271. Photograph of transverse section of the stem of *Lyginopteris oldhamia* (reproduced by the courtesy of Prof. F. W. Oliver, F.R.S.). *Bs.*, leaf traces; *S.*, sclerenchyma plates in outer cortex; *Sec.*, secondary wood; *X.*, primary xylem strand.

the simpler Ferns. The root was similar to that of recent plants, possessing from two to eight xylem-groups.

The *microsporangia* of *Lyginopteris* were borne on pinnæ, with much reduced laminæ. The pinna, with its elongated sporangia, had somewhat of the appearance of an epaulet (Fig. 272). The sporangia produced numerous small spores, which were presumably conveyed by the wind to the ovules, where they became lodged within the pollen chamber.   Of their further fate nothing is known, but it is probable that they developed a small male prothallus, giving rise to spermatozoids, somewhat like those of Cycads.

The *ovules* arose singly from the ends of short branches of the fronds, and showed the same plan of construction as in Cycads (Fig. 274), except that each possessed, in addition to the integument, a second protective covering. This took the form of a lobed cup-like structure (*Cu.*), comparable with the cupule of a Hazel-nut, and beset with the same glands as occur on the vegetative organs of *Lyginopteris* (cf. Fig. 273). The robust integument (Fig. 274, *I.*) was fused with the nucellus (sporangium-wall, *n.*), except for the apical portion, which was pierced by the narrow canal-like micropyle.

The tip of the nucellus was produced into a flask-shaped *pollen chamber* (*Pc.*), whose neck projected very slightly beyond the micropyle (cf. Fig. 273), so that the microspores reached the nucellus direct, a point of contrast to Cycads and most Seed Plants. The central portion of the pollen chamber was occupied by a dome of parenchymatous tissue, but between it and the surrounding wall was a narrow chink-like space (Fig. 274, *Pc.*) in which the pollen presumably germinated and liberation of the sperms ensued.

FIG. 272. Ultimate pinnules of the foliage of *Lyginopteris oldhamia*, with microsporangia. (From a photograph by the late Dr. R. Kidston, F.R.S.)

The single huge megaspore (*m.*) has been found filled with a uniform thin-walled prothallus, which bore the archegonia near its apex. The seed was supplied by a single vascular strand, which gave off branches to both envelopes. Those traversing the cupule (Fig. 274, *Vb.*) extended into its lobes, whilst those running in the integument (*I.b.*) penetrated to the neighbourhood of the micropyle, where the integument became free from the nucellus.

The recent plants described in this chapter are especially characterised by

FIG. 273. Restoration of the seed (*Lagenostoma lomaxi*) of *Lyginopteris oldhamia*, in its glandular cupule. (After Oliver.)

the method of fertilisation and the possession of seeds. As regards the former feature, the only essential difference from *Selaginella* lies in the germination of the microspores in close proximity to the megaspore, for which special devices such as the mucilaginous pollination drop and the pollen chamber are created. Moreover, with the help of the pollen tube, some nourishment is obtained from the adjacent nucellus.

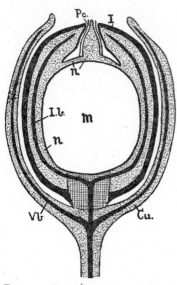

FIG. 274. Reconstruction of a longitudinal section through the seed of *Lyginopteris oldhamia* (after Oliver). *Cu.*, cupule; *I.*, integument; *I.b.*, bundle traversing integument; *m.*, megaspore; *n.*, nucellus; *Pc.*, pollen chamber; *Vb.*, bundle traversing cupule.

The *seed* may be looked upon as an extreme development of heterospory. Even in *Selaginella* it was noted that in some species there may be reduction to a single megaspore, which is retained within the sporangium till after fertilisation. Such reduction and retention are eminently characteristic of the seed-habit, where dehiscence of the megasporangium is dispensed with. The added protection, furnished by the integument, admits of a change in the character of the sporangium-wall, which becomes a thin-walled tissue serving as intermediary between the vascular system of the ovule and the developing megaspore and female prothallus.

The possession of a vascular system, another characteristic of the ovule, facilitates nutrition and the storing up of food-reserves for the young embryo. It is probably in consequence of the increased food-supply that ovules and seeds in general attain so large a size as compared with the sporangia of lower plants. As a general rule (*e.g.* most Conifers and Flowering Plants), however, the vascular system of the ovule stops short at its base. The elaborate vascular supply of the early seed-types, as contrasted with the more modern ones, may perhaps be related to the possession of motile spermatozoids, and to the relative degree of exposure and size of the ovules.

One important aspect of the permanent retention of the megaspore, involving considerable economy, is the possibility of postponing the accumulation of food-reserves to a relatively late stage, when fertilisation has taken place and the embryo has begun its development. The embryo is, moreover, more adequately protected, during its early phases, than is possible in Pteridophyta and Bryophyta, and, after attaining a certain stage, remains dormant and securely shielded until conditions arise suitable for its further growth.

Lyginopteris is but one representative of the large Palæozoic group of Pteridosperms, all possessing secondary thickening, Fern-like leaves, and reproducing by seeds. With them there flourished the

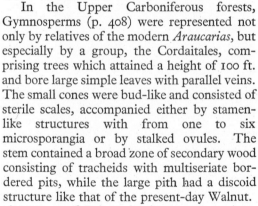

giant Horsetails and Clubmosses referred to in Chapter XXXIII, as well as other Vascular Cryptograms, among which the characteristic Sphenophyllales were prominent. They possessed whorled leaves (Fig. 274 *) and bore their sporangia on whorled and often forked appendages grouped in terminal cones.

In the Upper Carboniferous forests, Gymnosperms (p. 408) were represented not only by relatives of the modern *Araucarias*, but especially by a group, the Cordaitales, comprising trees which attained a height of 100 ft. and bore large simple leaves with parallel veins. The small cones were bud-like and consisted of sterile scales, accompanied either by stamen-like structures with from one to six

FIG. 274 *. *Spheno-* microsporangia or by stalked ovules. The
phyllum verticillatum stem contained a broad zone of secondary wood
(below) and leaf-whorl consisting of tracheids with multiseriate bor-
of *S. cuneifolium* dered pits, while the large pith had a discoid
(above) (after Potonié). structure like that of the present-day Walnut.

Most of the woody groups of Palæozoic times seem to have become extinct in later epochs, but a limited number of types persisted, often reduced in stature and no longer playing the same important rôle. Prominent in the vegetation of the succeeding Mesozoic era were relations of the Maiden-hair Tree (Ginkgoales), of the Cycads, and of another Cycad-like group, the Bennettitales which in part had hermaphrodite strobili. The dominance of these groups later gave way to that of the Flowering Plants which came to the front in late Mesozoic times.

CHAPTER XXXV

THE CONIFERS

ALL seed-plants, with the exception of certain fossil forms (*e.g.* some fossil Clubmosses), are grouped as Spermaphyta. The subdivisions of this class, viz. Gymnosperms and Angiosperms, are

characterised by the manner in which the ovules are borne; those of the former are not enclosed, whilst those of the latter, the Flowering Plants proper, are surrounded by a structure called the ovary. There are, however, other points of contrast, which will become apparent later. The Spermaphyta as a whole are further distinguished by a greater differentiation of the strobili than is found among Pteridophyta.

The *Gymnosperms* include, apart from the Cycads, the Maidenhair Tree (*Ginkgo biloba*, cf. p. 400), the important group of the Conifers, and the Cordaitales

FIG. 275. Branches of the Spruce Fir (*Picea abies*) with three ripe cones. [Photo. E. J. S.]

known only as fossils. The Conifers, to which belong such familiar plants as the Scot's Fir (*Pinus sylvestris*, Fig. 285), Larch (*Larix decidua*, Fig. 276), Yew (*Taxus baccata*, Fig. 284), etc., are essentially characteristic of temperate zones, some being the chief forest trees of colder regions (cf. p. 485). They furnish some of the most important sources of timber (p. 181), turpentine, resin, etc. (p. 91). There are some 350 known species, of which more than a fifth belong to the genus *Pinus*.

All the Conifers [1] are woody, and the majority are trees. The regular habit, so marked in the Spruce Fir (*Picea abies*) and Cypress (*Cupressus*), characterises the group and is an outcome of the monopodial branching (cf. p. 116). The feature which gives them their most distinctive stamp, however, is the foliage, which in general consists of small needle-like *leaves* (Figs. 275, 276 and 284). These usually persist for several years, although the Larch, for instance, is deciduous.

The needles are either borne on the ordinary long shoots (*e.g.* Yew, Fig. 284, A, and Silver Fir), or, as in several common genera (*Pinus, Larix, Cedrus*, all members of the Abietineæ), are usually restricted to *dwarf-shoots*. These arise in the axils of scale-leaves on the long shoots (Fig. 285), and bear a few dark-coloured scales below and a variable number of foliage leaves above. In the Pines the number of the latter is limited (five in *Pinus strobus*, two in *P. sylvestris*, Fig. 283, and only one in *P. monophylla*), and no further leaves are produced after the first season, the whole dwarf-shoot being shed at the end of two or three years. On the other hand, in the Larch (Fig. 276) and Cedar (*Cedrus*), where the dwarf-shoots are larger and bear a tuft of needles, quite a considerable number of new leaves is formed annually, although after some years this production ceases and the dwarf-

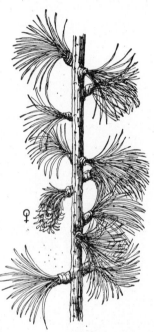

FIG. 276. Branch of the Larch (*Larix*), showing several dwarf-shoots, one of them bearing a young female cone. (Both about natural size.)

shoots die away. These two Conifers also differ from the Pines in the fact that the needles are not entirely confined to the dwarf-shoots, since, during the first season's growth, they occur on the long shoots also. It will be realised that only the normal shoots contribute to the permanent branch-system of the trees.

The leaves are most frequently sessile, although those of the Yew have a short stalk (Fig. 284, A). Their bases are often fused with the stem for a short distance, and persist after the leaves have fallen, leaving characteristic scars (*e.g.* Spruce Fir, *Picea*); in the

---

[1] For reference-books, see p. 425.

Scot's Fir similar scars are left by the shedding of the dwarf-shoots.

The peculiar appearance of the Arbor Vitæ (*Thuja*, Fig. 277) and the Cypress (*Cupressus*), both belonging to the Cupressineæ, is due to the presence of minute leaves arranged in decussate pairs, and almost fused with the stem upon which they are borne. Moreover, owing to the larger size of the lateral leaves, and the restriction of most of the branches to their axils, the shoot as a whole acquires a

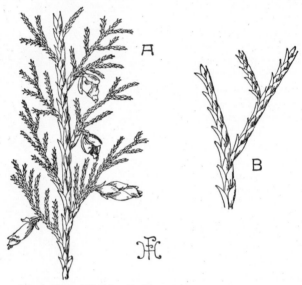

FIG. 277. Arbor Vitæ (*Thuja*). A, Branch with ripe female cones (about natural size). B, Small part of a branch enlarged to show the leaf-arrangement.

flattened appearance. In the common Juniper (*Juniperus*), which is likewise one of the Cupressineæ, three needle leaves arise at each node, and such a whorled arrangement is characteristic of this whole family. Large flattened leaves are seen in *Araucaria*, and a similar type of foliage is found in *Podocarpus*, which is the most important genus of Conifers in the Southern Hemisphere, comprising some sixty species, of which several furnish valuable timber.

In spite of the considerable diversity in the mature structure, the *seedlings* of most Conifers exhibit great uniformity, the young stem bearing ordinary needle-leaves for some little distance above the cotyledonary node (Fig. 278). The dwarf-shoots of *Pinus* and other Abietineæ, as well as the scale-like leaves found in the Cypress, etc., only appear at a later stage. The juvenile foliage sometimes persists, even in the adult condition, as in some cultivated varieties

of *Thuja* and *Cupressus* (the *Retinospora* of nurserymen).   Even the
deciduous habit of the Larch appears as a secondary acquisition,
since in the seedling the leaves persist for some time.   It is not
always that the varied specialisation which a group has undergone,

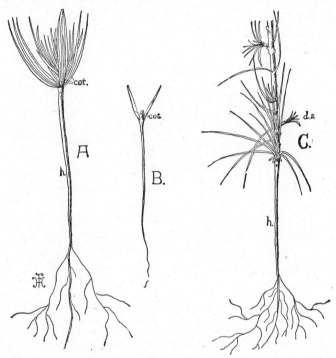

FIG. 278. Seedlings of various Conifers.   A, *Pinus sylvestris*.   B, *Cupressus*,
showing two cotyledons and plumule.   C, *Larix*, older seedling which has
already produced several dwarf-shoots.   *cot.*, cotyledons; *d.s.*, dwarf-shoot;
h., hypocotyl.

in evolving from a common ancestral type, is as plainly decipherable
as in the Conifers.

   The appearance of the *stem* in transverse section is very similar
to that of a Dicotyledon having secondary growth.   *Pinus* affords
a typical example (Fig. 279, A).   The irregular outline is due to the
adherent bases of the scale-leaves which are occupied by a large-
celled tissue (Fig. 279, B), on whose inner side the cork-cambium
(*ca.*) arises.   With the production of cork, therefore, the epidermis (*e.*) and the dwarf-shoots become exfoliated, so that the
older branches have a relatively smooth surface.   The narrow
cortex is rather lacunar, and contains schizogenous *resin-canals* (*r.*)

(cf. p. 93). These resin canals are particularly characteristic of Conifers (Fig. 279, C), and are found in all parts of the plant.

The primary and secondary vascular tissues are not easily distinguished from one another, particularly in the *phloem*, the broad zone of which is chiefly secondary in origin. This tissue (*ph*.) is strikingly uniform, its elements, which have thick white shining walls, exhibiting a radial arrangement. The rows of more

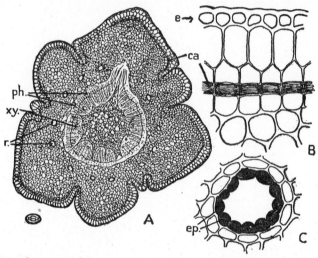

FIG. 279. Structure of the young stem of *Pinus sylvestris* in transverse section. A, Entire (diagrammatic). B, Small part of the peripheral tissues enlarged. C, Single resin-canal enlarged, showing the epithelium (*ep*.). *ca.*, cork cambium; *e.*, epidermis; *ph.*, phloem; *r.*, resin-canals; *xy.*, xylem.

or less empty-looking *sieve-tubes*, which have no companion cells, are interspersed with a smaller number of irregular files of phloem-parenchyma, whose cells contain dense contents. In longitudinal sections the sieve-tubes appear as long tapering elements bearing sieve-areas (Fig. 280, E, *Si.*) upon their sloping radial walls.

The secondary *wood* (Fig. 279, *xy.*), internal to the narrow cambial zone, also exhibits a very uniform, radially seriated structure. Except for the narrow parenchyma rays and occasional resin-canals, it consists entirely of fibre-like *tracheids*, which are differentiated among themselves only in respect of the distinctions between early (Fig. 280, A, *Sp.*) and late wood (*Au.*) [1] (see p. 177). The radial walls of the tracheids bear a single row of large circular bordered pits, especially evident in radial longitudinal (Fig. 280, C,

[1] Growth rings are, however, absent from some *Araucarias*, and from most of the fossil representatives of this group.

b.) sections, when the pits themselves are seen in surface view. In
the late wood the tangential walls are also pitted. The groups
of primary xylem, composed of spiral tracheids, project into the
small pith and are separated from one another by the primary
rays.

The stem-structure of *Pinus* is typical of most Conifers, but

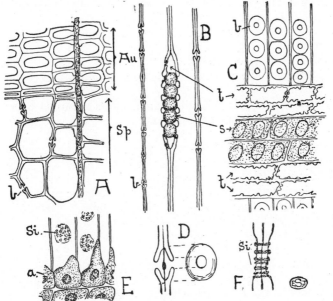

FIG. 280. Structure of the stem of *Pinus sylvestris*. A, Small part of the
secondary wood in transverse section, showing early (*Sp.*) and late
(*Au.*) wood; B, The same in tangential longitudinal section showing a parenchyma ray; C, The same in radial longitudinal section, with part of a parenchyma
ray; D, Single bordered pit in section (on the left) and from the surface (on
the right); E, Small part of the secondary phloem in radial longitudinal section;
F, Single sieve-tube in tangential longitudinal section. *a*, marginal cells of
parenchyma ray of phloem; *b*, bordered pits; *s*, storage cells of rays; *Si.*,
sieve-plates; *t*, tracheidal cells of rays.

resin-canals are absent from the wood in certain genera (being often
replaced by resin-cells), whilst in the *Araucarias*, and occasionally
in other members of the group (e.g. *Pinus palustris*), the tracheids
bear two or more rows of bordered pits. Resin-canals are lacking
in *Taxus*.

Radial and tangential longitudinal sections exhibit the same
arrangement of the *parenchyma rays* as in Dicotyledons (Fig. 280).
In some Conifers certain rays, which are relatively wide, are
traversed by resin-canals connecting those of the pith and cortex.

As a general rule the rays consist of uniform cells, whose walls usually bear simple pits. Several Abietineæ, including *Pinus*, show a complex differentiation of the rays, best seen in radial longitudinal sections. In the region of the wood the cells of the middle rows, which bear simple pits of exceptionally large size, are more particularly concerned with storage, and contain copious starch (Fig. 280, C, *s*.); the dead and empty cells of the marginal rows (*t*.), which bear small bordered pits and often exhibit peg-like ingrowths of the walls, have a conducting function. Where the rays traverse the phloem, all the cells have thin walls and dense cytoplasm, but those at the margin (Fig. 280, E, *a*.) are often drawn out into finger-like processes which are insinuated between the sieve-tubes.

The *root*, which is generally diarch, shows the usual structure, although characterised by the presence of a large resin-canal within each protoxylem-group.

The *leaves* of most Conifers are traversed by a single vein only, but, apart from that, their structure is somewhat varied. Its range can, however, be gauged from a consideration of the relatively simple dorsiventral leaf of *Taxus* (Fig. 281) and the more complex centric one of *Pinus* (Fig. 282). In the former the epidermis (Fig. 281, *ep*.) shows the thick cuticle and sunken stomata (Fig. 281, B) associated with transpiration-reduction; the pronounced papillæ on the lower surface (Fig. 281, B, C) are a special peculiarity. The mesophyll, comprising two layers of palisade cells (*p*.) and spongy tissue (*s*.), is traversed by the single bundle (*b*.), which exhibits the usual dorsiventral structure. On either side of the xylem, however, are occasional spirally or reticulately thickened elements (*t*.), which sometimes bear bordered pits. These dead cells constitute what is called *transfusion tissue*, and may serve both for the lateral conduction of water, thus compensating for the absence of side-veins, and as water-reservoirs.

The epidermal cells of the *Pinus*-leaf (Fig. 282, A, B) also have a very pronounced cuticle (*Cu*.), and are so strongly thickened that their cavity is often reduced to a mere dot (*ep*.); beneath the epidermis is a strongly thickened hypoderm (*h*.). The deeply sunken stomata (*St*.) occur at intervals all round a transverse section, but, if the leaf be examined with a lens, they are seen to be arranged in longitudinal rows. The mesophyll contains several prominent resin-canals (*r*.) and consists of more or less isodiametric cells, characterised by the presence of inwardly projecting folds of the wall (*i*.). As seen in transverse section it will be noticed that, apart from the respiratory cavities of the stomata, there are few intercellular spaces in the mesophyll. This tissue, however, consists of successive transverse lamellæ, which are separated from one another by narrow air-spaces (Fig. 281, E). The twin-bundles are connected by a group of thick-walled mechanical

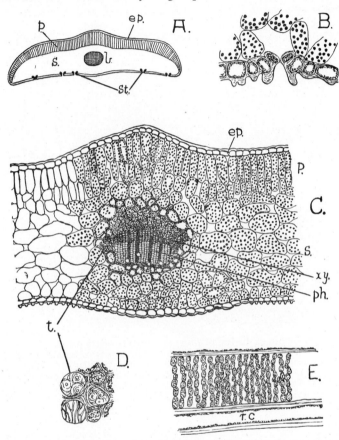

FIG. 281. A–D, Structure of the leaf of *Taxus baccata* in transverse section. A, Diagram of whole section; B, Single stoma enlarged; C, Central part; D, A few cells of the transfusion tissue. *b.*, bundle; *ep.*, epidermis; *p.*, palisade tissue; *ph.*, phloem; *s.*, spongy tissue; *St.*, stomata; *t.*, transfusion tissue; *xy.*, xylem. E, Tangential longitudinal section of leaf of *Pinus*, showing a resin-canal (*r.c.*) and the transverse lamellæ of photosynthetic cells.

cells (Fig. 282, A, D, *Scl.*) and are embedded in an extensive mass of tissue bounded by a well-marked bundle-sheath (*S.*). This tissue consists, in large part, of ordinary living parenchymatous cells containing starch-grains. Scattered among these are the dead and empty cells of the transfusion tissue (cf. especially Fig. 282, C, *tr.*), bearing small bordered pits (*b.*), which are seen both in section and from the surface.   At the outer edge of the phloem of each bundle is a group of cells, whose dark contents are rich in proteins (*a.*). In some species of *Pinus*, as well as in *Picea* and *Larix*, the leaf contains but a single bundle.

Whilst many of the features of Coniferous leaves are those

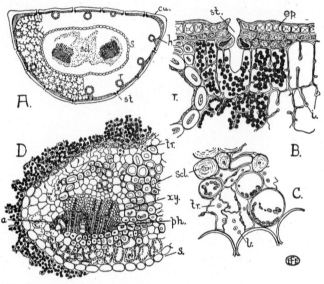

FIG. 282. Structure of the leaf of *Pinus* in transverse section.   A, Diagram of whole section.   B, Small part of the superficial tissues, enlarged.   C, A few cells of the transfusion tissue, etc., from the central vascular cylinder, greatly enlarged.   D, About half the central vascular cylinder.   *a.*, protein cells; *b.*, bordered pit on transfusion cell; *Cu.*, cuticle; *ep.*, epidermis; *h.*, hypoderm; *i.*, folds on walls of mesophyll-cells; *ph.*, phloem; *r.*, resin-canal; *S.*, bundle-sheath; *Scl.*, sclerenchyma; *st.*, stomata; *tr.*, elements of transfusion tissue; *xy.*, xylem.

usually found in plants which require to economise their water-supply, others such as the limited vascular supply and the trans-fusion tissue are special peculiarities of the group.   The relation between the vascular system of stem and leaf in Conifers is similar to that which obtains in Flowering Plants (cf. p. 168).

The sporophylls of Conifers, like those of Cycads, are grouped in cones (Fig. 283, 285), the two kinds being most commonly found on the same plant, though *Taxus* (Fig. 284), for instance, furnishes an exception.   The *male cones*, which often occur in clusters (Fig. 283), are yellow oval structures of diverse size, and frequently arise in the axils of the foliage-leaves (e.g. *Taxus*, Fig. 284, E;

Abies).   In *Pinus*, where they are axillary to scale-leaves, the male

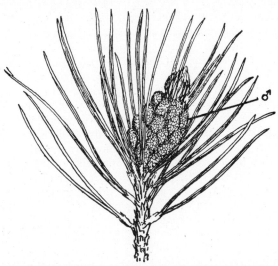

FIG. 283. Portion of a branch of *Pinus*, bearing male cones ($\male$) on the lower part of the year's growth (natural size).   Near the top of the latter are seen, closely crowded, a number of immature dwarf-shoots.

cones replace the dwarf-shoots (Fig. 283), but in the Larch, for instance, the latter bear leaves below the male cones.

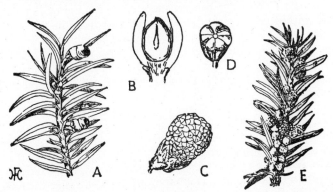

FIG. 284. *Taxus baccata*.   A, Branch bearing two ripe seeds; B, A ripe seed in longitudinal section, showing the aril; C, Single male cone, enlarged; D, Single microsporophyll; E, Branch with male cones.   (D, after Eichler; the rest original.)

The axis of the male cone (Fig. 286, A) supports large numbers of densely crowded microsporophylls, which mostly have the form

of flattened scales, whose upturned overlapping tips are alone
visible at the surface.   They usually bear two large microsporangia
(*pollen sacs*) on their under-surface (Fig. 286, B, *ps.*), although there
are sometimes several (e.g. *Cupressus*).   In *Taxus* the stamens are
peltate in form, with several (5 to 9) pollen sacs pendant from the
lower side of the lamina (Fig. 284, D).   In *Araucaria* also the
microsporophylls bear numerous (10 to 20) pollen sacs.

The young microsporangia are provided with a wall of several
layers which encloses large numbers of spore mother-cells, each
dividing in the customary manner to form four haploid microspores
(*pollen grains*).   The pollen sacs usually dehisce by means of a
broad split, and the pollen is distributed by the wind.   In *Pinus*
and its allies the microspores develop a pair of blister-like enlargements, between the cuticle and the inner layer of the membrane;
these contain water, which subsequently evaporates, thus leaving
two collapsed bladders which act as wings (Fig. 288, A, *w*).

The *ovules* (megasporangia) of the Yew (*Taxus*) usually occur
singly within small buds, which arise in the axils of the leaves;
they closely resemble the ordinary vegetative buds.   Each bears
several minute scales, the single ovule occupying a terminal position
with the micropyle facing outwards.   The ovule is peculiar in
possessing, apart from the usual integument, a second protective
covering termed the *aril*, which remains inconspicuous till after
fertilisation.   It then develops into a bright-coloured fleshy cup
investing the seed (Fig. 284, A, B;   Fig. 338, D–F).

In most Conifers, however, more or less numerous ovules are
found within each of the *female cones*, and these in the Monkey
Puzzles (*Araucaria*), for instance, may attain considerable dimensions.   The cones themselves occupy diverse positions.   Thus, in
Pinus (Fig. 285) they first appear as small reddish structures,
situated at the ends of short stalks, just beneath the apical bud of
the current year's growth.   In the Larch, where they are larger
and of a bright crimson colour, they terminate some of the dwarf-
shoots, with a rosette of green needles at their base (Fig. 276).   The
small cones of the Cypress and Arbor Vitæ (Fig. 277, A) likewise
occur at the ends of short branches.

The scale-like sporophylls generally show a spiral arrangement,
although in *Cupressus* and *Thuja* they are decussate, like the foliage-
leaves.   In *Pinus* and other Abietineæ (*Larix*, *Abies*, etc.) the axis
of the cone bears two different types of scales which are quite
distinct from one another, and occur in superposed pairs
(Fig. 286, D).   The lower or bract scale (*bs.*) of each pair is smaller
than the upper or ovuliferous scale (*Os.*).   The latter appears to
arise in the axil of the former, and bears, on its upper surface, two

ovules (*Ov.*) whose micropyles face towards the axis of the cone (Fig. 286, E). The difference in size becomes more pronounced

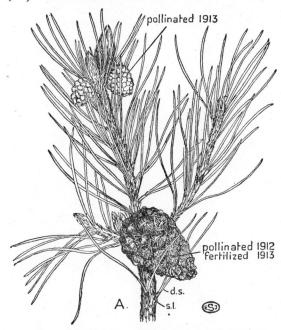

FIG. 285. Branch of *Pinus* bearing female cones of two ages (about one-half natural size). *d.s.*, dwarf-shoot; *s.l.*, scale-leaf.

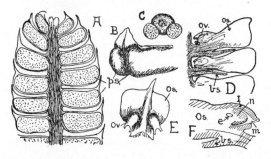

FIG. 286. A–B, Structure of male cone of *Pinus sylvestris*. A, Upper part in longitudinal section; B, Single sporophyll. *ps.*, pollen sacs. C, Pollen grain. D, Longitudinal section of female cone of *Pinus*. E, Single megasporophyll, from above. F, Part of D, enlarged. *bs.*, bract scale; *e.*, megaspore; *I*, integument; *m.*, micropyle; *n.*, nucellus; *Os.*, ovuliferous scale; *Ov.*, ovule.

as the cone grows older, the ovuliferous scale enlarging to a much greater extent than the bract scale. In the Wellingtonia (*Sequoia,*

Fig. 289, D) and Cupressineæ bract and ovuliferous scales are almost completely joined, whilst in some Conifers (e.g. *Cryptomeria*) the line of fusion is plainly recognisable. The scales in the Cupressineæ usually bear more than two ovules, situated with the micropyles directed outwards; not infrequently the uppermost

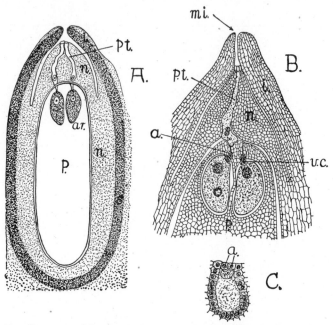

FIG. 287. Structure of Ovule of *Pinus*. A, Diagrammatic longitudinal section of mature ovule (after Coulter and Chamberlain). B, Front portion of same greatly enlarged, showing a pollen tube penetrating the nucellus (after Strasburger). C, Young archegonium showing the layer of nutritive cells investing the egg (after Ferguson). *a.*, neck of archegonium; *ar.*, archegonium; *i.*, integument; *mi.*, micropyle; *n.*, nucellus; *o.*, egg; *p.*, female prothallus; *p.t.*, pollen tube; *s.*, stony layer of integument; *v.c.*, ventral canal cell.

scales are sterile (e.g. *Thuja*). The Monkey Puzzles are peculiar in having but a single ovule on each megasporophyll.

The *ovules* in most Conifers possess a single thick integument (Fig. 286, F, *I*; Fig. 287, *i.*). This is partially fused on one side with the ovuliferous scale (Fig. 286, F), and, except in a few genera, the central nucellus is only free from the integument in the region of the micropyle (Fig. 287, B, *mi.*). A single megaspore (*p.*) is usually differentiated within the nucellus of the young ovule by the division of a mother-cell which arises hypodermally. This forms a linear tetrad of potential haploid spores of which only the innermost survives. The functioning spore rapidly enlarges and eventually displaces the greater part of the nucellus, though a pronounced cap of tissue still remains in the free portion beneath the micropyle (Fig. 287, *n.*). The thin-walled parenchymatous *female prothallus* (*p.*), which is richly supplied with food-material, as a rule arises only after pollination has occurred. The archegonia (*ar.*), which are often few in number (*e.g.* three in *Pinus sylvestris*), are generally differentiated at the micropylar end. Each consists of a huge ovum (*o.*) embedded in the tissue of the prothallus, a minute ventral canal cell (*v.c.*), and a very short inconspicuous neck (*a.*) composed of one or more tiers of cells. When the archegonia are numerous (as in most Cupressineæ), they are usually collected together in groups, opening into a common shallow depression (*archegonial chamber*), at the front end of the prothallus.

When the mature pollen is being scattered broadcast by the wind, the axis of the female cone elongates slightly, so that the cone-scales spread apart, thus giving access to the ovules. The mature pollen grains are caught on micropylar lobes of the integument which act like stigmas. At night a fluid secretion fills the micropylar canal and entraps the grains. By the gradual shrinking of the fluid the pollen grains are sucked through the micropyle on to the surface of the nucellar cap, and, soon after this, the scales of the female cone enlarge and once again fit tightly together. In *Taxus* the fluid exudes from the micropyle as a drop which receives the pollen grains direct. This process of *pollination* must be sharply distinguished from that of fertilisation which occurs at a later stage—often only after a prolonged interval.

When shed, the contents of the microspores have already undergone division, the cell, or cells, thus cut off from the general body lying against one side of the grain (Fig. 288, B); usually there is only an *antheridial* cell (*a.c.*), but in *Pinus* and related forms its formation is preceded by the cutting off of two very flat cells, which soon break down (Fig. 288, B, *v.c.*). The remaining and larger portion of the pollen grain forms the so-called tube cell (*t.n.*). On reaching the nucellus the outer membrane of the microspore is ruptured, and the tube cell grows out to form the *pollen tube* (Fig. 287, *p.t.*), into whose tip its nucleus wanders, whilst simultaneously the antheridial cell divides into two, the inner half (*body cell*) subsequently forming the two male cells.

The growth of the pollen tube into the nucellus soon ceases, and is not resumed till a short time before fertilisation. This interval between pollination and fertilisation is comparatively short (four to six weeks) where the seeds mature in the same year as that in which pollination occurs (e.g. *Thuja*, *Picea*), but is very prolonged (twelve to thirteen months) in the Pines, where pollination ensues in May or early June, whilst the seeds are not shed till the autumn of the following year. In *Pinus* there is very pronounced growth of the female cones and ovules in the interval between pollination and fertilisation (cf. Fig. 285).

With the resumption of growth the pollen tube penetrates

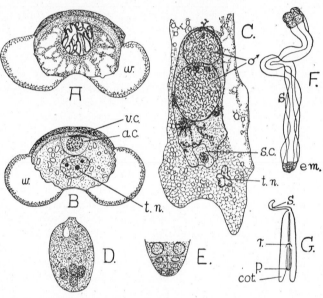

FIG. 288. Pollen and embryology of *Pinus*. A, Mature pollen grain, nucleus not yet divided; B, Pollen grain at time of pollination; C, Lower end of pollen tube a little before fertilisation. *a.c.*, antheridial cell; *s.c.*, stalk cell; *t.n.*, tube nucleus; *v.c.*, vegetative cell; *w.*, wing of pollen grain; ♂ (in C), the two male nuclei. D–G, Embryology. D, Fertilised ovum, with nucleus divided into four: E, Lower end of oospore, showing young pro-embryo; F, Much older pro-embryo; G, Almost mature embryo. *cot.*, cotyledon; *em.*, embryo; *p.*, plumule; *r.*, radicle; *S.*, suspensor. (A–D after Ferguson; the remainder after Strasburger.)

deeper into the nucellus (Fig. 287, *p.t.*), frequently exhibiting slight lobing, and the two naked *male cells*, resulting from the division of the body cell, pass down into its apex (Fig. 288, C, ♂). On reaching an archegonium the neck is crushed, and the pollen tube, breaking open at its tip, discharges its contents into the ovum. Subsequently one of the two male nuclei fuses with the egg-nucleus. In *Pinus* the second male nucleus is smaller (Fig. 288, C) and usually aborts, though in some genera (*e.g.* of Cupressineæ), where the archegonia occur in groups and the pollen tube discharges into the common archegonial chamber, both the male nuclei, which are here of equal size, may function.

The fertilised egg, becoming enveloped in a delicate membrane, almost immediately exhibits two successive divisions of its nucleus (Fig. 288, D). The four nuclei thus formed wander to the end of the egg remote from the micropyle, where they become grouped in a single plane. Further division, accompanied by the formation of separating walls, ultimately results in the development of three or four superposed tiers (Fig. 288, E), each usually consisting of four cells and occupying only a small part of the oospore. In the *proembryo* of *Pinus* the tier farthest from the micropyle gives rise to the new plant,[1] whilst the cells of the adjacent tier elongate very considerably (Fig. 288, F, S.) and form a *suspensor* (cf. *Selaginella*, p. 395), which carries the developing *embryo* (*em.*) down into the middle of the prothallus.

The cells of the embryonic tier divide repeatedly to form an extensive mass of tissue. At the end away from the micropyle a number of lobes soon grow out and form the cotyledons (Fig. 288, G, *cot.*). These surround the developing plumule (*p.*), whilst the radicle (*r.*) arises as a pointed structure at the opposite end, adjacent to the suspensor (*S.*). The number of cotyledons is very variable; there are only two in *Taxus* and Cupressineæ (Fig. 278, B), whilst in *Pinus* (Fig. 278, A) there are from three to seventeen, according to the species.

As the embryo enlarges it absorbs the food-reserves stored up in the prothallus and gradually displaces it. At the time when the *seed* is fully mature, however, a considerable part of this tissue still persists unaltered around the embryo and constitutes the *endosperm* (Fig. 289, A, *e*); the seed of Conifers is thus endospermic. The food-reserve is largely of the nature of fat, and is present in sufficient quantity to render the kernels of some species of Pines of nutritive value. The method of germination of the seeds is practically the same as that of a Castor Oil, the seedlings (Fig. 278) possessing long hypocotyls (*h.*) with epigeal cotyledons (*cot.*).

During the development of the embryo the entire ovule enlarges considerably, and at the same time the integument hardens to form the seed-coat, or *testa* (*s.*). The greater part of the latter comes to consist of very thick-walled tissue, foreshadowed as a dark zone in the integument of a young *Pinus*-ovule (Fig. 287, A, *s.*), and constituting the hard layer which is so conspicuous a feature in the seed of the Stone Pine (*Pinus pinea*). The micropyle appears

---

[1] In *Pinus* and some other genera the cells of the pro-embryo commonly separate, and as many as eight embryos may be formed, but, as in other Conifers, one only reaches maturity.

on the testa as a minute opening, and it will be realised, from the foregoing description, that the tip of the radicle lies just beneath this. In *Pinus* and some of its allies, a thin membranous flake becomes detached from the ovuliferous scale and adheres to the ripe seed, forming a wing which aids in dispersal by the wind (Fig. 289, E, *w*.). In *Cephalotaxus* and a few other genera the ripe seeds are plum-like, resembling those of Cycads.

FIG. 289. Seeds and cones of various Conifers. A, Longitudinal section of ripe seed of *Pinus pinea*, showing testa (*s*), perisperm (*n*, cf. p. 471), endosperm (*e*), and embryo with radicle (*r*) and numerous cotyledons (*Co.*); B, Young female cone, and C, Ripe cone of *Juniperus*; D, Outer edge of ripe cone-scale of *Sequoia*; E, Single cone-scale of *Pinus* bearing the two seeds with wings (*w*); F, Ripe cone-scales of *Pseudotsuga*. *b.s.*, bract scale; *o.s.*, ovuliferous scale. (B, after Antoine.)

The cones also undergo considerable enlargement in ripening, often becoming many times larger than they were prior to fertilisation (Fig. 285). The ripe cone-scales are usually woody, and gape apart to set free the seeds, although in the Cedar, for instance, they are shed with the latter. At this stage the bract-scales in *Pinus* are no longer recognisable, though in some of the related forms (*e.g.* the Douglas Fir, *Pseudotsuga taxifolia*, Fig. 289, F), they are conspicuous even in the mature cone. The Juniper is peculiar in that the cone-scales become fleshy, forming a berry-like structure (Fig. 289, C) in which the ripe seeds are embedded; the seeds are here distributed by birds.

In the life-history of the Conifers the method of fertilisation shows a considerable advance on that of Cycads, since the pollen tube, which is there but an organ for the absorption of nourishment from the nucellus (a function which it may also fulfil to a slight extent in the Conifers), is here utilised to convey the motionless male cells to the egg. Thereby the necessity for the presence of liquid water at the time of fertilisation is rendered unnecessary.

[For a more detailed treatment of Gymnosperms, see J. M. Coulter and C. J. Chamberlain, *Morphology of Gymnosperms*, Univ. Chicago Press, 2nd edit., 1917 (466 pp.); and W. Dallimore and A. Bruce Jackson, *A Handbook of Coniferæ*, Ed. Arnold, 2nd edit., 1931 (582 pp.). For taxonomic works, see p. 578.]

CHAPTER XXXVI

FLOWER-STRUCTURE

THE majority of the Angiosperms, the second subdivision of the Spermaphyta, are easily distinguished from the Gymnosperms by the possession of *flowers*, which are really highly specialised fertile shoots. In some, however, the flowers are relatively inconspicuous (*e.g.* Grasses), and scarcely conform to the popular notion of such structures. The Angiosperms are more markedly characterised by the enclosure of their ovules in a protective ovary, as well as by the possession of true vessels and of sieve-tubes of a special type (cf. p. 62).

The classification of Angiosperms into *Monocotyledons* and *Dicotyledons* is based on many morphological and anatomical features (leaf-form, number of cotyledons in the embryo, stem- and root-structure, and number of floral parts), the Monocotyledons being an essentially herbaceous group exhibiting a high perfection of means for perennation and hibernation (*e.g.* bulbs, corms, etc.). The evidence that the Dicotyledons and Monocotyledons were derived from a common stock is almost overwhelming. This fact is plainly indicated, for example, by the widespread traces of the presence of a cambium in Monocotyledons, and the extremely few characters, either of development or structure, that are entirely restricted to the one or the other group (cf. also p. 446).

The Angiosperms are the predominant vascular plants on the earth's surface at the present day, and comprise upwards of 150,000 species. In Britain this preponderance is especially marked. The native Angiosperms here number about 1500 species and the Gymnosperms 4 species; amongst the Cryptogams there are about 60 Pteridophyta, 600 Mosses, 250 Liverworts, several thousand species of Algæ, and at least 5000 species of Fungi. The Angiosperms first appear in the geological succession in the Cretaceous period,[1] but the study of these and of the abundant

---

[1] For further details on fossil Angiosperms, see L. Laurent, *Les Progrès de la paléobotanique angiospermique, etc.*, Progressus Rei Bot., I, 1917, p. 319 *et seq.*

Tertiary fossils, though affording much that is of interest, has so far shed no light whatsoever on the origin of the group, which is merged in obscurity. The details of the life-history betray a very high degree of specialisation, but afford practically no evidence as to how this has been attained.

The physiological activities of the Angiosperm may be said to culminate in the formation of flowers and seeds. The manner in which the flowers are borne is often of biological significance and sometimes characterises entire families or genera. Sometimes the flowers are solitary (Fig. 296), but more commonly a number occur together on a flower-bearing shoot termed the *inflorescence*. This exhibits one of the two types of branching found in the vegetative parts (cf. p. 116), or more rarely both types occur together. If the branching is monopodial the inflorescence is termed *racemose*,[1] if sympodial it is termed *cymose*. Each flower usually arises in the axil of a leaf (except in Cruciferæ), which often differs markedly from the foliage-leaves and is termed a *bract*. The bracts show much morphological resemblance to bud-scales. The ultimate branches of the inflorescence end in flowers, and their stalks (*peduncles*) often bear one or two scale-like leaves termed *bracteoles*. A flower-bud may arise in the axil of a bracteole so that the bracteole of one flower becomes the bract of a younger one.

Racemose inflorescences (Fig. 290, A) are characterised by the flowers opening from below upwards. Cymose inflorescences exhibit a reverse order of opening of the flowers (Fig. 290, G), from above downwards or, if flat-topped (cf. below), the oldest flowers are towards the centre. The growth of any axis in a cymose inflorescence is terminated by the production of a flower which opens before those on the lateral branches below.

The chief types of *racemose inflorescence* are: The simple raceme (Fig. 290, A), in which each flower is stalked (*e.g.* Currant, Lupine); the compound raceme (Fig. 290, D), where the branches are themselves racemes (*Festuca*); the corymb (Fig. 290, B), a simple raceme in which the lower peduncles become increasingly longer so that the flowers approximate to the same level (Candytuft, *Iberis*, Fig. 316); the spike (Fig. 290, E, and 291), a simple raceme with sessile flowers (*Plantago*, Fig. 313). Simple racemes and spikes, in which the internodes are not recognisable, are respectively termed umbels (*e.g.* Cowslip, Fig. 290, C) and capitula (*e.g.* Daisy, Dandelion, Fig. 290, F, and 312, A). In the corymb, umbel, and capitulum the opening of the flowers appears as from without inwards.

In most Umbelliferæ we have examples of compound umbels. Catkins are loose spikes in which the flowers contain either stamens or an ovary only (*e.g.* Hazel, *Corylus*, Fig. 314).

---

[1] For the definition of this and other terms, see the work of Jackson cited on p. 123.

The chief types of *cymose inflorescence* are: The simple cyme (e.g. *Geum*, Fig. 290, G), found in plants with alternate leaves; the dichasial cyme (e.g. *Lychnis*, Fig. 290, H), in plants with opposite leaves. The dichasial cyme appears forked below each of the older flowers, but one of the branches of the ultimate pairs is often suppressed. Cymose umbels (*e.g.* Onion), cymose capitula (*e.g.* Scabious), and cymose corymbs (*e.g.* Wayfaring tree, *Viburnum*) also occur.

Richly branched inflorescences often exhibit a racemose development of the main axis and laterals, whilst the ultimate branches develop in a cymose manner

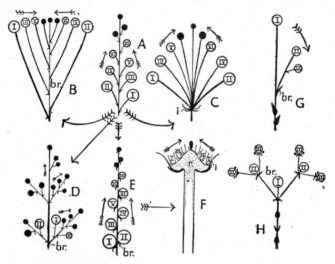

FIG. 290. A–F, Diagrams of different types of racemose inflorescences. A, Simple raceme. B, Corymb. C, Simple umbel. D, Compound raceme. E, Spike. F, Capitulum. G. H, Diagrams of cymose inflorescences. G, Simple cyme. H, Dichasial cyme. The Roman numerals, as well as the small arrows, indicate the order of opening of the flowers. The larger arrows show the relation of the different types to one another. Flower-buds shown black. *br.*, bracts; *i.*, involucre; *r.*, receptacle.

(e.g. *Æsculus, Syringa*). In the Labiatæ the axillary groups of flowers are dichasial cymes, but those at the base are the oldest and those at the tip the youngest.

The massing of small flowers into an inflorescence renders them more conspicuous. In very condensed types, such as capitula, the numerous bracts form a whorl or whorls at the base of the inflorescence, known as an *involucre*, and collectively constitute a protective investment (Fig. 290, F, *i*).

The individual flower is a compressed shoot, serving for purposes of reproduction and bearing a number of different structures which are usually not separated by internodes. Of these floral organs some are essential for the production of seed (stamens and ovary), whilst others constitute the non-essential *perianth* (calyx and corolla) which, however, mostly plays an important part in the protection of the flower and in the attraction of insect-visitors. When the flower, as in the Ash, contains only the essential organs it is said to be *naked* (Fig. 291).

The expanded end of the peduncle to which the different floral organs are attached is spoken of as the *receptacle* or *thalamus*. This is frequently more or less convex in form, bearing at its summit the ovary, with stamens and perianth (or corolla and calyx) at successively lower levels. Such flowers, in which the other parts arise from beneath the ovary, are said to be *hypogynous* (*e.g.* Buttercup, Fig. 293, A, and Hyacinth, Fig. 294, B). Occasionally the receptacle is flattened, and from this it is but a slight step to one which is more or less deeply concave or even flask-shaped; examples are

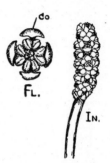

FIG. 291. Flower (*Fl.*) and inflorescence (*In.*) of *Potamogeton* (the flower enlarged, inflorescence natural size). *co.*, connective.

furnished by *Potentilla* (Fig. 292, C) and *Rosa* (Fig. 292, B), which show progressive hollowing out of the thalamus, so that the central ovary (which in the former is situated on a central protuberance)

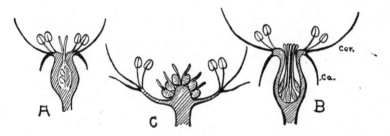

FIG. 292.—Diagrams to show different types of floral receptacle. A, Apple (epigynous flower). B, Rose (extreme perigynous type). C, *Potentilla* (perigynous flower). Receptacle shaded in all cases. *Ca.*, calyx; *Cor.*, corolla.

becomes more and more enclosed. Such flowers are described as *perigynous*. If the ovary becomes completely enveloped and altogether joined up with the receptacle (Fig. 292, A), whilst the remaining floral organs arise from its top, the flower becomes *epigynous*, as in the Umbelliferæ (Fig. 315, E) and Narcissus (Fig. 293, B). In the Apple (Fig. 292, A) ovary (core) and receptacle (flesh) are clearly distinguishable. In these flowers the ovary is situated below the other organs, *i.e.* is *inferior*, whilst in peri- and hypogynous flowers it is *superior*.

In those flowers, which for many reasons are regarded as relatively unspecialised (*e.g.* Ranunculaceæ and

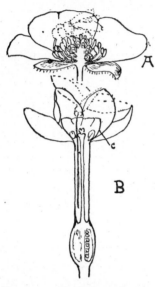

its allies), the floral receptacle is elongated,[1] bearing sepals, petals, stamens, and carpels at successively higher levels, and these parts are wholly or in part spirally arranged; the stamens and carpels, moreover, are usually numerous, and not joined in any way. The further evolution and specialisation of the flower has brought about increased efficiency and precision in pollination, and appears to have involved a gradual shortening of the floral receptacle, with the result that the different sets of organs became whorled and reduced in number. At the same time the members of a whorl, after their primary differentiation, tend to develop in unison (so-called *fusion*). Another development leads to better protection of the ovary, the receptacle gradually becoming more and more concave (progressive stages can be found in the perigynous Rosaceæ), until the flower is epigynous. Certain it is that the most highly specialised families (Umbelliferæ,

FIG. 293. Vertical sections of flowers of A, Buttercup (open type); B, Pheasant's-eye Narcissus (tubular type), showing hypogyny and epigyny respectively. The body of the pollinating insect is shown by dotted lines, the proboscis being indicated by a continuous line. *c*, corona.

Compositæ, Orchidaceæ) all possess such epigynous flowers, with the different members in whorls. Further specialisation is connected with the development of irregular flowers (p. 456).

The features hitherto considered are best illustrated by means of *longitudinal sections* through the middle of the flower, as in Fig. 292. In drawing such sections it is advisable to show only the actual cut surface (cf. Fig. 294, B). The section should faithfully represent the shape of the receptacle, as well as the exact position of the various floral organs, and should indicate the orientation of bracts and bracteoles with reference to the flower.

Apart from the longitudinal section, a *floral diagram* or ground-plan of the

---

[1] Extreme elongation of the floral receptacle is seen in *Myosurus* and *Ranunculus sceleratus*. In whorled flowers local development of internodes may occur, as between calyx and corolla (*Silene cucubalus*) or between corolla and stamens (*Passiflora*).

flower is necessary to complete the picture of its structure (cf. Fig. 294, A). The main axis (*m.a.*), on which the flower is borne, is shown by a dot and after that the exact position of the different floral whorls, as well as of the bracts and bracteoles, with reference to the main axis and to one another, is indicated (as in Fig. 294, A and C–F); all the members arising at one level are placed on the same circle and the ovary is shown in cross-section. The side of the flower adjacent to the axis of the inflorescence is *posterior*, whilst that away from it is

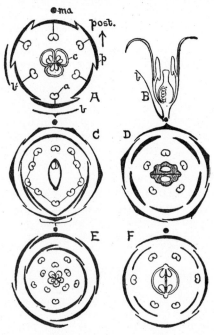

FIG. 294. Diagrams of floral structure. A and C–F, Floral diagrams. A, Hyacinth (Liliaceæ). C, Sweet-pea (Leguminosæ). D, Hogweed (Umbelliferæ). E, Geranium. F, Wallflower (Cruciferæ). *a*, stamen; *b*, bract; *b'*, bracteole; *c*, ovary; *m.a.*, main axis; *p*, perianth-member; *post.*, posterior side of flower. B, Longitudinal section of flower of Hyacinth, taken through the median plane. *b*, bract.

anterior. A longitudinal section which passes from the posterior to the anterior side of the flower passes through the *median plane* and is the customary one for longitudinal sections.

The floral diagram of the Hyacinth (Fig. 294, A) shows that all the different whorls have their parts in threes; this is found in many Monocotyledons and such a flower is said to be *trimerous*. On the other hand, *Geranium* (Fig. 294, E), a Dicotyledon, has its parts in fives and its flower is consequently described as *pentamerous*, a type of frequent occurrence in the latter group, although flowers with their parts in fours (i.e. *tetramerous*, as in *Epilobium*, Fig. 311), or twos (e.g. *Circæa*, Fig. 427, C, D), are also found.

The normal flower of both Monocotyledons and Dicotyledons has two whorls of perianth-members (Fig. 294). In Monocotyledons (Fig. 294, A) the

main axis lies opposite the interval between two members of the outer whorl—
that is to say, the third member is anterior, whereas in most Dicotyledons the
odd (fifth) member of the outer perianth-whorl is situated opposite the axis—
in other words is posterior (Fig. 294, D and E).   In the Leguminosæ (Fig.
294, C), however, the odd sepal is anterior.   In general the members of one
whorl alternate with those of the next and this is always so in the perianth.   In
Dicotyledons, however, it is not uncommon for the outer whorl of stamens to
stand opposite the petals (e.g. *Geranium*, Fig. 294, E).   The number of whorls,
moreover, varies in the flowers of different plants; apart from the absence of a
perianth (*e.g.* Ash, see p. 429), there may be only one whorl of stamens (*e.g.*
Umbelliferæ, Fig. 294, D) or more than two (*e.g.* Rosaceæ).   In the Hyacinth
(Fig. 294, A) and *Geranium* (Fig. 294, E) the same number of parts occurs in
each whorl, but this is by no means the general rule, the ovary frequently
consisting of less (two in Umbelliferæ, Fig. 294, D; one in Leguminosæ, Fig.
294, C), and not uncommonly this is true also of the stamens (e.g. *Veronica*,
with a tetramerous perianth and two stamens, Fig. 430, B).

   The two alternating *non-essential whorls*, when alike in colour
and texture (*e.g.* most Monocotyledons), are termed a perianth.   In
Dicotyledons, on the other hand, as well as in some Monocotyledons
(*e.g.* Water Plantain *Alisma*, Fig. 441, B), the outer whorl is generally green and protective, whilst the inner one is brightly coloured
and attractive, and we then speak of a *calyx* and *corolla* respectively.
Occasionally there is only one perianth-whorl, which is then generally green, and good examples of such *apetalous* flowers are furnished
by the Stinging Nettle and Dog's Mercury (Fig. 295).

FIG. 295. Apetalous, unisexual flowers
of the Dog's Mercury (somewhat enlarged).   The left-hand one is the
male, the right-hand one the female.

   The individual sepals of the calyx are with rare exceptions green
in colour.   Their protective character is well seen in most flower-
buds in which all the inner parts are completely enveloped by the
sepals.   The sepals may actually drop off as the flower expands
(*e.g.* Poppy, Fig. 163, *c*) and the necessity for protection becomes
less urgent.   As a general rule, however, the calyx is *persistent* and
may subsequently, long after the petals and stamens have withered,
afford protection to the fruit (*e.g.* Campion, Mallow, Fig. 334, C).
   The necessity of the calyx as a protective envelope is easily
demonstrated by carefully removing it from a number of young
buds (*e.g.* Poppy) without damaging the rest of the flower; as a
result the latter will be found either to dry up or to show half-
withered petals when it expands.
   Sometimes bracteoles grade off into the perianth, as in the Lesser
Celandine in which the outer members (actually modified bracteoles)
are green and may even exhibit a reduced lamina similar to that of

the foliage-leaves. Thus the protective sepals of the reproductive
bud or flower may be com-
pared with the scale-leaves
which protect the foliage-
bud. In the Winter Aconite
(Fig. 296) the functions of
the calyx are performed by
three much-divided brac-
teoles closely resembling the
foliage-leaves and arising
immediately beneath the
coloured perianth. This
recalls the state of affairs
seen in the Wood Anemone
in which, however, the three
bracteoles are situated some
little way below the flower.

We have likened the
flower to a compressed shoot,
and this analogy is em-
phasised by certain abnormal
flowers, such as the Double
Arabis; here, instead of
producing essential organs

FIG. 296. Flower of the Winter Aconite
(*Eranthis*) (natural size), showing the
three divided bracteoles which function
as a calyx.

the axis continues to grow, forming a series of successive flowers
with short separating internodes, the one within the other and
each consisting only of calyx and corolla.

The sepals are usually simple in form and either arise quite separately from
one another (*polysepalous*, Geranium, Fig. 294, E, and Wallflower, Fig. 317) or
are more or less completely joined to form a tube with free tips corresponding
to the component members (*gamosepalous*, Fig. 297, B and C, shown by joining
edges of sepals in floral diagram, cf. Fig. 422, C). When the individual lobes of
a gamosepalous calyx are of the same size it is said to be *regular* (Henbane, Fig.
297, B), but frequently owing to unequal development an *irregular* calyx is produced (*e.g.* the two-lipped calyx of many Leguminosæ, Fig. 320, A and B); less
commonly a polysepalous calyx shows irregularity, as in the Garden Nasturtium
(Fig. 297, A) in which one side is produced into a long *spur*. Where the flowers
are closely massed together in the bud, so that they afford one another mutual
protection, the calyx is often greatly reduced. Thus, in the Umbelliferæ it
merely forms a green rim, whilst in the capitula of Compositæ, in which additional protection is afforded by the involucre, the leaf-like character of the sepals
is altogether lost; the calyx here generally consist of a circle of hairs (the *pappus*,
Fig. 297, E, *p*) which aid in fruit-dispersal (cf. p. 480).

The *petals* of the corolla in Dicotyledons and of the perianth in Monocotyledons exhibit a great variety of form, developing either separately (*polypetalous*, Buttercup, Fig. 293, A, and Tulip) or being more or less joined together
so as to form a corolla-tube with free lobes (*gamo-* or *sympetalous*, Primrose,

Fig. 318, and Narcissus, Fig. 293, B).   Free petals are usually much larger than
the sepals and very commonly have an entire margin (Fig. 293, A; Fig. 298, B),

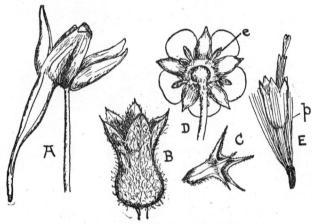

FIG. 297. Forms of calyx (A–D natural size, E enlarged).   A, *Tropæolum*
(spurred).   B, Henbane (*Hyoscyamus*) (gamosepalous).   C, *Lamium* (gamosepalous and slightly irregular).   D, *Geum*.   *e*, epicalyx.   E, Tubular floret of
Aster (Compositæ).   *p*, pappus.

although sometimes more or less deeply divided (*e.g.* Fig. 422, A and B).   As
a general rule the petal has only an extremely short stalk (Fig. 298, B), but
occasionally (*e.g.* Pink, Fig. 298, A, Wallflower) the
blade terminates a long claw (*cl.*) with which it forms
almost a right angle.

The sympetalous corolla shows considerable diversity
of form (cf. Fig. 299).   The corolla, like the calyx,
may be *regular* or *irregular*; examples of the latter
condition are furnished by the *bilabiate* corolla of the
Labiatæ (Fig. 299, D).   An irregular corolla may,
however, also occur amongst polypetalous forms, as
for example, the butterfly-shaped (*papilionaceous*) corolla
of the British Leguminosæ (Fig. 320) and that of
Orchids (Fig. 326).

FIG. 298. Forms of
petals (about two-
thirds natural size).
A, *Dianthus*.   B,
Geum.   *cl*, claw.

In the bud the sepals either fit edge to edge (*i.e.* are
valvate, as in *Clematis*) or more commonly overlap (*i.e.*
are *imbricate*, as in the Buttercup; cf. also Fig. 294, C–E).
Since the space within the flower-bud is as limited as
in a vegetative bud, the developing petals become folded
just as do the young foliage-leaves (cf. p. 129).   Most commonly the petals
overlap one another, so that their arrangement is *imbricate* (Fig. 294, C and E);
more rarely a crumpled folding (Poppy, Fig. 163, *b*) or a twisted arrangement
(*Gentiana*, Fig. 300, A and C) obtains.

In the same way as outgrowths, such as stipules and the ligule of Grasses
(p. 126), have been found arising at different points from foliage-leaves, so also
analogous structures occasionally develop in relation to the calyx and corolla.
Thus, in some plants leafy processes develop between the bases of adjacent

sepals, so that there appear to be two alternating whorls of the latter, the outer of which is then spoken of as an *epicalyx* (*e.g.* Strawberry; *Geum*, Fig. 297, D, *e*; Mallow).   Similarly tubular corollas may produce outgrowths, usually near the

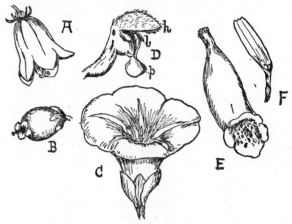

FIG. 299. Forms of gamopetalous corolla (all natural size). A, *Campanula*. B, *Erica*. C, *Calystegia*. D, *Lamium* (bilabiate). *h*, upper lip (hood); *l*, side-projections; *p*, lower lip (alighting platform). E, *Digitalis*. F, Ray-floret of Compositæ (ligulate).

top of the tube, which either arise independently from each petal (*e.g.* the teeth-like processes of the Campion) or form a united fringe (Fig. 300, B and D, *co.*), or a complete membranous tube (the *corona* of Daffodil and Narcissus, Fig. 293, B, *c*).

The sequence of development of the floral parts is usually from without inwards, viz. calyx, corolla, stamens, ovary.   Each *stamen* (Fig. 302, A) consists of a stalk or filament (*f*) and a swollen pollen-producing part or *anther* (*a*).   The latter exhibits two lobes joined by a continuation of the filament known as the *connective*.   The stamens are microsporophylls and comparable to foliar structures bearing marginal sporangia (the pollen sacs).   The lamina is represented by the connective.   The foliar nature of the stamen is indicated where the connective is developed as a flat petal-like structure (as in *Potamogeton*, Fig. 302, B, *Co.*), or where stipule-like outgrowths arise from the bases of the filaments (*Allium*, Fig. 302, C).

Most commonly the anther is rigidly attached to the filament (Fig. 301, A, C, and F), but occasionally (as in Grasses, Fig. 301, D) it is more or less loosely suspended from its end.

Sometimes appendages develop on the anthers (e.g. *Calluna*, Fig. 301, E, *ap.*) or rarely the connective branches (*e.g.* Sage, Fig. 322, E).   In the Violet (Fig. 325, B, *c*) the connective forms a membranous prolongation beyond the anther.

If more than one whorl of stamens is present, the individual whorls usually alternate with one another (Fig. 294, A and E). The outermost stamens commonly alternate with the inner series of perianth-leaves, but in the Primrose (Fig. 429) the five stamens are situated opposite the petals, whilst in *Geranium* (Fig. 294, E) the outermost whorl occupies a similar position. When the stamens are numerous, they are often spirally arranged, as in the Buttercup (Fig. 423), and their number is usually very variable; we then speak of them as

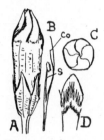

FIG. 300. Structure of flower of *Gentiana germanica* (natural size). A, Entire flower-bud, showing twisted arrangement of petals. B, Longitudinal section of petal, showing epipetalous stamen and corona. C, Petals in bud, seen from above. D, Single petal, showing corona. *co*, corona; *s*, stamen.

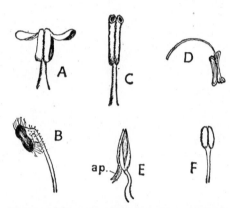

FIG. 301. Stamens and stamen-structure (all natural size). A, Bay-tree (*Laurus*), showing dehiscence. B, Dead-nettle. C, *Rhododendron*, showing dehiscence. D, Vernal Grass (*Anthoxanthum*). E, *Calluna*, showing dehiscence. *ap.*, appendages. F, *Ranunculus*.

indefinite. The stamens are most commonly of equal length, but many exceptions occur, *e.g.* four long and two short (*tetradynamous*, Cruciferæ, Fig. 424, A); two long and two short (*didynamous*, Labiatæ); five long and five short (*Stellaria*, Fig. 315, C). The stamens collectively constitute the *androecium*.

The number of stamens is often equal to, or some multiple of, the number of members in the perianth-whorls (Fig. 294, A and C–E). Exceptions are most usually found in flowers having only a single whorl of stamens and possessed of an irregular corolla, *e.g.* Labiatæ (Fig. 432) and Scrophulariaceæ (Fig. 430, C), in both of which there are generally only four stamens; other examples are furnished by *Veronica* (Fig. 430, B) and Rosemary (*Rosmarinus*) with only two, and *Tropæolum* with eight stamens. A careful study of the arrangement of the stamens in these flowers indicates that one or more have failed to develop, and confirmation is furnished by flowers in which a sterile structure or *staminode*[1] (not producing pollen) occupies the position of the missing stamen. This is well illustrated by the Figwort and *Pentstemon*, members of the Scrophulariaceæ, in which the staminode (Fig. 310, *St.*) occupies the posterior position in the stamen-whorl (Fig. 430, C), which, in most other members of this family and of Labiatæ, is vacant. In the Stork's

---

[1] In the floral diagram this is indicated by a small circle or in the way shown in Fig. 430, C; missing stamens are marked by a dot (cf. Fig. 430, B).

Bill (*Erodium*), an ally of *Geranium*, there are five staminodes opposite the petals and five fertile stamens.

The stamens may either be free from one another or joined together in various ways. Thus, in *Genista* (Fig. 426, A) and Gorse the ten filaments are united for the greater part of their length (*i.e.* are *monadelphous*), so as to form a tube round the young pod. A somewhat similar condition is seen in the Mallow, where the numerous stamens have joined filaments. In the Compositæ (Fig. 312) and *Jasione* (Fig. 436, E), on the other hand, the five filaments are free, whereas the anthers are connected (*syngenesious*). Moreover, in many flowers with tubular corollas the filaments of the stamens are more or less completely fused with the petals (*epipetalous*, Fig. 294, B; 300, B), since they appear to arise from the latter. Finally it may be noticed that in a few flowers the stamens exhibit branching, those of the St. John's Wort (*Hypericum*), for instance, forming five bundles each dividing into numerous filaments bearing anthers.

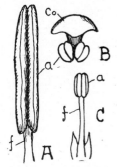

FIG. 302. Various forms of stamens. A, Tulip (ordinary form). B, *Potamogeton*, showing the enlarged connective (*Co.*). C, Onion (*Allium*), with stipular outgrowths from the base of the filament. *a.*, anthers; *f.*, filaments.

A single vascular bundle traverses filament and connective. The anther normally bears four *pollen sacs*,[1] two on either side of the connective (Fig. 303, A), although in the Mallow-family (Malvaceæ) the stamens bear but two pollen sacs. In transverse sections through immature flower-buds, the anthers are seen to consist of uniform thin-walled tissue bounded by a distinct epidermis, whilst a slight lobing foreshadows the future pollen sacs (Fig. 303, B). At a slightly later stage four subepidermal strips of varying width (often of only a single cell) become distinguishable, one in each lobe; these strips consist of cells with prominent nuclei and dense contents, and constitute the *archesporia* (Fig. 303, C, *a.*), each of which extends as a narrow band of tissue for almost the whole length of the anther. Each archesporial cell divides tangentially (Fig. 303, C), and, from the inner halves thus formed, the actual pollen-producing tissue arises, so that the *pollen mother-cells* are really subepidermal in origin. The outer half of each archesporial cell divides to form the wall of the pollen sac (Fig. 303, D), which consists of several layers.

In transverse section through older anthers (Fig. 303, A), the mass of spore mother-cells in the centre of each pollen sac is seen to be surrounded by a nutritive layer (*tapetum*, *t.*). This is composed of large, often palisade-like, cells with prominent nuclei and

---

[1] For details on reproductive morphology of Angiosperms, see J. M. Coulter and C. J. Chamberlain, *Morphology of Angiosperms*. Appleton, New York, 1915 (348 pp.); P. Maheshwari, *An Introduction to the Embryology of Angiosperms*. McGraw-Hill Book Co., 1950 (453 pp.).

dense contents. Between the tapetum (*t.*) and the epidermis (*ep.*) of
the anther are two or more layers, the outermost of which generally
consists of rather large, subsequently thickened cells (*fibrous layer,
f.*), whilst the others (*m.l.*) are usually very much flattened.

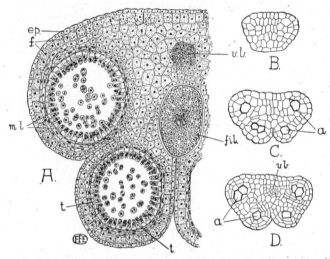

FIG. 303. Development of the anther. A, Section of part of anther of young
stamen, showing the pollen sacs at the mother-cell stage (the mother-cells
are seen in various stages of division). B, Section of young anther before the
archesporia are differentiated. C and D, Later stages. *a.*, dividing archesporial cells; *ep.*, epidermis of anther; *f.*, fibrous layer; *fil.*, filament; *m.l.*,
middle layers; *t.*, tapetum; *v.b.*, vascular bundle of connective   (A, original;
the remainder after Warming.)

Each pollen mother-cell, as in the groups previously studied,
undergoes two divisions (cf. Fig. 303, A), the first of which is the
reduction division.   The four *pollen grains*, thus formed within
each mother-cell, generally fall apart as the membrane of the
latter becomes dissolved.   But in a few plants the members of
each tetrad remain in connection, when the pollen is shed (e.g.
Typha, Neottia, Fig. 304, D, *a–c*; Ericaceæ, Fig. 304, D, *d*.), and
a more extreme condition is seen in Orchids, where all the pollen
grains formed by the single stamen cohere as two masses or *pollinia*
(Fig. 304, F).   Such cohesion is, however, only met with in insect-
pollinated flowers.   During the development of the pollen grains
the tapetum undergoes gradual disorganisation (Fig. 305, *t.*), prior
to which the cells often become bi- or multi-nucleate.

The mature pollen grain possesses a wall of two layers, the
outer of which is thick and cuticularised, whilst the inner is delicate.
Where the pollen is wind- or water-borne, its surface is commonly

smooth and dry, but when conveyed by insects it is usually sculptured
in various ways (Fig. 304, B, G) and covered with a sticky oil.
The outer layer is perforated, or rendered thin, by one or more
pores or pits (Fig. 304, C, *o*.), through one of which the pollen
tube is subsequently protruded. In this respect the pollen of
Angiosperms is more specialised than that of Gymnosperms, where
the outer layer of the membrane merely bursts in germination.

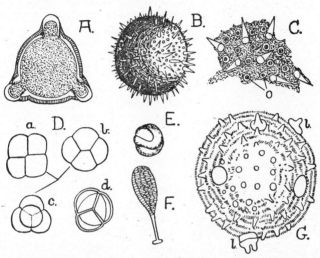

FIG. 304. Diverse types of pollen. A, *Epilobium*, with three thin spots in the
outer coat. B, Hollyhock (*Althœa*), with numerous pores. C, Small part of
same enlarged, showing the pores (*o*.). D, Pollen-tetrads, *a–c*, of *Neottia
nidus avis*; *d*, of Bilberry (*Vaccinium myrtillus*). E, Musk (*Mimulus moschatus*).
F, Pollinium of *Orchis morio*. G, Pollen grain of *Cucurbita pepo*, showing the
embossed lids (*l*.) of the outer coat, which become pushed off by the growing
pollen tubes. (A–D, after Sachs; D and F, after Wettstein; E, after Mohl;
G, after Schacht.)

As the pollen matures the walls of the cells composing the
fibrous layer become strengthened by radial bars of thickening
which are often connected on the inner tangential walls, and
simultaneously the cells lose their living contents (Fig. 305, *en*.);
many of the cells in the region of the connective, moreover, develop
similar thickenings. At this stage the two pollen sacs, in each
half of the anther, become confluent through the drying up of the
intervening thin-walled septa, and it is this same process of desiccation that ultimately leads to the setting free of the pollen. Drying
is usually due to direct loss of moisture to the air, but may result
from the withdrawal of water by neighbouring cells of high osmotic
content, belonging either to nectaries (e.g. *Stellaria*, Fig. 315, C)

or to sugar-containing tissue (e.g. *Digitalis*); hence dehiscence of the stamens ensues, even in a saturated atmosphere.

Actual splitting usually takes place longitudinally, along the middle line of each anther-lobe; the line of weakness is sometimes bounded on either side by a spindle-shaped group of enlarged epidermal cells (*e.g.* Lily). The thickenings of the cells of the fibrous layer (Fig. 305, *en.*) prevent radial contraction, so that the tangential shrinkage brings the bars together like the closing of the hood of a perambulator; it is the tension thus set up that finally results in rupture. The edges of the slit, thus formed (Fig. 424, C), curl back, but in damp air they often bend forwards into their original position and so protect the pollen. According as the connective develops mainly towards the outer or inner face, the lines of dehiscence of the anthers are towards (viz. *introrse*; *e.g.* Umbelliferæ, Fig. 294, D), or away from, the centre of the flower (i.e. *extrorse*; *e.g.* Buttercup, Fig. 423). In a few flowers dehiscence takes place in other ways, as, for instance, by apical pores (Ericaceæ, Fig. 301, C, E), or by the formation of subapical valves which hinge backwards to allow the shedding of the pollen (*e.g.* Barberry) (cf. also Fig. 301, A).

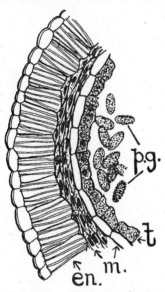

FIG. 305. Transverse section through part of a pollen sac of a ripe anther. *en.*, fibrous layer; *m.*, middle layers; *p.g.*, pollen grains; *t.*, disorganised tapetum.

The *ovary* of the Angiosperm consists of one or more *carpels* or *megasporophylls* which may either be joined together to form a *syncarpous* ovary (*e.g.* Liliaceæ, Fig. 294, A, *c*) or they are free (*apocarpous* ovary, Buttercup, Fig. 293, A; Fig. 306, C). The leaf-like structure of the carpels is best seen in ovaries of the latter type. Thus, in a young fruiting specimen of the Larkspur or Monkshood (Fig. 333, *b*) the outer surface of each carpel shows a distinct midrib (or *dorsal suture*, *m*), from which lateral veins (*l.v.*) are seen to arise; on the opposite side there is a slight furrow, where the somewhat enlarged edges of the carpels are joined and form two *placentæ*, each bearing a row of ovules. It is along this line (the *ventral suture*) that the fruit subsequently opens. Except for the inrolling, such a carpel might be compared to the megasporophyll of *Cycas* (cf. p. 398).

Similarly, if a young pod of a Pea be split lengthwise, it will be found to break more readily along the edge bearing the young seeds (*i.e.* the ventral suture); moreover, the latter are seen to occur on both valves, since some remain attached to one half and some to the other. In *Reseda* the margins of the carpels are not joined together, except at the base, even in the young ovary. The tip of each carpel terminates in the *stigma*, which is often borne on the end of a prolongation, the *style*.

In the syncarpous ovary the sides of adjacent carpels are more or less joined together. A slight fusion is seen in the Monkshood (Fig. 333, *b*) in which the individual carpels are frequently united at their bases by the ventral sutures. When the carpels are completely connected in this way, we obtain an ovary divided by *septa* into as many compartments or *loculi* as there are carpels, the structure being described as *bi-*, *tri-*, *quadri-*, or *multilocular* according to their number; thus the Umbelliferæ (Fig. 294, D) and the Scrophulariaceæ (Fig. 323, D) have a bilocular, the Hyacinth (Fig. 294, A) has a trilocular, the Willow-herb (Fig. 427, B) has a quadrilocular, and the Mallow a multilocular ovary. If only one carpel is present we have a *monocarpellary* ovary, as in Leguminosæ (Fig. 294, C).

A second mode of junction of the carpels in syncarpous ovaries is that in which the adjacent edges are united without the individual carpels being folded together, the ovary consequently having only one compartment (*i.e.* it is *unilocular*; e.g. Violet, Fig. 325, C). The ovary is then described as *bi-*, *tri-*, *quadri-*, or *multicarpellary* according to the number of component carpels, and this feature can be determined either by the character of the style and stigma or by the arrangement of the ovules.

Whatever the type of syncarpous ovary, the tips of the individual carpels are either free or more or less joined. Thus, in some ovaries the styles and stigmas are distinct (*e.g.* the St. John's Wort, Fig. 306, A) so that the number of component carpels is quite apparent. More usually, however, the styles of a syncarpous ovary are completely united to form a single structure, the stigma dividing into as many segments as there are carpels (*e.g.* three in *Campanula*, Fig. 306, F; two in Compositæ, Fig. 299, F). The stigma either divides into a number of narrow arms or is merely lobed. The actual sticky receptive surface (on which the pollen can alone germinate) is normally situated on the upper side. In the Primrose (Fig. 318), the stigma constitutes a small swelling (*capitate stigma*) at the end of the style. The almost flat top of the multi-carpellary ovary of the Poppy (Fig. 333, *h*) bears a number of dark radiating lines which represent stigmas of a peculiar type.

When the edges of the carpels of a syncarpous ovary meet at the centre, the ovules are naturally situated on the central column (placenta), formed by the fused swollen margins of the carpels (Figs. 293, B; 294, B); the arrangement or *placentation* of the ovules is then said to be *axile* (*e.g.* Hyacinth, Fig. 294, A). When the ovary is unilocular, the ovules are borne in rows (often double) along the lines of junction of the carpels, so that we can speak of marginal or *parietal* placentation (*e.g.* Violet, Fig. 325, C). The number of placentas here again gives an indication of the number of carpels composing the ovary. In some plants the parietal placentas project more or less markedly into the cavity,

29

as for instance in *Hypericum* (Fig. 306, B). A third type of placentation is seen
in the Caryophyllaceæ (*e.g.* Campion) and Primulaceæ (Fig. 318) in which the
ovules are borne on a central upgrowth arising from the base of the ovary, a
so-called *free central placenta*; in the former family septa are occasionally
found connecting the placenta with the ovary-wall. In the White Water-lily
(*Nymphæa*) and in the Flowering Rush (*Butomus*) the ovules arise in an unusual
way from the whole inner surface of the carpels.

The number of ovules in the ovary, or in its individual compartments, varies
considerably; thus, in the Scrophulariaceæ and Liliaceæ they are numerous,
whilst there are but two in each loculus in the Sycamore, and one only in each

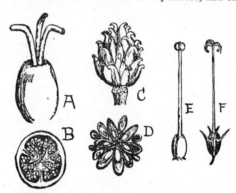

FIG. 306. Ovaries and ovary-structure (E and F natural size, the other figures
enlarged). A, Ovary of *Hypericum*. B, The same in cross-section. C,
Ovary of *Ranunculus*. D, The same in cross-section. E, Ovary of *Digitalis*.
F, Ovary of *Campanula*.

compartment in the Umbelliferæ (Fig. 294, D). When there is but one ovule
in the ovary it is generally either attached to the base (e.g. *Polygonum*) or
suspended from the apex. A small number of ovules is most frequent in the
more specialised families.

In certain families the loculi in the ovary become subdivided during the
development of the flower. In the Cruciferæ, for instance, the bicarpellary
ovary is at first unilocular, but becomes bilocular through the formation of a
partition joining the two parietal placentas (Fig. 294, F). Similarly, in the
Labiatæ (Fig. 432) and Boraginaceæ (Fig. 433, A) the ovary is bilocular in
early stages, but subsequently exhibits four compartments. In the Flax there
are ten loculi, but only five carpels.

When the ovary is apocarpous the individual carpels commonly
show a spiral arrangement. In such spiral flowers a marked
transition between stamens and petals is occasionally found, this
being very obvious in *Nymphæa*. The same phenomenon is
frequently observed in double flowers where the doubling is due
to a replacement of the stamens by petals (*e.g.* cultivated Roses and
Pinks).

The *ovules* of Angiosperms (Fig. 307), which in their general
construction are like those of Gymnosperms, usually possess two

integuments (inner, *I.i.*, and outer, *O.i.*). A single one is the rule amongst the gamopetalous Dicotyledons (Sympetalæ) and a few polypetalous families (*e.g.* Umbelliferæ, Salicaceæ, etc.). In these latter, however, the single integument is generally relatively robust, a fact which suggests its possible origin from the fusion of two; a partial union of this character is, indeed, seen in some members of the Ranunculaceæ.[1] The *nucellus* (*n.*), with very few exceptions, is only clearly separated from the integument at the apex, where it forms a cap of tissue extending between the large megaspore (embryo sac, *e.s.*, see p. 445) and the micropyle (*m.*). The part of the nucellus in contact with the integument can often be distinguished from the latter, in sections of the ovule, by the dense contents of its cells, which form a nutritive layer around the developing embryo sac.

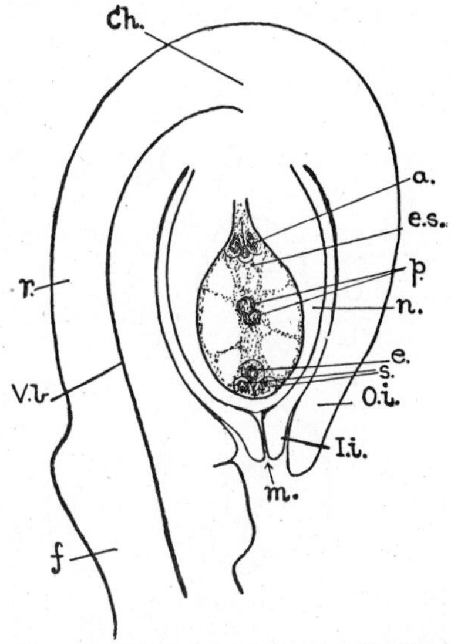

FIG. 307. Diagrammatic longitudinal section through an anatropous ovule, greatly magnified. *a.*, antipodal cells; *Ch.*, chalaza; *e.*, egg; *e.s.*, embryo sac; *f.*, funicle; *I.i.*, inner integument; *m.*, micropyle; *n.*, nucellus; *O.i.*, outer integument; *p.*, polar nuclei; *r.*, raphe; *s.*, synergidæ; *V.b.*, vascular bundle of raphe.

By far the commonest type of ovule is the *anatropous* one (Figs. 307 and 308, C), in which the main body is bent down against its stalk (*funicle*, *f.*), so that the micropyle (*m.*) is directed towards the placenta. The greater part of the funicle is connected with the adjacent portion of the outer integument, which is in consequence not easily distinguished on this side. This region, known as the *raphe* (*r.*), is traversed by the vascular bundle (*V.b.*) which enters the funicle from the placenta, and which extends as far as the base of the nucellus (a region known as the *chalaza*, *Ch.*).

Erect or *orthotropous* ovules, in which the micropyle faces away from the placenta, and lies at the opposite end to the usually short funicle (Fig. 308, B), are much less frequent, but are found, for example, in *Polygonum*. Another rare type, the *campylotropous*

---

[1] In a few Rosaceæ (e.g. *Geum*) there is only a single integument due to failure of the inner one to develop.

ovule (Fig. 308, E), seen in many Caryophyllaceæ, is bent in such a way that the stalk appears to be attached midway between the chalaza and micropyle. All Angiospermous ovules are supplied by a vascular bundle which runs through the funicle, but terminates at the chalaza, except in those rare instances where the nucellus is not in intimate contact with the integument. In *Myrica gale*, for

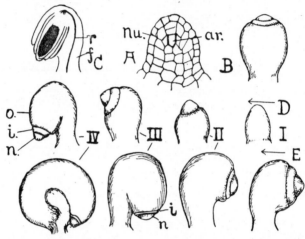

FIG. 308. Ovules and stages in their development (after Le Maout and Decaisne). A, Young ovule, before the integuments appear, showing nucellus (*Nu.*) and dividing archesporium (*ar.*). B, Orthotropous ovule of *Polygonum*. C, Anatropous ovule in longitudinal section, showing funicle (*f.*) and raphe (*r.*). D, I–IV (in the direction of the arrow), successive stages in the development of the anatropous ovule of *Chelidonium*. E, Successive stages (in the direction of the arrow) in the development of the campylotropous ovule of the Mallow (*Malva*). *i.*, inner integument; *n.*, nucellus; *o.*, outer integument.

instance, there is a well-developed vascular supply throughout the integument and the nucellus also contains conducting tissue.

The ovule invariably arises on the placenta as a small mound of thin-walled cells which represents the future nucellus (Fig. 308, A and D, I). Around the base of this the integuments subsequently develop as ring-like upgrowths, the inner being formed before the outer (II–IV). In the Spindle-tree (*Euonymus*) a third integument (*aril*) is present, which becomes conspicuous after fertilisation (Fig. 338, B, C). The caruncle of the Castor Oil seed (p. 23 and Fig. 15, A) is also of the nature of an aril.

All ovules are at first erect. The anatropous form, characteristic of the majority, is due to excessive growth on one side of the chalazal region of the rudiment, so that the latter gradually becomes curved till the micropyle points towards the placenta (cf.

Fig. 308, D). In campylotropous ovules the mature form is due to even more extreme asymmetrical growth of the chalazal region (Fig. 308, E). Stages in the development of anatropous ovules can be readily studied in transverse sections through young ovaries of the Poppy.

The first steps towards the development of a *megaspore* are to be found in very young ovules, usually before the integuments have become plainly differentiated (Fig. 308, A). As in the stamens, the *archesporium* (*ar.*) arises subepidermally, but here it usually comprises but a single cell situated near the apex of the nucellus. This divides tangentially (Fig. 308, A, *ar.*), the inner half generally constituting the mother-cell, which as a rule, by two successive divisions, of which the first is the reduction division, gives rise to a row of four spores, forming a tetrad within the nucellus. It is usually the innermost member of the tetrad that becomes the functioning megaspore (generally known as the *embryo sac*). This cell subsequently increases greatly in size so as to occupy most of the nucellus (Fig. 307, *e.s.*). In the Mistletoe-family (Loranthaceæ) no proper ovules are differentiated; a parenchymatous outgrowth, which arises from the base of the ovary and almost fills the latter, develops a number of archesporia, from each of which an embryo sac results. This affords another instance of the reduction characteristic of parasites (cf. p. 215).

Until it has reached a considerable size the embryo sac contains but a single nucleus, which usually lies in the middle of a strand of cytoplasm running from end to end of the sac and bridging a large central vacuole. Sooner or later, however, a nuclear division occurs, and the two resulting nuclei wander towards opposite ends of the embryo sac, where each again divides twice. Of the eight nuclei thus formed, three at the end remote from the micropyle, usually become separated by cell-walls and constitute the *antipodal cells* (Figs. 307, 309, 329, D, *a.*), which probably assist in the nourishment of the young embryo. They frequently enlarge after fertilisation, and may even divide to form an antipodal tissue (*e.g.* Burr-reed *Sparganium*).

Of the four nuclei at the micropylar end of the embryo sac, three become surrounded by an envelope of specialised cytoplasm, and constitute a group of naked cells known as the *egg-apparatus* (Fig. 307), which consists of the *egg* (*e.*) and two *synergidæ* (*s.*). The remaining nuclei (one at each end, one of them the sister-nucleus of the egg) pass back to the middle of the embryo sac, where these two *polar nuclei* (Figs. 307, *p.*; 329, D, *p.n.*) meet and ultimately fuse to form the *primary endosperm nucleus* (Fig. 309, *p.*). This is the stage reached by the embryo sac at the time of fertilisation.

The sequence of events during this development and the resulting structure of the embryo sac are practically identical in the vast majority of both Monocotyledons and Dicotyledons which have been investigated, and this uniformity constitutes one of the strongest arguments for the origin of the group from a common ancestry. Tubular sucker-like outgrowths from the chalazal or both ends of the embryo sac are met with in the Beech, Hornbeam, and some Sympetalæ (*Plantago lanceolata*, Scrophulariaceæ), and probably aid in the transference of food-material to the developing embryo. The same end is served by the haustorial outgrowths from the later-arising endosperm (p. 469) which occur in some genera.

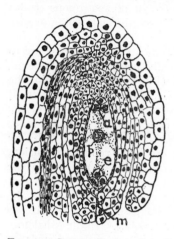

FIG. 309. Longitudinal section of ovule of Marsh Marigold (*Caltha*), showing the structure of the mature embryo sac. *a.*, antipodal cells; *e.*, egg; *m.*, micropyle; *p.*, primary endosperm nucleus.

The pollen grains and embryo sacs of Angiosperms are obviously comparable to the microspores and megaspores of Gymnosperms and *Selaginella*, and within them divisions take place which lead to the formation of the male and female gametes respectively. The contents of the embryo sac may therefore be regarded as a female prothallus, and the contents of the microspore (cf. p. 468) as a still more reduced male prothallus.

CHAPTER XXXVII

FLORAL MECHANISMS AND POLLINATION[1]

THE ovules do not, in most species, mature into seeds, unless pollen from the same kind of plant has been deposited upon the stigma at a time when the latter is still in a receptive condition. By carefully removing the stamens from a number of flowers, before their pollen is shed (*i.e.* in the bud-stage), and then covering each with a bag of fine muslin to prevent access of insects or of wind-borne pollen, the necessity of pollen for the formation of seed can be readily shown. If pollen from another plant of the same kind is transferred to the stigma of one of the flowers, with the help of a camel's-hair brush, ripe seed will, however, almost certainly be produced.

Experiments have also proved that in many plants a larger number of seeds and frequently more vigorous offspring are produced, if fertilisation is effected by pollen from the flower of a different individual of the same species. This is called *cross-pollination,* whereas the term *self-pollination* is applied when the pollen comes either from another flower of the same individual or from the stamens of the self-same flower, the former alternative being sometimes more beneficial than the latter. The advantage of cross- as compared with self-pollination is very apparent in some plants; for instance, Darwin found that the weight of Cabbages produced from seeds, formed as a result of cross-pollination, was very much greater than those grown from seeds which had been produced by self-pollination, the former varying between 74 and 130 ounces, the latter between $11\frac{1}{2}$ and 46 ounces.

In view of such facts it is not astonishing that a very large number of flowers exhibit a structure which tends to favour cross-pollination. Most flowers contain both stamens and ovaries—in other words, are *hermaphrodite* (indicated by the symbol ☿), but the two kinds of organs rarely ripen at exactly the same time. The stamens may ripen first (*protandrous* flowers), or the stigma matures before the pollen is shed (*protogynous* flowers). There

---

[1] For reference-books, see p. 466.

are, however, all transitions from flowers in which the essential organs ripen almost simultaneously (*e.g.* White Dead-nettle) to flowers in which the one kind of organ has withered before the

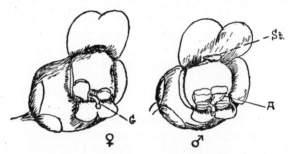

FIG. 310. Flowers of the Figwort (*Scrophularia*), to illustrate protogyny (enlarged). The left-hand flower is in the female stage, whilst in the right-hand one the stigma has withered and the stamens are mature. A, stamen; G, stigma; *St.*, staminode.

other is mature. Thus, extremely protandrous flowers are seen in the Canterbury Bell and Rose-bay Willow-herb (Fig. 311), whilst marked protogyny is exhibited by the Figwort (Fig. 310) and Plantain (Fig. 313).

The tetramerous flower of the Willow-herb has eight stamens and a four-lobed stigma, but until the stamens have finished

FIG. 311. Flowers of Rose-bay Willow-herb (*Chamænurion angustifolium*), to illustrate protandry (natural size). In the left-hand flower the stamens are alone mature; in the right-hand one they have withered, whilst the four stigmatic lobes are now spread out. *St.*, stigma. ♂, male stage; ♀, female stage.

shedding their pollen (*i.e.* until the male or staminate stage is over) the stigmatic lobes remain closely pressed together, so that their receptive surfaces are not exposed (Fig. 311, ♂). When the stamens wither, the four lobes of the stigma curl back (Fig. 311, ♀, *i.e.* the flowers are now in the female or pistillate stage), ready to receive pollen from some flower which has opened later. In the spike of the Plantain (Fig. 313) the lower flowers open first and exhibit a white feathery protruding stigma, but at this stage no stamens are to be seen; as the flowers in the upper part of the inflorescence develop, the stigmas of the lower ones wither and their place is taken in each flower by the four stamens. Since the flowers in the female stage (Fig. 313, ♀) are always above those in the male (Fig. 313, ♂), the pollen in falling cannot effect pollination.

In all such extreme instances, self-pollination is obviously prevented in the earlier stages of flowering, although a considerable number of such flowers may become self-pollinated just before fading (p. 465). If, however, prior to this, cross-pollination has taken place, pollen from the same flower is ineffective. In fact, in many Leguminosæ, for instance, such pollen often has no effect at all.

Of the commonly cultivated fruits, most of the bush-fruits and small fruit (e.g. Currants, Gooseberries, Raspberries, Blackberries, Strawberries, etc.) are self-fertile. This is also true of Medlar, Quince, Apricot, Almond, and Peach, but many varieties—though not all—of Apple, Pear, Plum, and Cherry are more or less self-incompatible—that is to say, self-pollination cannot normally be effected, very commonly owing to a marked retardation in the growth-rate of the pollen tube. Hence the desirability of growing several varieties together. Even in self-compatible varieties better crops usually result from cross-pollination.

Greater certainty of cross-pollination is ensured, when stamens and ovaries occur in distinct *unisexual* flowers. The two sexes are either found on the same individual (*monœcious*, e.g. Hazel, Fig. 314), or on different individuals (*diœcious*, e.g. Dog's Mercury, Fig. 295; Willow, Fig. 418). In the latter self-pollination is out of the question. Sometimes such unisexual flowers show remains of the other essential organ and so betray their derivation from an hermaphrodite condition. Thus, in the staminate flowers of the Buckthorn (*Rhamnus*) a rudimentary ovary surmounted by a style can be recognised at the base of the perianth-tube. We could regard such male flowers as extremely protandrous ones in which the female stage is never attained, and a similar explanation could be applied to pistillate flowers.

Quite a large number of plants possess unisexual flowers side by side with hermaphrodite ones. Thus, in many Compositæ the outermost flowers (*ray-florets*), with a strap-shaped (ligulate) corolla, are female (Fig. 299, F; Fig. 312, B), whilst those occupying the greater part of the capitulum (*disc-florets*) and having tubular corollas are hermaphrodite and protandrous (Fig. 297, E; Fig. 312, C). In the Coltsfoot (*Tussilago*), however, the disc-florets are male, having but a rudimentary ovary, whilst the ray-florets are, as before, female. It may be added that in certain groups of Flowering Plants all sorts of variations in the distribution of sexes are to be found. In *Lychnis*, for instance, male, female, and hermaphrodite flowers occur on distinct plants, whilst in the Ash (*Fraxinus*) all three types may be borne on the same individual.

Minor features that tend to favour cross-pollination are the extrorse dehiscence of stamens (p. 440) and arrangement of the

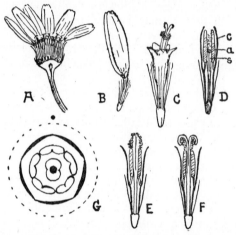

Fig. 312. Floral structure and pollination in *Senecio aquaticus* (A, natural size, other figures somewhat enlarged). A, Capitulum in longitudinal section. B, Ray-floret. C, Disc-floret in early female stage. D, Ditto, in longitudinal section, in early male stage. E, Ditto, with style just emerging. F, Ditto, late stage. G, Floral diagram of disc-floret. *a*, stamen; *c*, corolla; *s*, style.

anthers at a lower level than the stigma in many upright flowers or *vice versa* in hanging ones.

Pollination can be effected by various agencies, the commonest being insects and wind, more rarely water (p. 554). Wind-pollination (*anemophily*) is a mode of transference associated frequently with simple types of flowers, particularly unisexual ones. It is evident that this mode of pollination depends largely on chance and therefore, if it is to be successful, a much greater amount of pollen must be produced than is necessary to effect fertilisation. Wind-pollinated plants either have numerous stamens in their flowers (*e.g.* Poplar, Elm), or relatively large anthers producing copious pollen (*e.g.* Grasses, Fig. 439, A) or the male flowers are numerically in excess of the female (*e.g.* Hazel). Moreover, the stigma is frequently branched and feathery (*e.g.* Grasses, Fig. 439, A; Hazel, Fig. 314, ♀), so that pollen is the more easily caught.

The ready liberation of the pollen of anemophilous flowers is facilitated by the frequent occurrence of loose hanging inflorescences (*e.g.* Birch), or of anthers which are loosely hinged on long projecting filaments, so that they are moved by the least breath of wind (Grasses, Figs. 301, D, and 439, A; Plantain, Fig. 313). The dry and powdery pollen grains do not adhere to one another, thus facilitating a wider distribution.

The flowers of wind-pollinated plants are usually inconspicuous and green, either possessing a simple perianth (*e.g.* Dog's Mercury, Fig. 295) or are naked (*e.g.* Ash). They naturally lack all those attractive mechanisms which are so marked a feature of the insect-pollinated flower.

Entomophilous flowers are visited by insects either for

FIG. 313. Spike of the Black Plantain or Ribwort (*Plantago*) (natural size). The upper flowers, which have opened most recently, are in the female (♀) stage, whilst the middle ones are in the male (♂) stage, and the lowest of all are already fading (cf. p. 448).

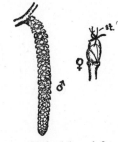

FIG. 314. Male (♂) and female (♀) catkins of the Hazel (*Corylus*) (natural size). *st.*, stigmas.

their nectar or pollen and are usually very conspicuous. Nectar is the most frequent attraction and is produced in *nectaries* (p. 198) which may be situated on almost any protected part of the flower. Dark lines, known as *nectar-guides* (*e.g.* Pansy, Fig. 325, A), are sometimes found upon the petals converging towards their base where the nectar is formed. Experiments have shown that such markings probably aid the more intelligent insects in finding the nectar rapidly.

Nectaries are frequently located at the base of the flower and most often on an enlargement of the thalamus known as a *disc* (*e.g.* the Rue, Fig. 315, B, *n*) which may be confined to the anterior side of the ovary (as in many Labiatæ and Scrophulariaceæ). In flowers with an inferior ovary (p. 430) the disc is situated on the top of the latter (*e.g.* Umbelliferæ, Fig. 315, E, *n*). Many members of the Liliaceæ have nectar-secreting tissue lining the sides of narrow slits in the ovary-wall and visible when the latter is cut across. In other flowers the nectaries are produced on the expanded bases of the stamens (Fig. 315, C, *n*, and other Caryophyllaceæ).

In different members of the Ranunculaceæ all conditions are found between petals with a nectary at the base, protected by a small flap (Buttercup, Fig. 315, A), and little trumpet-shaped

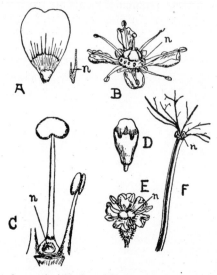

Fig. 315. Forms of nectaries (A, B and F, natural size; other figures enlarged). A, Petal of Buttercup, showing flap covering nectary; the right-hand figure, the same in longitudinal section. B, Flower of Rue (*Ruta*). C, Stamens of *Stellaria*. D, Honey-petal of *Helleborus*. E, Flower of Hogweed (*Heracleum*). F, Part of leaf of *Viburnum opulus*, showing extrafloral nectaries. *n*, nectaries.

structures (as in the Christmas Rose, Fig. 315, D; and Winter Aconite, Fig. 296) situated just outside the stamens.

Nectaries often produce such large quantities of nectar that it overflows from the depressions in which it is secreted and may in some flowers accumulate in special *spurs*. These are but slightly developed in the Cruciferæ (Fig. 317, *b*) where they are formed by the pouch-like bases of the lateral sepals situated opposite the two short stamens bearing nectaries (cf. Fig. 424, A). In the Toadflax and Garden Nasturtium (Fig. 297, A) they appear as tube-like outgrowths of the perianth. The spur may, however, not merely function as a receptacle for nectar, but may actually produce it at its tip; this is seen in Orchids (Fig. 326, B, *sp.*) and in *Aquilegia*, each petal of the latter being prolonged into a spur. In such flowers a special outgrowth has developed in relation to the production of nectar. A similar feature can be seen in the Pansy (Fig. 325, A and B, *n*) and Larkspur in which two processes, from the stamens in the former and the petals in the latter, project into the spur and secrete nectar into it.

Not all entomophilous flowers, however, produce nectar, a limited number possessing no other bait than pollen. Such *pollen-flowers* (e.g. *Hypericum, Papaver*) usually possess a large number of stamens, so that there is an adequate surplus of pollen for pollination. Even in flowers having nectaries, Bees generally take a certain amount of pollen as food for their larvæ.

Many flowers are so constructed that nectaries and pollen are protected from the injurious effects of dew or rain. The simplest method of pollen-protection is for the dehisced anther to close up more or less completely (cf. p. 440). The closing of flowers or capitula at night (p. 268) serves to shield both nectar and pollen, and the same end is attained by the hanging position occupied by many flowers (e.g. *Campanula*, Fig. 299, A). The individual flowers in many catkins (*e.g.* Hazel, Fig. 314, ♂) are protected by the bracts which appear as roofs above them.

While nectar and pollen are the attraction, the colours, odours, and grouping of flowers render them conspicuous. As a general rule the perianth provides the *attractive apparatus*,[1] but sometimes stamens (*e.g.* Willows, *Thalictrum*) or even bracteoles (*e.g.* some cultivated Sages, *Bougainvillea*) may play a part. A great feature in plants possessing small flowers is the massing together of the latter, whereby a conspicuous inflorescence is formed (cf. p. 428). Moreover, where the inflorescence is flat-topped, the outermost flowers are often irregular and exhibit a one-sided enlargement of the corolla tending towards greater conspicuity, a feature which is well illustrated by the Candytuft (Fig. 316), Hogweed, Daisy, etc.; not uncommonly these outer flowers are unisexual (many Compositæ, p. 449 and Fig. 312, B) or altogether devoid of essential organs (*i.e.* are *neuter*, as in the Guelder-rose (*Viburnum opulus*) and *Centaurea*, Fig. 435, B), so that they are purely attractive in function.

Since, provided they are visited, pollination is almost a certainty in entomophilous flowers, particularly those frequented by Bees, a much greater economy in pollen is possible than in anemophilous plants. There is usually (except in pollen-flowers) a relatively small number of stamens, a feature which becomes the more marked the

[1] The importance of the perianth in this respect may be shown by removing all the petals from one specimen of a certain plant, out of doors, and noting the behaviour of insects in relation to it, as compared with a normal plant.

more efficient the mechanism for pollination.   The rough or sticky coat of the pollen causes it to adhere readily to the insect's body, whilst the stigma has a sticky receptive surface and is not as richly branched as in most wind-pollinated types.

The chief pollinating insects are Bees, Butterflies, Moths, Flies, and Beetles.   The Honey Bee and other Hymenoptera are most important, but Diptera play a large part in the pollination of some flowers (*e.g.* Blackberry).   All pollinating insects, except Beetles, possess a special sucking organ, the *proboscis*, arising from the under

FIG. 316. Inflorescence of the Candytuft (*Iberis*) (natural size), showing the enlarged marginal flowers.

side of the head, very short in Flies and exceptionally long in Butterflies and Moths, where it is coiled up when not in use.   When visiting a flower the position taken up by an insect depends largely on the length of its proboscis and the situation of the nectary.   In fact, flowers possessing a long narrow corolla-tube (Fig. 293, B) or a spur are not accessible for nectar to any but long-tongued insects, whilst wide open flowers (Fig. 293, A) provide nectar for a variety of visitors, both with long and short proboscides.   Certain insects (*e.g.* the small Bumble-bee), however, not un-commonly puncture the base of the corolla-tube, when this is too long for them to reach the nectary by legitimate means, and thus steal nectar without effecting pollination.

In the majority of flowers the insects concerned actually alight on the perianth, although many Moths hover in front of the flowers they visit.   As a result of the different, though for the same flower usually constant, positions taken up by pollinating insects very diverse parts of the body (viz. proboscis, head, back, or abdomen) may become dusted with pollen, and these are often covered with hairs to which the pollen readily adheres.   Sooner or later the stamens and stigma in any given entomophilous flower come to occupy similar positions, so that the pollen taken from the anthers of one flower will be likely to get rubbed against the stigma of another.

The simplest kinds of *pollination-mechanisms* are seen in regular flowers, amongst which two principal types can be distinguished. The first are flowers with an open shallow corolla (*e.g.* Buttercup, Fig. 293, A), and from these almost any insect-visitor can obtain nectar.   The insect here alights either on the corolla or on the essential organs, so that either its head or its under side becomes dusted with pollen. Flowers of this type are often visited by small insects which may in their erratic wanderings effect pollination, although no doubt it is often only pollen from the same flower that is transferred. Insects commonly crawl about on the flat tops of umbels, corymbs, and capitula, and, since many of the plants concerned are markedly protandrous, pollen is transferred from the younger flowers in the centre to the older ones near the margin.

FIG. 317. Flower of the Wallflower (*Cheiranthus*), showing the tube produced by the four upright sepals and the claws of the petals (natural size). *b*, one of the pouched sepals.

The second type of regular flower, the *tubular* one, possesses a perianth-tube of varying length and formed in one of two ways. Most usually, as in the Primrose (Fig. 318) and *Narcissus* (Fig. 293, B), the corolla or perianth is gamopetalous, the united portions producing the tube. But where the petals of a polypetalous corolla have long claws (Fig. 298, A) they, together with the upright sepals, constitute a tube (*e.g.* Cruciferæ, Fig. 317). In all such flowers the expanded ends of the petals form an alighting platform (Fig. 293, B) and

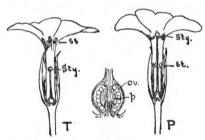

FIG. 318. Floral structure of *Primula*, showing longitudinal sections of thrum-eyed (T) and pin-eyed (P) forms (natural size). *St.*, stamens; *Sty.*, stigma. The middle figure shows the ovary in longitudinal section, considerably enlarged. *ov.*, ovule; *p*, free central placenta.

the pollen is brushed off either on to the proboscis or the head of the insect, according to the level at which the anthers stand in the tube. Such flowers are only visited with profit by long-tongued insects, the variety of visitors becoming the more restricted the greater the length of the tube.

A special device, spoken of as *heterostyly* and tending to favour cross-pollination, is seen in certain tubular flowers (*e.g.* Primrose, Fig. 318) in which more than one type of flower is produced. Some individuals have the stigma situated at the mouth of the corolla-tube (pin-eyed form), the stamens occupying a position half-way down (Fig. 318, P), whilst in others the relative positions of stamens and stigma are reversed (thrum-eyed form, Fig. 318, T). As a consequence the pollen received upon the proboscis from a flower of the pin-eyed type will only be at the appropriate level for effecting pollination in one of the thrum-eyed type, and *vice versa*.

More perfect pollination-mechanisms are found in flowers having an irregular corolla, which results in a greater restriction of insect-visitors. In such flowers the agent is compelled to take up a definite position with reference to the essential organs and must frequently be strong enough to force open the more or less closed corolla.

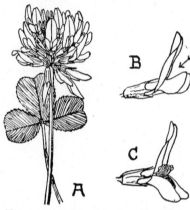

As a first example the flowers of British Leguminosæ may be studied. Here the corolla (Fig. 320, A; cf. also Fig. 294, C) consists of: (i) a large posterior petal, the standard, usually vertical (Fig. 320, A and C, *s*); (ii) a pair of wings (*w*) situated at the sides; and (iii) a pair of anterior petals, more or less joined together to form the boat-shaped keel (*k*). The essential organs are completely enclosed within the keel (see Fig. 321, E) and are thus efficiently protected; they consist of ten stamens (cf. Fig. 294, C), often of two lengths, the filaments forming a tube around the central pod-like

FIG. 319. Pollination in the Clover (*Trifolium*) (A, natural size; B and C enlarged). A, Inflorescence and leaf. B, Single flower seen from the side, in its normal condition. The arrow indicates the direction of approach of the pollinating insect. C, The same, showing position of parts at time of pollination when wings and keel are depressed.

ovary which is provided with a long style ending in a stigma (Fig. 321, D, *St.*). Nectar is usually produced on the inner sides of the bases of the filaments and accumulates in the trough formed by them. In such nectar-producing flowers the posterior stamen is always free (cf. Fig. 294, C), thus leaving a slit in the stamen-tube through which the proboscis is inserted. Some Leguminosæ (*e.g.* the Broom, Lupine), however, produce no nectar, and in these pollen-flowers all the ten stamens are united (cf. Fig. 426, A).

The wings form the alighting platform, the head of the insect being directed towards the conspicuous standard (cf. Fig. 319, B). Since obviously neither nectar nor pollen are easily reached, these flowers can only be visited with profit by sufficiently intelligent insects and by such as are heavy enough to expose the essential organs; Bees fulfil both requirements and are indeed amongst the commonest visitors. The base of each wing is provided with an

outgrowth which fits into a hollow in the adjacent petal of the keel
(Fig. 320, D) and thus, when a Bee alights on the wings, these and
the keel are depressed simultaneously. As a result the essential
organs are exposed and rub against the *under surface* of the insect's
body (cf. Fig. 319, C). Although the stigma is often surrounded

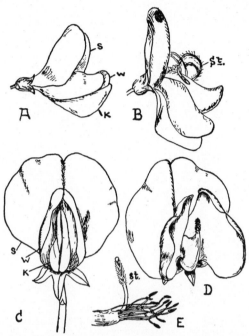

FIG. 320. Pollination in Broom (*Sarothamnus scoparius*) and Sweet-pea (*Lathyrus
odoratus*) (natural size, E enlarged). A, Flower of Broom before pollination,
seen from the side. B, Ditto after pollination. C, Flower of Sweet-pea,
seen from the anterior side. D, Ditto, with stigma and stylar brush emerging,
as during pollination. E, Essential organs enlarged, showing position when
released from keel. *k*, keel; *s*, standard; *St.*, style; *w*, wings.

by pollen, as it lies hidden in the keel, self-pollination does not
occur owing to self-incompatibility (p. 449). When the insect
flies away, the parts of the flower return to their original positions
and the keel again screens the essential organs. This simple type
of pollination-mechanism is seen in the Clover, Sainfoin, and
Melilot.

In the Sweet-pea and Vetches the style, just beneath the small
stigma, bears a dense brush of hairs (Fig. 320, E, *st.*) upon which
the pollen is shed. The tip of the keel in the Sweet-pea is prolonged into an upright beak (Fig. 320, D) in which are situated

30

the anthers of the ten stamens, surrounding the stigma and stylar brush.   When a Bee alights on the wings and the keel is depressed, the style emerges (Fig. 320, D) brushing out the pollen onto the insect's under surface, whilst the stamens remain concealed; the relative positions of style and stamens are now approximately as in Fig. 320, E.

In the Lupine and Bird's-foot Trefoil (Fig. 321) the two petals

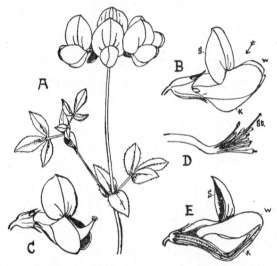

FIG. 321. Pollination in the Bird's-foot Trefoil (*Lotus corniculatus*) (A, natural size; B–E enlarged). A, Portion of plant with inflorescence. B, Side-view of flower before pollination; arrow marks direction of approach of insect. C, Flower during pollination, showing emergence of pollen. D, Essential organs. E, Longitudinal section of flower. *k*, keel; *s*, standard; *St.*, style; *w*, wings.

of the keel are joined along both their lower and upper edges, leaving, however, a small circular opening near the pointed tip (Fig. 321, C and E).   The tops of the filaments of the five longer stamens are swollen (Fig. 321, D), so as to form collectively a piston by means of which the pollen collecting in the tip of the keel is forced out of the opening, when the keel is depressed (Fig. 321, C).   The style is appreciably longer than the stamens, so that the stigma is the first to protrude, when an insect alights on the flower.   In all these flowers the different parts return to their normal positions when the visitor flies away.

In the *explosive flowers* of the Broom (Fig. 320, A and B) and Gorse, however, the style and stamen-tube are compressed into a relatively small keel so that, when an insect of sufficient weight alights on the wings, the depression of the keel leads to a sudden release of the essential organs; the latter emerge with a jerk and a shower of pollen is sent over the visitor. No return of the floral organs to their previous positions takes place; the flower is "exploded" and stamens and stigma remain projecting from it (Fig. 320, B).

The pollination of the Broom is so far exceptional in that some of the pollen is deposited *on the back* of the insect. When the latter alights, the five shorter stamens first emerge and strike its under surface, but immediately afterwards the five longer stamens and the stigma spring out (Fig. 320, B) and strike the insect's back. The pollen received by the lower side of the body probably serves as food.

In the Labiatæ and in many Scrophulariaceæ all the pollen is deposited *on the back* of the insect. The usually horizontal flowers of most Labiatæ exhibit a corolla-tube (Fig. 299, D), the upper part of which is drawn out into a helmet-shaped hood (*h*), formed by the two posterior petals and constituting a roof over the four stamens and the bilobed stigma. The anterior part of the corolla forms an alighting platform (*p*), whilst projections (*l*) on either side of the throat give a hold to the fore-feet of the insect during pollination. Nectar is secreted by a disc (p. 451) at the base of the ovary but, owing to the presence of a corolla-tube, can only be reached by long-tongued insects, such as will have a body sufficiently large to fill the space between the upper and lower lips. Frequently hairs are present in the upper part of the tube, which tend to prevent the intrusion of small insects which would steal nectar without effecting pollination. In probing the nectary the visitor brings its back into contact with the essential organs and thus effects pollination. The flowers are commonly protandrous, the stamens first projecting downwards to a slight extent so that they are bound to touch legitimate visitors, the stigma at this stage being above them and with its two lobes pressed together; subsequently the latter diverge and the stigma comes to lie a little below the position previously held by the stamens.

A more specialised condition is seen in *Salvia* (Fig. 322) whose flowers have only two stamens, each with a much elongated connective joining the two anther-lobes (cf. p. 435 and Fig. 322, E, *co*.). One arm of the connective is somewhat longer than the other, and the anther-lobe at the end of the short arm produces no pollen. These sterile lobes are so placed in the throat of the corolla-tube that an insect probing for nectar must push against them (Fig. 322, A and D), thus bringing the fertile lobes down upon its back (Fig. 322, B). In the female stage the stigma projects to a very marked extent (see Fig. 322, C), so that its lobes are bound to touch the back of an insect-visitor.

Amongst the Scrophulariaceæ we have flowers with a pollination-mechanism very similar to that of Labiatæ (*e.g.* Red Eyebright, *Odontites*, Fig. 372, A). The same type of construction is seen also in the flowers of the Musk, the sensitive stigma of which (cf. p. 266) is a special device that prevents self-pollination. The folding together of the two lobes (Fig. 171, B) is brought about by contact with the pollen-bearing proboscis of the retreating insect so that self-pollination is prevented. In *Antirrhinum* (Fig. 323) and *Linaria* the mouth of the corolla is completely closed by a pouch-like outgrowth from the lower lip (Fig. 323, A and C, *p*). In this way

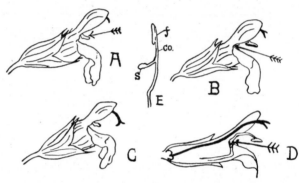

FIG. 322. Pollination in *Salvia* (all figures natural size). A, Flower before pollination, in male stage. B, Flower during pollination. C, Female stage. D, Flower in longitudinal section, showing mode of pollination. E, Single stamen (slightly enlarged). The arrows show direction of approach of pollinating insect. *co.*, connective; *f*, fertile lobe; *s*, sterile lobe of stamen.

pollen and nectar are not only amply protected from outside moisture, but the flower is alone accessible to insects (*e.g.* Bumble-bees) which are strong enough to force open the flower. In the Figwort (Fig. 310) the stigma (♀) and stamens (♂) successively occupy positions against the lower lip, so that the under side of the insect (often a Wasp) is effective in pollination.

Further examples of special pollination-mechanisms are furnished by the Monkshood, Pansy, and Orchids. In the first, each flower has a petaloid perianth composed of a large posterior hood (Fig. 324, *h*), overlapping the four lower segments (*l, a*). Within the hood are situated two long-stalked nectaries (Fig. 324, B, *n*), numerous stamens (*s*), and an apocarpous ovary (*o*). The insects (Bumble-bees) alight on the lateral and anterior members of the perianth and probe for nectar beneath the hood, so that their under side becomes dusted with pollen in the first (male) stage of the protandrous flower. Subsequently the stamens curl right back, so that in the female stage the stigmas touch the Bee's abdomen.

In the Pansy (Fig. 325) the anterior petal (*a*) serves as the landing-place for the insect, which then pushes its proboscis (the arrow in Fig. 325, A) into the spur (*sp.*, cf. p. 453) containing the nectaries borne by the two anterior stamens (Fig. 325, B, C). The five stamens fit closely around the style. The receptive portion of the stigma (Fig. 325, D) is a small hollow on its anterior face (*st.*) covered by a flap (*fl.*) hinged towards the base of the flower. The

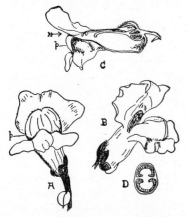

FIG. 323. Pollination in *Antirrhinum* (D enlarged, other figures about two-thirds natural size). A, Complete flower seen from the anterior side. B, Flower in side-view, with the corolla forced open to display the essential organs beneath the upper lip. C, Flower in longitudinal section. The arrow marks the direction of approach of the insect. D, Cross-section of ovary, showing the large axile placenta. *p*, pouch formed by lower lip of corolla.

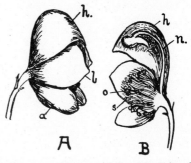

FIG. 324. Flowers of the Monkshood (*Aconitum*) (natural size). A, Entire flower seen from the side. B, Flower in longitudinal section. *a*, anterior member; *h*, hood (posterior member); *l*, lateral member; *n*, nectary; *o*, ovary; *s*, stamens.

pollen is shed on the proboscis, and, in its withdrawal, the flap over the stigmatic surface is closed, so that self-pollination in these flowers is impossible (cf. p. 465). When visiting another flower the proboscis pushes back the flap and the pollen is thus deposited on the stigmatic surface. The Violets have quite similar flowers, but the style is differently shaped and the flap is often lacking.

Many British Orchids show a very complex mechanism. In the Early Purple Orchis (Fig. 326) the irregular perianth consists of two whorls, each of three members (cf. Fig. 326, C), the posterior petal (*labellum*) of the inner series forming an alighting platform (*l*) and being drawn out into a long spur (*sp.*). Owing to the twisting of the sessile flower through half a circle, in the course of its development, the labellum occupies an anterior position, the twisting of the inferior ovary (*o*), which is elongated and resembles a flower-stalk, being very apparent. The remaining five petals form a protective hood over the essential organs (Fig. 326, A and B). The latter (Fig. 326, D) occupy the centre of the flower and are

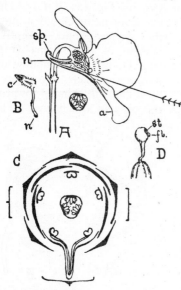

FIG. 325. A–C, Structure of flower of Pansy (*Viola tricolor*). A, Longitudinal section of flower (natural size). B, Single stamen (enlarged). C, Floral diagram. D, Ovary, etc., of *V. arvensis* (enlarged). *a*, alighting platform; *c*, connective of anther; *fl.*, flap below stigmatic surface; *n*, nectary; *sp.*, spur; *st.*, stigma.

situated on a short column (*c*), the upper part of which bears a single large stamen with two very distinct anther-lobes. Each lobe contains a mass of pollen grains (*pollinium*, p. 438) cohering by sticky threads which are continued below into short stalks (*ca.*); the latter end in little sticky swollen discs contained in a shallow pouch (*r*) which forms a slight projection on the column, somewhat overhanging the mouth of the spur. Below this pouch, and on either side of it, are seen the two broad flat stigmatic surfaces (*s*) which are more or less joined together. Above them two small teeth, representing barren stamens or staminodes (*Std.*), are distinguishable.

An insect settling on the labellum has to pierce the tissue at the base of the spur for nectar and, whilst thus occupied, its head necessarily comes

into contact with the pouch (*r*). As a result the pollinia adhere to it and, when the visitor flies away, it carries them projecting vertically from its head. In the space of half a minute their stalks bend forwards through a right angle. When a new flower is visited, the pollinia are therefore in the correct position to strike against the stigmas.

The Compositæ exhibit a pollination-mechanism quite different from those hitherto considered, and as a general rule the hermaphrodite florets alone produce seed. Pollen is shed into the tube formed by the five joined anthers (Fig. 312, D). At this stage the two receptive surfaces of the stigma are in contact, the style being

quite short.   When the stamens have dehisced the style grows so
that the numerous hairs on its upper part gradually brush the
pollen out of the top of the anther-tube (Fig. 312, E).   By continued
growth the stigma is carried beyond the anthers and soon after its
two lobes diverge (Fig. 312, C), thus exposing the receptive surfaces
above the mass of pollen.

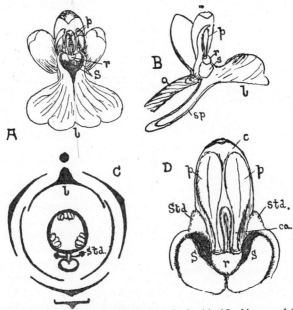

FIG. 326. Structure of flower of Early Purple Orchis (*Orchis mascula*) (A and
B somewhat enlarged, D considerably magnified). A, Entire flower, seen
from the front.   B, Flower in longitudinal section, except for ovary which is
shown entire. C, Floral diagram. D, Column with essential organs. *c*,
column; *ca.*, stalk of pollinium; *l*, labellum; *o*, ovary; *p*, pollinium; *r*, pouch;
s, stigma; *sp.*, spur; *Std.*, staminode.

The nectar is produced around the base of the style.   Owing to
the relatively short corolla-tube the capitula are visited by a variety
of insects, chiefly Bees and Flies.   These become dusted with
pollen on their under surface and, as often as not, merely transfer
it from one floret of the capitulum to another.   As the flower gets
older the lobes of the stigma continue to diverge till they curl right
back, as in Fig. 312, F, thus bringing their receptive surfaces into
contact with the pollen still adhering to the hairs on the style.   In
this way self-pollination is assured, if cross-pollination has not
already taken place (cf. p. 465).

The different kinds of Bees are by far the commonest insect-visitors to the irregular flowers considered above, and especially those which are blue or purple, colours for which Bees seem to have a decided preference (cf. p. 466). Owing to the fact that many Bees visit only one kind of flower at a time, they are the most useful agents in pollination. Butterflies, on the other hand, seem to be attracted chiefly by white and red flowers and, where these have a relatively long corolla-tube, these insects may be the most important visitors (*Lychnis, Silene*). A considerable number of flowers have

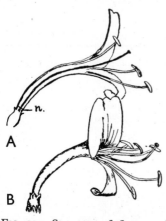

become markedly adapted to pollination by night-flying Moths (*e.g.* Evening Primrose, Tobacco, Honeysuckle, Fig. 327, White Jasmine), inasmuch as many only open at night and at this time alone emit a strong scent. Such flowers are mostly white or yellow so that they are relatively conspicuous in the dusk and, since Moths usually hover in front of the flower (p. 454), no alighting platform is necessary and the flowers are frequently regular.

FIG. 327. Structure of flowers of Honeysuckle (*Lonicera*) (natural size). A, In longitudinal section. B, Entire flower in side-view. *n*, nectary.

Flowers visited chiefly by flies are often characterised by a fœtid odour and a dirty brown or purplish colour, as in Herb Paris (*Paris quadrifolia*) and Cuckoo-pint. Pollination in the latter (Fig. 328) results from imprisonment of the insects concerned. The fleshy spike bears the naked unisexual flowers on its lower portion only, those at the very base being female (each consisting of one carpel) and those above male (each with 2 to 4 stamens); beyond these are a number of downwardly curved hairs (*h*) which wither about the time that the stamens shed their pollen. The upper half of the spike is dilated to form a purple club-shaped structure. The whole inflorescence is enveloped in a large sheathing bract, the lower part of which forms a tube narrowing to a waist, at the level where the hairs above mentioned are situated, whilst the upper portion expands into an open leafy structure exposing the swollen tip of the axis (Fig. 328, A). Small Flies (Midges), attracted by the latter and the evil odour, crawl down into the swollen base of the tube; their escape is temporarily prevented by a slippery, oily surface, which disappears as the inflorescence gets older. The female flowers are mature some time before the male, so that if the insect bears pollen from another individual it will in its wanderings effect cross-pollination. In escaping, the Fly must pass the stamens of the male flowers which have now dehisced, so that it becomes coated with a fresh load of pollen.

In many flowers, whose construction favours cross-pollination, eventual self-pollination takes place, as already noticed in Compositæ (p. 463 and Fig. 312, F). Other examples are afforded by the Canterbury Bell (*Campanula*) and Willow Herb (*Epilobium*). Certain plants produce flowers which are only capable of self-pollination, since they never open. Such *cleistogamic flowers* have minute unattractive petals and form very little pollen. Those of the Violet and Wood Sorrel (*Oxalis*) are produced after the showy flowers (which in the Violet are capable only of cross-pollination, cf. p. 461) and, owing to their short peduncles, remain hidden amongst the foliage-leaves. They are developed in the summer, when the trees above these woodland-plants have formed a dense crown of foliage, so that the light which reaches them is of relatively low intensity.

Our study of pollination has shown that, by contrast with the usually protective and relatively uniform calyx, the corolla exhibits great variety of form, and not only renders the flower conspicuous to

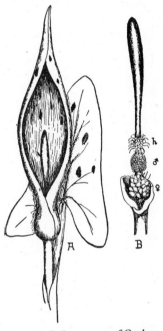

FIG. 328. Inflorescence of Cuckoo-pint (*Arum maculatum*) (slightly reduced). A, Leaf with complete inflorescence showing the bract. B, Spike with bract removed. *h*, hairs; ♂, male flowers; ♀, female flowers.

insects, but usually shows obvious modifications enhancing the effectiveness of their visits and the exclusion of undesirables. The relative positions occupied by the floral leaves, and especially the extent to which they form a tube with or without fusion, play no small part in determining the nature and efficiency of the pollinating agent. It is thus mainly the latter that gives the clue to floral structure, whether the agency be insects, wind, or water. Plants developing the most effective mechanism will tend to set the greatest amount of seed and produce the most offspring.

Moreover, the increased certainty of pollination, where insects are the transferring agents, allows, except in pollen-flowers, of a reduction in the number of stamens and in output of pollen—in other words, an economy of material. Such specialisation, if extreme, may, however, defeat its own ends by unduly restricting the variety of pollinating insects.

Bees are known to be the most methodical of the insect-visitors of flowers, since they commonly visit but a single kind of plant until that has been fully exploited. It is probable that colour is the means of attraction from afar, whilst scent enables the Bee to select a specific flower amongst others of similar colour. That Bees are able to discriminate in this way has been shown by the fact that, after being trained to visit blue-coloured sheets of paper baited with watch-glasses containing sugar-solution and distributed among sheets of other colours not so baited, they subsequently, when the bait was removed and the different-coloured sheets were arranged at random, flew only to the blue sheets. Flies and Beetles are probably more strongly attracted by scent than Bees.

[For further details regarding pollination, see P. Knuth, *Handbook of Flower Pollination* (Engl. transl. by J. R. Ainsworth Davis), 3 vols., Clarendon Press, Oxford, 1906–1909; and F. E. Clements and F. L. Long, *Experimental Pollination*, Carnegie Instit., 1923 (274 pp.), which contains a useful historical summary and an account of recent experimental methods for studying pollination. See also the work of J. C. Willis cited on p. 609 and G. Erdtman, *Pollen Morphology and Plant Taxonomy*, Chronica Botanica, 1952.]

CHAPTER XXXVIII

FERTILISATION AND EMBRYO-DEVELOPMENT

SINCE the ovules of Angiosperms are enclosed, the pollen cannot reach the micropyle direct as in Gymnosperms, but is received by the special receptive surface of the carpel, the *stigma*. This bears

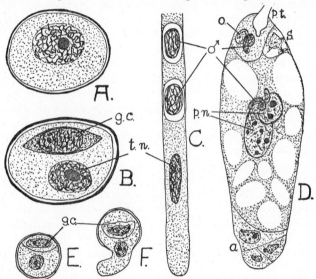

FIG. 329. Germination of pollen and fertilisation. A–D, *Lilium* (after Guignard). E–F, *Tulipa* (after Ernst). A, Mature pollen grain, showing the single nucleus. B and E, Later stage, showing generative cell (*g.c.*) and tube nucleus (*t.n.*). C, Tip of pollen tube with tube nucleus (*t.n.*) and two male cells (♂). D, Embryo sac at the moment of fertilisation, showing antipodals (*a.*), polar nuclei (*p.n.*), ovum (*o.*), one synergid (*s.*), and the two vermiform male cells (♂) discharged from the tip of the pollen tube (*p.t.*). F, Early stage in formation of pollen tube.

numerous papilla-like hairs, whose secretion nourishes the developing pollen. Before the pollen grain is shed its nucleus divides into two [1] (Fig. 329, B). One of these becomes surrounded by

[1] For further details, see the work by Coulter and Chamberlain cited on p. 437.

denser cytoplasm (*generative cell, g.c.*), whilst the other (*tube nucleus, t.n.*) lies freely in the general body of the grain. In this condition the pollen is transferred to the stigma, and here germination takes place (Fig. 329, F). The tube nucleus passes into the tip of the pollen tube, and the naked generative cell sooner or later follows suit (Fig. 329, C). The former usually remains undivided, whilst the latter ultimately produces two male nuclei.

In its downward growth the *pollen tube* is sometimes nourished by secretions from papillæ forming a continuous lining to the canal or canals traversing the style and extending uninterruptedly into the loculi of the ovary (*e.g.* Tulip and Violet). Often, however, the style is solid, the pollen tube penetrating through the axial core of thin-walled tissue, nourished by the sugary sap which the tissue contains. In some cleistogamic flowers (*e.g.* Purple Deadnettle) the pollen grains germinate in the anthers, and the pollen tubes grow from there to the stigma.

The period of time occupied by the pollen tube in growing down to the ovules varies greatly in different species, and bears no relation to the distance to be traversed. In the Crocus, where the style is 6–10 cm. long, the interval is only from one to three days, whilst in the Meadow Saffron (*Colchicum*), with a style of about the same length, it is six months (from autumn, when pollination occurs, to the following spring). A similar prolonged interval not uncommonly obtains in woody plants (*e.g.* Hazel), though the distance traversed is short, and in some Oaks the ovules do not even commence development until after pollination. In most spring-flowering plants the anthers develop as far as the mother-cell stage in the previous autumn, although in the Hazel ripe pollen can be found in the male catkins during midwinter.

As a general rule the pollen tube traverses the cavity of the ovary, and thus reaches the micropyle of one of the ovules (porogamy, Fig. 330, A). But, in certain trees and shrubs (*e.g.* Elm, Beech, Hazel), it grows through the placental tissue and enters the ovule near the chalazal end (chalazogamy, Fig. 330, B). The growth of the pollen tube may therefore be compared to that of a fungal hypha, and its power to penetrate tissues, and eventually the megaspore membrane, is doubtless due to an analogous secretion of digestive enzymes.

The downward growth of the pollen tube is mainly determined by a chemotropic stimulus due to substances contained in the ovules or in the ovary-wall. This fact can be experimentally demonstrated by sowing pollen grains of the Wild Hyacinth (*Scilla*) in a 5 per cent., or of *Echeveria retusa* in a 15 per cent., solution of cane-sugar around a fragment of the ovary, taking care to avoid the inclusion of air-bubbles. The pollen tubes tend to grow in the direction of the piece of ovary.

Having passed through the micropyle, the pollen tube penetrates the overlying nucellar cap, and thus reaches the embryo sac. Meanwhile the generative cell has divided to form two *male nuclei* (Fig. 329, C, ♂), which are extruded from the tip of the pollen tube, and, entering the embryo sac, fuse respectively [1] (*a*) with the egg, and (*b*) with the two polar nuclei (cf. Fig. 329, D), or with the nucleus formed by the fusion of the latter. The former fusion

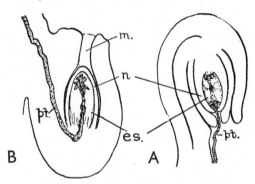

FIG. 330. Diagrams illustrating normal fertilisation (porogamy, A) and chalazogamy (B). *e.s.*, embryo sac; *m.*, micropyle; *n.*, nucellus; *pt.*, pollen tube.

results, in the usual way, in the production of an embryo, but the latter also leads to abundant division, whereby a nutritive tissue, the *endosperm*, is formed. In the utilisation of both male nuclei for these different purposes, Angiosperms exhibit a characteristic difference from Gymnosperms.

The product of the second fusion, which is really built up of three nuclei (one from either end of the embryo sac and one male nucleus), divides repeatedly, till the sac becomes filled with numerous free nuclei distributed uniformly throughout its protoplasmic content. Formation of separating walls now takes place almost simultaneously, so that the sac becomes occupied by a continuous thin-walled tissue, the endosperm, which stores food for the developing embryo.

During the nuclear divisions leading to endosperm-formation, the fertilised egg, now provided with a cell-wall, enlarges considerably and begins to segment. The first division is unequal, a smaller cell situated at the end away from the micropyle being cut off from the large remaining portion. The latter forms the sac-like

[1] This process is often spoken of as "double fertilisation."

basal cell (Fig. 331, I–VI, *b*.) and plays no further part in the
development of the embryo. The smaller segment undergoes
successive transverse divisions, so as to give rise to a short elongating
suspensor (Fig. 331, *S*.). Hereby the slightly larger hemispherical
terminal cell (*e*.), which subsequently produces the embryo proper,

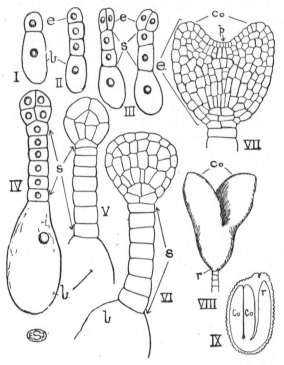

FIG. 331. Embryology of the Shepherd's Purse (*Capsella bursa-pastoris*). The
successive stages are numbered I–IX. In VII and VIII only the embryo and
a small part of the adjacent suspensor are shown. IX is a longitudinal section
of a mature seed, showing the bent embryo. *b*., basal cell; *Co*., cotyledons;
e., embryo; *p*., plumule; *r*., radicle; *S*., suspensor.

is carried down into the heart of the developing endosperm. Young
pro-embryos at this stage of development, with a suspensor composed
of a number of flat cells, are readily squeezed out of very young
seeds of the Shepherd's Purse, such as can be removed from the
ovaries of flowers which have not yet faded; the seeds are best
mounted in water, and sudden pressure applied by tapping the
cover-glass.

More advanced stages can be obtained in the same way from
progressively older seeds. These show rather longer suspensors

and an increasing number of divisions in the enlarging embryonal cell (Fig. 331, IV–VI). The latter soon segments into octants, by three walls at right angles to one another (III, IV), and subsequent walls parallel to the surface (V, VI) delimit the future epidermis, cortex, and vascular system. Meanwhile the embryo assumes a more or less flattened form, and, at its wider free end, the future *cotyledons* appear as two lobes (VII, *Co.*) between which the *plumule* (*p.*) develops. The attached end of the embryo invariably becomes the *radicle* (VIII, *r.*), which thus faces towards the micropyle. Such embryos are to be found in seeds from almost ripe fruits (cf. IX).

The general method of embryo-development just described is that characteristic of a large number of Dicotyledons, although there are numerous differences in detail which are beyond the scope of this book. In Monocotyledons (Fig. 332, A–E), where the suspensor is often a more bulky structure (cf. especially Fig. 332, G), the single cotyledon (*Co.*) occupies the terminal position, whilst the plumule (*p.*) arises towards one side. Pro-embryos with a bulky suspensor are also found in some Leguminosæ (Fig. 332, I). It will be noticed that the embryos of Gymnosperms and Angiosperms do not develop a special absorptive organ (foot), such as characterises those of Bryophyta and Pteridophyta, although sometimes haustorial outgrowths arise from the suspensor.

The stimulus of fertilisation leads to increase in size and other changes in both ovules and ovary and may even affect adjacent floral parts (p. 478). The outcome is the ripe fruit in which the enlarged ovary-wall becomes the *pericarp* and the integuments, or integument, the *testa*. A proportion of the ripening fruits often drop prematurely which may appreciably reduce the crop. It is possible to prevent this by spraying fruit-trees with growth-promoting substances.

The testa is of varied durability and thickness, while the surface often shows distinctive sculpturing (*e.g.* Corn Cockle, *Agrostemma*), by which the seed can be identified. The endosperm may be absorbed before the embryo enters upon its resting-stage (non-endospermic seeds, *e.g.* Pea) or part may persist until germination (endospermic seeds, *e.g.* Castor Oil, most Monocotyledons). In a few plants (*e.g.* many Caryophyllaceæ) the nucellus is not entirely replaced by the endosperm; in such, a thin layer (*perisperm*) persists, even in the ripe seed, and functions for the storage of food. The degree of differentiation attained by the *embryo*, at the time when it enters upon its resting-stage, varies considerably. Thus, in the Runner Bean, even the venation of the first pair of plumular leaves is distinguishable. In the Castor Oil the plumule is merely a peg-like structure, whilst in the Lesser Celandine (*Ficaria*) and Orchids (Fig. 332, H) the entire embryo is an undifferentiated mass of cells, a condition likewise encountered in the embryos of most parasites. In some plants, moreover, there

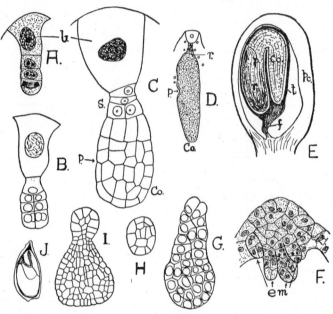

FIG. 332. Embryology of various plants. A–D, Successive stages in the development of the embryo of the Arrowhead (*Sagittaria*) (after Schaffner). E, Longitudinal section of ripe achene of the Water Plantain (*Alisma*) (original). F, Formation of several embryos (*em.*) from a massive suspensor, by budding, in *Erythronium americanum* (Liliaceæ) (after Jeffrey). G, Pro-embryo, with massive suspensor, of *Lilium* (after Coulter). H, Embryo of Twayblade (*Listera ovata*), at time when seed is shed (after Pfitzer). I, Pro-embryo of *Spartium junceum* (Leguminosæ) (after Guignard). J, Longitudinal section of Orange pip (*Citrus*) (with two embryos) (after Wettstein). *b.*, basal cell; *Co.*, cotyledon; *f.*, funicle; *p.*, plumule; *pc.*, pericap; *r.*, radicle; *S.*, suspensor; *t.*, testa.

is no resting period (*e.g.* in the tropical Mangroves), whilst in many trees the seeds germinate most readily if sown immediately on reaching maturity.

Exceptions to the normal sequence of events described in the foregoing pages are by no means uncommon. *Apogamy* (cf. p. 385), for example, has been recorded in quite a large number of Compositæ (*e.g.* Dandelion, Hawkweed), as well as in some species of Lady's Mantle (*Alchemilla*), which produce seed without fertilisation. Here the reduction division does not appear to occur, and the embryo arises from an unfertilised cell of the embryo sac having the diploid number of chromosomes. Such apogamy is of course akin to vegetative propagation, but gains the advantages afforded by the mechanism for seed-dispersal. Despite the non-occurrence of a sexual process in such apogamous forms, pollination sometimes appears to furnish a necessary stimulus for embryo-formation. More rarely it is an ordinary cell of the nucellus that divides to form the embryo (e.g. *Citrus*), a condition analogous to the *apospory* described among Ferns (p. 384). In the Hawkweeds (*Hieracium*) all three conditions—apogamy, apospory, and normal fertilisation— have been observed. Apogamy and apospory (often collectively spoken of as *apomyxis*) appear to be particularly prevalent among plants with high chromosome-numbers exhibiting polyploidy (p. 601) and are especially frequent in northern types. In such apomyctic plants every vegetative mutation not only persists but breeds true (see p. 586).

The occasional presence of more than one embryo within a seed may be due to several causes. Sometimes more than one member of the tetrad, formed by the megaspore mother-cell, develops into an embryo sac, so that several embryos can exist from the first. But more frequently accessory embryos arise by vegetative budding from the pro-embryo (Fig. 332, F). Orange pips frequently contain several embryos, of which one is the outcome of a sexual fusion, whilst the others are derived from nucellar cells which are presumably stimulated to growth as a result of fertilisation (Fig. 332, J).

The general course of the life-history in Angiosperms is obviously very similar to that of Gymnosperms. In both the young embryo lives, as a parasite, within the ovule, which forms a protective envelope around it until the time of germination. As with the young Fern, however, its independence is soon established. In contrast to Gymnosperms, the most striking features are connected with the very efficient arrangements for the protection and nourishment of the developing embryos and seeds, and the highly perfected mechanism for pollination, by virtue of which the most intimate relation often obtains between the flower and the pollinating agent.

31

CHAPTER XXXIX

FRUITS, SEEDS, AND DISPERSAL

As a result of fertilisation the wall of the ovary enlarges to form the *pericarp*, which is either hard and dry, or fleshy, the fruit itself being described as dry or succulent according to the character of its wall. It will be realised, therefore, that the fruit corresponds to the whole ripened ovary, whilst the seeds are the matured ovules contained within it. When there is any doubt as to the nature of a given structure (*e.g.* in Gramineæ, where the testa of the single seed is completely joined up with the pericarp, cf. p. 29), a seed can always be distinguished from a fruit by the fact that it exhibits only one scar (the hilum, p. 21), whereas the fruit shows two, one marking the former attachment to the plant, the other the remains of the style.

Where the ovary is syncarpous a *simple fruit* develops from it, but when the ovary is apocarpous each carpel matures separately and the aggregate is a *compound fruit*. Two types of dry fruits may be distinguished, the one usually remaining attached to the parent-plant and splitting open to liberate the contained seeds (dehiscent fruits), whilst in the other the fruits are detached and the pericarp merely decays away (indehiscent fruits). Practically all indehiscent fruits are one-seeded, whilst many-seeded ones are dehiscent. The necessity for dehiscence in the latter class is obvious, since otherwise all the seeds would come to germinate at the same spot and the offspring would harm one another by mutual competition.

Examples of *dry indehiscent fruits* are furnished by *achenes* with a membranous, and *nuts* with a hard woody pericarp. The fruit of Compositæ and Gramineæ is an achene which is peculiar in the fusion of pericarp and testa. That of the Buttercup (Fig. 333, *a*) consists of a collection of achenes. The Hazel and the Acorn provide instances of nuts, each of which is enclosed in a cupule [1] formed by joined bracts and bracteoles. Some of the nuts of

---

[1] This forms the cup of the Acorn and the prickly covering of the fruits of the Sweet Chestnut (*Castanea*).

commerce (*e.g.* Walnut, see p. 478) are not true nuts, while Brazil Nuts are seeds formed within an extremely hard indehiscent fruit.

Not uncommonly fruits derived from multilocular ovaries, containing more than one ovule, split along the septa into compartments, each with a single seed and equivalent to as many achenes; such fruits are said to be *schizocarpic*. Thus, in the Umbelliferæ the fruit at maturity splits into two achenes (Fig. 334, A), whilst

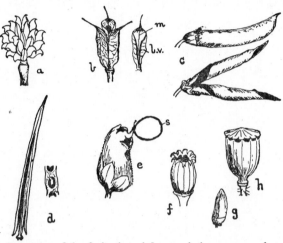

FIG. 333. Examples of dry fruits (*a* and *d*, natural size; *g*, somewhat enlarged; others slightly reduced). *a*, Buttercup (collection of achenes). *b*, *Aconitum* (three follicles). *m*, midrib of carpel; *l.v.*, lateral vein of same. *c*, *Vicia* (legume); lower figure shows pod after dehiscence. *d*, Wallflower (siliqua); right-hand figure shows portion of false septum with seeds. *e*, *Antirrhinum* (capsule with apical pores). *s*, style. *f*, Campion (capsule with teeth). *g*, Plantain (capsule with lid). *h*, Poppy (porous capsule).

the Labiatæ exhibit four achenes (Fig. 334, D) produced by an early fission of the ovary, and the Mallow (Fig. 334, C) as many achenes as there were loculi in the original ovary. A similar splitting of the ripe fruit into compartments is seen in the Crane's Bill (Fig. 334, B), but here the contained seeds are subsequently shot out of the opening segments.

The simplest type of *dehiscent fruit* is the *follicle*, seen in the Marsh Marigold, Monkshood (Fig. 333, *b*), etc., in which the dry pericarp formed from a single carpel dehisces along the ventral suture (p. 440). This constitutes the most essential difference from the *legume* of Leguminosæ (Fig. 333, *c*) in which dehiscence takes place along both sutures, the two valves often twisting when ripe. A somewhat similar fruit is the *siliqua* characteristic of Cruciferæ (*e.g.* Honesty, Wallflower, Fig. 333, *d*). Here dehiscence takes place along both edges and commences at the base of the elongated fruit, so that the two carpels separate from below but remain cohering above. The septum (p. 442), spread out on a framework formed by the parietal placentas, remains standing vertically and the seeds attached to the latter (cf. right-hand drawing in Fig. 333, *d*) are gradually shaken off by the wind. Many members of the Cruciferæ have very short siliquas known as *siliculas* (*e.g.* Shepherd's-purse, Fig. 4, B) which dehisce in just

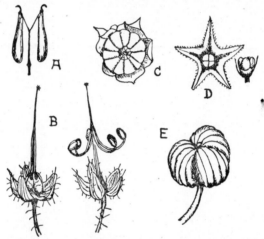

Fig. 334. Types of schizocarpic fruits (A enlarged, other figures natural size). A, *Anthriscus*. B, Crane's Bill (*Geranium*); left-hand figure before, right-hand figure after, splitting into achenes. C, Mallow. D, White Dead-nettle; right-hand figure shows fruit, with calyx removed, in side-view. E, *Tropæolum*.

the same way. All dehiscent fruits arising from a syncarpous ovary are described as *capsules*, the siliqua just mentioned being a special form of the latter.

Capsules differ chiefly amongst one another in the number of compartments and the mode of dehiscence. Most commonly opening takes places by longitudinal slits in the pericarp along the dorsal suture of each carpel (*loculicidal*, *e.g.* Iris, Willow-herb), whilst much more rarely the slits appear along the lines of junction of the carpels (*septicidal*, *e.g.* St. John's Wort). In the Caryophyllaceæ and the Primrose the top of the unilocular fruit splits into a number of teeth which curl right back in dry air (Fig. 333, *f*), whereas in the Pimpernel (*Anagallis*), Henbane, and Plantain (Fig. 333, *g*) it breaks off cleanly as a lid. The ripe fruit of the Poppy (Fig. 333, *h*) exhibits a series of pores beneath the flat top (*porous dehiscence*), due to the wall between each pair of placentas curling slightly outwards at these points; pores are formed in a similar manner at the base of the hanging capsule of the Harebell. In *Antirrhinum* (Fig. 333, *e*) there are three openings at the apex of the fruit, each of which is surrounded by several small teeth.

The Crane's Bill (Fig. 334, B) shows that even one-seeded compartments may dehisce, and the same is observed in the Horse Chestnut in which the prickly pericarp splits into three valves at maturity. The fruit of this tree, however, sometimes includes two or even three seeds, so that dehiscence is advantageous. The occasional presence of more than one seed is due to the fact that each of the three loculi of the ovary contains two ovules, although as a general rule only one of the six ripens. The majority of indehiscent fruits are one-seeded from the first, but in some this condition is attained, as in the Horse Chestnut, by all but one of the ovules dying away; thus the ovary of the Oak is trilocular with two ovules in each compartment, but five of these invariably fail to ripen, leaving the Acorn one-seeded.

The two principal types of *fleshy fruits*, both indehiscent, are the *berry* and the *drupe*. The former has a pericarp which is

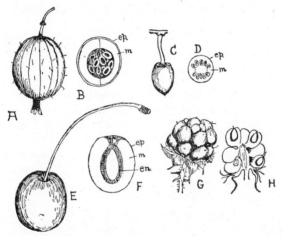

FIG. 335. Types of fleshy fruits (slightly reduced). A–B, Gooseberry (*Ribes uva-crispa*), entire and in cross-section. C–D, Bittersweet (*Solanum dulcamara*) (berry), entire and in cross-section. E–F, Cherry (drupe), entire and in longitudinal section. G–H, Blackberry (collection of drupes), entire and in longitudinal section. *en.*, endocarp; *ep.*, epicarp; *m.*, mesocarp.

fleshy throughout, whilst in the latter the inner part is hard and stony. We can, consequently, in the berry (Fig. 335, A–B) distinguish between the surface-skin or *epicarp* (*ep.*) and the fleshy portion or *mesocarp* (*m.*), whilst in the drupe (Fig. 335, E–F) we have in addition the hard *endocarp* (*en.*). Examples of berries are furnished by the Currant, Gooseberry (Fig. 335, A–B), Bittersweet (Fig. 335, C–D), and Tomato, the first two having parietal (Fig. 335, B), the last two axile placentas (Fig. 335, D). The Date (*Phœnix*) is a single-seeded berry in which the hard stone is constituted by the endosperm, the actual testa forming the delicate membrane around the latter. Other special kinds of berries are the Orange, Lemon, Grape, Banana, Cucumber, and Vegetable Marrow. In the two first the fleshy part is constituted by succulent hairs which are outgrowths of the carpel walls, while the Banana is a berry that is seedless in the cultivated varieties.

Typical drupes are the Plum, Cherry (Fig. 335, E–F), Almond, Peach, etc., whilst the Walnut (*Juglans*) and Coco-nut are drupes in which, however, the layers outside the endocarp are generally removed before they are placed on the market. The Raspberry and Blackberry (Fig. 335, G and H) furnish instances of compound fruits (p. 474) composed of many small drupes. Whereas berries are generally many-seeded, drupes usually contain but one seed. The hard endocarp renders the drupe equivalent to a nut, while the individual seeds of a berry get scattered when the fruit is eaten by animals.

In some plants the fruit is not composed of the ovary alone, other parts of the flower (especially the receptacle) participating in its formation, when we speak of it as a *false fruit*. Thus, in the Strawberry (Fig. 336, D) the true fruit consists of a number of minute achenes (*a*), but these are carried up on the much enlarged and fleshy receptacle (*r*) which constitutes the actual edible part. In the Apple (Fig. 336, E) and Pear the flesh is formed by the receptacle (*r*) in which the inferior ovary (the core, *ov.*) is embedded. The hip of the Rose (Fig. 336, C) is another false fruit in which the coloured flask-shaped envelope develops from the deeply hollowed thalamus (*r*), whilst the fruit proper is constituted by the contained achenes (*a*).

Some false fruits are formed from complete inflorescences. In the Mulberry (Fig. 336, A) the individual fruits are achenes, each covered by four fleshy perianth-members (*p*). The Fig (Fig. 336, B) originates from a peculiar inflorescence in which the fleshy axis (*a.i.*) is deeply hollowed out, the cavity being lined with numerous minute flowers.[1] The Pineapple (*Ananas*) is likewise an entire inflorescence.

Many young fruits are protected by the persistent calyx (*e.g.* Caryophyllaceæ, Fig. 422, E, and Labiatæ, Fig. 334, D), whilst in Compositæ the same function is fulfilled by the involucre (p. 428). In mature fruits, which have dehisced, the seeds are often shielded during wet weather by a more or less marked closing of the valves; thus, in the Caryophyllaceæ the teeth at the top of the capsule (Fig. 333, *f*) come together when the air is damp, a feature due to un-equal absorption of moisture by their two sides.

[1] Information on fruits of tropical plants will be found in H. F. Macmillan, *Tropical Planting and Gardening*, Macmillan & Co., 4th edit., 1935 (560 pp.); W. Popenoe, *Manual of Tropical and Subtropical Fruits*, Macmillan & Co., 1920 (474 pp.).

Far more important than an enumeration of the characters of fruits is the relation which these bear to the *dispersal*[1] of the seeds. Reproduction by seeds is superior to vegetative multiplication, because seeds are usually carried some distance away from the parent, though a large proportion of those shed by a plant will be conveyed to situations unsuitable for further growth. In view of the great mortality, it is of advantage that a plant should produce far more seeds than can ultimately develop into seedlings and that these should be widely scattered, since in this way some

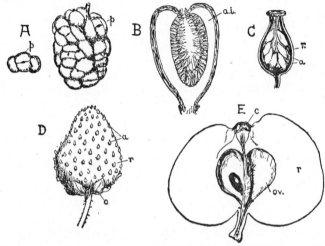

FIG. 336. Examples of false fruits (slightly reduced). A, Mulberry (*Morus*); single fruit shown on left. B, Fig (*Ficus*), in longitudinal section. *a.i.*, axis of inflorescence. C, Hip of Rose, in longitudinal section. D, Strawberry (*Fragaria*). E, Apple, in longitudinal section. *a*, achenes; *c*, calyx; *ov.*, ovary; *p*, perianth-member (in A); *r*, receptacle.

are certain to reach a suitable situation. Moreover, the risk of competition with the parent or with one another is diminished. If many seeds are deposited close together, there will be marked competition among the resulting seedlings, as can be observed in any seed-bed that has been too densely sown, when only a small number survive. There is less competition between seedlings of different kinds of plants, and a seed-bed containing mixed seed will support a considerably greater number of individuals. For most plants wind or animals[2] are the agents of seed-dispersal.

A very simple feature facilitating *wind-dispersal* consists in the production of minute and light seeds (*e.g.* Foxglove), an extreme

---

[1] For a detailed treatment, see H. N. Ridley, *The Dispersal of Plants.* L. Reeve, 1930 (744 pp.).   [2] Regarding dispersal by water, see p. 554.

instance being seen in the Orchids in which they form a powdery mass. Many other plants, however, propagate by light seeds of small size, which are capable of being carried considerable distances by the wind. In most of these the fruits are attached to the plant in such a way that the seeds are readily shaken out. Thus, in the Harebell the hanging fruits are disturbed by every breeze (censer-mechanism) and, in their oscillations, the seeds are gradually dispersed through the pores of the capsule. In many Caryophyllaceæ and the Poppy (Fig. 333, *e, f, h*), the ripe fruits are borne at the ends of stiff upright elastic peduncles which bend with sudden gusts of wind and then spring back to their normal position, thus shooting out some of the seeds like a catapult.

In a number of plants (*e.g.* Gorse, *Impatiens*) the different layers of the pericarp dry to an unequal extent during ripening, so that a tension is created which leads, at the slightest touch, to an explosive rupture of the fruit, the seeds being projected some little distance.

An expansion of the pericarp in the shape of a *wing* often helps in the distribution of one-seeded fruits, good instances being afforded by the Ash (Fig. 337, A) and the Elm. Similarly, in the Sycamore (Fig. 337, B) the ripe schizocarp splits into two winged achenes. Each group of fruits in the Lime (Fig. 337, C) is suspended from the middle of a strap-shaped bract (*br.*) which aids in dispersal. A similar co-operation of bracts in fruit-distribution is seen in the Hornbeam (*Carpinus*, Fig. 419, C). Winged seeds are rarer, but are found, for instance, in the Field Spurrey (*Spergula arvensis*) and Honesty (*Lunaria*).

The pericarp or testa is often produced into hairs. Good examples of such *plumed* seeds are seen in the Willow and Willow-herb (Fig. 337, D), both of which have capsules. In *Clematis* (Fig. 337, F) and *Anemone pulsatilla* the style of each achene is feathery and enlarges after fertilisation to form a plume. In the Compositæ the calyx of the individual florets is usually developed as a number of fine hairs (*pappus*) arising from the top of the inferior ovary (cf. p. 433, and Fig. 312, B and C), thus forming a plumed fruit. These hairs form a kind of parachute by means of which the achenes drift readily in the air; when, as in *Tragopogon*, the hairs of the pappus are themselves feathery, they are still more effective. In the Dandelion (Fig. 337, E) and *Tragopogon* a long stalk (*s*) develops after fertilisation between the pappus and the ovary.

The individual hairs of the pappus spread out more or less horizontally when the air is dry, but close together vertically when it is damp. Thus, the fruits are only dispersed under favourable conditions, whilst, when once on the wing, they fall to the ground

with the advent of rainy weather, during which they are likely
to become washed into the soil.

Succulent fruits depend for their dispersal on animals. Their
adaptational features are the usual bright colouring, the fleshy
edible character of part or whole of the pericarp, and the protection

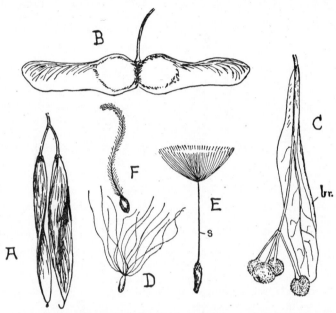

FIG. 337. Winged and plumed fruits and seeds (all natural size). A, Ash
(*Fraxinus*) (two winged achenes). B, Sycamore (*Acer*) (schizocarpic, splitting
into two winged achenes). C, Lime (*Tilia*). *br.*, bract. D, Plumed seed of
Willow-herb. E, Dandelion (*Taraxacum*) (achene with superior pappus).
s, stalk. F, *Clematis* (achene with feathery style).

of the seed-contents of all these fruits by a hard covering furnished
either by the endocarp (drupes) or the testa (berries). As a consequence of the last feature, such seeds are able to pass through
the digestive tracts of animals without the embryo coming to harm,
the seed being deposited with the fæces; thus a certain amount of
manure is available for the seedling which subsequently develops.
It may be noted in this connection that the seeds of the Hawthorn
(*Cratægus*) and others, which are normally swallowed and pass
through the alimentary tract of animals, germinate much more
readily after having been acted upon by the gastric juices. Even
when the stone is not swallowed, the bird or other animal generally
carries the fruits some little distance from the parent before dropping

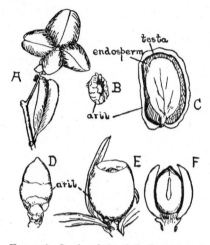

FIG. 338. Seeds of the Spindle-tree and
Yew (C considerably enlarged, other
figures natural size). A–C, Spindle-tree
(*Euonymus*). A, Single fruit. B, Young
seed with aril. C, Ripe seed in longitudinal section. D–F, *Taxus*. D, Young
seed. E, Older seed. F, Ditto in longitudinal section.

the seeds. In the Mistletoe
part of the flesh of the fruit
is very sticky, so that the
contained seed adheres to the
bill of the bird who rubs it
off on to the branch of a
tree; the seedling is thus
from the first attached to the
plant on which it lives (p.
217).

Fleshy seeds are rare in
our country. In the Spindle-
tree, the single seed found in
each of the four compartments
of the fruit (Fig. 338, A) is
enveloped by a bright-orange
puckered envelope (*aril*, Fig.
338, B and C) which is very
conspicuous when the capsule
dehisces. Another example
is furnished by the Yew (Fig.
338, D, E). In these two
forms the seeds are distributed
by Birds, but in the Gorse, whose seeds have a small fleshy swelling
at one end, Ants are stated to act as the agent of dispersal.

A considerable number of
low-growing herbs develop
hooks on their fruits or on
adjacent parts of the flower,
and such *burr-fruits* are usually
distributed by hairy animals.
Thus, in Cleavers (*Galium
aparine*) and *Circæa* (Fig. 339, B)
the hooks are borne on the fruits
themselves, whilst in *Geum* (Fig.
339, D) a portion of the style of
each achene forms a long stiff
claw. On the other hand, in the
Burr Marigold (*Bidens*, Fig. 339,
C) it is the calyx that is modified,
the customary pappus being here
replaced by two or three stiff
bristles with backwardly directed
barbs. The top part of the

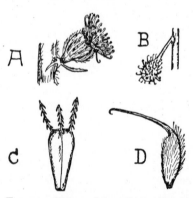

FIG. 339. Types of burr-fruits (A and
B, natural size; C and D somewhat
enlarged). A, *Agrimonia* (hooks on
receptacle). B, Enchanter's Nightshade
(*Circæa*) (hooked fruit). C, Burr Marigold (*Bidens*) (hooked calyx). D, *Geum*
(hooked style).

receptacle of the Agrimony (Fig. 339, A), again, is beset with numerous hooks, whilst in the Burdock (*Arctium*) the involucre is similarly equipped. Seeds, which become sticky when wet (*e.g.* Plantain, Chickweed), may adhere to bird's feathers and so be dispersed.

We have already on p. 20 described the general way in which fruits and seeds get buried in the soil. In the Stork's Bill (*Erodium*) the segments of the style, which separate with the indehiscent achenes of the schizocarpic fruit (as in Fig. 334, B), coil up when dry, but uncoil when moist; a similar behaviour is shown by the awns (p. 631, and Fig. 439, A, *a*) on the fruits of the Oat (*Avena*) Since the hairy or rough surface of the awn causes it to cling to the soil, its extension, when the latter is damp and consequently soft, results in the fruit being driven into the ground.

Whilst many fruits and seeds thus possess special mechanisms facilitating distribution, it should be recognised that highly efficient dispersal may occur without any marked adaptation. A striking example is furnished by the spread of the Pineapple Weed (*Matricaria matricarioides*), a wayside plant, the fruits of which are carried in the mud picked up by the patterned treads of motor tyres. Long distances may be traversed before the dried mud containing the fruits becomes detached.

As already noted (p. 133) the initiation of flower-buds, especially in woody plants, often takes place at a period considerably antecedent to actual flowering. In so far as weather-conditions influence flowering, those of one year may thus determine the amount of blossom and so of fruit on fruit-trees in the year following. Each of the critical phases leading to fruit-formation, viz. blooming, pollination, fertilisation, etc. will, moreover, be affected by the climatic conditions (see p. 485) at the times when these events occur and not merely by those prevailing during any single phase.

CHAPTER XL

THE PLANT-ENVIRONMENT

WE have so far considered plants separately, that is, as isolated individuals, but in nature they generally grow together in communities, the separate members of which not only mutually affect one another, but have to accommodate themselves to all the circumstances of their surroundings. These collectively, that is to say both the physical conditions, due to soil and climate, and the biotic conditions produced by other plants and animals, constitute what is termed the *environment* of the plant. The nature of this environment is in fact the result of present conditions, but it is also to a considerable extent the outcome of its past history. Moreover, the biotic conditions are not fixed, partly because plants themselves modify their environment and also because they are markedly plastic. The situation in which a plant grows, having regard to all the conditions of its environment, is termed its *habitat*, and the study of the relation of plants to their environment and to one another is termed *ecology*.

The various conditions afforded by the environment are spoken of as the *habitat factors*, and these may be grouped into several categories. For instance, the conditions determined by soil are the *edaphic* factors, while those due to surface changes are the physiographic factors. There are also climatic and historic factors, as well as *biotic* factors, the latter depending upon the influence of other plants and animals. It is important to realise that these groupings though convenient are rather arbitrary, since different factors interact with one another. Thus changes in topography, such as increase of altitude, affect climatic conditions, whilst the influence of soil on vegetation varies according to the climate with which it is associated. So too a biotic factor (*e.g.* shading of one plant by another) may vary in its effect, according as the water supply is high or low, whilst the species of plants making up a community will be determined in no small degree by the past history of the area concerned.

The *climatic factors* comprise temperature, precipitation,

484

humidity, wind, and light. Of these temperature is particularly significant, if the world as a whole is considered, while in more limited areas it is important with respect to seasonal changes and the length of the growing season, especially when there are marked differences in altitude. Rainfall, humidity, and temperature are obviously interrelated, since the higher the temperature and the greater the saturation deficit of the air the less will be the effective value of any particular rainfall. Seasonal distribution of rainfall is more significant than the total annual amount and, as with other factors (*e.g.* temperature), the extremes may influence growth far more than the averages which may indeed be altogether misleading. Thus, a low rainfall concentrated in a few thunderstorms will be inadequate to support anything but desert vegetation, whilst a single killing frost will exclude plants that could tolerate the average. Precipitation during the growing season is more important than that which falls during the period of rest, whilst periodic droughts may alter the character of the plant-covering (*e.g.* some deserts), despite adequate water supply during intervening periods. Amongst the climatic factors rainfall is of prime importance.

Wind by its drying action accentuates water-shortage and prevents the growth of plants with high water-requirements. Since its velocity increases with height, tall vegetation requires more water, or must be more resistant to desiccation, apart from needing greater mechanical strength. Wind-effects are especially marked on wind-swept coasts (Ch. XLVI) and at high altitudes (p. 527).

Light, though comparatively uniform over large areas of the earth's surface, varies markedly in intensity with latitude and from one part of the year to another, so that a degree of shading that is tolerated in summer may well prevent growth in spring. Moreover, the duration of daily illumination exhibits similar changes (p. 247).

The effect of climate is well illustrated by the distribution of forest, grassland, and desert over the earth's surface. In general, forest occupies the regions of highest, and desert those of lowest, rainfall, whilst grassland occurs in areas of medium, rather uniformly distributed, rainfall; the influence of man or of winds may, however, profoundly modify the applicability of this generalisation. In northern latitudes forests are composed of such trees as Birch, Pine, and Spruce (*Picea*), whilst in temperate zones deciduous trees, such as Beech, Oak, and Ash, predominate. On the slopes of high mountains, like those of Switzerland, the same relative distribution occurs, with deciduous forests below and Coniferous ones above.

Amongst *biotic factors* the competition between different species or between individuals of the same species is most important. Plants, when free from competition, develop much more extensive root-systems than when growing together, and their capacity to form root and shoot when associated together, varies both with the competing species and with the other habitat factors. This competition often begins at the seedling stage, before the overground parts are even in contact with one another. Just as the antibiotic substances formed by Fungi like *Penicillium notatum* and *Streptomyces griseus* (p. 339) serve to eliminate Bacteria competing for existence in the same substratum, the roots of higher plants secrete substances which check the growth of the roots of their competitors. Competition for light is one of the commonest aspects of the effect of plant on plant, as is especially evident in woodlands (cf. p. 519).

The interaction between plants and animals may be either beneficial or non-beneficial. Beneficial relationships are exemplified by the rôle of insects as pollinating agents and of other animals as agents in the dispersal of fruits and seeds. Moles, rabbits, and earthworms serve as natural cultivators of the soil. But, since animals are directly or indirectly dependent upon plants for their food, it naturally follows that animals often have a deleterious effect upon plants, influencing it may be the frequency of particular species or altering the prevalent physiognomy of the vegetation. Thus the grazing of herbivorous animals maintains grassland in areas that would otherwise become scrub or woodland (p. 531) and overstocking has in arid areas of Australia led to such depletion of the plant-cover as to result in soil erosion and desert conditions. In Britain and even more in less populated areas the rabbit has had a profound effect in checking plant-growth, especially with respect to seedlings of woody species. The ravages of Caterpillars may sometimes destroy a plant entirely in a small area (*e.g.* the Five-spot Burnet attacking Bird's-foot Trefoil), although such devastation by insects is much more extensive in warmer parts of the earth (*e.g.* by swarms of Locusts). Many plants possess some protection in the form of spines (cf. p. 507), of distasteful substances, of needle-like crystals, etc.

The presence of characteristic species in any particular type of situation is evidence of some benefit or benefits which they gain, either directly, through the nature of the soil or climate, or indirectly, through being relieved from the severity of competition with plants that, in other conditions, would prove more successful (cf. p. 519). But, whilst every habitat may be said to confer a benefit upon its legitimate inhabitants, it is equally true that adaptation to its special conditions is also involved, in particular to those conditions which are most pronounced. Thus, in any given locality that particular factor which most nearly approaches the minimum requisite for life or which is present in excess, whether it be water, light, temperature, or food-supply, will be that one which most profoundly affects the character of the vegetation. For, if the other essential conditions are amply sufficient for most, if not all, of the species present, the successful plants in the struggle for existence will be those best able to flourish under the particular extremes, either of deficiency or excess. The more specialised the habitat, the more specialised must the plant be to survive there. Thus, the only forms that can live in a desert are plants that can withstand great water loss, while further examples are furnished by aquatics. It must be realised, however, that, although a certain plant may be eminently successful in conditions to which its structure is adapted, these very modifications may often render it unsuited to another environment (*e.g.* aquatics, succulents, cf. p. 510). Moreover, just as certain morphological and physiological features, which ensure success under one set of habitat factors, may be an incubus in others, so too the vegetation, that was adapted to conditions which were widespread on the surface of the earth in past epochs, may nowadays be unable to survive or have become restricted to certain areas (cf. Cycads, p. 397).

[Important general reference-works are: J. Braun-Blanquet, *Plant Sociology* (Engl. transl. by G. D. Fuller and H. S. Conrad), McGraw-Hill Book Co., 1932 (439 pp.), which contains a good presentation of the more floristic aspects of plant geography; H. Lundegardh, *Environment and Plant Development* (transl. by E. Ashby), Ed. Arnold, 1931 (330 pp.), a useful account of the chief habitat factors; C. Raunkiaer, *Life-forms of Plants and Statistical Plant Geography*, Clarendon Press, 1934 (632 pp.); A. G. Tansley, *Practical Plant Ecology*, Allen & Unwin, 1923 (228 pp.); A. G. Tansley, *The British Islands and their Vegetation*, 2 vols., Cambridge Univ. Press, 1949; E. J. Salisbury, *Downs and Dunes*, G. Bell & Sons, 1952 (328 pp.); W. H. Pearsall, *Mountains and Moorlands*, Collins, 1950 (312 pp.); E. J. Salisbury, "The Geographical Distribution of Plants in relation to Climatic Factors," *Geographical Journal*, 1926, pp. 312–342. For ecological conditions in relation to garden plants, see E. J. Salisbury, *The Living Garden*, G. Bell & Sons, 1935 (338 pp.).]

CHAPTER XLI

THE SOIL (EDAPHIC FACTORS)

THE soil from which the roots of plants derive so much of their nourishment is, considered physically, a more or less loose aggregation of two kinds of particles. On the one hand there are the mineral particles formed by the breaking down of rocks under the influence of atmospheric and other agencies; on the other hand there are the organic particles consisting of the decaying remains of plants and animals that have previously lived on the soil in question, such organic material being spoken of collectively as *humus*. This dead matrix is permeated by a soil-atmosphere and a soil-solution. In addition there is a teeming population of microscopic animal and vegetable organisms, some of which are essential to the well-being of the larger plants (p. 349).

The mineral particles, which usually exceed the organic in amount, depend in their nature on the kind of rock from which they have been derived. Thus, the soil in a sandstone or gravel area will tend to consist in the main of sandy particles, *i.e.* of relatively large grains of semi-transparent quartz which are, however, frequently coloured red or brown by iron-compounds. Similarly, in a chalk area we find a considerable proportion of chalk particles in the soil (calcareous soil), which in consequence is often conspicuous by its greyish-white colour. A mineral matrix of a more mixed character is found where the rocks are of volcanic origin (igneous rocks, *e.g.* granite, basalt, etc.), since these are composed of many different kinds of minerals (*e.g.* quartz, felspar, mica, and hornblende, the commonest constituents of granites).

In all these instances we are dealing with soils formed *in situ*, and there is thus, apart from such chemical changes as may have taken place, a close relation between the character of the soil and the nature of the underlying rock. But this need not necessarily be so. The material formed by the breaking down of rocks may be carried away by running water which, according to its rate of flow, has the power of transporting particles of varying size, and the latter are thus progressively deposited with the gradual decrease in rapidity of the current. In this way there arise the gravel banks and the large stretches of alluvial soil, so commonly found near the mouths of rivers. Movement of glaciers during the Glacial Period has also been instrumental in the transference of material, and by the disintegration of the boulders, etc., transported upon the ice, large areas of clay and gravel have been produced (*e.g.* Hertfordshire Boulder clay, glacial drifts of Norfolk). As a general rule the soils one meets with in nature are mixed soils in which, however, one kind of particle often predominates; pure soils are relatively rare.

The considerable volume of air present in a soil will be realised if one or two lumps of *unbroken* earth are placed in water and moved about to displace the air from their surfaces; if they now be broken up, bubbles arise from them showing the presence of air within the soil. The amount of this soil-atmosphere can be estimated in the following way.

A tin which must not leak is filled to the brim with water and completely immersed in a tall glass cylinder partly filled with the same liquid; the level of the water in the cylinder is then marked by a piece of gummed paper. The tin, still full, is removed, and after the moisture from its surface has been allowed to drip into the cylinder, the contained water is poured away and a number of holes punched in its base. Thereupon the open end is driven down into the soil *in situ*, until the tin is completely filled, after which it is dug out and the soil in the tin cut off flush with the top edge. The whole is now placed in the cylinder and the contained soil is scooped out under the surface of the water, so as to ensure complete displacement of the soil-air. The water in the cylinder now stands at a lower level than that previously marked by the paper. By adding water from a measuring-glass until the marked level is reached, we obtain an approximate estimate of the amount of air in the volume of soil used.

There must thus be a more or less considerable number of spaces in the soil which are occupied by soil-air (Fig. 340, *a*). The latter stands in connection with the atmospheric air and is continually circulating from one part of the soil to another, being of immense importance in the respiration of roots and of the organisms (*e.g.* Bacteria, Protozoa), which live near the surface. The soil-atmosphere differs, however, from that of the air in having a much higher proportion of carbon dioxide and less oxygen. Whenever the soil is dug up or otherwise worked, the amount of air in the interspaces increases, so that such soil occupies a larger volume than before. A correct estimation of the natural air-content can therefore only be obtained, if the method described

32

in the last paragraph is adopted.

Although a considerable space in the soil is occupied by air, the solid particles and the associated water form the bulk. If a small quantity of moist earth is spread out in a thin layer on a sheet of white paper, the individual particles have a fresh or glistening surface. The paper with the soil may now be dried and again examined, whereupon the particles appear dull. The glistening was due to a very thin film of water which coated each soil-particle and disappeared on evaporation. In a soil which is capable of supporting a healthy growth of plants, the moisture occurs mainly as such films (Fig. 340, *w*), which coalesce so as to fill the smaller interspaces, but surround the air in the larger ones. Most bodies after immersion in water show a similar film which is due to an adhesive force operating between the water and the surface of the body.

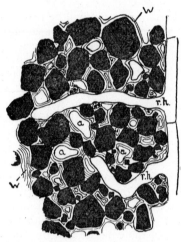

FIG. 340. Diagram of soil with root-hairs (*r.h.*) to show the distribution of air (*a*) and water (*w*) (much enlarged). Soil-particles in black.

If it be desired to determine the *water-content* of the soil, 100 grams are placed in a weighed evaporating dish, after which dish and soil are heated over a water-bath for several hours at a temperature slightly below 100° C. After cooling, the whole is reweighed and the heating is continued until the weight is constant. The difference between the first and the final weights represents the water-content in 100 grams of the soil, the result being usually expressed as a percentage of the dry weight.

The proportions of different-sized particles are best determined by sifting soils through sieves with meshes of a standard size; it is usual to distinguish coarse sand (2·0–0·2 mm.), fine sand (0·2–0·02 mm.), silt (0·02–0·002 mm.), and clay (less than 0·002 mm.). A rough *mechanical analysis* can be carried out by thoroughly stirring a small quantity of soil in a tall glass cylinder, nearly filled with water, until the latter is uniformly turbid, and then allowing the soil to settle. The coarser sandy particles soon collect at the bottom and are quickly followed by others of progressively smaller size, till finally (after many hours or days) the clayey silt deposits as the uppermost layer, leaving the water nearly clear. In this way a separation of the soil into particles of diverse sizes is obtained, and the approximate amount of each can be determined by measuring the thickness of each layer. That portion of the soil that remains floating at the surface of the water and consists of dark-looking fragments, is the organic fraction (humus), the vegetable nature of which can often be recognised.

The *organic content* can be roughly determined by strongly heating a weighed portion of the *dried* soil in a crucible for some hours to constant weight. The loss represents not only the organic material (including the colloidal humus), but also water not driven off at 100° C. and carbon dioxide given off from carbonates. Most soils contain some humus to which they owe their dark colour. It is this which more or less sharply distinguishes the true soil from the subsoil, *i.e.* the half-disintegrated underlying rock which is in process of conversion into soil and is often readily distinguishable on the exposed faces of railway cuttings, etc. (Fig. 341).

Soils from various localities not only differ widely in their air, water and organic contents, but also in the relative proportions of coarse and fine particles. The extremes are sandy gravels with practically nothing but coarse particles (*e.g.* a pebble-beach), and clayey soils (*e.g.* those of the London clay) and the estuarine alluvial silts composed almost wholly of fine particles. Between the two extremes are many intermediate types. Soils with practically equal amounts of sandy and clayey particles are known as *loams* and usually contain little calcium carbonate (*i.e.* are non-calcareous); the plants inhabiting them are commonly absent from chalky soils and are described as *calcifuge*. Other clayey soils (so-called *marls*), however, contain much calcium (*i.e.* are calcareous), whilst still more lime is often present when the subsoil is chalk or limestone. Species inhabiting such soils are described as *calcicole*.

It must be emphasised, however, that the terms calcareous and non-calcareous are only relative, since even plants like Rhododendrons that are wholly intolerant of carbonates require some calcium The presence of calcium pectate in the primary walls (p. 59) indeed renders the calcium ions indispensable.

Sandy soils differ from the sandy gravels in the smaller average size of the particles and the small amount or absence of clay; examples are furnished by the wind-blown sand of dunes and the soil of the Breckland district of Suffolk.

The action of rainfall, combined with chemical change, plays a considerable part in determining soil-structure, tending to bring about a spatial segregation of soil-particles and dissolved salts.

As a general rule no very large amount of organic material is present, although a thin layer of almost pure humus is often found at the surface, but in woodland-soils and garden-mould, for instance, a much larger quantity occurs. Such humus is almost completely disintegrated, chiefly owing to the action of Earthworms, whereas the *peat* which is found in moorland districts consists of vegetable remains which, owing to the unfavourable conditions for decay, have undergone little change and, moreover, often accumulate to a great depth (see p. 537).

FIG. 341. Photograph to show soil (*a*) and subsoil (*b*). The strip of white paper represents a length of 1 foot. No-man's-land, Hertfordshire. [Photo. E. J. S.]

In relation to the plant the important characteristics of a soil are its capacity to furnish the necessary mineral salts, its air-content, and its power of absorbing and giving up water. Since water is mainly held as a thin film round each particle, a fine-grained soil, offering as it does a much larger total surface for the water-films than a coarse-grained one, will in an equal volume of soil hold a greater quantity. This can be shown in the following way:—

Two equal-sized tins, with small holes drilled in the bottoms and lids, are filled with a clayey and sandy soil[1] respectively and left standing for an hour in a bowl, filled to about half an inch with water; the water may require renewal. After removal the excess water is allowed to drip off, the tins are weighed, and then heated to constant weight, as described on p. 490. The difference between

[1] Not completely dry since moisture passes only very slowly into dry soils.

the first and final weighings shows that the clayey soil has a considerably greater *water-capacity* than the sandy one.

Water is held in the soil by surface forces around the soil-particles and by imbibition in the gel-like colloidal fraction, which is derived from part of the clay and from some of the humus. When it is absorbed by the root-hairs of a plant (p. 193), they have to overcome the forces with which it is attracted to the surfaces of the particles, as well as the imbibitional forces. But, as water is progressively absorbed, the forces in question increase and consequently at a certain stage of dryness the moisture is held by the soil-particles so firmly that the roots cannot absorb it. In a fine-grained soil, owing to the much larger film-surface, this state will be reached when quite a considerable amount of water still remains, whereas in a coarse-grained soil with its smaller surface the amount of moisture left when the films have thinned out to this limit will be relatively small. There is therefore both water which is *available* and water which is *non-available*, the latter being that which is left in the soil and which can be driven off by heating after plants growing in it show signs of wilting. Whilst a fine-grained soil still containing 12 per cent. of water may already be dry so far as the plant is concerned, a coarse-grained one with 5 per cent. of water would still probably provide sufficient moisture. But the amount of non-available water varies with the external conditions, particularly the rate of water-loss from the plant, and to a much smaller degree with the type of plant concerned, which may, or may not, be capable of creating a high suction potential.

There are two principal sources of the water in the soil: the greater part is derived directly from atmospheric precipitation from above, some of which is absorbed as it slowly trickles through the earth. Part of the moisture, however, may be drawn up by capillarity from the underground water-table if this be near the surface. Different soils vary greatly in the facility with which they permit the water that falls on their surface to pass through them—in other words, their *permeability* differs. Thus, a coarse-grained sandy soil allows water to drain very rapidly through the large spaces between the particles, so that but little is retained; in such a soil, however, the interspaces are usually occupied by air and there is no risk of water-logging, unless the soil be shallow and situated upon some impermeable layer. The greater the percentage of fine-grained particles, the less permeable does the soil become; the water passes through very slowly, tends to accumulate in the interspaces, and consequently in such a soil there is always a danger of inadequate aeration. A clayey soil, for instance, when once thoroughly wet, comes to be almost impermeable, a property made use of in the puddling of ponds. This is readily shown by the following experiment (Fig. 342).

Two small tins have their bases perforated by a number of fine holes and are then half-filled with closely packed sandy and clayey soils respectively. Both are then suspended over beakers, and an equal volume of water is added to each. In a given space of time far more water runs through the sandy than through the clayey soil (Fig. 342), and indeed the latter may be quite impermeable. It will be realised, therefore, that coarse-grained soils contain little water but are well aerated, while fine-grained soils have plenty of water but tend to be badly aerated, so that a soil with a duly balanced amount of coarse and fine particles (*e.g.* a loam) will give the most satisfactory combination as regards water- and air-content.

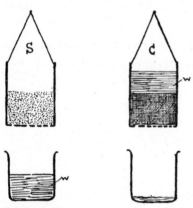

FIG. 342. Experiment to show relative permeability of sand (*S*) and clay (*C*) to water (*w*). The water in the two beakers is shown as it would appear at the end of the experiment.

The permeability of different soils to air can be compared in the following way (Fig. 343): A glass funnel is filled with closely packed wet clayey soil which is prevented from extending into the stem of the funnel by a small pad of cotton-wool. A piece of glass tubing, slightly wider than the stem of the funnel, is fitted at each end with a short length of rubber tubing, one of these being closed with a clip. The glass tube is now filled with water and attached in an air-tight manner by the second piece of rubber tubing to the stem of the funnel. A second similar apparatus is fitted up, employing a wet sandy soil. When the clip closing the base of each tube is opened, water rapidly runs out of the apparatus containing the sandy soil, through which air has passed to take its place, whilst little or none escapes from that containing the clay.

In times of prolonged drought the abundant evaporation from the surface-layers of the soil brings about a kind of suction from below. Inasmuch as the air-spaces form one continuous system, they constitute a series of capillary channels through which the water may rise. The height to which the water can be drawn is, however, not considerable and depends on the small size of these spaces, and therefore such capillary suction comes into play much more effectively in a fine-grained clayey soil than in a coarse-grained sandy one.

The amount of evaporation of water from the surface of the soil depends on a great many features. In the first place, what has been said above about the strength of attraction between the particles and the water-films has an important bearing on this matter, since in evaporating the water has to overcome this attractive force which, as already explained, increases as the soil becomes drier. The nature of the surface also plays a great part in determining the amount of evaporation. If the surface is kept finely divided (*e.g.* by ploughing, raking, etc.),—in other words, is kept in good tilth, —the uppermost layer of the soil will be dry, but will consist of numerous loose particles with large air-spaces between them. This surface-layer or *mulch* of dry well-aerated earth checks evaporation, inasmuch as heat-conduction of the surface-layer is greatly reduced so that the soil below is cooler. Furthermore, the continuity of the fine capillary channels has been greatly diminished so that, whilst the rise of water by capillary action goes on as readily as before up to the level of the mulch, the loss from the latter is much less. The interchange of gases between soil and atmosphere is facilitated

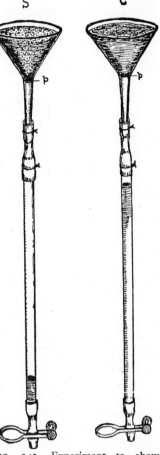

FIG. 343. Experiment to show relative permeability of moist sand (*S*) and clay (*C*) to air. *p*, pad of cotton-wool. The level of the water in the two tubes is shown as it would appear at the end of the experiment.

owing to the larger pore-space and the marked expansion and contraction of the air in the mulch-layer due to temperature changes as between day and night. In many soils natural tillage is effected by the action of Earthworms, Moles, etc.

A surface-crust provides numerous capillary channels for the upward passage of the evaporating water, besides impeding the ready gaseous exchange between soil and air. An instructive experiment can be performed to illustrate this fact. Two pots are filled with some moist clayey soil and weighed, the surface-layer in the one being kept finely divided, whilst that in the other is pressed down to form a crust. The latter will be found to lose weight much more rapidly than the former. It may be added that in gardens, besides the broken surface of the soil itself, mulches of

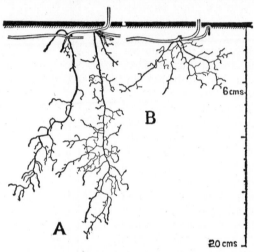

FIG. 344. Root-systems of *Mercurialis perennis* grown in light (A) and heavy soil (B). (After Salisbury.)

straw and dung are often employed. So, too, the soil often remains moist beneath a large stone.

Clay soils have a considerable capacity to imbibe water which causes them to swell and become sticky when wet and to shrink on drying. The changes on wetting are largely responsible for the impermeability of such soils to water and air. As a result, soils containing a considerable proportion of minute particles are hard to dig and are spoken of as *heavy* in contrast to coarse-grained soils, with little cohesion between the particles, which are easily dug and are termed *light*. Such differences in soil-texture also materially affect the extent of the root-system (Fig. 344 and p. 511). The special characteristics of clay soils are due to the large proportion of minute particles determining the colloidal fraction which is also of great importance in the absorption and exchange of inorganic ions (cf. also p. 498).

Clay soils can be improved in one of several ways, the simplest (though difficult to apply on a large scale) being to mix sand thoroughly with the soil. A method extensively employed is to add a top-dressing of lime, for which chalk is often substituted. The positively charged calcium ions interact with the negatively charged particles of the colloidal clay, causing flocculation and crumb-formation and increasing the permeability of the soil to water and air. Whereas the finer clay particles will remain in suspension in a vessel of water for days, the water soon clears if 10 per cent. lime water or a little acid be added when the clay becomes flocculated.

The water-retaining power of a sandy soil can be increased by adding clay. Both light and heavy soils are improved by the addition of organic material. The relatively large size of the undecomposed portions promotes good aeration, whilst the colloidal portion or humus is efficient in the retention of water, a fact which is especially obvious in peat. The mixing of organic matter with a sandy soil therefore considerably increases the water-capacity, whilst it also helps to lighten a heavy soil and is used in gardens for this purpose.

The chief value of humus, however, lies in the very large colloidal surface it presents, on which valuable nutrient ions are retained. It thus provides a reserve upon which the plant can draw by base exchange. In fact, a sandy soil without humus furnishes practically no food at all.

Lime is less of a fertiliser than an improver of the soil conditions, both neutralising acidity and altering the texture. Earthworms, in addition to their cultivating action, tend to reduce the acidity of the surface soil in which they chiefly feed, through the influence of their chalk glands. In untilled soils especially, the continued action of rain, charged with carbon dioxide, washes out the soluble salts into the drainage water. It is due to this constant impoverishment, or *leaching*, that the surface soil of old pastures overlying chalk or limestone, for example, may be almost destitute of calcium salts and even acid in reaction; this leads to a change in the vegetation.

The mineral food in the soil is contained in a heterogeneous system, consisting of the colloidal gel-complex holding ions in the imbibed water and the soil-solution forming the liquid phase. Nitrates and chlorides occur only in the latter, but other ions are present in both phases. The nutrient ions are taken up by a process of exchange. Hydrogen ions, for example, pass out from the root-hairs to replace basic nutrient ions, and this further accentuates the loss due to leaching. Under natural conditions plants (and animals) die and rot in the soil on which they have lived, and much of the substance which they have taken from the ground returns to it again in the form of humus and other products of decay. When, as in agricultural practice, the bulk of the vegetation is removed and does not decay *in situ*, the soil becomes year by year more and more impoverished unless nutrients are artificially replaced. Hence the necessity, under cultivation, for the frequent application of fertilisers which serve to replenish the stock of mineral food-substances required by the plant for building up its body. The most frequently employed *manures* are nitrogenous (*e.g.* ammonium sulphate), potassic (*e.g.* potassium sulphate), and phosphatic (*e.g.* superphosphate).

Not uncommonly soils supply inadequate amounts of certain of the nutrients, although such deficiencies are frequently not due to absence, but to non-availability of the particular nutrient. As already pointed out (p. 208), the trace-elements (boron, copper, zinc, manganese, molybdenum), which are almost certainly involved either directly or indirectly in the catalysing of essential reactions, are required only in extremely small amounts. Molybdenum is particularly important for many Leguminosæ and probably plays an essential part in the reduction of nitrates. The capacity to obtain and accumulate the rarer elements sometimes differs markedly in one species as compared with another. Thus, Clovers readily absorb molybdenum and the Sun Spurge boron, whilst Grasses growing on the same soil contain but little. On soils containing selenium certain species of *Astragulus* accumulate it to such an extent, as to cause the death of cattle feeding upon these plants.

The soil-reaction affects plant-distribution to a considerable extent, very largely in consequence of the hydrogen ion concentration of the soil-solution. This not only has a direct influence, but acts indirectly by affecting the solubility of nutrient salts or of toxic substances, such as ions of alumina and iron. As the reaction favouring absorption differs for the various trace-elements and also affects their concentration in the soil, the diverse requirements of higher plants in respect of these elements is a factor affecting their distribution in nature.

[Important reference-books are: E. J. Russell, *Soil Conditions and Plant-growth*, Longmans, Green & Co., 18th edit., 1950 (635 pp.); T. Wallace, *Diagnoses of Mineral Deficiencies of Plants*, H.M. Stat. Off., 2nd edit., 1951; S. A. Waksman, *Principles of Soil Microbiology*, Balliere, Tindall & Cox, 2nd edit., 1931 (894 pp.); S. A. Waksman, *Humus*, Balliere, Tindall & Cox, 1936 (494 pp.). For details as to soil structure cf. E. J. Salisbury, "Soil Structure in relation to Vegetation," *Science Progress*, pp. 409–425, 1935.]

CHAPTER XLII

STRUCTURE IN RELATION TO HABITAT

THE fundamental organisation of the plant is essentially the same for that of the desert as for that of the lake or mountain-top, but the detailed structure is nevertheless subject to considerable modifications in harmony with the differing conditions of the environment. The most striking of these modifications are related to the conditions of water-supply in the varied habitats in which vegetation occurs, but light and other factors may also play a part in moulding the structure of the plant. The effect of diverse conditions is most patent when the self-same species occupies two different habitats, as when the same plant grows in both sunny and shady localities or when an aquatic grows on land. Many of the structural peculiarities, associated with environments which necessitate water-economy, are of the nature of *transpiration-checks*, whilst others are connected with the storage of water during times of plenty to be gradually utilised during periods of drought. Among the former the most important are: development of a thick cuticle, depression of the stomata below the general surface (cf. p. 152), restriction of the latter to grooves or pits, copious production of hairs (p. 158), and reduction of the leaf-surface.

Plants with broad thin blades, generally characterised by the absence of transpiration-checks, are commonly termed *mesophytes* (*e.g.* Lime, *Circæa*). Their most marked characteristic is that they wilt when loss of water is comparatively small; hence they are not suited to arid conditions. By contrast so-called *xerophytes*, which often exhibit marked transpiration-checks, can endure pronounced water-loss without wilting, and, if wilted, can recover from a considerable degree of desiccation. Despite the restriction due to the possession of transpiration-checks, xerophytes frequently transpire as rapidly as many mesophytes. The external features, such as small, often scale-like foliage-leaves, cushion-like habit, extreme hairiness, succulence, etc., which tend to retard transpiration, are usually spoken of as *xeromorphic characters*.

Most deciduous trees and shrubs have mesophytic foliage, but by shedding this at the end of the season become xeromorphic, since the whole exposed surface is covered with cork. Perennial herbs exhibit an analogous winter-change through the dying down of the aerial shoots in the autumn (cf. p. 13).

The simplest method of economising the water-supply is perhaps thickening of the cuticle, sometimes supplemented by secretion of wax. The unspecialised annual or perennial herb usually grows under conditions in which the slight variations in the amount of water furnished by the soil are sufficiently compensated by changes in the suction potential of the plant (p. 202). The leaves are thin and flexible and have a thin cuticle, so that some slight evaporation takes place all over their surface; as compared with the transpiration through the stomata, however, this *cuticular transpiration* is generally quite negligible, except in immature leaves where the cuticle is not yet fully formed. The more strongly the cuticle is developed, the more leathery the texture of the leaf and the less the cuticular transpiration. Such plants are often evergreen and able to retain their foliage throughout the winter, when absorption by the roots is often very slow (cf. p. 13). Plants possessing leaves with a thick cuticle (e.g. *Vaccinium*; Sea Holly, *Eryngium*) can thrive in drier situations because the period during which they remain turgid, at times of water-scarcity, is prolonged.

Plants which grow in a variety of situations show considerable differences in the thickness of the cuticle. Thus, the leaves of the Bracken or Bilberry (*Vaccinium*) growing on an open heath are thick and leathery, whilst those of the same species growing in the moist atmosphere of a wood are thin and flexible. The efficacy of cuticle thickness in restricting transpiration can be demonstrated by the cobalt method. Leaves with stomata confined to the lower surface are employed, and stomatal transpiration is prevented by means of vaseline.

Dense coverings of hairs increase the thickness of the nonturbulent layer of air in contact with the leaf-surface and check rise of temperature of the leaf (cf. p. 158). The maintenance of a layer of damp air above the stomatal surface is an important aid in checking transpiration, and this can be accentuated in other ways than by the development of a hairy covering. Thus, in many xeromorphic leaves the stomata are depressed below the general surface so that a column of damp air accumulates above each. In the Holly (Fig. 345, A), for example, the stoma is situated at the base of a pit (the *vestibule*) which is formed mainly as a result of the great thickening of the cuticle around the pore. Similar protected stomata occur on the stem-spines of the Gorse (Fig. 345, B), where the cuticle is also very thick.

Plants of damp situations offer a marked contrast in these respects, the cuticle being relatively thin and the stomata often slightly raised above the general surface (Fig. 345, C, D).[1]

Retarded transpiration in wind is also very effectively attained by *restriction of the stomata to grooves or hollows* whose communication with the exterior is often partially occluded by an outgrowth of hairs. A good example is furnished by the common Oleander (*Nerium oleander*). If the lower surface of a leaf be examined with a lens, a large number of light-coloured patches appear dotted

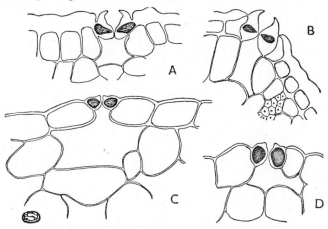

FIG. 345. Stomata. A, Holly (*Ilex aquifolium*). B, Gorse (*Ulex europæus*). C, Brooklime (*Veronica beccabunga*). D, Yellow Pimpernel (*Lysimachia nemorum*).

between the principal veins, each patch being due to a tuft of hairs arising from one of the numerous hollows. In transverse sections (Fig. 346) the latter are seen to extend inwards for slightly more than one-third the thickness of the leaf. The stomata (*St.*) are confined to the portions of the epidermis within these depressions, and interspersed among them are numerous thick-walled unicellular hairs. Each stoma is raised, on a papilla-like ring of cells, above the level of the epidermis lining the hollows, a fact which is not surprising when it is realised that, since the depressions contain a damp atmosphere, the stomata within them develop under the same conditions as those of ordinary leaves growing in moist situations. Other striking features of the Oleander-leaf, apart from the thick cuticle on the exposed surface, are the extremely

---

[1] Plugging of the stomatal apertures with particles of wax is observed in some plants (*e.g.* certain Conifers), which thereby impede the escape of water-vapour and consequently check transpiration, which is almost entirely cuticular.

lacunar spongy tissue, and the presence of two layers of water-storing hypoderm.

In the Heather (*Calluna*, Fig. 347, A, B) the stomata are confined to a groove (*stomatal chamber, st.*) situated on the under-surface of the leaf. The upper or outer surface is protected by a thick cuticle, and the aperture of the groove is closed by interlacing

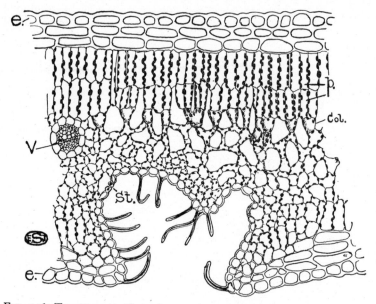

FIG. 346. Transverse section of part of the leaf of the Oleander (*Nerium oleander*) showing a stomatal chamber.   *Col.*, collecting cells; *e.*, epidermis; *p.*, palisade layers; *St.*, stoma; *V*, vascular bundle.

hairs (Fig. 347, B).   The form of the transverse section is roughly that of an inverted triangle, with the groove occupying a small area in the lower angle and surrounded by the very lacunar meso-phyll.   The *rolled leaves* of the Crowberry (*Empetrum*) have a similar organisation, except that the stomatal chamber (*st.*) is much larger (Fig. 347, D).   More extreme types are found in Grasses (Fig. 347, C), where, moreover, the leaf is often capable of rolling and unrolling in response to changes in humidity (cf. p. 562).

The massing of the foliage in dense rosettes (seen in the Thrift, many Saxifrages, and very commonly in alpine plants) brings the transpiring surfaces into close contact, so that semi-saturated air accumulates in the spaces between them; moreover, such plants are usually of low growth, only sending up a vertical axis in the flowering season, and are therefore relatively little exposed to wind-currents.

Such massing together of the transpiring surfaces is well illustrated by trees growing in exposed wind-swept situations. New shoots that arise on the side of the crown sheltered from the prevailing winds develop normally, but those on the exposed windward side are cut off owing to excessive transpiration. In this and in other ways growth becomes more or less restricted to the leeward side, so that the familiar asymmetrical crown results (Fig. 348).

The deciduous plant meets the conditions of drought in winter by shedding its leaves—that is to say, the transpiring surface becomes greatly reduced. A reduction of surface is, however, exhibited by many plants throughout the year (cf. the rolled leaves shown in Fig. 347). Other examples are seen in the small leaves of Conifers and *Lycopodium* (Fig. 261, A). A feature which often accompanies such reduced leaf-surface is the absence of markedly dorsiventral structure. In its extreme form this results in the leaf acquiring centric organisation (p. 169).

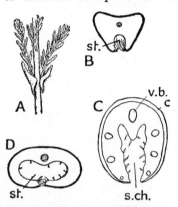

Fig. 347. Reduction of the transpiring surface in xerophytes (A, slightly reduced; the others magnified). A, Small portion of plant of *Calluna*. B, Cross-section of leaf of same. C, Cross-section of rolled leaf of *Festuca*. D, Cross-section of leaf of *Empetrum*. *c.*, cuticle; *s.ch.*, chamber containing damp air; *st.*, stomatal chamber; *v.b.* vascular strands.

This is well seen in a transverse section through a pinna of the compound leaf of *Hakea*, a native of Australia; the cylindrical pinnæ are slightly flattened on the upper surface. The epidermis shows the customary thick cuticle and deeply sunken stomata. Beneath it are two palisade layers completely encircling a central tract of parenchyma which contains three prominent vascular bundles, with strands of sclerenchyma on their upper and lower sides. Occasional elongate thick-walled cells, with slightly dilated ends, extend between the epidermis and the central vascular region. Mechanical elements like these, offering considerable resistance to shrinkage and thus to water-loss, are a frequent accompaniment of other transpiration-checks in xeromorphic leaves. The central region in *Hakea* in which the bundles are embedded consists of colourless water-storing (aqueous) tissue in which are scattered occasional large tannin-cells having deep brown contents. A comparable type of centric leaf is seen in *Pinus* (cf. p. 416).

In the so-called *switch-plants* the leaves are often reduced to mere scales, more or less destitute of chlorophyll, their functions being transferred to the stem. The presence of chloroplasts in the outer cells of young stems (cf. p. 145) has already been noted; but, where the leaf-surface is small, the stem may retain its photo-synthetic powers for some years after the inception of secondary

Fig. 348. Wind-trimmed trees at Criccieth, North Wales. Note that the crowns of the trees are almost at right angles to the trunks.
[Photo. E. J. S.]

thickening, and may even become enlarged by wing-like outgrowths whereby its efficiency is increased. The Broom (*Sarothamnus sco-parius*), the Whortleberry (*Vaccinium myrtillus*, Fig. 349), the Rush (*Juncus*), and *Equisetum* (p. 386) furnish examples of such *photo-synthetic stems*. In the first-named downward prolongations from the margins of the leaf-bases give the stem a ridged appearance. A cross-section shows the usual thick-walled epidermis beneath which, in each ridge, there is a strand of fibres; but, except for these, the whole periphery of the cortex consists of a layer of palisade tissue succeeded by four or five layers of closely packed cells, also containing chloroplasts. The stomata occur at intervals throughout the parts of the epidermis overlying the photosynthetic tissue. In other respects the stem exhibits the normal structure of a secondarily thickened axis.

The leaves of the Whortleberry, though not greatly reduced, are usually deciduous, so that during the winter the plant carries on photosynthesis only by means of its winged stem. Beneath the epidermis is a continuous zone of photosynthetic tissue (Fig. 349, *as.*),

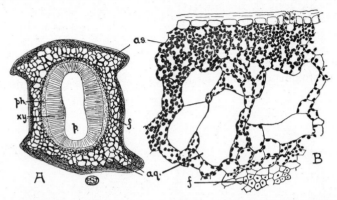

FIG. 349. Diagram of transverse section (A), and detail of small portion (B), of the green stem of the Whortleberry (*Vaccinium myrtillus*). *aq.*, aqueous tissue; *as.*, photosynthetic tissue; *f.*, fibres; *p.*, pith; *ph.*, phloem; *xy.*, xylem.

consisting of rounded or polygonal cells, uninterrupted by fibres. The inner cortex is formed by a network of chlorophyll-containing

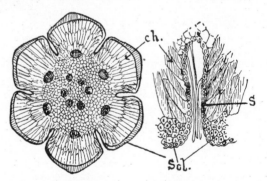

FIG. 350. Transverse section of a young green stem of the She-Oak (*Casuarina*) with the stomatal grooves; one of the latter is shown enlarged on the right. *ch.*, photosynthetic tissue; *S.*, stoma; *Scl.*, sclerenchyma.

cells in which the meshes are occupied by large aqueous elements (*aq.*).

In the She-Oaks (*Casuarina*) of Australia, which supply valuable timbers, the leaves are scale-like. The green twigs possess longitudinal grooves (Fig. 350) to which the stomata (*S.*), protected by hairs, are restricted. The stomata are located at the sides of each furrow, and are situated close to the photosynthetic tissue (*ch.*).

33

An extreme example of a green stem is afforded by species of *Juncus* in which the leaves are reduced to mere brown scales situated, as in *J. striatus*, at the base of the flowering and non-flowering stems. A transverse section across the stem (Fig. 351) presents an epidermis with thick outer walls and a pronounced cuticle. The sunken stomata are distributed at intervals around the whole periphery, but in surface sections are seen to be arranged in approximately longitudinal series. Beneath the epidermis is a

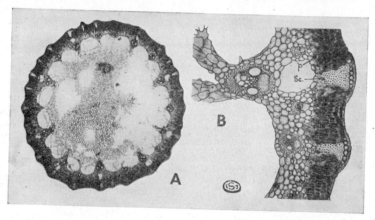

FIG. 351. Transverse section of stem of *Juncus striatus*. A, Complete section under low magnification. The photosynthetic tissue appears as a black peripheral zone interrupted by light patches constituting the mechanical tissue; a ring of over 20 bundles is seen bordering the very large pith composed of stellate cells. B, A small portion on a larger scale, showing one large and three small bundles. *p.*, photosynthetic tissue; *Sc.*, sclerenchyma.

typical palisade tissue interrupted by groups of fibres and the large respiratory cavities of the stomata. Within follows an irregular ring of typical Monocotyledonous bundles accompanied by sclerenchyma. The large pith consists of stellate parenchyma. Rushes afford excellent examples of plants which, though growing in wet places, exhibit a xeromorphic structure. The reason is not yet fully understood.

A peculiar type of xeromorphy is seen in the Butcher's Broom (Fig. 353, B) and *Asparagus* (Fig. 352), where, as in the switch-plants, the leaves are reduced to mere scales, whilst their photosynthetic functions are taken over by specially modified branches known as *cladodes*; such are met with quite commonly in the desert-regions of the earth. In *Asparagus* a tuft of narrow leaf-like branches, on some of which the flowers are borne (in reality a dwarf shoot-system), arises from the axil of each scaly leaf

(Fig. 352, *l*), whilst in the Butcher's Broom the cladodes arise singly and are broad leathery leaf-like structures which, through a twisting of the base, are placed more or less vertically (Fig. 353, B, *cl.*). They are axillary to scale-leaves (*l*) and, on the upper surface of each cladode, there is a small scale-leaf (*s*) in whose axil one or two flowers appear in March or April.

A similar structural modification is seen in many species of *Acacia* where the leaf-blade has become reduced or suppressed, while the vertically expanded petiole or *phyllode* takes its place (Fig. 417).

A cross-section of the cladode of the Butcher's Broom (Fig. 354) shows an epidermis (*ep.*) with thick outer walls, but no appreciable depression of the stomata. The latter (*St.*) are protected by two pairs of ridges which extend around the pore, creating a double vestibule. The upper and lower epidermis are alike, and this, as well as the absence of a marked palisade layer, can be related to the "edge-on" position which this modified branch assumes. The photosynthetic tissue is almost uniformly developed. The central region of the cladode is occupied by large water-storing cells (aqueous tissue, *Aq.*; cf. below p. 510). The arrangement of the vascular tissue is analogous to that of a petiole. Phyllodes have a similar structure to cladodes, and the leaves of many Monocotyledons show an analogous organisation.

FIG. 352. Small portion of a branch of *Asparagus* with cladodes (natural size). *l*, scale-leaves on main stem; *cl.*, cladodes.

The replacement of a leaf by a photosynthetic stem, in conditions of possible water-shortage, provides a structure better able to resist shrinkage, since mechanical tissue is more effectively differentiated in branches (and petioles) than in the lamina. In some plants of dry habitats, however, copious sclerenchyma is formed in the blade itself, with the result that the leaves are highly resistant to conditions of drought (cf. p. 503).

A comparable condition is seen in leaves or branches which are modified to form stiff *spines* containing abundant sclerenchyma. A good example is afforded by the Gorse or Furze (Fig. 355, D) where both leaf and branch spines occur. If grown in a moist atmosphere few or no spines are formed and normal flexible foliage-leaves, although of small size, are produced. The seedling

508

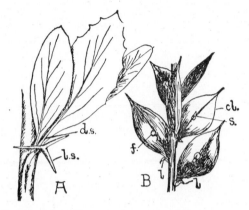

FIG. 353. A, Small portion of branch of Barberry (*Berberis*), showing the three-branched leaf-spines (*l.s.*) (natural size); the foliage-leaves arise from a dwarf-shoot (*d.s.*) in the axil of the spine. B, Branch of Butcher's Broom (*Ruscus*) with cladodes (natural size). *cl.*, cladode; *f.*, flower; *l.*, scale-leaves on main stem; *s.*, ditto on cladodes.

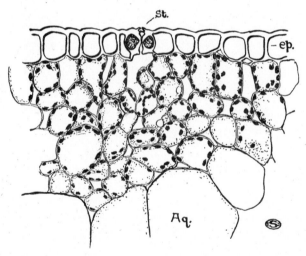

FIG. 354. Transverse section through part of a cladode of the Butcher's Broom (*Ruscus aculeatus*), showing a single stoma (*St.*), the thick-walled epidermis (*ep.*), and the aqueous tissue (*Aq.*) below the photosynthetic zone. The chloroplasts are shown black.

of the Gorse (Fig. 356), moreover, does not immediately bear spines, these only appearing when the shoot has grown to some height above the surface of the ground; this may be related to the fact that the air immediately above the soil is relatively moist, as compared with that at higher levels.

Instances of leaf-spines are furnished by the Barberry (Fig. 353, A, l.s.), where the leaves on the long shoots are replaced by three-branched spines, in whose axils arise dwarf-shoots (d.s.) bearing ordinary foliage-leaves and inflorescences. In the Gooseberry

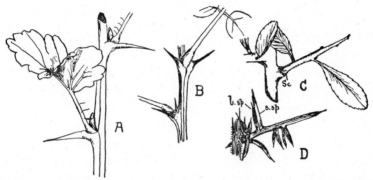

FIG. 355. Examples of spinous plants (all figures natural size). A, Gooseberry (*Ribes uva-crispa*) (leaf-spines). B, False Acacia (*Robinia*) (stipular spines). C, Sloe (*Prunus spinosa*) (stem-spines). *sc.*, leaf-scar. D, Gorse (*Ulex*) (leaf- and stem-spines). *l.sp.*, leaf-spine; *s.sp.*, stem-spine.

(Fig. 355, A) the spines, which are simple or branched, can be recognised on the summer-shoots as outgrowths from the leaf-base, whilst in the False Acacia (Fig. 355, B) they arise in pairs at the base of the petiole and are modified stipules.

Stem-spines are seen in the Sloe (Fig. 355, C), the Hawthorn, etc., and are recognised not only by their axillary position, but also by the fact that they often bear leaves. Many xeromorphic plants have leaves with spiny margins, as in the Holly, Thistles, etc.

Spines are no doubt in most, if not in all, instances an expression of the tendency to increase woody tissue under conditions of reduced water-supply, but when they occur they may often be of value to the plant in keeping off browsing animals.

Apart from the development of transpiration-checks there is a second method of providing against shortage of water, often found in combination with the first. Thus, many xerophytes store up water in aqueous tissue and, when this represents a large part of the plant, the latter acquires a succulent character.

The Stonecrops and Houseleeks (Fig. 357) afford good examples of leaf-succulents, whilst stem-succulents are well illustrated by Cacti, in which the leaves themselves are represented by spines. Such succulents can exist for a very prolonged period without external supply of water, during which they gradually shrivel more and more. Owing to their very thick cuticles they transpire very slowly and hence the moisture stored up within them lasts for a long time. Most of these forms have become so suited to dry conditions that their roots rot in a soil of average dampness.

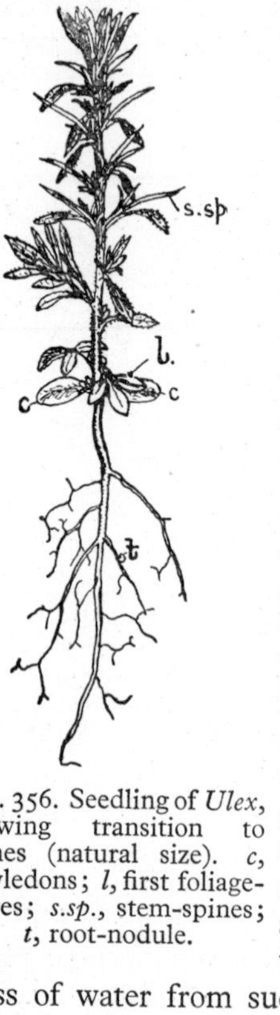

Aqueous tissue, already observed in the Butcher's Broom (Fig. 354, Aq.) and Hakea, is a most prominent feature of succulents. In the leaves of the Stonecrop (Sedum), the Prickly Saltwort (Salsola kali), and the Sea-blite (Suæda), the large colourless and thin-walled cells in which water is stored up form the bulk of the leaf-tissue. The aqueous tissue occupies the centre of the leaf, with the photosynthetic tissue towards the periphery; in Salsola these tissues are sharply marked off from one another (cf. also Fig. 90, A, p. 150), but in the other two there is a gradual transition between them. Similar water-storing tissue is encountered in stem-succulents (e.g. Cactus). Through the loss of water, by transpiration and absorption by the adjacent green cells during periods of drought, the cells of the aqueous tissue shrink, and this results in the walls becoming thrown into small folds which disappear, during the wet season, as the plant regains turgidity.

FIG. 356. Seedling of Ulex, showing transition to spines (natural size). c, cotyledons; l, first foliage-leaves; s.sp., stem-spines; t, root-nodule.

Loss of water from such aqueous tissue is often retarded by the presence of thin mucilage in the cell-contents which exudes from a broken surface as a slimy fluid (e.g. Mesembryanthemum).

A certain amount of protection from excessive transpiration in strong sunlight is obtained in a few plants by the leaf-blades occupying a more or less vertical position (e.g. Iris). The advantage of the upright position lies in the fact that the incident rays are oblique, and therefore in great part reflected; thus, their heating effect is much diminished. This is seen in the so-called "Compass-plants" (e.g. Lactuca serriola). In a shady situation their leaves are spread out in the usual horizontal position, whilst in a sunny

locality the blades are vertical with the edges facing north and
south, so that the edge is always presented to the sun at the hottest
part of the day.   The leaflets of the Wood Sorrel are often found,
on a hot summer's day, more or less drooping as in the night-
position (cf. p. 268 and Fig. 173), whilst those of the False Acacia
(*Robinia*) under these circumstances become tilted upwards at an
acute angle;   this is a position opposite to that assumed at night,
when the leaflets droop downwards.

The modifications of the shoot discussed in the preceding pages
all serve to harmonise the plant with its surroundings;   so that a

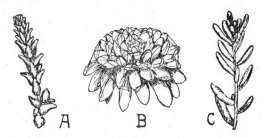

FIG. 357. Examples of leaf-succulents (all natural size).   A, Yellow Stonecrop
(*Sedum acre*).   B, Houseleek (*Sempervivum arachnoideum*).   C, White Stonecrop (*Sedum album*).

comparison of different kinds of plants growing under similar
conditions, even in widely separated regions of the earth's
surface, often reveals a similar physiognomy.   But, even in the
individual itself mesophytic and xeromorphic features may be
united (*e.g.* deciduous trees), bearing a definite relation to changing
circumstances.   So, too, the seedling does not necessarily resemble
the adult (cf. the Gorse).   Finally it should be added that, though
some of the modifications cited vary with the conditions of growth,
others are more or less fixed and tend to put a limit to the variety of
circumstances under which the plants possessing them can thrive.

The occasional presence of xeromorphic features in plants living in
damp habitats, as in the succulent *Sedum villosum* which grows in bogs
(cf. also *Juncus*, p. 506), is probably due to the limitations imposed
by hereditary constitution.   Many plants are, however, extremely
plastic, particularly with respect to leaf-structure (pp. 521, 551).

Variation in root-growth should not be overlooked.   In some
species this growth is rather uniform, whilst in others the mode of
development and extent of the root-system is profoundly modified
by competition and especially by the density of the soil, as can be
demonstrated by growing the same species in a root-observation
box (p. 106) in a light sand or in a heavy clay (Fig. 344).

CHAPTER XLIII

THE ECOLOGY OF WOODLANDS

THE study of the social life of plants [1] can be begun by a consideration of woodlands, because this type of vegetation has a designation
which is at once used in popular parlance and further coincides
with a botanical conception. All woods are characterised by trees
as the most conspicuous feature of their vegetation. Beneath these
there are usually shrubs or smaller trees (Fig. 360), forming an
undergrowth which is more or less dense according to the type
of wood, and, on the ground, a growth of herbaceous plants (the
ground-flora, Figs. 359 and 361).

With marked differences in soil-characters are associated
differences in the tree-layer so that woodlands of diverse types
can be distinguished. Thus, on non-calcareous soils (cf. p. 491)
one generally finds woods of Oak (*Quercus*) or Birch (*Betula*),
whilst calcareous soils frequently bear woods of Beech (*Fagus*) and
Ash (*Fraxinus*). Where there are intermediate types of soils the
woodlands may show a mixed character (*e.g.* the Oak-Ash woods
found commonly on marls). Hand in hand with differences in
the dominant [2] tree, the kind as well as amount of undergrowth
and ground-flora will be found to change. But whilst the component species may vary to such an extent that two woods have
few kinds of trees, shrubs, or herbs in common, yet those found
in the first are replaced by similar physiognomic types in the
second, bearing the same relation to one another. Such a definite
kind of vegetation as deciduous woodland can be recognised as a
major type of *plant-community* in which the leafless period is
associated with unfavourable climatic conditions. The different
types are characterised by the prevalence of different trees (Oak,
Ash, etc.) and associated shrubs and herbs.

[1] A simple description of most of the commoner British communities is
to be found in H. Drabble, *Plant Ecology*, Ed. Arnold, 1937 (142 pp.). For
other works, see p. 487.

[2] A dominant is a species which by its height and area plays a predominant
part in determining the biotic conditions. When there is a single dominant
we speak of a *consociation*; where more than one plant shares the dominance,
the community is termed an *association*.

The woodland is therefore a plant-community having a definite structure with three tiers, viz. the trees, the undergrowth, and the ground-flora. Light is the factor which most markedly limits or restricts the kinds of plants that can persist in the undergrowth and ground-flora. This depends on the more or less dense canopy of foliage belonging to the uppermost tier of trees or the second tier of shrubs or more commonly on their combined effect; as a consequence the character of the flora of a woodland depends largely on the amount of shade cast by the constituent members. In the deciduous woodland, however, we must distinguish between the "*light-phase*" during the winter months, when trees and shrubs are devoid of leaves, and the "*shade-phase*" from about May to November, when the canopy of foliage cuts off a large proportion of the light.

The light-intensity requisite for the growth of a particular species must be one at which the rate of gain by photosynthesis exceeds the loss due to respiration. The intensity at which these processes balance is the *compensation point* (p. 240) and its value varies with the species concerned.

The conditions in each stratum of the woodland differ in respect to humidity, light-intensity, the supply of carbon dioxide, and other factors. Hence within the woodland community itself, we can distinguish what may be termed *partial habitats* and such can often be recognised in other types of vegetation.

LIGHT-INTENSITIES IN WOODLANDS AS PERCENTAGES OF THAT IN THE OPEN
(After Salisbury).

Woodland Type.	Light-phase (Winter). Per cent.	Shade-phase (Summer). Per cent.	Ground-flora.
Beechwood (*Fagetum*) .	17–40	0·4–21	Scanty or 0.
Oakwood (*Quercetum roburis*).	19–61	0·2–17	Vernal.
Oakwood (*Quercetum petræce*	33–90	0·9–27	Vernal and æstival.
Birchwood (*Betuletum*) .	40–63	18–57	Æstival.

Of our woodland trees the Beech, found on chalky soils in the south-east of England, usually casts the deepest shade both in the light- and shade-phases, owing to its extensive branching and perfect leaf-mosaic (p 122). Furthermore, the "packing" of the relatively flat Beech leaves when wet probably checks gaseous exchange between air and soil. Hence the conditions of aeration are poor, whilst the shallow, richly branched roots of the Beech trees tend to render the surface-soil dry. A striking feature of such a wood is the paucity of vegetation upon the ground and the almost entire absence, except at the edge, of shrubby undergrowth (Fig. 358). The species, as well as the individuals, of the ground-flora are few, but, wherever there is a clearing (Fig. 359) or the trees are sparsely scattered, the abrupt increase of vegetation shows at once that the soil is not at fault.

In the Beech-wood consocation depth of soil plays an important rôle in determining the character of the herb layer, Dog's Mercury

FIG. 358. Interior of a Beech-wood, Pitstone Hill, near Tring, Herts. Note the absence of undergrowth. [Photo. E. J. S.]

(*Mercurialis*), Solomon's Seal (*Polygonatum*), and Woodruff (*Asperula*) being most abundant on the deeper soils, while the Sanicle, White Helleborine (Fig. 359) and Wall Lettuce are found more especially on the shallow ones. The commonest herb is *Mercurialis*, one of the earliest native plants to form new leaves, while, in the better-lighted parts, Enchanter's Nightshade (*Circæa*), Sanicle (Fig. 359), Woodruff and Wild Strawberry (*Fragaria*) are sometimes abundant. The last three retain part of their foliage during the light-phase and carry on photosynthesis, whenever the temperature permits. There are also usually a number of Orchids, whilst the saprophytes *Neottia* (Fig. 132) and *Monotropa*, which occur in the height of the summer, can flourish in deep shade, where they are replaced in autumn by numerous Fungi growing in the humus formed by the fallen leaves. The Yew and White

Beam (*Sorbus aria*) are characteristic associates of the Beech. Where, as at the edge of the wood, undergrowth develops, the most frequent shrubs are the Hawthorn, *Viburnum lantana*, *Cornus sanguinea*, *Euonymus europæus*, and *Acer campestris*, while climbers are represented by *Tamus* and *Clematis*.

In marked contrast to the Beech-woods, but likewise occurring on calcareous soils, particularly limestones, are consociations

FIG. 359. Ground-flora of a clearing in a Beech-wood on shallow soil. The vegetation consists chiefly of *Sanicula*, with *Mercurialis* in the foreground; on the right are two leaves of the Wood Burdock (*Arctium vulgare*); just to the left of these is a plant of the White Helleborine (*Cephalanthera damasonium*), bearing three flowers. [Photo. E. J. S.]

of the Ash (*Fraxinus excelsior*) (Fig. 360). This tree casts much less shade and comes into leaf late in the season; in correspondence with this there is usually a varied and abundant undergrowth and ground-flora, though the extreme development of the shrub-layer may itself lead to the production of so dense a canopy as almost to prevent the growth of herbs beneath.

A frequent associate of the Ash is the Wych Elm (*Ulmus glabra*), and the commoner shrubs include the Hawthorn, Hazel, Maple, Privet, *Viburnum lantana*, and other species common also in scrub on calcareous soils. *Mercurialis perennis* is often abundant, whilst among the characteristic species of the herb-layer are the Solomon's Seal and Herb Paris (*Paris quadrifolia*). Where, as in the flushes, the soil is damper, *Allium ursinum, Colchicum autumnale,* and *Adoxa moschatellina* are often common.

Since Oak-woods are very common in many parts of England, they may be considered in greater detail. The amount of shade cast by the Oak is more or less intermediate between that cast by the Beech and Ash. Two species of Oak are found in Britain, each of which forms woods on appropriate soils. The most

FIG. 360. Interior of an Ash-wood, Clifton Woods, Bristol. The dense shrubby undergrowth is seen below, whilst in the fork of the tree in the foreground a plant of *Polypodium* occurs as an epiphyte. [Photo. E. J. S.]

frequent species, and that usually planted, is the Pedunculate Oak (*Quercus robur*) in which the leaves are often glabrous on both surfaces and the lamina ends somewhat abruptly, at its point of insertion upon the often short petiole, in a pair of lobes with the margins slightly turned over (Fig. 362, A). The other species, the Sessile-fruited Oak (*Quercus petræa*), bears star-shaped hairs on the under sides of its leaves and the blade tapers towards its insertion on the relatively long petiole (Fig. 362, B).

Quercus robur forms woods chiefly upon deep and heavy soils, such as clays and clayey loams which are well supplied with nutrient salts, and the community to which it gives rise may be termed the *Pedunculate Oak-wood* (Fig. 361). Other trees besides the Oak are frequently found and of these the commonest are

FIG. 361. Ground-flora of a Pedunculate Oak-wood in early spring. The vegetation consists chiefly of *Scilla* and *Mercurialis*. In the background are seen the stems of Hazel and Hornbeam forming the undergrowth. [Photo. E. J. S.]

usually the Wild Cherry, Birch, Maple (*Acer campestris*), Ash (*Fraxinus*), Holly (*Ilex*), and sometimes the Crab. In certain localities the Hornbeam (*Carpinus*) is a prominent feature, though when it occurs it is frequently coppiced (*i.e.* cut down periodically) and then forms the main feature of the under-growth (*e.g.* on the less calcareous clays of North London). The Horn-beam which has a leaf-mosaic like that of the Beech (cf. Fig. 71), forms a much denser canopy and the result is a ground-flora poor in number of species and much resembling that of a Beech-wood. As a general rule, however, the shrub-layer consists

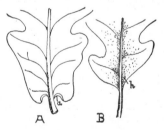

FIG. 362. Portion of leaf of A, *Quercus robur*, and B, *Q. petræa* (about two-thirds natural size). *a*, basal lobe showing margin turned over. *h*, hairs.

mainly of Hazel (*Corylus*), amongst which commonly occur bushes of Hawthorn, Sloe, Dogwood, Willows, Roses, and Brambles, as well as the Honeysuckle (*Lonicera*).

The most frequent members of the ground-flora in such a wood, often forming large expanses (Figs. 361, 363), are the Wild Hyacinth (*Scilla*, Fig. 363), Primrose, Lesser Celandine (*Ficaria*), Wood Anemone, Yellow Deadnettle (*Galeobdolon*), Dog's Mercury (Fig. 363), and in less abundance various kinds of Dog-violet. Of great frequency, but not forming such pronounced sheets, are a large number of species, the more familiar of which are the Bugle (*Ajuga*), *Ranunculus auricomus*, Wood Sorrel (*Oxalis*), Barren

FIG. 363. Ground-flora of a Pedunculate Oak-wood in early spring, showing *Scilla* and *Mercurialis*.

Strawberry (*Potentilla sterilis*), Enchanter's Nightshade, Ground Ivy (*Glechoma*), Cuckoo-pint (*Arum*), and several Grasses (Melic, Vernal, False Brome Grass, etc.). In the Oak-woods of Kent the Milkmaid (*Cardamine pratensis*) often covers large areas, whilst on the more loamy soils the Wood Sandwort (*Mœhringia trinervia*), Woodruff (*Asperula*), Wood Sanicle (*Sanicula*), Wood Sage (*Teucrium*), Foxglove, and Bracken are conspicuous.

If we follow the story of the wood from the early days of spring to the fall of the year, we are confronted with the problem as to how the soil is able to accommodate and nourish so many individuals and such a constant succession of forms. The solution is in part furnished by the subterranean architecture of the wood, for just as we find the aerial organs forming three definite tiers, each utilising the sunlight that has passed through the layer above, so too in the soil beneath we find a layering of the root-systems.

Those of the trees and shrubs are naturally the deepest, whilst the shallow ones of Grasses and of some of the herbs are nearest the surface. The intervening layers are occupied by many roots, frequently belonging to plants with underground storage-organs, such as the Wild Hyacinth (*Scilla*) and Cuckoo-pint. Owing to this stratification root-competition is diminished, whilst owing to the successive development of the overground shoots they mainly compete with those expanded contemporaneously. Moreover, the woodland soil is itself stratified, the surface layer being often acid, even when the subsoil is markedly calcareous so that species with differing requirements can occupy the same area.

Woodland plants probably receive a two-fold benefit from their habitat, namely shelter and absence of sun-loving competitors. It will be familiar that, in gardens, the majority of plants in deep shade bloom either very sparsely or, more frequently, not at all, and this is equally true of wild species. The early flowering of most woodland plants can be related to the fact that at this time of the year the overhead canopy has not yet formed. It may be recalled that a higher light-intensity is often necessary for flower-formation than for the development of vegetative organs (p. 247). All the commonest plants found in the interior of woodlands such as the Anemone, Dog's Mercury, Primrose, Wild Hyacinth, and Lesser Celandine have finished blooming, and often have formed their seeds, before the canopy is complete. Not only does the shade prevent the development of the flowers of most plants, but also, where these possess attractive mechanisms for insects, their conspicuousness would be to a great extent lost. It is probably in relation to this that many of the later-flowering woodland plants are highly scented, *e.g.* Woodruff (*Asperula odorata*), Honeysuckle, Butterfly Orchis (*Platanthera chlorantha*), etc. Most of the later-flowering woodland plants are either found where the canopy is more open or at the edge and by the sides, constituting the so-called marginal flora.

No less essential than the development of flowers, however, is the formation of food-material for growth and reproduction. It is therefore of supreme importance to the members of under-growth and ground-flora that their leaves should be produced early, so that photosynthesis may proceed whilst light is plentiful. In many plants of other habitats the period of maximum growth and subsequent flowering does not take place till after the first-formed leaves have provided the necessary material. But in a woodland the bulk of the growth and flowering is accomplished at the outset, and in relation to this we find that most members of the ground-flora are perennials possessed of some kind of storage-organ in which food-substances, elaborated during the previous season, are held in readiness to supply the material for growth and reproduction in the following spring. Examples are seen in the bulbs of the Wild Hyacinth, Daffodil (*Narcissus*), and Broad-leaved Garlic (*Allium ursinum*), the corms of the Cuckoo-pint and *Colchicum*, the tuberous roots of the Lesser Celandine, and the fleshy rhizomes of the Wood Anemone, Moschatel (*Adoxa*), and Enchanter's Nightshade (*Circæa*)

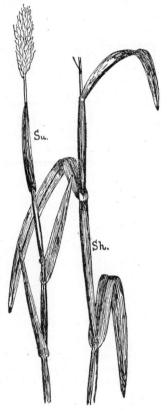

With the advent of the shade-phase the foliage of many species withers (e.g. *Scilla, Adoxa, Ficaria, Anemone*, etc.), but other less pronounced shade-species (e.g. *Ajuga, Primula*) retain their foliage throughout the summer, although the rate of photosynthesis is then considerably diminished. The efficiency of the leaves in this respect is, however, to some extent compensated by further growth in area, so that a larger surface is presented to the light. The protection from wind and the heat of the sun, afforded at this stage by the canopy above and the vegetation around, now probably makes this possible, since there is little risk of excessive transpiration. It should, however, be emphasised that the summer-green species are usually found only where the light-intensity during the shade-phase is not very low. Just as many of the herbs form their new leaves before those of the woody plants expand, so too the foliage of the shrubs usually develops before that of the trees above. Each layer thus benefits to some extent by the greater illumination of the "light phase."

Fig. 364. Sun- (*Su.*) and shade- (*Sh.*) forms of *Holcus mollis* (about two-thirds natural size).

The long internodes of many woodland plants (p. 246) leads to a wide separation of the leaves and consequently little mutual shading. Moreover, during development, the blades of such shade-plants take up the position best suited to receive the incident light (cf. p. 122), excellent examples being afforded by the Bracken and *Holcus mollis*. Both these plants, when growing in bright sunlight, place their leaves at an acute angle with the direction of the sun's rays, thus minimising their effect (Fig. 364, *Su.*); in light

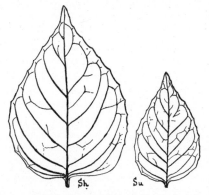

FIG. 365. Sun- (*Su.*) and shade-leaves (*Sh.*) of *Circæa lutetiana* (about one-half natural size).

of medium intensity, however, the blades of the Grass and the pinnæ of the Bracken are arranged so as to receive the light at right angles to the surface, whilst under the deep shade of trees the whole

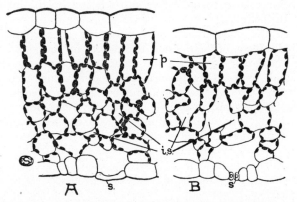

FIG. 366. Transverse sections of the sun- (A) and shade- (B) leaves of the Yellow Deadnettle (*Galeobdolon*), on the same scale. *i.s.*, intercellular spaces; *p.*, palisade tissue; *s.*, stoma (in A, cut longitudinally).

leaf bends over so as to absorb the oblique rays that come in under the canopy of overhead foliage (Fig. 364, *Sh.*).

Plants when growing in the shade exhibit structural adaptation to the changed conditions. In general *shade-leaves* are larger (Fig. 365), thinner (cf. Fig. 366), and very commonly, if the leaf

34

be lobed or compound, not so deeply cut as the corresponding sun-forms. The colour is usually a fresher green, owing to a high chlorophyll-content, less decomposition of the chlorophyll through absence of strong light, and the greater translucency of the leaf; moreover, chloroplasts are not infrequent in the epidermal cells (*e.g.* Bracken). Production of hairs is usually much reduced in the shade-form (*e.g.* Yellow Deadnettle, Dog's Mercury).

The cuticle and outer epidermal walls of the shade-forms are thinner than in the sun-forms (Fig. 366), a feature which can be related to the greater humidity of the air. A comparison of strips of epidermis from the two kinds of leaves shows that the lateral walls of the epidermal cells tend to be straighter in the sun-form where the leaves are thicker (cf. p. 150). The palisade cells (*p.*) are shorter and the number of palisade layers, as compared with leaves growing in bright light, may exhibit reduction (*e.g.* Beech), accompanying which there is a relative increase of spongy tissue, whose intercellular spaces (*i.s.*) become much more conspicuous. The last-named feature may perhaps facilitate transpiration in a humid atmosphere. As a general rule the stomata are not depressed in the shade-form, whilst this condition is very common in the sun-form. On the other hand, they are generally more numerous in the latter, the fewer stomata found per unit area in the shade-form being related to the larger size attained by the intervening cells. In shade-leaves the vascular tissue is less developed.

When the undergrowth of a wood has been coppiced, the increased access of light finds expression in the much greater vigour and larger amount of the ground-flora, thus showing that light, and not soil-conditions, was the limiting factor. The majority of Oak-Hazel woods are periodically coppiced at more or less regular intervals, so that the herbaceous vegetation waxes and wanes, being least when the undergrowth is thickest, and most abundant about the second or third year after coppicing.

Many herbaceous plants (Pig-nut (*Conopodium*), Yellow Deadnettle, etc.) flower little, if at all, when growing in deep shade, at or near their compensation point, but do so profusely after the wood is coppiced.

Upon loams, sands, shallow siliceous soils, and even on those heavy clays which are likewise poor in mineral salts and often acid in reaction, the characteristic tree is *Quercus petræa*, forming the *Durmast Oak-wood*; the same tree also frequently occurs on the sides of rocky valleys (*e.g.* on the slates of Wales and the sandstones of Yorkshire, Fig. 367), where it may form woods up to 1000–1200 feet altitude. Some of the commonest species of the ground-flora in this community are the Bracken, *Holcus mollis*,

Deschampsia flexuosa, Wood Sage, Whortleberry (*Vaccinium*), Foxglove, Great Woodrush (*Luzula*), Golden Rod (*Solidago*), Hawkweeds, and Ferns. The shrubby layer shows few of the representatives found in the Pedunculate Oak-wood, but Honeysuckle, Brambles, and Holly (*Ilex*) are often common. In the rocky districts above mentioned the ground-flora not infrequently consists

FIG. 367. Durmast Oak-wood, lining the sides of a moorland valley in Yorkshire. On the left, in the foreground and elsewhere at the sides of the stream, are seen bushes of Alder. [Photo. E. J. S.]

almost exclusively of a carpet of Mosses composed of numerous species (Fig. 368).

On many of the heaths with light sandy soils, *Pinus sylvestris* and Birch (*Betula*) cover extensive areas, frequently occurring intermingled as colonisers, every grade between woods and heath being found. Where the Pine-trees grow close together they form evergreen woods, casting a dense shade, and the ground is usually devoid of vegetation except for a number of Fungi in the latter part of the year. There are also various Mosses, amongst which one known as *Leucobryum* forming grey tussocks is most conspicuous. This Moss shows a structure comparable to that of *Sphagnum* (p. 357), the leaf possessing a single layer of green living cells placed between dead, hyaline, water-retaining elements.

When the Pine-trees are less densely aggregated, a sparse vegetation appears which consists chiefly of Bracken, Whortleberry (*Vaccinium*), *Calluna, Erica,* Tormentil (*Potentilla erecta*), and occasional Grasses (particularly *Deschampsia flexuosa*), all in varying amounts. The greater the amount of light penetrating to the ground, the more numerous the heath-species that can survive.

Natural Pine-forests are found in Scotland upon morainic soils up to an altitude of 1500 feet.

Natural *Birch-woods* occur above the Oak-woods in mountain

FIG. 368. Interior of a Durmast Oak-wood on slates, Wales, showing the type of ground-flora consisting almost entirely of Mosses. [Photo. E. J. S.]

districts, usually at an altitude of 1000–1200 feet. The dominance of this tree here is an outcome of its great tolerance of exposure. Owing to the efficient dispersal of the wind-borne fruits of the Birch it often colonises felled areas in woodlands on lighter soils. There thus arise semi-natural Birch-woods that are usually replaced in time by other trees that cast a deeper shade, but have a less efficient dispersal. On heavier and damper soils similar colonisation is often effected by the Ash.

By the sides of streams, where the reaction of the soil is usually nearly neutral and the water-content high, woods of Alder (Fig. 367) and Willow frequently occur. The light-intensity in these woods is low in summer. Ferns and Mosses are common, and many marsh-species, such as *Filipendula ulmaria* and *Chrysosplenium oppositifolium* are frequent. In the West of England this is the characteristic home of the Welsh Poppy (*Meconopsis cambrica*).

A general feature of woodland species is the larger size of their fruits or seeds, as compared with members of the same genus inhabiting open habitats. The greater food-supply in the former can perhaps be related to the competition for light to which seedlings in a shady habitat are subjected. The species most characteristic of woodland clearings often have a large output of seed, which permits of rapid colonisation of such areas. A single plant of a Foxglove or Mullein, for example, may produce nearly half a million seeds.

It should be realised that most soils in our climate, except those which are too shallow or water-logged or which retain too little moisture (*e.g.* pure sand), can support woodlands. Where woodlands do not occur and edaphic conditions like those just mentioned do not obtain, it is usually because there is some factor or factors inhibiting tree-growth. Thus, most grasslands if left untouched would develop into scrub and ultimately woodland. The various phases which the vegetation exhibits until it attains equilibrium with the environment constitute collectively the *plant-succession*, and in this country woodlands represent what is termed the *climatic climax*, being the final phase of equilibrium (cf. also p. 568).

The exact composition at any one phase in the succession depends upon the facilities for colonisation, among which proximity to areas already occupied by vegetation is important. The propagules (seeds, fruits, bulbils, etc.) are conveyed by various agencies, and of these, dispersal by animals figures more conspicuously in woodland communities than in most others. The prevalence of plants with succulent fruits eaten by birds (Cherry, Sloe, Elder, Woody Nightshade, Whortleberry) is noteworthy. Many of the herbs of the ground-flora (Woodruff, Sanicle, Enchanter's Nightshade), on the other hand, have fruits adapted to external carriage.

CHAPTER XLIV

SEMI-NATURAL COMMUNITIES (SCRUB, GRASSLAND, HEATH, ETC.)

WHEREVER woodlands have been cut down, in the drier parts of the country, their place is taken either by communities of shrubs (scrub) or by heaths, which differ in character according to the soil upon which they grow. Thus, on non-calcareous soils formerly occupied by Oak-wood, we often find a *scrub* notable for the prickly nature of many of the component bushes. So-called commons often bear vegetation of this type, the Gorse being one of the most conspicuous plants. Intermingled with it are numerous scattered bushes of Hawthorn and Sloe, whilst the prickly scrambling stems of Wild Roses and Blackberries are everywhere frequent. Where the shrubby members are less abundant, Grasses, such as the Rye-grass (*Lolium*), Sweet Vernal Grass (*Anthoxanthum*), Dog's-tail (*Cynosurus*), Bent (*Agrostis*), and *Holcus lanatus* are the dominant feature, associated with various perennials. The most frequent are Buttercups, Clovers, Plantains, Sorrels, Cat's-ear (*Hypochæris*), Bird's-foot Trefoil, etc. Along the tracks Plantains, *Polygonum aviculare* and Rye-grass are conspicuous, the zonation on either side of them being an expression of the different degrees of tolerance of the species to the frequency of impact of human feet.

On chalky soils the scrub (Fig. 369) contains, in addition to Hawthorn and Sloe, Spindle-tree (*Euonymus*), Buckthorn (*Rhamnus catharticus*), White Beam (*Sorbus aria*), Elder (*Sambucus*), Wayfaring Tree, Privet, and *Clematis*.

Scrub-vegetation is perhaps the richest in species among British plant-communities, which may be related to its transitional character (cf. p. 568). The environmental conditions are not highly specialised and the species are those of meadows and of the marginal flora of woods. Most *hedges* are planted, but some represent the last remnants of the broad uncultivated belts of scrub and trees which were left to act as wind-breaks around the cultivated land and which are recalled by the broad haughs of the west country. Hedgerows (cf. Fig. 11, p. 18) in general correspond very closely, both as regards the constituent shrubs and the accompanying herbs, with the vegetation at the margin of a wood. Just as the latter differs markedly according to the aspect, so too there are striking differences in the vegetation, as well as in the number of species and individuals, on the north and south sides of a hedgerow running from east to west. The flora is both more abundant and varied on the south side. The relationship to woodland is seen in the

FIG. 369. Chalk-scrub, Berkhamsted Common. The vegetation is mainly composed of Furze, Hawthorn (most of the large bushes in the background), and Sloe. In the foreground, on the right, is a mass of *Clematis* in fruit and, on the left, a bush of *Rhamnus catharticus*. [Photo. E. J. S.]

frequent presence in ancient hedgerows of such plants as the Primrose, Wood Anemone, and Wild Hyacinth. The commonest shrubs are Hawthorn, Hazel, Sloe, Maple, Dogwood (*Cornus*), and Elder, while on chalky soils the Spindle-tree, Buckthorn, and *Clematis* are often conspicuous. Climbers, both woody and herbaceous, are common. The hedge, moreover, is the special home of the Beaked Parsley (*Anthriscus*), Hogweed (*Heracleum*), Chervil (*Torilis*), Jack-by-the-Hedge (*Alliaria petiolata*), and Hedge Woundwort (*Stachys sylvatica*). The frequency of species with succulent fruits, here and at the wood margin, is a feature probably related to the prevalence of birds in both these habitats.

Above the zone of forest on the slopes of our higher mountains there usually follows scrub vegetation which, as the exposure increases, gives place to *alpine pasture* in which the viviparous *Festuca alpina*, the Mat-grass (*Nardus stricta*), and sometimes the alpine Lady's Mantle (*Alchemilla alpina*) are conspicuous features. But beyond this continuous carpet there follows the vegetation of the rocky summit where, partly owing to lack of soil and partly to exposure (except in the rock-crevices), the plant-growth is discontinuous and characteristically dwarf, including many Mosses and Lichens. Among the species present in the alpine pasture

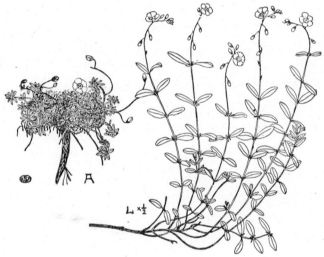

Fig. 370. Alpine (*A.*) and lowland (*L.*) forms of the Rock Rose (*Helianthemum chamæcistus*). (After Bonnier.)

are many (*e.g.* Dandelion) which also occur at lower levels, and these show differences in habit and leaf-anatomy analogous to those exhibited between sun- and shade-leaves. In this country, owing to the relatively low height of the mountains and the humid atmosphere at their summits, such differences are not well marked. But elsewhere (*e.g.* in the Alps) the leaves are commonly thicker and smaller, and have a better-developed palisade tissue, than those of the corresponding lowland form, though they possess a looser texture owing to the large intercellular spaces. A rosette- or dwarf-habit is very common (cf. Fig. 370); and to this may probably be related the frequent presence of more numerous stomata on the upper, as compared with the under, surfaces of the leaves, since the latter are closely adpressed to the humid soil.

Grassland communities are mostly semi-natural in the sense that they would pass into scrub or woodland but for human or other interference, though natural grasslands occur on very shallow soil and above the tree-limit on mountains. Of the semi-natural grasslands two main types can be distinguished according to the treatment they undergo, viz. *meadows* which are cut once or twice a year and *pastures* which are constantly browsed. In both types the pruning prevents passage to scrub or woodland, but whereas meadow-land is often characterised by tall associated herbs, pastures are mostly distinguished by the presence of rosette-plants.

FIG. 371. Vegetation of a meadow. The chief plants are Dutch Clover, Buttercups, Daisies, Yellow Rattle, and Grasses. [Photo. E. J. S.]

The vegetation of *meadows* consists typically of a number of robust Grasses, such as the Meadow Foxtail (*Alopecurus pratensis*), Timothy Grass (*Phleum pratense*), the taller Fescues (*Festuca pratensis*), *Poa pratensis*, *Arrhenatherum*, etc. With these are associated a great variety of other perennial herbs, many of which are tall when in flower. Amongst these *Ranunculus acris*, the Sorrel (*Rumex acetosa*), and Dog-daisy (*Chrysanthemum leucanthemum*) are often abundant, whilst other common species are the Yarrow (*Achillea millefolium*) and Clovers. The damper meadows, often spoken of as water-meadows, frequently contain a number of typical marsh-species (p. 538), and others, such as the Meadow Rue (*Thalictrum flavum*), Water Avens (*Geum rivale*), *Geranium pratense*, etc., are conspicuous features.

Owing to the density of meadow vegetation the air near the

ground is very humid and becomes drier as the tops of the Grasses are approached. This feature is reflected in the structure of the leaves of the rosette species, those near the ground being much less hairy than those borne on the flowering stems.

The low-growing *grassland of calcareous soils* (*e.g.* of chalk-downs) has since remote times been the grazing ground for sheep. It is usually dominated by *Festuca rubra*, together with Quaking-grass (*Briza media*), *Bromus erectus*, *Helictotrichon pratense*, *H. pubescens*, etc., which form a close turf. One of the most striking features, however, of this type of pasture is the wealth of blossom in the early summer. The numerous chalk-loving plants which form these floral carpets include the Milkwort (*Polygala*), Purging Flax (*Linum catharticum*), *Anthyllis vulneraria*, Horseshoe-vetch (*Hippo-crepis*), Salad Burnet (*Poterium sanguisorba*), Sheep's Scabious (*Scabiosa columbaria*), Dwarf Thistle (*Cirsium acaule*), *Campanula glomerata*, *Asperula cynanchica*, *Helianthemum*, *Centaurea scabiosa*, *Blackstonia perfoliata*, *Gentiana amarella*, and Orchids. All of these are of low growth, except when flowering.

The level tops of chalk-downs often exhibit marked leaching of the surface layers of the soil, as a result of which they may be entirely depleted of carbonates, and the calcareous vegetation is replaced by species of acid soils, such as the Heather.

In *pastures* which are not markedly calcareous, species in which the leaves form rosettes close to the surface of the ground are abundant, *e.g.* Daisy, Cat's Ear (*Hypochœris radicata*), *Plantago lanceolata*, and Dandelion. The cricket-pitch or tennis-lawn illustrate in an even more marked degree the effect of repeated artificial restriction of the height of the vegetation. The capacity of the Grasses to compete with and suppress the rosette-herbs is diminished and they tend to multiply at the expense of the turf. Whereas in pastures annuals are usually absent, in close-cut turf bare patches often serve as suitable locations for colonisation by such species as *Sagina procumbens*, *Trifolium micranthum*, etc.

In poor grasslands with thin herbage, where competition is not so severe, there not infrequently occur annuals which are semi-parasitic, such as the Eye-bright (*Euphrasia*), the Red Eye-Bright (*Odontites*, Fig. 372, A), and the Yellow Rattle (*Rhinanthus*), all of which are parasitic on the roots of the Grasses. These still retain the power of active photosynthesis by means of their green leaves, which, though relatively small, are often larger than those of a true parasite. As a result, many can grow independently of a host, although under these circumstances they are far less vigorous. If one of these plants is carefully dug up with the accompanying soil and the latter gently washed away, the small root-system of the parasite will be found attached at certain points to the roots of the host (Fig. 372, B and C) by minute disc-like haustoria (*S*). From these, processes penetrate to the vascular tissue of the host and thus absorb nourishment, and in particular augment the water-supply.

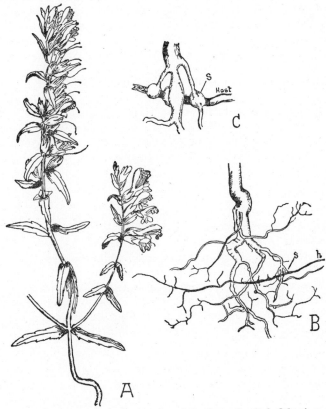

FIG. 372. A, Overground portion of a flowering plant of *Odontites verna* (natural size). B, Root-system of the same, showing connection with roots of host (somewhat enlarged). C, A small part of the last (much enlarged). *h*, root of host; *S*, haustorium.

The under sides of the leaves are beset with numerous dome-shaped hydathodes (Fig. 118, B) that act as safety-valves when an excess of water is taken up from the host.

Much of the existing pasture would perhaps pass into scrub and eventually into woodland, but that its condition is artificially maintained by browsing and by fires. The high winds on mountain-tops probably operate in a similar manner. Other causes contributing to the formation of pasture, both there and elsewhere, are probably the small amount of humus and the dryness of the soil in summer.

The periodical and comparatively frequent disturbance of the soil of *cultivated ground* effectively prevents most perennials from persisting. Indeed, apart from deep-rooted perennials such as Coltsfoot (*Tussilago farfara*), *Equisetum arvense*, Bindweed (*Calystegia*), etc., the only species which perpetually recur are those which can survive tillage operations, either as seeds or as vegetative fragments. Thus most of the weeds of gardens and arable fields are annuals, such as the Shepherd's Purse, the Groundsel (*Senecio vulgaris*), Fumitory (*Fumaria*), and Charlock (*Sinapis arvensis*). Some are winter annuals whose seeds germinate in the autumn (*e.g.* Poppy), others such as the Petty Spurge (*Euphorbia peplis*) and the Scarlet Pimpernel (*Anagallis*) are summer annuals, and these differences in the season of their activity play no small part in determining abundance in relation to particular crops and particular rotations.

The effect of soil is seen in the prevalence of Sheep's Sorrel (*Rumex acetosella*), Knawel (*Scleranthus*), and Field Spurrey (*Spergula arvensis*) on light acid soils, and of Venus's Looking-glass (*Specularia hybrida*), *Galeopsis angustifolium*, and Sun Spurge (*Euphorbia helioscopia*) on chalky soils, while the Red Eye-Bright and the Field Mint (*Mentha arvensis*) are a feature of heavy clays. Such perennials as do persist in cultivated soil are chiefly species, like the Creeping Thistle (*Cirsium arvense*) and the Bindweed, whose rhizomes and roots are not only deep-seated, but fragments of which broken up by cultivation grow into new individuals (cf. also p. 537).

Heaths (Fig. 374), which are a type of scrub, occur on soils poor in mineral salts (*e.g.* sands and gravels) and acid in reaction, either owing to the nature of the underlying rock or because of the leaching action of high rainfall (p. 497). Heath is characterised by the presence of a usually shallow layer of relatively dry peat containing a considerable proportion of sand. The dominant plant is the Heather or Ling (*Calluna*), sometimes (especially on old heaths) almost pure, or accompanied by the Cross- and Fine-leaved Heaths (*Erica tetralix*, Fig. 373, and *E. cinerea*) and the Whortleberry or Bilberry (*Vaccinium myrtillus*). Occasionally, as in parts of Dorset and Surrey, such heaths become extensively colonised by *Pinus* (cf. p. 523), which eventually kills off the heath-flora.

The typical heath, owing to the deep shade cast by the densely branched *Calluna*, has a relatively scanty flora, sometimes consisting, apart from the dominant plant, almost entirely of Mosses and

Lichens. Where the heath is not so pure the commonest associates of *Calluna*, in addition to *Erica* and *Vaccinium*, are the Dwarf Furze (*Ulex minor*), Broom, Tormentil, Heath Bedstraw (*Galium hercynicum*), Heath Speedwell (*Veronica officinalis*), Woodsage (*Teucrium*), Juniper (*Juniperus*), and Bracken, as well as various Grasses, of which *Deschampsia flexuosa* is the most characteristic. The parasitic *Cuscuta* (p. 214) is also not uncommonly found attacking numerous members of the heath-community.

In the wetter parts of the heath a slightly thicker layer of peat is met with, bearing particularly *Vaccinium* and sometimes *Sphagnum*. The vegetation in such habitats is transitional to that of typical moorland (cf. below).

The soil of a heath is very shallow and generally sandy; moreover, the surface-layer of peat, owing to the large quantity of moisture which it absorbs, largely prevents the access of rain-water to lower levels, so that most of it evaporates again in subsequent warm weather. The peat further absorbs the heat-rays of the sun, so that the surface becomes very warm on a sunny day, a fact which is familiar from the quivering of the air just above the ground at such times. Most heaths finally are exposed and wind-swept. In correspondence with this the characteristic members of the heath-flora are xeromorphic. Moreover, a considerable number of the typical heath-plants are ever-greens, for conditions are scarcely more un-favourable in winter than in summer.

FIG. 373. Portion of a plant of the Cross-leaved Heath (*Erica tetralix*, natural size).

The upland *moors* (*e.g* those of Yorkshire, Fig. 375) are probably to be regarded, like the majority of heaths, mainly as occupying soil formerly dominated by woodland which has been destroyed, either by man or natural agencies. For just as heath replaces woodland in the drier districts, so is moorland found on the site of former forest in those parts where a moderately high rainfall usually obtains. That many of our moors have thus taken the place of woodland can often be seen from the presence of tree-trunks, mostly of Birch, embedded in the peat (Fig. 376). Lowland moors, such as those of the New Forest, on the other hand, appear to have developed from fens (cf. p. 555).

Moors are usually characterised by a soil having a greater depth of peat than heaths and a smaller percentage of inter-mingled sand, so that the soil has an increased water-retaining

FIG. 374. Heath, Hindhead Common, Surrey.   A large proportion of the vegetation on the farther slope consists of *Calluna*.   [Photo. F. E. F.]

FIG. 375. Distant view of Heather-moors, Yorkshire.   The plants in the foreground are mainly *Calluna* and *Vaccinium*, whilst the grassy patch consists chiefly of Cotton-grass and Rushes.   [Photo. E. J. S.]

FIG. 376. Section of peat on a Yorkshire moorland, showing embedded trunks of the Birch. The vegetation on the slope above consists of *Calluna* and Bracken. [Photo. E. J. S.]

FIG. 377. Wet part of a Yorkshire moor. In the foreground and on the left is a dense growth of Bog-myrtle (*Myrica*), whilst in the background a considerable quantity of Bracken is seen. [Photo. E. J. S.]

capacity. In the wetter parts the peat may attain to considerable thickness, as a result of its rapid formation by such plants as *Sphagnum*, Cotton-grass (*Eriophorum*), etc. Owing to the large amount of acid humus present, the soil-water of the moor is acid in its reaction and thus contrasts very markedly with the often alkaline character of fen-water (cf. p. 555).

In the commonest type of moorland, namely, the *heather-moor* (Fig. 375), the dominant plants, amongst which *Calluna, Erica*, and *Vaccinium* (all members of the Ericaceæ) are most prominent, all possess xeromorphic foliage, whilst most are devoid of root-hairs, the function of which is taken over by mycorrhiza (cf. p. 218). In view of the relative wetness of the soil, the xeromorphic character appears surprising, but the poor aeration owing to its water-logged character, the low temperature of the soil, and the toxicity of the soil-water all tend to lower the rate of absorption by the roots. Moreover, moorlands are usually to be found in more or less exposed wind-swept situations tending to accentuate transpiration. The retentive capacity of the peat for water may also play a part, but this is to a large extent compensated by the heavy rains and mists in the districts where moors occur.

The commonest of the shrubby associates of *Calluna* on such a moor are species of *Erica* (Fig. 373), *Empetrum*, and *Vaccinium*. These together form a vegetation with somewhat low growth and of a more or less even level, so that the plants afford one another mutual protection. The last of these shrubs has deciduous leaves with a thick cuticle and becomes a switch-plant in winter (cf. p. 504). Frequent moorland plants are the Blue Moor-grass (*Molinia cœrulea*), the Bog-rush (*Juncus squarrosus*), the Deer Sedge (*Scirpus cæspitosus*), and the Bracken, besides numerous Mosses of which *Polytrichum* is the chief. In the damper parts (Fig. 377) the insectivorous Sundew (Fig. 134) and Butterwort (Fig. 135) flourish, together with Sweet-gale or Bog-myrtle (*Myrica*), Cranberry (*Oxycoccus palustris*), Bog Asphodel (*Narthecium*), *Viola palustris*, various Rushes, *Eriophorum*, Sedges (*Carex*), and *Sphagnum*. The Mat-grass (*Nardus stricta*) often forms almost pure communities on eroding edges of the peat.

It is more particularly on the deeper peat that the Whortle-berry finds its chief home, here frequently becoming the dominant plant. In some areas, where the peat is still deeper, an extremely wet soil results bearing a community dominated by *Eriophorum vaginatum* (*Cotton-grass moor*). This plant, which forms peat with very great rapidity, has narrow leaves with a very thick cuticle and is thus suited to exposed situations, whilst its rhizomes traversed by numerous air-canals enable it to grow in a soil that is completely water-logged (cf. p. 544).

The different types of moorland-communities appear to be determined partly by the water-content of the soil and partly by the degree of acidity and the amount of nutrient salts, features that are often related to the rate of peat-formation, to its depth, and to the amount of associated mineral matter. The dry heather-moor is formed on peat relatively rich in mineral substance and either shallow or up to 4 feet in depth. The very wet Cotton-grass moor, on the other hand, is associated with peat very poor in mineral matter, usually very acid, and attaining a depth of from 5 to as much as 30 feet.

Burning of heath and moorland is often resorted to as a means of encouraging new growth for stock or game. Salts are liberated from the burnt plant-tissues which ameliorate the edaphic conditions and thus tend to modify the character of the vegetation. Such areas often exhibit a distinctive growth which persists for a considerable period, e.g. the "swiddens" of the Yorkshire moors. Another method of amelioration of acid moorlands is by means of artificial dykes which flush the soil with drainage water containing mineral salts leached out from higher ground. Such flushes, like the "flushes" in acid woodlands, support a vegetation more like that on neutral soils.

The vegetation of *cornfields* is an artificially induced assemblage, composed mainly of annual weeds that here find relative freedom from the competition of perennials which tend to be eliminated by the periodic cultivation (cf. p. 532). The persistence of these annuals depends in part upon their having a growing period which synchronises with that of the crop so that the arable phase coincides with that of their seed-stage, in part on the capacity of the seeds to remain dormant in the soil until conditions are favourable for germination. The artificial successions, involved in crop-rotation as practised by agriculturists, and the establishment of pastures, known as *temporary leys*, for one or more years, each have their effect upon the composition of the weed-flora. The significance of the ley is that the decay of the relatively deep roots of some Grasses (*e.g.* Perennial Rye Grass), which are renewed annually, incorporates organic material throughout the soil and brings about improved texture and increased fertility.

35

CHAPTER XLV

THE ECOLOGY OF MARSH-
AND WATER-FLORAS

IN low-lying meadows we find considerable variation in the depth at which the underground water-table is situated and, where the latter approaches near to the surface, any depression may furnish a *marsh-flora*, such as is found more particularly round the edges of lakes and ponds and by the sides of sluggish streams. In such a marsh the underground organs of the plants are often submerged, but there may, for the greater part of the year, be no free water apparent above the soil. In these situations (Fig. 378) we find typical marsh-plants, the more characteristic being the Marsh Marigold (*Caltha*), Water-mint (*Mentha aquatica*), Ragged Robin (*Lychnis flos-cuculi*), Forget-me-not (*Myosotis palustris*), Milkmaid, Marsh Thistle (*Cirsium palustre*), Marsh Ragwort (*Senecio aquaticus*), Meadow-sweet (*Filipendula*), Marsh Horsetail (*Equisetum palustre*), Rushes (*Juncus*), Sedges (*Carex*), and Small Valerian (*Valeriana dioica*); if the soil is somewhat peaty, one meets with additional species, such as Lesser Spearwort (*Ranunculus flammula*), Pennywort (*Hydrocotyle*), Lousewort (*Pedicularis palustris*), Water Blinks (*Montia*), Marsh Violet (*Viola palustris*), Devil's-bit Scabious (*Scabiosa pratensis*), and Sneezewort (*Achillea ptarmica*).

Further towards the open water we come to a *swamp-flora* (Fig. 380) in which a certain amount of standing water is usually present above the soil-level, the vegetation often showing a more or less marked zonation corresponding to the depth to which the soil is submerged. Typically three such zones are distinguishable. Beginning with the Sedge-zone on the landward side, there follows a belt of Reeds (*Phragmites*), which is again succeeded by a zone of Bulrushes (*Scirpus lacustris*) next the open water. Among the more characteristic plants of the Sedge- and Reed-zones are *Iris pseudacorus*, Flowering Rush (*Butomus*), Bur-reed (*Sparganium*), Water Plantain (*Alisma plantago*), Reed-mace (*Typha*), Spike-rush (*Eleocharis*), Reed Canary-grass (*Phalaris arundinacea*), *Glyceria maxima*, Great Water Dock (*Rumex hydrolapathum*), Water Dropwort (*Œnanthe*), Purple Loosestrife (*Lythrum*), Hemp Agrimony (*Eupatorium*), Gipsywort (*Lycopus*), Brooklime (*Veronica beccabunga*), Bog-bean (*Menyanthes*), and *Equisetum fluviatile*. The only common associate of the Bulrush is the *Hippuris* (Fig. 381).

The species, however, vary locally in distribution and do not always necessarily occur in the belt mentioned; thus, some marsh-plants are frequently found in the swamp-flora and *vice versa*.

FIG. 378. Marsh-flora. In the foreground are seen various Sedges (*Carex*), with Marsh Marigolds (*Caltha*) and, more particularly in the background, the leaves of the Meadow-sweet (*Filipendula*). [Photo. E. J. S.]

Moreover, one or other zone is commonly absent, when the floor slopes steeply. Depth of water is the most important factor influencing the zonation as such, but the specific composition of the zones is usually determined by the depth of silt and mud in which the plants are rooted and whether this substratum is rich or poor in nutrients, and well aerated and oxidising or poorly aerated and reducing. The swamp-flora is distinguished by the prevalent upright habit and the vertically placed leaves (Fig. 380), which equip it well to meet wind-movement.

Marsh-plants frequently show conspicuous hydathodes, most commonly at the leaf-tip, as in *Myosotis palustris* and *Alisma plantago*. In the latter the tissue above the bundle-ends breaks down completely so that the escaping water-vapour passes directly to the exterior.   The underground organs exist in a medium which is deficient in oxygen.   This is to some extent counteracted by copious intercellular spaces which are continued also into the aerial parts.   Some members of this flora (e.g. *Lythrum salicaria, Lycopus europæus, Epilobium hirsutum*) develop on their submerged stems and roots a special aerating tissue which appears as a white spongy swelling.   This *aerenchyma* is a very lacunar secondary tissue,

FIG. 379. White Water Lily (*Nymphæa*) growing amongst Reeds (*Phragmites*), Wicken Fen.   The floating leaves and flowers of the former are seen.
[Photo. E. J. S.]

formed in place of cork by the phellogen, which cuts off cells only on the outside.   These remain thin-walled and living and, as they enlarge, partially separate, and so produce a system of wide air-spaces (often concentric in their arrangement) to which the spongy character is due.   The function of this tissue is to supply air to the submerged parts, and it is particularly well developed in plants growing in water-logged soil.

As soon as the region with free-standing water is entered *aquatics* begin to appear, so that many of them are found among the members of the swamp-flora (cf. Fig. 379, Fig. 380).   Moreover, these aquatics themselves exhibit a zonation, associated with the depth of the water.   Near the shore are plants rooted to the bottom and developing floating leaves, but, as the water deepens, the limit

FIG. 380. Swamp-flora, Wisley. The vegetation consists of a thick growth of Water St. John's Wort (*Hypericum elodes*), amongst which is seen the Spike-rush (*Eleocharis*) on the right and *Carex pseudocyperus* on the left. [Photo. E. J. S.]

FIG. 381. Aquatic flora, Water-end, Herts. Numerous upright shoots of the Mare's-tail (*Hippuris*) are seen projecting from the water, in which the dark patches indicate the position of submerged plants of the Hornwort. In the middle the floating rosettes of the Water Starwort (*Callitriche*). [Photo. E. J. S.]

of depth from which they can bring these leaves to the surface is reached and beyond this zone aquatics with floating leaves are absent. Examples are furnished by the White (*Nymphæa*, Fig. 379) and Yellow Water Lilies (*Nuphar*), Water Starworts (*Callitriche*, Fig. 389), Water Crowfoot (*Ranunculus aquatilis*, Fig. 386), Floating Pondweed (*Potamogeton natans*), and *Polygonum amphibium*. In this same zone we get other rooted plants, such as the Arrowhead (*Sagittaria*, Fig. 387) and *Hypericum elodes* (Fig. 380), which raise some of their leaves into the air, and still others, in which only the flowers appear above the water-level, *e.g.* Floating Bur-reed (*Sparganium natans*), Water Violet (*Hottonia*), and Water Milfoil (*Myriophyllum*, Fig. 388), the first two occurring in relatively shallow water. Amongst all these forms are found a number of free-floating aquatics, such as the Duckweed (*Lemna*), Frog-bit (*Hydrocharis*), and Bladderwort (*Utricularia*).

Beyond the belt of floating aquatics which, starting from the shore, extends into considerably deeper water than the Bulrush-zone of the swamp-flora, a number of typical submerged forms can exist at a still greater depth. Such are *Potamogeton lucens*, *Ceratophyllum* (Fig. 382), and *Elodea*. At a still greater depth all aquatic Flowering Plants disappear and we only find the Moss *Fontinalis* and the Stoneworts (*Chara*) and subsequently nothing but Algæ. The latter occur in varying quantity in all parts of the water at certain times of the year, and on rocky shores of lakes, where the marsh-community is not developed, conspicuous growths of *Cladophora*, *Ulothrix*, Cyanophyceæ, etc., may be seen.

In streams the rate of flow greatly affects the character of the aquatic flora. Where the current is rapid, free-floating plants are absent and such species as *Sagittaria* and *Œnanthe fluviatilis* grow completely submerged, though they may develop floating leaves in quieter waters. The capacity to carry particles in suspension depending on the rate of flow, the former are deposited near the banks in proportion as the flow is checked. Under sheltered conditions the deposits tend to consist of varying proportions of fine inorganic and organic silt, whilst where there is constant movement coarse mineral particles will mainly accumulate. Such differences in texture and composition of the bottom deposits have a marked influence on the character of the vegetation. Where the deposit is mainly organic, *Scirpus lacustris* is frequently dominant, whilst when the deposits are richer in mineral salts the Reed-mace (*Typha latifolia*) is often conspicuous.

The submerged parts of all water-plants are surrounded by a medium which is much denser than that enveloping the shoot of a land-plant, so that they receive considerable support. Aquatics do not therefore require much mechanical tissue. In fact the principal strain to which they are subjected is, as in the roots of terrestrial plants (cf. pp. 6, 109), a longitudinal pull due to currents in the water. Indeed, such mechanical tissue as the aquatic possesses is usually contained in a central strand of vascular tissue (cf. Fig. 382).

Water contains far less oxygen than an equivalent volume of air, so that the amount thus available for respiration is small in

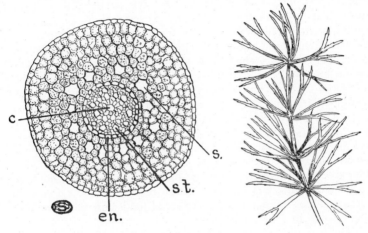

FIG. 382. Habit, and transverse section of the stem, of the Hornwort (*Ceratophyllum demersum*). *c.*, xylem-canal; *en.*, endodermis; *s.*, intercellular space of cortex; *s.t.*, sieve-tube.

aquatics. Carbon dioxide, on the other hand, is more readily dissolved by water and the aquatic consequently has a larger amount at its disposal, bulk for bulk, than a land-plant. Moreover, the supply of carbon dioxide is constantly enriched through the oxidation of organic materials in the mud.

The physiological processes carried out by submerged aquatics, whether Flowering Plants or Algæ, may appreciably alter the proportions of these gases. During active photosynthesis there is considerable removal of carbon dioxide, even from bicarbonates, which may lead to the precipitation of carbonates and a decrease in hydrogen-ion concentration. Moreover, oxygen-enrichment may be brought about, especially by the action of Algæ, both attached and free-floating (plankton).

Since there are usually no stomata on the submerged parts of aquatics, both oxygen and carbon dioxide have to enter by diffusion over the whole surface through the very thin cuticle. This is in itself a slow process. The difficulty in gaseous exchange is compensated by very thin foliage or extreme division of the leaves (Figs. 386, 388), *i.e.* the creation of a large absorptive surface and by the development of a special internal atmosphere occupying the abundant intercellular spaces (Fig. 383).

The relation between anatomical structure and habitat is nowhere more plainly shown than in the *aquatics* among Flowering Plants, which, however, usually betray distinct evidence of their origin from terrestrial ancestors. All the submerged organs of such plants are modified to suit the exceptional conditions of the environment. This is well exemplified by a study of the transverse section of the *stem* of an aquatic like the Hornwort (*Ceratophyllum demersum*, Fig. 382), which grows completely under water. A small intercellular space (*c.*), surrounded by three or four layers of thin-walled parenchyma-cells, occupies the centre of the single vascular strand. This space is actually a longitudinal canal (*xylem-canal*) formed by the breaking down of elements of the procambial strand which, in less specialised aquatics (e.g. *Myriophyllum*), give rise to xylem. Beyond the enveloping parenchyma lies the phloem, which can be recognised by its large sieve-tubes (Fig. 382, *s.t.*). The absence of xylem, whilst the phloem is well represented, can be related to the fact that absorption takes place over the whole surface, whilst conduction of elaborated food-materials remains as necessary as in a terrestrial plant.

The vascular strand is sharply bounded towards the cortex by a well-defined endodermis (Figs. 382 and 384, *en.*), showing suberised thickenings on the radial walls, and immediately within is a pericycle, just as in many young roots. The wide cortex beyond consists of thin-walled parenchyma in which a ring of intercellular spaces (*s.*) surrounds the central strand. These are much larger and often more numerous in other aquatics (cf. Fig. 383). The epidermal cells have thin outer walls with a very thin cuticle, and there are no stomata.

An atmosphere consisting largely of oxygen is produced within the plant during photosynthesis which, owing to the relatively large amount of carbon dioxide, goes on readily; the oxygen formed does not escape into the water, but passes into the numerous large canal-like intercellular spaces of the cortex which traverse all parts of the aquatic (Fig. 383). When it was demonstrated that a water-plant gives off oxygen during photosynthesis (cf. p. 211), the gas collected was escaping from this *internal atmosphere.* The presence of these air-chambers furthermore gives the aquatic considerable buoyancy, and thus helps to maintain rooted forms in an erect position in the water.

The numerous large air-canals of aquatics are often segmented by plate-like septa or *diaphragms* composed of many small cells separated by minute intercellular perforations. These latter are too small to admit of the passage of water, and thus prevent the injection of the air-canals, when fragments of water-plants become detached, as normally occurs in vegetative reproduction; owing to the perforations the flow of air is not obstructed.

Those aquatics, whose lower parts only are submerged, approach more nearly to land-plants in their internal structure. In the Mare's-tail (*Hippuris*, Fig. 384), for instance, the xylem (*Xy.*), which is necessary to supply water to the aerial parts, though not extensive, forms an obvious zone situated within the phloem (*p.*) and surrounding a large central pith (*pi.*). The wide vascular cylinder can be related to the growth of the shoots above the water and the consequent bending stresses to which these are exposed. Hence a more peripheral disposition of the mechanical elements than occurs in submerged plants is rendered necessary.

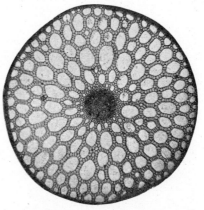

FIG. 383. Transverse section of the stem of *Hippuris*, showing the small central stele and the very wide lacunar cortex.

Even the more extreme aquatics, however, often preserve indications of their terrestrial ancestry in their *vascular system*. Thus spiral vessels commonly persist at the nodes (e.g. *Potamogeton*), and transient spiral vessels occur in the young internodes. In the different species of *Potamogeton* can be found various stages of the concentration and reduction of the vascular system. These features are least pronounced in *P. natans*, which develops a relatively large inflorescence rising some two or three inches out of the water, and further possesses floating leaves. The large central cylinder (Fig. 385) encloses eight to ten fairly well-defined vascular bundles, each of which is separated from its neighbours by two to three layers of thin-walled parenchyma, and consists of a large xylem-canal (*C.*) with accompanying phloem (*P.*). The likewise broad-leaved, but completely submerged, *P. lucens* presents a more marked concentration of the bundles, whose individuality is consequently less pronounced. Lastly, the narrow-leaved *P. pectinatus*, which is also totally submerged, exhibits but a single xylem-canal surrounded by phloem, as in *Ceratophyllum*. It may be noted that the leaf-traces exhibit a similar reduction, one bundle passing to each leaf in the last-named species, whilst in the two former the trace consists of three bundles. In view

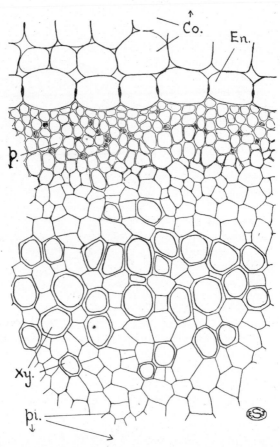

FIG. 384. Portion of transverse section of the stem of the Mare's-tail (*Hippuris*). *Co.*, lacunar cortex; *En.*, endodermis; *p.*, phloem; *pi.*, pith; *Xy.*, xylem.

of the reduction which water-plants show in respect to the vascular tissue, it is scarcely surprising that they rarely exhibit cambial activity. A trace of cambium can, however, be detected in the stem of the Mare's-tail (*Hippuris vulgaris*).

Another consequence, resulting from life in water, is the reduced illumination to which submerged aquatics are exposed, due to much of the obliquely incident light being reflected from the surface, whilst that which penetrates is rapidly absorbed as it passes to deeper and deeper levels. For this reason, it is imperative

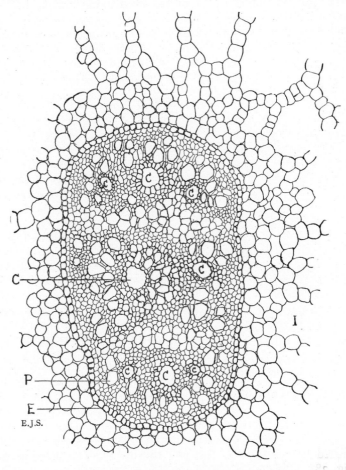

FIG. 385. Transverse section of the vascular strand of the Floating Pondweed (*Potamogeton natans*). *C.*, xylem-canals; *E.*, endodermis; *I.*, air-canal; *P.*, sieve-tube.

for most water-plants to bring their photosynthetic organs relatively near to the surface, and their compensation point largely determines the depth at which submerged aquatics can grow. Naturally the depth to which light penetrates varies with the turbidity of the water.

The *submerged leaves* of water-plants are either very thin or deeply divided, as in *Myriophyllum* (Fig. 388) and *Ranunculus aquatilis* (Fig. 386). Divided leaves not only afford a larger surface for the absorption of carbon dioxide and oxygen, but are mechanically more efficient, since currents flow readily between the segments. The long undivided leaves of *Potamogeton pectinatus*, which readily trail out with the current, are equally well adapted to offer but slight resistance. Occasionally submerged leaves have a broader surface, as in *Potamogeton lucens* and *Nuphar* where, however, the leaves are very thin and flexible.

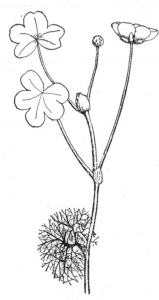

Aquatics which produce floating leaves as a rule also have a varying number of submerged ones; the latter are generally quite different from the floating leaves, the most notable exception being *Nuphar*, where they are similar in form but very much thinner. The difference is well illustrated by *Ranunculus aquatilis* (Fig. 386), in which the submerged leaves are much divided and feathery, whilst those floating at the surface are reniform. In *Nymphæa* the few submerged leaves are generally ribbon-shaped, whilst the floating ones are deeply cordate with a roughly oval lamina (Fig. 379). A particularly interesting example is afforded by *Sagittaria* (Fig. 387). In still shallow water, three kinds of leaves are produced: firstly, ribbon-shaped submerged ones (Fig. 387, A); secondly, lanceolate or cordate floating ones, often with a deeply notched base (Fig. 387, B); and thirdly, sagittate aerial leaves (Fig. 387, C) standing out of the water; in running (cf. p. 542) or very deep water, however, only the submerged type of leaf is produced.

FIG. 386. Portion of a plant of *Ranunculus aquatilis* (about two-thirds natural size), showing floating and submerged leaves.

Floating leaves (Figs. 379, 386, 387, B) agree in mostly having an entire edge and in the fact that the petiole is attached more or less near the centre of the glabrous blade (cf. especially Fig. 379), so that the pull of the leaf-stalk acts centrally and the lamina is kept flat on the surface of the water. ·The floating leaves of the Water Lilies arise from a stout perennating rhizome; they have very long petioles, whereby the blade is maintained at the surface, even in relatively deep water, and enough play is permitted for currents to carry it to and fro without submergence.

In *Potamogeton natans* and *Polygonum amphibium,* on the

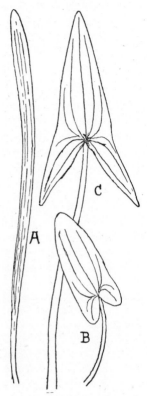

FIG. 387. Different types of leaves of the Arrowhead (*Sagittaria*) (considerably reduced). A, submerged. B, floating. C, aerial.

FIG. 388. Portion of a plant of the Water Milfoil (*Myriophyllum*), showing the inflorescence (consisting of four female flowers at the base and male flowers above) supported by the parachute-like arrangement of the whorled leaves (about natural size).

other hand, the petioles are short, the blades being brought to the surface by the elongation of the stem. In these two plants the floating leaves are separated by much shorter internodes than the submerged leaves, a fact which is more particularly apparent in the Water Starwort (*Callitriche*). Here the opposite leaves on the submerged part of the stem are borne at widely separated nodes, but at the water-surface the internodes are scarcely developed, the leaves being crowded together to form the familiar floating rosettes

(Fig. 389, *W*). The longer internodes of the more deeply submerged portions of the stem in these plants are probably to be related to the reduced light-intensity, a feature which may also be responsible in part for the thin texture of the submerged foliage in many aquatics.

An important function of many floating leaves is that of forming a supporting platform around the base of the aerial inflorescence (cf. Fig. 386). The same function is fulfilled in some plants having only submerged foliage by a parachute-like arrangement of the whorled leaves just beneath the water-level (e.g. *Hottonia*, *Myriophyllum*, Fig. 388).

The leaves of submerged water-plants usually bear no stomata, whilst in floating leaves they are restricted to the upper surface, and exhibit marked differences from the ordinary type. The guard-cells, in transverse section, are roughly triangular through the inner walls being bevelled off towards the outer edge of the pore, where the thickening is most pronounced. By means of their stomata floating leaves maintain a connection between the air-spaces of the submerged portions and the outside atmosphere. As the upper surface of such floating leaves is usually covered by a fine waxy bloom (e.g. *Nymphæa*), this side of the leaf is not readily wetted, and hence the formation of water-films across the stomatal apertures is prevented.

Submerged leaves are generally very simple in structure and, when dissected, are usually centric, as is well illustrated by the leaf of *Ranunculus aquatilis* (Fig. 391, *W*). This centric structure may be related to the absence of illumination from any particular direction, owing to the diffuse character of the light and the constant displacement of the segments by water-currents. Intercellular spaces, as in the stem, are usually abundant. Non-dissected types of leaf, as already noted, are often very thin and may consist between the veins of only two layers of cells (e.g. *Elodea*). Chloroplasts are invariably present in the epidermis (cf. p. 148 and Fig. 391, W).

The roots of water-plants are generally all adventitious, forming white slender little-branched structures functioning mainly as organs of attachment, since absorption of water and mineral salts takes place over the whole surface. Some aquatics are rootless, as in *Ceratophyllum* and the Bladderwort (*Utricularia*). In the free-floating *Lemna* and Frog-bit (*Hydrocharis*) the roots hang down into the water, and not only absorb, but also serve to keep the plant balanced in the normal position.

There are comparatively few Flowering Plants that grow in the sea. Amongst the commonest are the Eel-grass (*Zostera*) found in shallow water and *Ruppia* which grows in brackish ditches. The former has long, thin, grass-like leaves.

Aquatics display a remarkable plasticity of structure, particularly in relation to their anatomy, as a result of which many (e.g. *Callitriche*, *Ranunculus aquatilis*) can grow either completely submerged, or on mud, or even on dry land. A comparison of such *land-* and *water-forms*, belonging to the same species, clearly shows the adaptational significance of most of the characters of aquatics. In the *land-forms* the internodes become extremely short, so that the whole plant appears stunted (cf. Fig. 389, *L*); further, the leaves are thicker and smaller (Fig. 389, *L*) and, when divided, show broader and fewer segments, whilst roots are more strongly developed. In *Polygonum amphibium* the land- and water-forms are strikingly different. The leaves of the former are lanceolate and covered with bristly hairs, whilst the floating leaves of the aquatic form are cordate and quite glabrous.

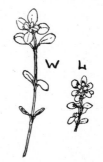

FIG. 389. Land-form (*L*) and Water-form (*W*) of the Water Starwort (*Callitriche*) (natural size).

It is noteworthy that the submerged leaves correspond closely to the juvenile foliage of the same species growing on land, whilst the adult leaves, even of completely submerged aquatics, sometimes approach those of their land-form. In general, conditions which promote increased photosynthesis appear to favour the development of the terrestrial type of foliage.

In a cross-section of the stem of the land-form of *Callitriche* (Fig. 390, *a*) the cortex consists of closely packed rounded cells with small intercellular spaces between them, whilst that of the water-form (Fig. 390, *d*) is mainly occupied by two large air-canals separated only by narrow strips of tissue. Thicker outer walls and a distinct cuticle characterise the epidermal cells of the land-form (cf. Fig. 390, *b* and *e*). The vascular strand of the latter has an almost continuous ring of xylem (Fig. 390, *c*) in contrast to the one or two xylem elements bordering the central canal (*la.*) in the water-form, whose vascular strand is slightly smaller (Fig. 390, *f*). Similar differences are exhibited by the structure of the stems of the two forms in other aquatics.

The leaves of the Starwort do not differ markedly in the two forms, but there is a distinct cuticle and a better developed vascular system in that of the land-plant. Since stomata are present even on the submerged leaves, the only difference is that they remain closed in the water-form. A marked contrast is, however, presented by the leaves of the two forms of *Ranunculus aquatilis* (Fig. 391). Those of the land-form (*L*) have a definite palisade layer, which occupies the bulk of the mesophyll, and the epidermis is devoid

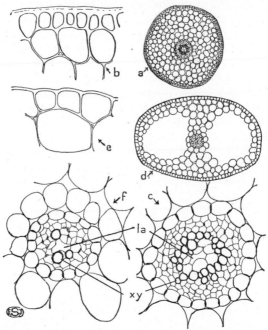

FIG. 390. Transverse sections of the stems of the land- (*a–c*) and water-form (*d–f*) of the Starwort (*Callitriche stagnalis*). *a* and *d*, entire sections; *b* and *e*, epidermis; *c* and *f*, vascular strands. *la.*, xylem-canal; *Xy.*, xylem-vessels.

of chloroplasts and provided with stomata through which gaseous exchange takes place. In the leaves of the water-form (*W*), on the

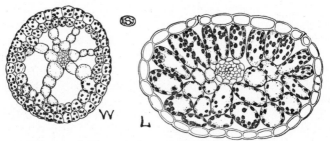

FIG. 391. Transverse sections of the leaves of the land (*L*) and water (*W*) forms of *Ranunculus aquatilis*.

other hand, palisade tissue is absent and there are very conspicuous intercellular spaces. There are no stomata in the epidermis whose cells contain chloroplasts. Similar differences can be observed between the floating and submerged leaves of this plant, but the anatomical contrast is more striking in the Mare's-tail (*Hippuris*), where the leaves borne above and below water are of the same external form.

A combination of aquatic characteristics with others, usually encountered in the vegetation of dry habitats, is not uncommonly exhibited by plants rooted in boggy ground, but whose shoots are exposed to conditions tending to encourage excessive transpiration. These conditions may in part explain the phenomenon, which is, however, probably an outcome of complex causes. Excellent examples are furnished by the Cotton Grass (*Eriophorum*), the Rush (cf. p. 506), and the Bulrush (*Scirpus*), all typical of such localities. The principal feature reminiscent of aquatics is the vast system of intercellular air-canals which serves to supply the underground organs with oxygen (cf. p. 536).

A feature of aquatic life is the abundant supply of water and often of mineral salts as well. This enables exceedingly rapid and prolific growth to take place, a fact which is strikingly illustrated by the Canadian Pondweed. This plant (Fig. 404) was introduced into this country in 1847 and spread with such rapidity that at one time it constituted a serious pest by choking up canals and other waterways. In view of this prolific growth vegetative reproduction is generally a marked feature of aquatics. Mere detachment of branches is very common, and such fragmentation is facilitated by the brittle condition engendered by the turgid state of the cells, e.g. *Elodea*, *Ceratophyllum*, both of which only rarely reproduce by seeds.

With the approach of winter many aquatics produce numerous *winter-buds* (Fig. 392), *i.e.* ends of shoots in which the leaves are very closely crowded together and filled with starch (e.g. *Elodea*, Fig. 392, A; *Myriophyllum*, Fig. 392, B); when the parent dies away, these sink to the bottom. In the following spring, with the increase of illumination, the buds sprout and grow to the surface. Such winter-buds resemble the summer-buds (cf. p. 130) of land-plants in having no bud-scales. They are often copiously covered with mucilage formed by secretory hairs.

The buds of *Hydrocharis* and the Water Soldier (*Stratiotes*) are formed at the ends of long more or less horizontal runners, and are produced, not only in the autumn, but also during the summer. Other methods of persistence during the winter are seen in the Duckweed, where entire plants often become full of starch in the autumn and sink to the bottom, and in *Sagittaria*, where small tubers are carried out on branches of the rhizome.

36 ·

In a mild winter, moreover, many water-plants (Canadian Pond-weed, Duckweed, Water Starwort) persist in an unaltered state.

The bulk of aquatics raise their flowers above the water-level and thus betray their derivation from terrestrial plants. Some are entomophilous (e.g. *Nuphar*). Others are anemophilous (e.g. *Myriophyllum*, Fig. 388; *Potamogeton*, Fig. 291), though occasionally pollinated by insects frequenting the surface of the water (*e.g.* Water-gnats). The peduncles often bend down after flowering is over and carry the developing fruits under water, so that they are well protected (e.g. *Ranunculus aquatilis*).

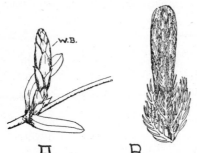

FIG. 392. Winter-buds of A, *Elodea*, and B, *Myriophyllum* (slightly enlarged). *w.b.*, winter-bud.

A few aquatics have become so highly adapted to life in water that even their flowers are submerged. In *Ceratophyllum* these flowers are developed in the axils of the leaves and have a small inconspicuous perianth. They are unisexual with both sexes on the same plant; the male flower has from twelve to sixteen stamens, while the female has a superior ovary with a single ovule. In all such water-pollinated plants the pollen grains are smooth and float readily in the water, currents carrying them to the stigmas; pollination is therefore as uncertain as in anemophilous plants and, in correspondence with this, a considerable amount of pollen is formed. Such water-borne pollen is sometimes highly specialised, that of the Eel-grass (*Zostera*), for example, being tubular, of the same specific gravity as sea-water, and without any cuticularised layer. Many aquatics, which ordinarily raise their flowers above the water, fail to do so if, just before the time of flowering, the water-level rises rapidly; under these circumstances the flower-buds do not open and are cleistogamic (p. 465).

Many of the plants growing by the water-side have fruits which float readily and are not damaged by prolonged submergence. In consequence they become distributed by water-currents.

When vegetation colonises a pond-floor or river-bed, the freedom of water-movement is checked and, as a result, the rate of deposition of water-borne particles is accelerated. These accumulate round the submerged plants with a consequent rise in the level of the bed. The overlying water thus becomes shallower, so that other species can grow and what was once free water becomes a marsh. The swamp-flora is always encroaching in this manner upon the aquatic vegetation, and in a similar way the reed-swamp, as it becomes more and more dense and the level of the floor rises, is invaded by the marsh-flora. In East Anglia large areas are covered by such dense reed-swamps in which the predominating plants are Grasses and Sedges, *e.g.* Reed (*Phragmites*), Blue Moorgrass (*Molinia*), Reed Canary-grass (*Phalaris arundinacea*), Bog-rush (*Schoenus*), Twig-rush (*Cladium*), etc. A certain amount of peat is formed in such situations, but this contains a large proportion of mineral substance and the soil-water, unlike that of moorlands (cf. p. 536), is often alkaline. This type of community is known as a *fen*. Other characteristic plants are *Lychnis flos-cuculi*, *Valeriana officinalis*, *Ranunculus lingua*, *Thalictrum flavum*, *Filipendula ulmaria*, etc.

In this dense fen-community there is a stratification comparable to that in woodlands. Such species as *Valeriana dioica* and *Hydrocotyle vulgaris* form a stratum, equivalent to the ground-flora. In *Filipendula ulmaria*, which is a tall-growing species bearing leaves in different strata and therefore subject to decreasing humidity with increase of height above the ground, the lower protected leaves are smooth and green on the under side, whilst the corresponding surface of the exposed upper leaves is of a greyish tinge owing to a thick felt of downy hairs.

Eventually the soil built up by the accumulation of mineral and organic material may become colonised by trees, such as Alder (*Alnus*), Willow, *Rhamnus catharticus*, etc., and a fen-wood or *carr* is produced, which may eventually pass into Oak-wood. We have here again a *succession*, in which one type of plant-community replaces another in a definite sequence, leading to a comparatively stable *climax-community*, the character of which is largely determined by the prevalent climatic conditions (cf. p. 525).

CHAPTER XLVI

VEGETATION OF THE SEASHORE

THE rock-fragments produced by the erosion of the sea coast are distributed through the agency of water and wind. Their capacity for carrying such fragments depends on their velocity. On parts of the coast where wave-action is considerable, reduction in velocity leads to the deposition of the very coarse material as shingle to form shingle-beaches. In quieter waters the finest material is deposited as mud and sand to form salt-marshes, whilst wind-borne sand gives rise above tide-levels to dunes. Exposure to wind is a general feature of coastal situations, shared equally by the beach, sand-dune, and salt-marsh.

Below spring-tide level there is an abundant growth on our shores consisting of large Brown Seaweeds like *Laminaria* and numerous Red Seaweeds; many of the latter grow only in deep water and in their zonation light-intensity plays an important part. Between tide-levels we often find a rich Seaweed-vegetation, among which Fucaceæ are conspicuous, but there are also a considerable number of Green (*Ulva*, *Cladophora*) and some Red Algæ, the latter commonly growing where they are partially shaded. On rocky shores the brown forms show a marked zonation, depending probably on a varying capacity to withstand desiccation.

Pelvetia (Fig. 188) and *Fucus spiralis* occupy the uppermost zone, and many of the plants occur in situations which, except at spring tides, are only reached by spray; the more exposed individuals exhibit a marked dwarfing. Above this spray-belt the cliff-surface constitutes the characteristic home of a number of Lichens and certain Flowering Plants, notably the wild Cabbage (*Brassica oleracea*), *Spergularia rupicola*, *Crithmum maritimum*, and *Inula crithmoides*. Below the level of the spray-belt the intertidal region is occupied in the upper part mainly by *Fucus vesiculosus* (Fig. 186), often accompanied by the related *Ascophyllum*, whilst *Fucus serratus* (Fig. 187) is more abundant in the lower part of this zone. A very typical Seaweed at low-tide level on exposed coasts is another member of Fucaceae, *Himanthalia*, with forked strap-like fertile thalli.

The abundant mucilage of Seaweeds helps to retain moisture and so minimises the effect of alternate submergence and drying to which all forms living between tide-limits are exposed.

The *Beach* itself, above high-tide level, is not infrequently composed of more or less water-worn fragments or pebbles forming a fringe of shingle to the shore (*e.g.* at Pevensey) or constituting a bar or spit (*e.g.* Chesil Bank, Hurst Castle Bank). Inhospitable as these situations seem, exposed to the full force of the wind, and with a barren soil composed of shingle, sand, and a small amount of drift (*i.e.* plant-remains cast up by the sea or from salt-marshes), yet these habitats are the chief home of many plants that are almost or entirely confined to such localities. Amongst the commonest may be mentioned the Yellow Horned Poppy (*Glaucium flavum*), Wild Beetroot (*Beta maritima*), Sea Campion (*Silene maritima*), Sea Purslane (*Honkenya peploides*), and Crisped Dock (*Rumex crispus* var. *trigranulatus*); more locally *Suæda fruticosa*, Sea-kale (*Crambe*), and the Maritime Pea (*Lathyrus maritimus*) are conspicuous features. Most of these plants have deep roots and fleshy leaves.

The controlling conditions upon the shingle-beach are primarily those of the soil with its extreme mobility,[1] small amount of humus, and lack of capacity for water-retention. The plants inhabiting a pebble-beach are at times partially buried under the shingle carried up during storms, and their presence in such habitats is only possible owing to their capacity for growing through to the new surface. The vegetation appears to depend for its existence largely upon a regular supply of humus to the shingle and, as a consequence, fringing banks which only receive a small amount of drift from the sea are often very bare, whilst those forming a bar or spit exhibit more extensive vegetation, as a result of the more abundant humus derived mainly from the marshes behind.

If we place our hand on a shingle-beach on a sunny day, the surface-pebbles will be found to be quite hot, but if these are scraped away the pebbles below feel cool and are often wet with moisture that is not salt to the taste. Owing to the loose character of the shingle, it is a poor conductor of heat, so that the radiant energy falling on the surface is not appreciably transmitted to lower levels. The hot air between the surface pebbles rises and these convection currents draw in warm moist air, from over the sea or adjacent marshes, which impinging on the cool stones of the interior leads to condensation or so-called *internal dew-formation*. This is an important source of water-supply to the vegetation, especially as it is most plentiful in sunny weather when there is no rain.

---

[1] Where the shingle is relatively stable, small Lichens of a black or grey colour often cover the surface of the pebbles (cf. p. 341).

The vegetation is mainly perennial and of low, mat-like, growth, only developing tall erect stems, if at all, at the time of flowering. After the seeds are shed the upper parts die away, so that during the stress of winter and the winds of early spring the foliage appears either as a rosette closely pressed against the ground (*e.g.* Horned Poppy), or takes the form of winter-buds situated upon the subterranean portion of the stem (as in *Honkenya peploides*).

The *sand-dune* (Fig. 393–4) has much in common with the shingle-beach, also showing internal dew-formation, but the smaller size of the particles, which include many calcareous shell-fragments, whilst rendering the soil more retentive of water, vastly increases its mobility. This shifting character is indeed a prime factor determining the vegetation.

In any locality where sand-hills abound (*e.g.* Southport, Braunton) it will be noticed that those nearest the sea are small and bear very little vegetation (Fig. 393); as we pass landwards, however, the dunes become larger and merge one into another, whilst the clothing of vegetation becomes more and more complete. The foremost dunes in which the sand is still readily moved by the wind are spoken of as *shifting* or *yellow dunes*. Here, as in the shingle-beach, it is the surface-layers that are transported when the requisite velocity is attained. Nearly all the plants found upon these young dunes are perennial and capable of repeated growth, when buried by the wind-borne sand. Any dead object projecting above the surface will check the speed of the wind and cause some of its burden to be shed. The pioneer plants as they grow offer an increasing obstacle to the wind and so, increasing deposition, bring about a rise in level.

In the earliest stages the first small heaps of sand usually collect around plants of the Marram-grass (*Ammophila arenaria*, Fig. 393), the Sea Couch-grass (*Agropyron junceiforme*), or, less frequently, the Lyme-grass (*Elymus*); the Marram-grass is much more sensitive to sea-water than the Couch-grass, so that the latter can form dunes lower down the shore. As layer upon layer accumulates, the shoots of the Grasses become successively covered, but no sooner does this take place than further growth from the rhizomes is stimulated and fresh tufts of leaves are formed at the surface (cf. Fig. 395). These not only accelerate deposition, but provide protection against removal.

The same process goes on repeatedly, each fresh layer of sand thus becoming bound to those beneath, so that the enlarging dune is permeated by a skeletal system formed of the branched rhizomes of the Grasses concerned. In this way the whole is knit together and a certain degree of stability is imparted to the extremely mobile

FIG. 393. Young dunes, Blakeney, Norfolk, showing collection of sand behind young plants of the Marram-grass. Older stages are seen in the background. [Photo. E. J. S.]

FIG. 394. "Blow-out" in a dune, Blakeney, Norfolk. The dense covering of Marram-grass is seen in profile, whilst owing to the action of the wind the rhizomes are seen exposed below. [Photo. E. J. S.]

soil-particles. Fresh sand will always tend to collect on the side away from the direction of the prevailing winds, owing to the shelter which the plants and, in later stages, the dunes themselves afford. If strong winds obtain for any length of time in a contrary direction, a considerable quantity of the accumulated sand may be removed and in this way "blow-outs" (*i.e.* excavations in the dune) will be produced, exposing to view the repeatedly branched rhizomes of the Grasses (Fig. 394), the older parts of which are, however, dead.

FIG. 395. Portion of an *Ammophila* - plant (about one-half natural size), showing leaf-production at successive levels of dune-surface, these levels being indicated by dotted lines.

Other plants that act as sand-binders are the Sea Holly (*Eryngium*), Sea Convolvulus (*Calystegia soldanella*), Sand Fescue (*Festuca arenaria*), and Sand Sedge (*Carex arenaria*), the last two, in virtue of the numerous tufts of foliage arising from their horizontal creeping rhizomes, tending to stabilise the surface-layers. The sea-front of the dunes, where there is abundant humus due to drift, is usually inhabited by the Sea Rocket (*Cakile maritima*), Prickly Saltwort (*Salsola kali*), and Orach (*Atriplex* spp.).

On the slightly older and more *fixed dunes*, which are lower than the yellow dunes, numerous shallow-rooted annuals are generally to be found, especially on the lee side. These germinate in the autumn and pass through their life-cycle in the winter and spring, whilst surface-moisture is plentiful, and dry up with the advent of summer. Examples are furnished by species of Mouse-ear Chickweed (*Cerastium tetrandrum* and *C. semidecandrum*), Lamb's Lettuce (*Valerianella*), Whitlow-grass (*Erophila verna*), *Myosotis hispida*, *Phleum arenarium* (Fig. 396), etc. Unlike the perennials, these do not exhibit repeated growth, but this is the less essential since the superficial moisture during the few months of their existence tends to "lay" the fine sand at the surface, which latter they themselves protect against the wind. At this phase Mosses, particularly *Tortula ruraliformis*, add to the vegetation carpet.

As the dunes become more stable, other plants, less tolerant of mobile sand, begin to appear upon the lee face, gradually creeping to the windward side as this becomes sheltered by the dunes in front. Amongst such plants are *Sedum acre, Galium verum, Senecio jacobæa, Erodium neglectum, Lotus corniculatus, Rosa spinosissima, Ononis repens,* and *Taraxacum erythrospermum.* At a relatively advanced stage in dune-fixation numerous Lichens (e.g. *Cladonia* spp., *Peltigera*) appear and their presence gives the sandhills a general grey colour. Hence fixed dunes are sometimes

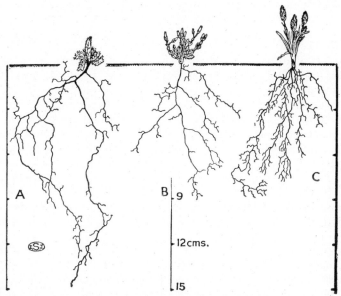

Fig. 396. Root-systems of dune annuals, showing the shallow depth of penetration. A, *Myosotis hispida.* B, *Cerastium semidecandrum.* C, *Phleum arenarium.* (After Salisbury.)

spoken of as *grey dunes*, in contrast to the mobile or yellow dunes. Eventually a scrub may form upon the dunes in which the Sea Buckthorn (*Hippophaë rhamnoides*), Elder (*Sambucus*), Bittersweet (*Solanum dulcamara*), Brambles, and occasionally Privet, are conspicuous forms. Between the dune-ridges moisture tends to accumulate, constituting what are termed *dune-slacks*, and here a marshy type of vegetation is established with Creeping Willow (*Salix repens*) as a common species. Here too, as on some of the dune-ridges of intermediate age, characteristic calcicole species are frequent, through the leaching down of carbonates.

The progressive increase in the number of species is rendered possible by the gradual amelioration of the extreme conditions. Not only does the stability increase but, as the plant population multiplies, organic matter is continually added to the soil, so that its water-retaining capacity is augmented and its fertility improved. Hand in hand with these changes the soil becomes more acid, as the carbonates in the shell-fragments (p. 558) are removed by leaching. The changes above described constitute a very definite plant-succession. Owing to its mode of formation in successive ridges parallel to the coast, the sand-dune community is peculiar in that the phases of succession in time correspond to their sequence in space, the youngest being nearest the sea, the oldest inland.

The plants inhabiting the dune are practically all xeromorphic with rolled leaves (*e.g.* the Grasses), fleshy leaves (*e.g.* Stone-crop, Sea Convolvulus), very hairy leaves (Sea Buckthorn, Stork's Bill), spines (Sea Holly, Sea Buckthorn), sunken stomata, etc. This xeromorphic habit is due not only to the poor capacity of the soil for water-retention, but also to exposure to winds and the strong heating of the surface-layers of the sand on sunny days. Most of the perennials inhabiting the dune have deep and extensive (cf. p. 496) roots which reach the subsoil moisture, in part provided by internal dew-formation. The powdery surface forms a mulch (p. 495), diminishing loss by evaporation from the layers below.

The thick cuticle of many of the dune-plants not only prevents excessive transpiration, but also protects them from injury due to impact of sand-grains. The pioneer Grasses are characterised by a specialised leaf-anatomy that enables the transpiring surface to be adjusted to the water-income. An excellent example is afforded by *Ammophila*. A section across the rolled-up leaf is more or less circular in outline (Fig. 397, A), and is bounded on the outer (*i.e.* under) surface by an epidermis provided with a thick cuticle (*Cu.*) and devoid of stomata; within are several layers of rounded thick-walled cells (Fig. 397, B, *m.*). The inner (*i.e.* upper) surface has a corrugated appearance, being produced into a number of longitudinal ridges, each of which is traversed by a vascular bundle (*V.b.*). The intervening grooves are flanked by photo-synthetic tissue consisting of more or less rounded cells (*A.t.*). The scattered stomata (*S.*) correspond in position with this tissue and are consequently confined to the furrows, where additional protection is furnished by numerous stiff interlocking hairs (Fig. 397, A).

The epidermal cells at the base of each groove are exceptionally large (*hinge-cells*, Fig. 397, *h.* and *h.c.*) and, being relatively thin-walled, are the first to lose water and shrink when transpiration is excessive. As a result the inner surface of the leaf contracts in width (*i.e.* transversely), so that the flat edges formed by the marginal ridges are brought together, and the leaf as a whole

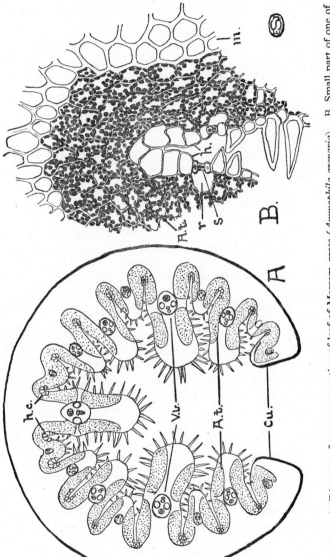

Fig. 397. A, Diagram of transverse section of leaf of Marram-grass (*Ammophila arenaria*). B, Small part of one of the grooves, with adjacent tissues, enlarged. *A.t.*, photosynthetic tissue; *Cu.*, cuticle; *h.* and *h.c.*, hinge-cells; *m.*, mechanical tissue; *r.*, respiratory cavity; *S.*, stoma; *V.b.*, vascular bundles.

becomes tubular. When the water-supply is plentiful the reverse action takes place and the blade becomes flattened.

In the more sheltered situations along the shore (*e.g.* bays and estuaries) large tracts of mud, or mud and sand, intersected by water-channels, frequently accumulate. Such areas which are periodically inundated by the tides constitute the habitat known as the *salt-marsh* (Fig. 398), and are frequented by plants very tolerant of saline conditions (*halophytes*). The first obvious colonisers in these situations are usually annual species of Marsh Samphire or Glasswort (*Salicornia*, Fig. 400) which, however, probably always follow small filamentous Green and Blue-green Algæ that have already to some extent bound together the surface-layers. On the south coast, especially that of Hampshire, the mud-flats are colonised by the Eel-grass (*Zostera*) and the Cordgrass (*Spartina Townsendii*), the latter eventually forming a dense community like a maritime Reed-bed.

The colonising Glasswort forms an obstacle to the incoming tide and silt is deposited from it. As the level rises the vegetation becomes less scanty and several additional species appear, such as the Sea Plantain (*Plantago maritima*), Arrow-grass (*Triglochin maritimum*), Sea Aster (*Aster tripolium*), Sea Blite (*Suæda maritima*), and the Sea Manna-grass (*Puccinellia maritima*). As further silt collects and the level of the marsh as a whole rises still higher, the number of species and the density of the vegetation increase; in this intermediate condition (Fig. 398) the Sea Pink (*Armeria maritima*), Sand Spurrey (*Spergularia marginata*), Sea Lavender (*Limonium*), and Sea Mugwort (*Artemisia maritima*) are often found in abundance. Sandy salt-marshes are particularly characterised by the Perennial Glasswort (*Salicornia perennis*), *Glaux maritima*, and Sea Heath (*Frankenia lævis*), all found more especially towards the landward edge. The Silver Goosefoot (*Halimione portulacoides*) sometimes invades the more sandy types of salt-marsh, first of all colonising the borders of the creeks (or water-channels) and then gradually spreading over the whole, until the former occupants are almost entirely driven out. In the final stage, when the level of the marsh is such that it is not covered even by the highest tides, a *salt-pasture* is formed, characterised, as the salt becomes leached out, by the presence of such Grasses as Bent-grass, Fescue, etc. Much of the flat land reclaimed from the sea occupies the former site of such salt-pastures (Fig. 399) which have been drained and cut off by dykes from the inroads of exceptionally high tides.

Salt-marshes again exhibit a succession (cf. p. 525), with a few highly specialised species in the initial stages,

FIG. 398. Intermediate stage in salt-marsh formation, Hunstanton, Norfolk.
The most conspicuous plant is *Armeria maritima* (in flower); the remaining
vegetation consists of *Salicornia, Statice, Plantago maritima*, etc. On the
horizon is seen a range of low sand-dunes. [Photo. E. J. S.]

FIG. 399. Reclaimed salt-marshes, Bristol Channel. The flat-lying fields in
the middle distance have been reclaimed from the sea. The dark areas in the
distance, just beyond the shore-line, are salt-marshes in an early stage of
colonisation. [Photo. E. J. S.]

giving place to a larger assemblage, as the influence of tidal inundation is progressively diminished. So long as this is frequent and prolonged, fresh sand, silt and mud are deposited at frequent intervals. The lowest part of the marsh is therefore raised most rapidly, while by contrast the highest rises only slowly. In this way the level contour, so characteristic of this type of vegetation is produced. In many salt-marshes certain plants occupy definite zones, corresponding to frequency of tidal inundation, a feature which is pronounced when the Sea-rush (*Juncus maritimus*) and *Artemisia maritima* are present. They form fringes at the upper edge of the marsh, the former conspicuous by its height, the latter by its white hairy leaves.

The salt-marsh soil contains a considerable proportion of chlorides, especially great during intertidal periods as a result of evaporation, but relatively small if heavy rainfall occurs at such times. The importance of the latter in washing out the salt is shown by the dwarf character of the vegetation in dry summers. After inundation by the sea the soil-solution has a high osmotic potential so that, by reason of its concentration, absorption may present difficulty. Actually the root-cells of salt-marsh plants are exceptionally permeable to chlorides so that their osmotic potential tends to vary *pari passu* with that of the soil-solution. The plants however, benefit greatly from dilution of the latter by rain, although thus subjected to marked fluctuations of osmotic potential.

The succulent character of many of the halophytes inhabiting salt-marshes is due to the development of large numbers of water-storing cells (aqueous tissue, cf. p. 510). This is well seen in *Salicornia* (Fig. 400), in which the opposite leaves ensheathe the stem and give the plant a jointed appearance, the flowers being embedded in threes in the tissue of the shoot (cf. Fig. 400). This succulence appears to be related to the presence of salt in the soil, since a considerable number of plants develop a similar fleshy habit when growing in saline situations (*e.g.* Bird's-foot Trefoil, *Plantago coronopus*). The majority of salt-marsh plants are perennials, although *Salicornia stricta* and *Suæda maritima* are summer annuals.

It has been stated that salt-marsh soil may be either sandy or muddy in character, with varying proportions of organic silt. This depends on the nature of the tide-borne material, to which that brought down by streams into the estuary contributes. When the salt-marsh is muddy, the conditions of aeration for the root-systems may be poor and then the *Salicornias* not infrequently develop aerenchyma (Fig. 401), comparable to that of plants of the fresh-water marsh.

This brief account of plant-communities may be concluded by a consideration of the processes of *colonisation*. Wherever fresh soil is exposed (*e.g.* land-slides, railway embankments, quarries, Fig. 402), it sooner or later becomes covered with vegetation, and in this succession various phases are again recognisable. Frequently Algæ, Lichens and Mosses are the pioneers, particularly where the subsoil is sand or rock, and thus constitute a primary source of humus.

As a soil develops, higher plants are able to establish themselves,

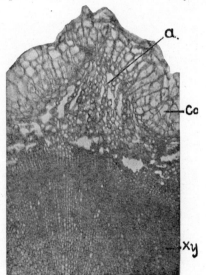

FIG. 400. Small plant of the Glasswort (*Salicornia*, about two-thirds natural size).

FIG. 401. Photomicrograph of a small portion of the aerenchyma (*a*) of the Marsh Samphire (*Salicornia*). *Co.*, cortex; *Xy.*, xylem. [Photo. E. J. S.]

either simultaneously with or subsequent to the pioneers. Most of the former are usually annuals, which grow in the adjacent districts and possess a good dispersal-mechanism (e.g. *Poa annua, Senecio vulgaris*, etc.). The broken surface of arable land (cf. p. 532) may be said never to get beyond this early phase in the succession. In later stages of natural colonisation an increasing number of perennials are found, these gradually ousting the annuals by competition, the order of their appearance often corresponding to the efficiency of their means of dispersal (*e.g.* Grasses, Willow-herbs, numerous Compositæ, Creeping Buttercup, etc.).

In early stages of all successions the vegetation is open, *i.e.* there are considerable areas of bare ground between the plants,

which latter are few as regards the number of species. Subsequently the vegetation becomes denser and denser, and for a
time we have a relatively large number of forms battling for
supremacy, until eventually the successful ones alone hold the
field, these being mainly perennials. If the soil remains undisturbed,
shrubs and trees will after some time begin to assert themselves
(Fig. 402), and thus we may ultimately get a dense scrub, analogous

Fig. 402. Colonisation of a disused quarry, Yorkshire. In the foreground
are Ferns, Furze, Brambles, Wood-sage, etc.   The barer parts are only occupied
by Mosses and Heather.   In the background are bushes of Broom.
[Photo. E. J. S.]

to that described on p. 526, or even woodland.   A similar succession
from an open to a closed community has been noticed above in
our description of the succession on sand-dunes and salt-marshes.
It will be noted that in general the dominant species increase in
size as the succession progresses.

A somewhat analogous series of phases can be observed after
the coppicing of a wood (p. 522) or the devastation of a heath by
fire, although here there is not only colonisation but also sprouting of the underground parts of the woody plants.   We may take
the reclothing of a burnt *Calluna*-heath as an example.   In the
first years after a fire a considerable number of species (Rose-bay
Willow-herb, Wood-sage, Tormentil, Milkwort, etc.) appear in

large quantity; subsequently as the new shoots sprouting from
the shrubby members of the heath-flora (Gorse, Fig. 403, Heather,
etc.) assert themselves, these earlier colonisers become more and
more crowded out, until finally the original condition may be
re-established.

Each phase of a succession is marked by a definite physiognomy,

FIG. 403. Colonisation of burnt heath, Hindhead, Surrey. The vegetation
consists largely of the sprouting stumps of the Dwarf Furze (*Ulex minor*).
[Photo. W. B. Johnson.]

and its members are often characterised by common morphological
and anatomical features. Thus, the pioneers on a salt-marsh and
arable land are alike annuals, whilst most of the species characteristic of later phases are perennials. The common species in a
Callunetum often have small leaves with the stomata confined to
grooves, and the plants of a salt-marsh are mostly succulents.
Furthermore, we may note that the general trend of succession is
to render conditions less extreme, so that the desert-like sand-
dune on the one hand, and the water-logged swamp on the other,
both come by a sequence of natural changes to approximate to
a similar type of climax community, namely, woodland, which may
itself be specialised with respect to shade conditions.

There is experimental evidence to show that in the later phases
of plant-succession, some species at least can form substances that
are inimical to the growth of their competitors. They thus tend to
contribute towards their own permanent establishment.

CHAPTER XLVII

THE GEOGRAPHICAL ELEMENTS OF THE BRITISH FLORA

THE geographical distribution of plants over the surface of the earth is mainly related to differences of climate, the distribution of a species often depending on its tolerance of cold or heat, dry or wet conditions, etc. But, apart from such instances in which the range of species is limited by their inability to withstand competition under adverse climatic conditions, certain species, genera, or even families are found to be restricted to particular areas of the earth's surface, though others may also be well suited to their existence. This fact is constantly being illustrated by the successful spread of species after their first introduction into a country. For example, the Canadian Pondweed (*Elodea canadensis*), which was brought to England from America about 1847, now occupies almost every waterway in this country (cf. Fig. 404). A similar phenomenon, on land, is presented by the Prickly Pear (*Opuntia*) in Australia. It may be supposed, in respect to such plants, that the ordinary agencies of dispersal have not sufficed to bring the species to all regions in which it can thrive successfully, though often such extension of range is only possible where human influence has diminished the severity of competition.

The natural barriers to the spread of plants are oceans, mountain ranges, deserts, etc., and it is significant that isolated islands (*e.g.* New Zealand) are peculiarly the home of species, so-called *endemics*, which are found there, and there alone. The capacity of a species to extend its range in new territory depends on an efficient seed-dispersal, the rapidity of its spread by this or by vegetative means, and its vigour in competition with others.

The British Isles afford an outstanding example of the con-tinuous colonisation of an island from the adjacent land masses. They present very varied conditions alike in respect to climate, to geology, and to economic development. In the west the rainfall tends to be high and the climate humid and more equable, whereas in the east the rainfall is low and conditions generally are drier and more extreme. The south-eastern area is, moreover, a region of dense population and great industrialisation, and has from remote times been most subject to human influence. It is a consequence of

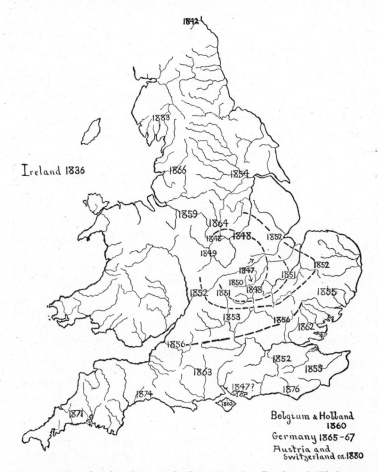

FIG. 404. Map showing the spread of the Canadian Pondweed (*Elodea cana-densis*) after its appearance in England in 1847. The broken lines connect identical years.

these facts that, not only does Britain present a wide range of habitat conditions, but there tends to be a segregation into two major environmental regions, the transition zone between which has a general south-west to north-east trend. This is very marked with respect to many southern and continental species (e.g. *Iberis amara* and *Muscari racemosum,* Fig. 405) which show a northern limit roughly south of a line from the Bristol Channel to the Wash.

The vascular plants of Britain number some 1500 species, of which probably not more than twenty are endemic. Most of the others are also found on the European mainland, though a few are American species (e.g. *Sisyrinchium angustifolium*). Some of the hardier members of our flora probably persisted from preglacial times in unglaciated areas, but the majority are species that re-colonised this country after the retreat of the ice. This process of colonisation has doubtless been a continuous one from post-glacial times to the present day. Evidence furnished by seeds, pollen grains, leaves, etc., preserved in peat, indicates a succession of climatic changes, each of which would have favoured the establish-ment of species with particular environmental preferences.

In the earliest post-glacial times (the preboreal period) the vegetation would seem to have been tundra-like in character with a preponderance of Dwarf Birch (*Betula nana*), Dwarf Willows (e.g. *Salix herbacea, S. reticulata*), *Dryas octopetala*, and other species, such as are common in Arctic regions to-day. The later part of the pre-boreal period was marked by the development of extensive Birch-woods, perhaps of a scrubby character, in which Pines became more and more conspicuous, leading to a Pine-maximum. The boreal period which followed was characterised by climatic conditions typical of continental areas, namely, relatively low humidity and extremes of temperature. During this period *Pinus* diminished in frequency and the Hazel attained a predominant position, although Birch and Pine were probably still common.

In the succeeding phase the climate would appear to have entirely altered; it was markedly oceanic with a relatively high humidity and mild conditions. This Atlantic period witnessed the development of extensive mixed woods of Oak with Birch, Elm, Lime, and Hazel. The high humidity of this epoch favoured increase of the Alder that had now immigrated into Britain, whilst the equable climatic conditions were responsible for woodlands attaining, during this Atlantic period, their altitudinal maximum, marked to-day perhaps by the upper limit of communities of *Calluna* in Britain and of species of *Rhododendron* in the Alps.

A return to more continental conditions characterised the succeeding sub-boreal period, after which an oceanic climate returned in a less marked degree, constituting the sub-Atlantic period, when the Beech and Hornbeam probably first immigrated into Britain.

During the earlier part of post-glacial times nomadic palæolithic man may have occasionally set fire to forests to augment the pasturage for the grazing animals which he hunted. His rather crude implements were unsuited to the felling of timber, and indeed his activities in this direction would normally involve the cutting of mere firewood of small girth. However, with the advent of neolithic man, who was an agriculturist, permanent destruction of forests began, affecting especially, until the age of metals, the softer timber trees such as Pine and Birch. The felling of *Pinus sylvestris* by neolithic man probably accelerated, if it did not actually cause, the disappearance of natural forests of this species in the greater part of England and Ireland.

The smelting of iron made enormous demands on wood for the manufacture of charcoal, and is known to have been a prime cause of the disafforestation of the Weald of Kent. As an outcome of the extension of agriculture, the growing demand for pasturage to serve the flourishing wool-industry, and the ever-increasing fuel-requirements until the general adoption of coal, the extensive forests of former times are to-day represented by mere remnants. Despite this, however, the high proportion of woodland species in the existing flora of Britain is a witness to the former importance of this type of habitat.

The large areas of grasslands, moorlands, and heaths, which occupy erstwhile forest regions, provide for the species of the former habitats a much more extended area than in primitive times. The increase of habitations and the creation of a network of roads, canals, and railways in more modern times again have furnished open communities of plants by their sides, permitting of colonisation by newly introduced species, many of which maintain but a precarious tenure, whilst others become permanent features of our flora.

The distinction between native and introduced species is rather arbitrary, being a difference of degree rather than of kind. It is, however, of importance to recognise that, whilst many species of our flora flourish in wild habitats enduring the full rigour of competition, others only persist where, as in arable fields, waysides, etc., artificial interference by man restricts biotic factors. Most so-called native species belong to the former category, those known to have been introduced mostly to the latter. But some, recorded as definite immigrants in recent years, such as *Elodea canadensis* and *Impatiens capensis*, can flourish in communities where competition is severe and unrestricted.

We can recognise in our flora various geographical elements, each of which is characterised by certain marked environmental preferences, as shown by the distribution of the constituent species on the European mainland. The presence of these groups is

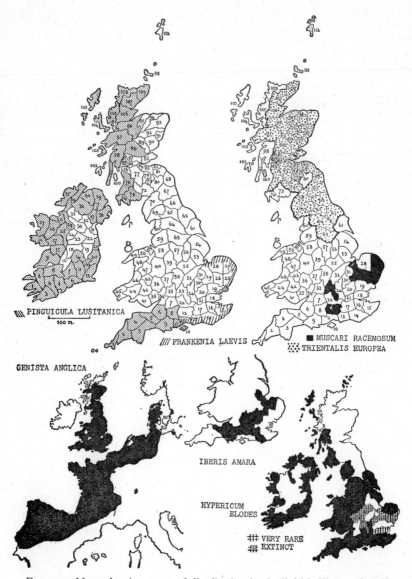

FIG. 405. Maps showing types of distribution in the British Flora. Oceanic types are represented by *Genista anglica*, *Hypericum elodes*, and markedly oceanic types by *Pinguicula lusitanica*. The continental type is represented by *Muscari racemosum*. Southern types are represented by *Iberis amara* and the Mediterranean *Frankenia lœvis*, whilst *Trientalis europea* is a northern species. (After Salisbury.)

perhaps a result of the striking climatic vicissitudes of the past, to which reference has already been made. For instance, there are in our flora some 100 species that are normal constituents of Arctic and sub-Arctic vegetation. With the rising tide of temperature after the boreal period, these were left stranded on the summits of our higher mountains, isolated by the sea of lowland warmth. Examples of such Arctic relics, which persist to the present day, are furnished by *Salix herbacea*, *Saxifraga oppositifolia* (Fig. 406), and *Dryas octopetala*. Even more striking perhaps is the small Alpine element, of which *Gentiana verna* and *Cherleria sedoides* furnish examples. This comprises about nine species, which do not occur in northern regions, but are characteristic of the Alps of Southern Europe and which may well have been enabled to cross the intervening plains by the cold of the glacial period. Amongst the more frequent species of the "Northern Element" in Britain may be mentioned the Globe Flower (*Trollius europæus*), the Bird's-eye Primrose (*Primula farinosa*), and *Trientalis europæa* (Fig. 405).

The large oceanic component of our flora is composed of species mainly found in Western Europe and often absent from the drier eastern side of Britain. Their northern limit tends to approximate to a line extending from the north-west to the south-east. Colonisation by and spread of these species was probably favoured during Atlantic times. In this group we can recognise a markedly oceanic element, the species of which are restricted to the Atlantic seaboard of Europe, and especially to that of the Iberian Peninsula. This is sometimes termed the Lusitanian element and in Britain has its chief home in the West of Ireland, the Cornish Peninsula, and Dorset. It includes the Cornish and Dorset Heaths (*Erica vagans* and *E. ciliaris*, Fig. 406), *Pinguicula lusitanica* (Fig. 405), *Scilla verna*, *Ranunculus lenormandi*, etc. A less restricted element, but still definitely oceanic, comprises such species as *Genista anglica* (Fig. 405) and *Erica cinerea*, whilst the Wild Hyacinth, though definitely western, extends as far east as Germany.

The southern component in our flora includes a Mediterranean group, of which *Suæda fruticosa*, *Frankenia lævis* (Fig. 405), and *Limonium bellidifolium* furnish examples. The southern element, in a less restricted sense, comprises plants especially found in southern England, and includes many cornfield weeds, such as *Antirrhinum orontium*, *Anagallis, cærulea* and *Silene anglica*.

On the sandy heaths of East Anglica the porous soil and the low rainfall, which is often under twenty inches, combine to produce conditions simulating those of Central Europe. The plants of this

FIG. 406. Above, *Erica ciliaris* (oceanic type); below, *Saxifraga oppositifolia* (Arctic relic).

"continental element" embrace a number of mostly rare species, such as the Grape Hyacinth (*Muscari racemosum*, Fig. 405), *Phleum phleoides*, and *Silene conica*.

A large number of native plants (about half our flora) have a wide distribution on the Continent and, in Britain, mostly exhibit no very marked climatic preferences. The great variety of soils, due in part to a wide geological range, and the absence of a highly differentiated climate, have combined to favour the establishment of species from diverse habitats, and, as we have seen, from a variety of sources. Accretions to our flora continue, but whilst most persist only in semi-artificial habitats, some like the hybrid *Spartina townsendii* or *Mimulus luteus* remain as permanent constituents of natural or semi-natural communities.

The number of species known to have been lost to the British flora is very small, including only a very few marsh-plants, though a large number have disappeared during the past hundred years from some of their former localities. Among such diminishing species plants of wet habitats are the most frequent, a feature associated with a general lowering of the water-table. On the other hand, man's activities, resulting in a marked increase in the area of disturbed soil, has promoted the temporary establishment of many aliens.

The British flora is much less rich in species than that of the European mainland, as is indicated by the fact that in France some 4000 vascular plants are to be found. So too the flora of Ireland contains fewer species than England and Scotland. There are only about 1000 species of vascular plants in Ireland, and amongst the commoner English species which are absent may be cited *Genista anglica* (cf. Fig. 405), the Rest Harrow (*Ononis spinosa*), *Scabiosa columbaria*, and *Helictotrichon pratense*. Others, such as the Rock Rose (*Helianthemum chamæcistus*), *Geranium pratense*, and *Adoxa moschatellina*, which are widely distributed in England and Scotland, are rare in Ireland. On the other hand, there are about a dozen species found in Ireland that do not occur in Britain; such are the Mediterranean Strawberry Tree (*Arbutus unedo*), *Erica mediterranea*, and *Dabœcia cantabrica*, as well as the American *Sisyrinchium* and *Spiranthes ramonzoffiana*. Most of these floristic differences are probably due to greater climatic specialisation and other environmental factors in Ireland, rather than to inadequacy of dispersal.

For further details on HISTORY AND DISTRIBUTION OF THE BRITISH FLORA, see:

CLEMENT REID, *The Origin of the British Flora*, 1899 (191 pp., out of print), a useful summary of the recent geological history of British vascular plants.

E. J. SALISBURY, *The East Anglian Flora*, Norfolk and Norwich Nat. Soc., 1932 (173 pp.), a study of comparative plant-geography in relation to the whole British flora, including distribution maps of over a hundred species.

E. J. SALISBURY, *The Influence of Man on Vegetation*. Trans. South-Eastern Union Scient. Soc., 1933 (17 pp.).

R. L. PRAEGER, *The Botanist in Ireland*, Hodges, Figgis & Co., Dublin, 1934 (250 pp.), an attractive account of plant-distribution in Ireland.

H. C. WATSON, *Topographical Botany*, 2nd edit., London 1883 (612 pp.); together with the two supplements (*Journal of Botany*, 1905 and 1929–30), gives the comital and vice-comital records for England and Scotland.

A. WILSON, *The Altitudinal Range of British Plants*. T. Buncle, Arbroath, 1931 (105 pp.).

R. GOOD, *The Geography of the Flowering Plants*, Longmans, Green & Co., 1947 (403 pp.).

The following are standard British FLORAS for the diverse classes:—

(a) *Spermaphyta* and *Pteridophyta*

H. D. HOOKER, *The Students' Flora of the British Isles*. Macmillan & Co., 1930.

A. R. CLAPHAM, T. G. TUTIN and E. F. WARBURG, *Flora of the British Isles*, Cambridge Univ. Press, 1952.

G. C. DRUCE, *Hayward's Botanists' Pocket Book*. Bell & Sons, 19th edit., 1930 (useful in the field).

W. H. FITCH and W. G. SMITH, *Illustrations of the British Flora*. L. Reeve, 1924.

R. W. BUTCHER and F. E. STRUDWICK, *Further Illustrations of British Plants*. L. Reeve, 1930.

S. ROSS-CRAIG, *Drawings of British Plants*. G. Bell & Sons, 1948.

V. S. SUMMERHAYES, *The Wild Orchids of Britain*. Collins, 1951 (366 pp.).

For CULTIVATED PLANTS, see:

F. J. CHITTENDEN, *Dictionary of Gardening*, 4 vols. Oxford, 1952.

W. J. BEAN, *Trees and Shrubs hardy in the British Isles*. Murray, 3 vols., 2nd edit., 1951.

W. DALLIMORE and A. BRUCE JACKSON, *Handbook of Coniferæ*. Arnold, 1931.

J. W. C. KIRK, *A British Garden Flora*, Arnold, 1927 (584 pp.), which provides a key for the identification of the genera of cultivated plants.

For the identification of ALIEN SPECIES occurring in Britain, the *Illustrated Flora of the Northern States and Canada*, by BRITTON and BROWN (Scribner, New York, 3 vols., 2nd edit., 1913), will be found most helpful for American species. Of the standard European Floras, the most generally useful is perhaps COSTE'S illustrated *Flore de France* (3 vols., Paris, 1906, reissue with supplement, 1938), which, covering as it does the whole of France and its borders, as well as Corsica, and illustrating upwards of 4000 species, will serve to identify most species of European origin likely to be found in Britain, and contains most species likely to be found when travelling in Western Europe. Visitors to Switzerland should consult the well-illustrated work, *Das Pflanzenleben der Alpen*, by K. SCHROETER (2nd edit., 1288 pp.), and *Die Vegetation der Schweiz*, by H. BROCKMANN-JEROSCH (1929, 499 pp.).

(b) *Bryophyta*

H. N. DIXON and H. G. JAMESON, *The Student's Handbook of British Mosses.* 2nd edit., V. V. Sumfield, Eastbourne, 1904.

J. B. DUNCAN, *A Census Catalogue of British Mosses,* 2nd edit., Berwick, 1926 (66 pp.), which gives comital and vice-comital distribution.

W. R. SHERRIN, *An Illustrated Handbook of the British Sphagna.* Taylor & Francis (74 pp.).

S. M. MACVICAR and H. G. JAMESON, *The Student's Handbook of British Hepatics.* 2nd edit., V. V: Sumfield, Eastbourne, 1926 (figures of all species).

W. INGRAM, *A Census Catalogue of British Hepatics.* Darwen, 2nd edit., 1913 (35 pp.), which gives distribution data.

(c) *Algæ*

G. S. WEST and F. E. FRITSCH, *A Treatise on the British Freshwater Algæ,* Cambridge Univ. Press, 1927 (out of print), a general account suitable for the identification of genera. For the identification of species, see A. Pascher, *Die Süsswasserflora Deutschlands, Oesterreichs und der Schweiz,* in several vols., Jena, 1914 and onwards.

W. WEST and G. S. WEST, *British Desmidiaceæ,* Ray Society, 1904–1923, 5 vols. (vol. 5 edited by N. Carter), which gives figures of all species.

G. M. SMITH, *Freshwater Algæ of the United States,* McGraw-Hill Book Co., 2nd edit., 1950, also useful for the identification of genera.

W. H. HARVEY, *Phycologia Britanica.* London, 1846–51 (Coloured plates of most British Seaweeds).

L. NEWTON, *A Handbook of British Seaweeds.* Brit. Mus. Publ., 1931 (illustrated).

W. R. TAYLOR, *Marine Algæ of the North-eastern Coast of North America.* Univ. of Michigan Press, 1937 (illustrations of many Seaweeds).

J. GROVES and G. R. BULLOCK-WEBSTER, *British Charophyta.* 2 vols., Ray Society, 1917 and 1924 (Figures of all species).

(d) *Fungi*

J. RAMSBOTTOM, *A Handbook of the Larger British Fungi.* Brit. Mus. Publ., 1923 (illustrated).

E. M. WAKEFIELD and R. W. G. DENNIS, *Common British Fungi.* Gawthorn, 1951 (290 pp.) (coloured illustrations).

CARLETON REA, *British Basidiomycetæ.* Cambridge Univ. Press, 1922 (799 pp.).

W. B. GROVE, *British Stem and Leaf-Fungi (Cœlomycetes).* Cambridge Univ. Press, 1933 (488 pp.).

W. B. GROVE, *The British Rust Fungi,* 1913 (412 pp.).

A. and G. LISTER, *A Monograph of the Mycetozoa.* Brit. Mus. Publ., 3rd edit., 1925 (296 pp., illustrations of all the species).

A. LORRAINE SMITH, *Handbook of British Lichens.* Brit. Mus. Publ., 1921 (158 pp.).

CHAPTER XLVIII

HEREDITY AND EVOLUTION[1]

THE features exhibited by any particular individual are determined by two sets of factors, namely those due to heredity and those due to environment. There is abundant evidence that inheritance is particulate and since, except for vegetative propagation, each individual develops from a single cell, this must contain all the determinants for the potentialities of the adult (*genotype*). These determinants, the *genes*, are mostly located in the chromosomes and every gene normally divides at mitosis so that the daughter-cells receive an equal complement of all.

When a large population of a given species is examined clear-cut differences in respect of certain characteristics (flower-colour, shape of leaf, etc.) are often found, so that the individuals can be classified into distinct groups (*discontinuous variation*), whilst in respect of other characteristics (*e.g.* size) there is almost complete gradation and such classification is impossible (*continuous variation*). The numerous seedlings grown from the seeds of a self-pollinated Foxglove, for example, evidently inherit the same general characters, but differ among one another in diverse minor details (cf. also Fig. 407); they afford examples of continuous variation. Some of the observable distinctions are mainly due to environmental differences, but most are the outcome of hereditary influences. "Nature and nurture", however, commonly combine to produce the characters we recognise (*phenotype*).

Continuous variations may be of two kinds. They are *qualitative* or *substantive*, when, for instance, they concern the shape or size of the entire plant (Fig. 407) or of any of its parts, the degree of hairiness, the type of colouration (Fig. 408), etc. They are *quantitative* or *meristic*, when they involve differences in the number of constituent parts, such as perianth-segments, leaflets in a compound leaf, etc. Both kinds are determined by a number of genes (polygenes).

It is easiest to study variation if some character is selected which is capable of exact measurement, as, for instance, the length of the leaf in the Privet, the length of the Runner Bean seed, or the number

[1] See end of Chapter for general works of reference.

of ray-florets in the Daisy. Taking the first of these as an example, it will be found that if, say, a thousand leaves are measured, the difference between the length of the shortest and the longest is quite considerable, and that the majority of the leaves are of an average size. If all the leaves be classified into separate groups, differing by increments of one millimetre, the groups arranged in sequence, and the number of leaves in each group counted, those containing the smallest numbers will be found to be situated at the two extremes. Between these the number of leaves of each particular length will

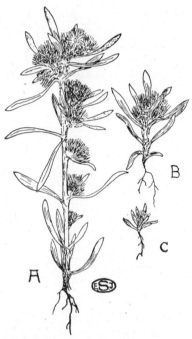

FIG. 407. Three individuals of equal age of the Marsh Cudweed (*Gnaphalium uliginosum*) from the same locality, showing individual variation. All three are in fruit. (Natural size.)

FIG. 408. Seeds of different varieties of Castor Oil (*Ricinus*), to illustrate variation within a species. [Photo. E. J. S.]

be found to increase with considerable regularity, as the size of its individuals approaches that exhibited by the majority. This most frequent size is termed the *mode*, and often corresponds very closely to the arithmetical mean of all the measurements.

By plotting a curve, in which the ordinates represent the number of individuals in each group, and the abscissæ the respective lengths, the variation can be graphically represented (Fig. 409). The larger the number of individuals taken into account, the smoother the outline of and the more symmetrical the curve. Such *variation curves* are most commonly symmetrical (Fig. 409, left), but they may be one-sided or asymmetrical (Fig. 409, right), as in meristic variation of the corolla-segments of many flowers, where there are often relatively few examples with *less* than the normal number of parts.[1]

The symmetrical curve of variation (normal variation curve)

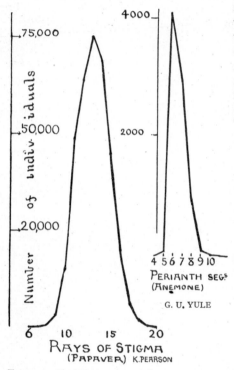

RAYS OF STIGMA
(PAPAVER) K.PEARSON

PERIANTH SEG.ˢ
(ANEMONE)

G. U. YULE

FIG. 409. Variation curves, symmetrical on the left and asymmetrical on the right.

agrees very closely with that representing variation depending on pure chance, a feature which in itself suggests that a multiplicity of controlling factors (including the environment) is involved. The classical example of such chance variation is afforded by the repeated tossing up of two coins, the combination of one head and one tail being most frequent (forming about 50 per cent.), whilst the combinations two heads or two tails occur with about equal infrequency. A more illustrative curve of chance variation would be obtained if ten coins were tossed simultaneously for a sufficiently large number of times.

In meristic variation the difference between the extremes is much greater when the mode corresponds to a large number than when it coincides with a small one. Thus, if variation due to fission of parts (say of the corolla of a flower) be equal in two species, the one having a mode of five (*i.e.* usually five petals) and the other having a mode of ten (*i.e.* usually ten petals), there would be just double the chances of fission occurring in the latter as in the former. The extreme condition (*i.e.* 10 and 20 petals) would be attained where all the petals underwent

---

[1] See G. U. Yule, *An Introduction to the Theory of Statistics*, Griffin & Co., 11th edit. 1937 (570 pp.); R. H. Fisher, *Statistical Methods for Research-workers*, Oliver & Boyd, 1936 (339 pp.).

fission. That is, the range would be greater in the one than in the other, although the actual frequency of fission of the individual segments was the same in the two species. Hence a comparison of variation, where the modes are dissimilar, can only be made by taking such dissimilarity into consideration, a comparison of the curves alone being misleading. The position of the mode can often be to some extent changed by modifying the environmental conditions, although the range of variation remains practically unaltered.

Within a *pure line* [1] the average of the race is usually maintained, since individual variations are here mostly due to environment. This has been established by sowing seeds from a single individual of pure descent which has been self-fertilised, the seed produced by the resulting plants (likewise self-fertilised) being sown in separate groups, and the same procedure followed for several successive generations. It was thus found that the average size of individuals derived from small parents is practically identical with that of individuals grown from large parents; also that heavy seeds do not beget heavier-seeded offspring than those derived from light seeds. The following data, which serve to illustrate this point, are taken from Johansen's experiments with Beans which were self-pollinated:

Weight of seeds of parents.	Average weight of seeds of offspring.
350–400 mg.	572 mg.
450–500 ,,	535 ,,
500–550 ,,	570 ,,
550–600 ,,	565 ,,
600–650 ,,	566 ,,
650–700 ,,	555 ,,

When dealing with a population consisting of members possessing varied hereditary constitution (*i.e.* not a pure line), a pure strain can often be obtained by selecting individuals which show a particular desired character and breeding from these, with due precautions against cross-pollination. In this way it might, for example, be possible by repeated *artificial selection* amongst the progeny of self-fertilisation to obtain pure lines, exhibiting a given character, *e.g.* a tall or dwarf habit. Under natural conditions the environment may often effect a similar elimination (so-called *natural selection*), since the possession of a particular character is sometimes decisive in determining which plant shall survive in the

---

[1] A pure line is a pure bred strain produced by self-fertilisation from a single individual and normally homozygous (p. 594) for the visible characters used in selection. A *clone* is a population produced by vegetative propagation (division) from a single individual.

face of competition and adverse habitat conditions. Even in a pure strain, repeated selective action may lead to the ultimate elimination of all but the heaviest, shortest, etc., individuals. This was the essence of Darwin's theory of the origin of new species, based mainly on a study of domesticated plants and animals.

The majority of plants produce such an abundance of either spores or seeds that, even with the most efficient dispersal, it would usually be impossible for more than a fraction of the offspring to become established. Many a common plant would, indeed, if the means of dispersal were adequate, and all the progeny of successive generations survived, rapidly cover a large surface of the globe. That this does not happen is due to that ceaseless competition of living organisms with one another which is known as the *struggle for existence.* A Mullein plant, for example, may produce as many as 700,000 seeds. The resulting seedlings are not of equal vigour, and those first to succumb in the struggle for existence are obviously the weakest. The latter, applying the term in its widest sense, owe their lack of vigour partly to inherited characteristics and partly to adverse environmental conditions. Just as a human being with a "weak constitution" may have inherited his defect or owe it to the surroundings in which he grows up.

Unlike most animals, plants cannot choose their place of habitation. The seeds or spores are carried passively to a variety of situations, and their chances of developing into mature plants depend upon their power of accommodating themselves to the environment in which they may be placed. But many plants exhibit this power of *adaptation* to a very marked degree, as is well illustrated by those aquatics which can grow either totally submerged or on exposed mud (cf. p. 551), by the sun- and shade-forms of woodland plants (p. 521), and by the alpine forms of lowland plants (p. 528, Fig. 370).

It has long been a matter of dispute as to whether or no the changes, impressed upon an organism by the environment, bring about any corresponding internal modification by means of which the new characters can be transmitted to the offspring. So far attempts to demonstrate satisfactorily the inheritance of such *acquired characters* in plants have proved a failure. It is indeed difficult to conceive of means by which characters, acquired by the plant in the course of its lifetime, could affect and modify the hereditary mechanism which must obviously be contained within the fusing gametes. On the other hand, the marked adaptations of plants in the wild state to their normal environment, features often retained when the organism is transferred to another habitat, naturally suggest the possibility of the unstable acquired characters becoming ultimately stabilised. This view has led to the conception of the origin of new species, etc., through cumulative selection and hereditary transmission of favourable variations (or mutations, cf. p. 586), tending towards more complete harmony between the plant and its environment. It still remains an open question,

FIG. 410. A new form or mutant which arose from a pure strain of Duke of Albany Pea and which differs in the narrow lanceolate stipules. The type on the right, the mutant on the left. [By permission of the late Prof. Bateson, F.R.S., and Miss Pellew.]

however, whether adaptation to the environment is due merely to selection among variations appearing at random or whether it is, in part at least, a result of direct response to changed surroundings and effected through a moulding influence on the structure of the plant, exerted by the environment. The problem is seen in the appearance of strains of *Staphylococcus* (Bacteria), more or less resistant to the sulphonamide drugs, and of comparable instances met with among pathogenic Fungi. These may be variations that have come to the front through elimination of their less resistant

38

competitors, but there is evidence which suggests that they may result from a changed pattern of chemical reaction within the cells themselves induced by the altered environment.

Seeing that the individual variations above considered are apparently to a large extent encompassed within the usually fixed range of the species (cf. p. 583), we must notice other kinds of changes that could more readily lead to the evolution of new forms. Among occasional populations of higher plants, and even in pure cultures of lower organisms, slight or even pronounced departures from the mode are sometimes encountered. If such discontinuous variations are capable of propagation, they breed true to their new characters from the very outset, *i.e.* are hereditarily transmitted. Such *mutations*, which are usually far more pronounced than the continuous variations hitherto considered and consequently obvious even to superficial examination (Fig. 410), are known to be related to two types of changes in the nucleus, either affecting a gene (*gene-mutations*, p. 600) or more frequently the chromosome-complement of the individual (*chromosome-mutations*, p. 601). Both kinds of changes can be induced artificially by exposure to X-rays, while chromosome-mutations have also been obtained by exposure to sudden temperature-extremes and treatment with certain chemicals (mustard gas and its derivatives); no specific mutations can be produced at will and all are random. The mutations obtained artificially are, for the most part, the same as occur spontaneously, the treatment merely increasing the frequency of mutation which in nature is usually of a very low order. The causes of spontaneous mutation are unknown, but it may be suspected that something in the external environment may provide the stimulus that brings about the internal change. Old seed of Snapdragon has been found to produce a higher percentage of mutants than fresh seed. Many of the observed mutations (and especially the gene-mutations artificially induced) are more or less pathological in nature and sometimes lethal.

The term mutation was first used by De Vries, who emphasised the importance of such major changes in producing new species. He observed the sudden and large-scale appearance in a field near Amsterdam of new forms of the Evening Primrose (*Oenothera lamarckiana*), markedly distinct from the parent and breeding true. It has since been shown that these mutations are an outcome of the possession by this species of a complex heterozygous chromosome-complement (cf. p. 603), but mutations are known to arise (*e.g.* in fungal cultures) also from pure-bred strains. A familiar mutation is that of the Irish Yew (*Taxus baccata* var. *fastigiata*) which differs from its parent in its darker foliage and cypress-like habit. Muta-

tions sometimes arise in the vegetative parts, appearing only on a
few branches of a plant. The propagation of such *vegetative
mutations* (sports) has afforded the cut-leaved varieties of Alder,
Beech (Fig. 411), etc., the leaves of which are normally undivided.

The most important mode of origin of new forms is the recom-
bination of characters which takes place when two different races,
varieties, or (more rarely) species constitute the respective parents.
In such instances the fertilised eggs are, of course, produced by the
participation of both parents, one furnishing the female and the

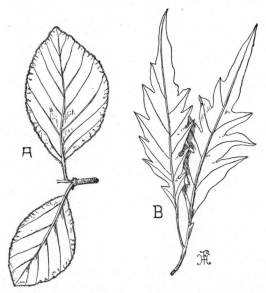

Fig. 411. Twigs of A, ordinary Beech, and B, cut-leaved Beech, illustrating
a vegetative mutation.

other the male sexual cell. Such "crossing" is often a failure, no
seed being set, but when successful the next generation is an
admixture of the characters of the two parents, some features
belonging to the one and some to the other.[1]

In respect of certain pairs of contrasting characters (*e.g.* tall and
dwarf habit, hairy and glabrous surface), however, that of one
parent frequently altogether predominates, all the offspring showing
the one feature only, although sometimes the hybrid is intermediate
with regard to a given character (p. 596). Since the determinants
for the characteristics of both parents must have been included in

[1] See the reference books cited at the end of the chapter.

the zygote, that of the one must, in the former instance, have remained *latent* during development. Indeed, if such hybrid plants are self-fertilised, the latent character reappears in a certain proportion of the individuals arising from the resulting seeds, a fact which proves its presence, although it was not outwardly manifest.

A quantitative study of the phenomena of *hybridisation* was first published by Mendel, an Austrian monk, who considered the behaviour of single pairs of characters only. In one of his earliest experiments he crossed tall and dwarf Peas, the whole of the resulting offspring (first generation) being tall. The seeds produced from these, by self-fertilisation, afforded two classes of individuals, three-quarters being tall and one-quarter dwarf. But of these tall Peas of the second generation (if again self-fertilised) only one-third bred true, the remainder behaving just like the original hybrids of the first generation, and giving rise to talls and dwarfs in the proportion of three to one. The dwarfs invariably bred true. In the second generation of such a cross, then, as regards any one particular pair of characters, half the offspring are pure (one quarter resembling one parent, another quarter the other parent), whilst the other half are impure and bear the characters of both. Representing the tall Pea by T and the dwarf Pea by d, these results can be graphically expressed as follows:

First generation: 100% Td (all tall).
Second generation: 25% TT: 25% dd: 50% Td (one tall: one dwarf: two hybrids).

Pairs of factors, which behave in this way and segregate in the second generation, are spoken of as *Mendelian factors*. To this law of segregation there are few exceptions which remain unexplained.

The latent character is usually spoken of as the *recessive* and the one, that appears in the first hybrid generation (designated F1), as the *dominant*. Pairs of characters determined by single genes, which thus combine in the hybrid and segregate in the subsequent generations, are termed *allelomorphs*. It has been suggested that the recessive character might be caused by the absence of something determining the dominant, in other words that the dwarf habit, for example, might be due to the absence of a gene for tallness or a glabrous form to the absence of a gene for hairiness. Both allelomorphs of various genes have, however, been shown to mutate into the opposite factor, and other considerations also render the presence and absence hypothesis untenable. The following are further examples of allelomorphs, the dominant character being that first named:—

Yellow and green, round and wrinkled seeds in Peas.
Prickly and smooth fruits (Thornapple, Field Buttercup).
Susceptibility and resistance to Rust in Wheat.
Starchy and sugary endosperm in Maize.
Hard (glutinous) and soft (starchy) endosperm in Wheat.

A feature which may be of great significance is that almost all the mutants so far studied behave as recessives to the parent stocks from which they sprang. It may be added that recent research has shown that many apparently simple characters can be analysed into a number of subordinate ones, which, however, are very commonly inherited together.

The most important principle, demonstrated by the experiments of Mendel and subsequent workers in this field, is that the characters introduced by either parent do not become inextricably intermingled in the hybrid, but remain distinct and segregate again in the gametes; each of the latter thus bears only one of a pair of allelomorphs. It is only on this basis that the reappearance of a latent character in the second generation can be explained. There is no doubt that in hybrid-organisms, during the formation of each tetrad of spores, and in conjunction with the reduction division (p. 438), the determinants of the characters become separated, so that each spore, and consequently each of the gametes, to which it ultimately gives rise, bears one only of each pair of determinants. In the reduction division, therefore, the allelomorphs will become segregated so that pure recessives and pure dominants can be bred.

It has been repeatedly noted that the fusion of the nuclei of the gametes appears to be the most important step in *sexual reproduction*. This is supported by the fact that, in all the higher plants, the male cell consists of little else than the nucleus (cf. pp. 422, 469), and that, in hybrid-experiments, it is usually [1] immaterial whether the one or the other parent functions as the male. The nucleus has also been seen to play a very important part in the activity of the cell, and, when dividing, to pass through a very complex series of changes. Moreover, the number of chromosomes is usually constant among all the individuals of a species. The division-stages have as their outcome an equal distribution of the chromosome substance, which indeed is the only part of the nucleus that remains recognisable throughout all the phases of division (p. 55). The chromosomes are thus well suited to be the carriers of the hereditary qualities of the organism. It should, however, be

---

[1] Some forms of *Œnothera* and *Epilobium* appear to constitute an exception to this generalisation.

emphasised that the nucleus and its chromosomes can only exist in a cytoplasmic environment and that inheritance through the cytoplasm has also been established (cf. p. 600).

It will be helpful at this stage to consider in some detail the changes occurring during the reduction divisions which, since they involve more than a mere halving of the diploid chromosome number, are more usually spoken of as *meiosis*.[1] The two nuclear divisions concerned differ in important respects from the mitosis typical of vegetative cells (cf. p. 54). The *prophase* of the first division is prolonged and several successive stages are distinguishable. In the earliest (leptotene) the same number of long, thin, more or less coiled chromosomes (Fig. 412, A) appears within the nucleus as in the early prophase of mitosis in the particular species. The chromosomes are not, however, divided longitudinally into chromatids, as in the corresponding stage of mitosis, and often exhibit a bead-like structure, with numerous deeply staining *chromomeres*, commonly of unequal size (Fig. 412 *, C), separated by less deeply stained regions.

During the ensuing stage (zygotene) the chromosomes begin to pair lengthwise at one or more points (Fig. 412, B), finally as a general rule becoming completely associated to form *bivalents*.[2] The pairing chromosomes are of the same length and their centromeres are situated at corresponding places upon them; they are in fact the homologous chromosomes referred to on p. 58, each member of a pair being derived from one of the individual's two parents. There is now a superficial resemblance to the early prophase of mitosis, but the paired threads observable in zygotene are entire chromosomes, each with its own centromere, whereas in mitosis they are split chromosomes or chromatids, with a common centromere. The correspondence between the pairs forming a bivalent is such that, where larger and smaller chromomeres are distinguishable, the larger lie at identical points on the apposed chromosomes. During zygotene the chromosomes commence to shorten and thicken owing to spiralisation (p. 56) and those of a bivalent often become wound round one another like the wires of an electric flex. The number of bivalents is of course half the diploid chromosome-number.

In the next stage (pachytene) the chromosomes split into chromatids (Fig. 412, C) so that each bivalent comes to consist of four threads. The mutual attraction between sister-chromatids

---

[1] See the works cited on p. 54, footnote 2.

[2] At the time of pairing the chromosomes, in fixed material, sometimes appear aggregated towards one side of the nucleus; this appearance, referred to as *synezesis*, is probably an artifact. In the past it was erroneously termed *synapsis*, a designation originally applied to chromosome-pairing.

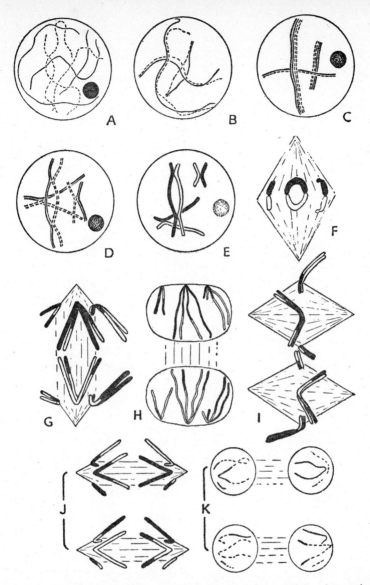

FIG. 412. Diagrams to illustrate behaviour of a nucleus, containing three pairs of chromosomes, at meiosis. One member of each chromosome pair is shown either as a continuous line, or black, the other as a broken line or white. Centromeres not shown. A–E, Prophase of first division. A, Early prophase (leptotene), with six long thin chromosomes. B, Commencing pairing between homologous chromosomes (zygotene). C, Pairing complete (pachytene); in two of the bivalents each chromosome has divided longitudinally into two chromatids. D, The paired chromosomes have separated, except at the chiasmata (diplotene). E, The paired chromosomes have shortened and thickened and the division into chromatids is obscured (diakinesis); nucleolus and nuclear membrane about to disappear. F, Metaphase, terminalisation complete; chromatids still obscured. G, Anaphase, with whole chromosomes, now with obvious chromatids, passing to poles; crossing over (p. 592) has occurred, and the spindle has lengthened. H, Telophase, with widely separated sister-chromatids. I, Metaphase of second division. J, Anaphase, half-chromosomes (chromatids) separating. K, Telophase.

now takes the place of that hitherto operating between the chromosomes of a bivalent, which commence to repel one another and to separate (diplotene). The separation is, however, incomplete, since the bivalents are held together by one or more connections between their chromatids termed *chiasmata* (Fig. 412, D), although, where there are no chiasmata the chromosomes repel one another strongly. A bivalent with a median chiasma will have the form of an X (Fig. 412, E), whilst one with several chiasmata will display

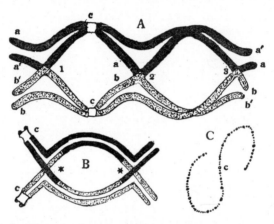

FIG. 412 *. A, Diagram of two homologous chromosomes at diplotene of meiosis, showing three chiasmata; at 1 and 2 crossing over has taken place between the chromatids *a'* and *b'*, at 3 between the chromatids *a* and *b*. B, Diagram showing terminalisation in process; the points at which the two chiasmata were originally formed are indicated by *. C, Leptotene chromosome with chromomeres. *c*, centromeres.

a series of loops, the successive ones in planes at right angles to one another owing to rotation of the regions between adjacent chiasmata.

Where a chiasma occurs, one chromatid in each chromosome of the bivalent has ruptured, and the broken ends have not rejoined, but have united with those of the other broken chromatid. If each chromatid of the one chromosome is represented as *ABCDEF* and each chromatid of the other chromosome as *abcdef*, then, where there is a median chiasma, the four chromatids of the bivalent will be *ABCDEF* and *ABCdef*, *abcdef* and *abcDEF*. An interchange of chromatid segments, spoken of as *crossing over*, has taken place so that one chromatid now differs from the other chromatid of the same chromosome (cf. also Fig. 412 *, A). As many as ten chiasmata have been observed in a bivalent; when there is more than one, the same chromatids are not always concerned and all four may become involved, although only two can be concerned in any one chiasma.

Chiasmata are probably formed as a result of mechanical strains among the four threads of the bivalent, consequent upon the simultaneous operation of forces of attraction and repulsion between the various constituents. They can probably arise anywhere along a bivalent, except in the immediate vicinity of the centromere, but neighbouring chiasmata are always some distance apart.

Towards the end of diplotene the places where the two chromosomes are held together commence to shift towards the ends of the bivalents, a process called *terminalisation* (Fig. 412 *, B) and believed to be due to the same repelling force as causes the earlier separation of the chromosomes. The shifting of course affects only the contacts between chromatids and not the actual points of crossing over. The continued shortening and thickening of the bivalents reaches its peak towards the end of prophase (diakinesis, Fig. 412, E), where, as in mitosis, the chromosomes may not appear to consist of chromatids. At the same time the nucleolus or nucleoli disappear.

The *metaphase* spindle is organised as in mitosis. The two centromeres of each bivalent, belonging respectively to the paternal and maternal chromosomes, however, repel one another so that, as a general rule, they are from the first markedly separated at metaphase and lie at equal distances on either side of the equator of the spindle (Fig. 412, F). There is *no* division of centromeres which, as they continue to diverge during *anaphase*, drag their associated chromatids towards the poles (Fig. 412, G). Complete chromosomes are thus separated at this division; whether a given chromosome of a bivalent passes to one or other pole depends on chance. The interchange during crossing over results in differences between the chromatids of a chromosome so that partly at least they repel one another and are often (cf. Fig. 412, G) readily distinguishable. After *telophase* a resting stage, usually of brief duration, with almost unstainable chromosomes, may ensue. Not uncommonly, however, the chromosomes persist unaltered and pass almost direct from telophase of the first to metaphase of the second meiotic division. A nuclear membrane is, however, always organised around each product of the first division.

The second division is not unlike a mitosis in diploid tissue, although only half as many chromosomes are present (Fig. 412, H). Moreover the chromatids of individual chromosomes diverge widely and are held together only by the unsplit centromere, although at metaphase (Fig. 412, I) they are for a time more closely approximated. Separation of the chromatids during anaphase is initiated by division of the centromere and the process of repulsion operating between its two halves (Fig. 412, J). The half-chromosomes, which travel to the poles in the second meiotic division, are the chromatids, modified by crossing over, which were defined by the split appearing during the prophase of the first division.

It is thus the first meiotic division, which differs materially from an ordinary vegetative one. In all plants, except some Thallophyta (cf. p. 314), meiosis is associated with tetrad-formation in the spore mother-cells. There can be no doubt that the bivalents, organised during prophase of the first division, comprise corresponding (homologous) chromosomes from the paternal and maternal nuclei, which have been brought together in fertilisation and have remained distinct during all ensuing mitotic divisions. Since the two chromosomes of a bivalent are distributed at random to the daughter-nuclei at the first division, this not only brings about reduction, but also a redistribution of the parental material. Moreover, the two chromatids of these chromosomes, which separate during the second division, are not identical with the chromatids, formed during the mitotic divisions of the same plant, because more or less extensive crossing over has taken place between them and those of the homologous chromosome. Meiosis therefore results in four cells with the haploid number of chromosomes, the make-up of the individual chromosomes not as a general rule being identical in any two of them. The consequent reassortment of genes affords scope for great variation, upon which natural selection can operate. Meiosis, identical in all essential respects, but there usually taking place during the formation of the sexual cells, plays the same important rôle in the Animal Kingdom.

The determinants for any allelomorphic pair among the Mendelian factors discussed on p. 588, must reside in the same bivalent, the one chromosome containing the dominant, the other the recessive gene. If the dominant and recessive be represented by A and a respectively, then the fertilised eggs produced by crossing will all have the constitution Aa, and the resulting plants will show the dominant character only; such individuals are termed *heterozygotes*.

During self-fertilisation, and assuming the gametes to meet according to the laws of chance, there are four possible combinations: viz. (1) a male gamete bearing A and a female bearing A; (2) a male bearing A and a female bearing a; (3) a male bearing a and a female bearing A; and (4) a male bearing a and a female bearing a. That is to say, among each four fertilised eggs that result, there will tend to be 1 AA, 2Aa, and 1aa. Seeing that A is invariably dominant, there will in the second generation be three individuals with the dominant to one individual showing the recessive character; of the former, however, two will be heterozygotes, which would exhibit segregation according to the same principle in the ensuing generation, whilst the other, as well as the individuals possessing the recessive character, are *homozygotes* and can be bred true to type.

Further evidence in support of this hypothesis is furnished by the result of crossing the hybrid of the first generation with either parent (i.e. $Aa \times AA$ or $Aa \times aa$). In such a *back-cross* only two kinds of combinations will be obtained, viz. AA and Aa, when the hybrid is crossed with the parent having the dominant character, and there are obviously equal chances for either combination to occur. The second generation does, as a matter of fact, afford individuals half of which are hybrid and half pure. Moreover, when it is recalled that the endosperm of Angiosperms develops as the result of a nuclear fusion (p. 469), it is of interest that, if varieties of Maize possessing different types of endosperm (*i.e.* variously coloured or containing sugar and starch respectively) are crossed, the endosperm of the resulting seeds exhibits evidence of its hybrid origin.

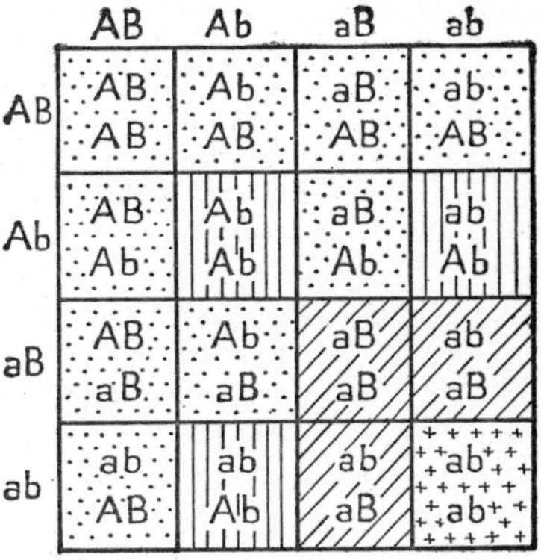

FIG. 413. Scheme to illustrate the progeny of the second generation when two pairs of characters (Aa, Bb) are taken into consideration. The individuals of the first generation will all have the constitution $AaBb$. When segregation occurs, the resulting gametes will have the constitutions AB, Ab, aB, ab[1], and the scheme shows the possible combinations of such gametes. When both dominants are present (in nine out of sixteen) the squares are dotted; when the dominant A is present (three squares) vertical shading is employed; when B is present (three squares) sloping shading; when neither dominant occurs the square is marked with crosses.

If the inheritance of two pairs of characters is investigated, the hybrid shows both dominants, but the second generation, unless there is linkage (cf. p. 598), exhibits independent assortment of the various allelomorphs, the individuals tending to occur in the proportions: 9 with both dominant characters, 3 with one dominant and one recessive, 3 with the other dominant and the other recessive, and 1 showing both recessives. The relations will be plain if the diagram in Fig. 413 is studied. Thus, if yellow round Peas are crossed with green angular ones, the first generation all bear yellow round Peas; in the second generation there will be 9 yellow round: 3 yellow angular: 3 green round: 1 green angular. Of the nine individuals showing both dominant characters only one breeds

---

[1] The combinations Aa and Bb do not arise, since dominant and recessive characters are segregated.

true, as also that bearing both recessive characters. These two are homozygous, but the remaining fourteen are heterozygous and, on being self-fertilised, segregate according to the contained characters.

Dominance, in the many instances in which it occurs, is important only for elucidating the facts of heredity. The principle of segregation is, however, equally applicable when the heterozygote is intermediate in certain characters between the two parents, as

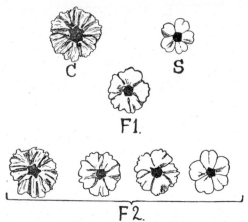

FIG. 414. Hybrids between Chinese (*Primula sinensis*) and Star Primroses (*P. stellata*). At the top the two parents, the Chinese (C.) with large, rather wavy, much crenated petals, and the Star (S.) with smaller flat petals exhibiting only a notch. The F1 generation is intermediate between the two in these respects. In the F2 segregation takes place in the usual way. (After Punnett.)

when the Star and Chinese Primroses are crossed. The petals in the first generation are intermediate in character between those of the parents (Fig. 414); in the second generation segregation takes place in the usual way, the hybrid-individuals (one-half) still showing flowers of the intermediate type, whilst the remainder consist of Star and Chinese Primroses in equal numbers. Similarly the hybrid between a red- and white-flowered Snapdragon has pink flowers, the second generation comprising one red, one white, and two pink.

Hybridisation experiments, apart from demonstrating segregation, show that external appearance (phenotypic expression) is no certain guide to potential characteristics (genotypic constitution). This is strikingly illustrated by the effect of crossing particular pure-bred strains of white-flowered Sweet Peas. We should naturally expect all the offspring to be white-flowered too, but in reality all have coloured flowers, with a purple standard and blue wings. Actually one white parent contains the determinant for a colour-producing substance, while the other white parent bears the determinant for an oxidase, and it is only when both determinants are associated in the same individual that a coloured flower is produced. By breeding plants the limited knowledge obtained by mere examination of the genotypic constitution of any organism, that is, of its hereditary potentialities, can be to some extent supplemented.

When two varieties cross in nature, the appearance of the hybrid is of course influenced by all the characters present in the parents. Whether it resembles one or other parent, or is roughly intermediate between them, will depend on whether one

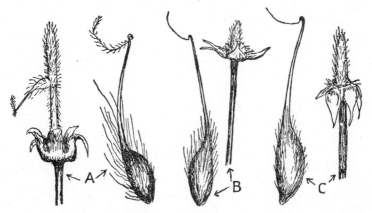

FIG. 415. *Geum rivale* (A), *Geum urbanum* (C), and the hybrid between them, *Geum intermedium* (B). In each the receptacle and calyx are shown, together with an enlargement of a single carpel.

parent contributes a greater proportion of dominant, or more conspicuous, characters than the other. Common examples of such hybrids in the wild state are afforded by various Willows, *Geum intermedium* (Fig. 415, B), *Quercus intermedia*, etc.

Sexual fusion acts in two ways, firstly it provides a stimulus leading to further development, secondly it affords a means of combining and of rearranging the characters of the two parents. The former result may be brought about by other stimuli. Amongst animals, for example, the eggs of Frogs have been caused to develop by mere pricking with a glass needle covered with blood serum, whilst among plants eggs of *Fucus* have been stimulated to divide by treatment with solutions having a higher osmotic potential than sea-water. The polyembryonic seeds of the Orange (cf. p. 473) furnish an analogous example; here certain cells, apart from the fertilised egg, develop into embryos, but the apomyctically produced seedlings are not less vigorous than those resulting from sexual fusion. Further, many simple Algæ can multiply asexually for long periods without loss of vigour. The real importance of sexual reproduction therefore probably lies in the possibility of producing organisms with a slightly different genotypic constitution, such as may be capable of survival under conditions that would be unfavourable to the pure parent strain. In other words, sexual reproduction provides material upon which natural selection can operate.

The offspring produced in *vegetative propagation*, on the other hand, normally exhibit no change of character as compared with the parent, although the occasional mutations (cf. p. 586) may serve to maintain the race in harmony with its environment. Despite the comparative infrequency of such mutations, it must be remembered that in groups like Bacteria and Cyanophyceæ, which multiply mainly by vegetative means, such multiplication is often very rapid so that opportunities for mutation are proportionately increased.

Many characters, both of plants and animals, have been shown experimentally to be associated with definite chromosomes and even with particular regions of a chromosome. For this reason particulate determinants of the characters, referred to as the *genes* previously mentioned, are assumed to exist within the chromosomes. Since the number of chromosomes is limited (cf. p. 602) and commonly quite small, numerous genes must be situated in one and the same chromosome, and the evidence points to their being arranged in linear sequence. In the examples above considered (p. 595) of the inheritance of pairs of characters, the allelomorphs selected occur in different bivalents and can therefore be sorted out independently in the second generation, but this will clearly often not be so. Indeed many characters are commonly linked and inherited together. The number of such groups of *linked characters* has in various species been shown to correspond to the number of chromosomes (seven in the Sweet Pea, for example), and this implies that the genes in any one linkage group are located in the same chromosome.

Complete linkage is, however, very exceptional, since the groups are repeatedly varied by *crossing over* (Fig. 412, G; 412 *, A) during diplotene of meiosis, with the result that new combinations appear in the offspring. For instance, the hybrid (*TtFf*) between a tall Tomato with smooth fruits (*TF*) and a short one with hairy fruits (*tf*) affords a 3 : 1 segregation with respect to either character in the second generation, but neither sorting out nor linkage are complete. The back-cross between the hybrid and the double recessive (*tf*) gives about 47·5 per cent. *TF*, 47·5 per cent. *tf*, and 2·5 per cent. of each of the other combinations (*tF* and *Tf*). Linkage therefore often results in incomplete segregation of parental characters in the hybrid and engenders changes in the gene-complex.

Since chiasma-formation (breakage and rejoining of chromatids)

can presumably take place almost anywhere along a bivalent
(p. 593), the frequency with which it occurs probably depends on
the distance between two points of crossing over. This frequency
(5 per cent. in the instance cited above) has been estimated, in
field-experiments, for many different characters of certain plants,
and from it the order in which the respective genes are arranged
along their chromosomes has been determined and chromosome-
maps prepared. It is not possible to go into further detail, but
corroboration of the arrangements of genes thus deduced is furnished
by the fact that, when a section of a chromosome is lost (p. 603), the

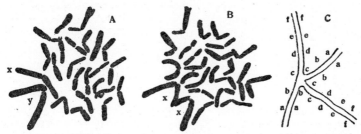

FIG. 415 *. A, B, *Melandrium album* (after Westergaard), chromosome-complement of male (A) and female (B) plants; in the former there are dissimilar
(*x* and *y*) chromosomes, in the latter two similar (*x*) chromosomes. C, Diagram
illustrating zygotene-pairing in an autopolyploid with three pairs of chromosomes.

characters attributed to genes in that part of the chromosome-map
are affected in the offspring.

Segregation of sex, even where the individuals are alike morphologically as in many isogamous Algæ, usually occurs during meiosis
so that sex-determination is genotypic. The respective genes must
be located in homologous chromosomes, since individuals of opposite
sex are produced in approximately equal numbers. In dioecious
plants, the chromosome-complement may include special pairs of
sex-chromosomes, dissimilar (X- and Y-chromosomes) in the male
and similar (two X-chromosomes) in the female (Fig. 415 *, A, B).
Thus, in *Melandrium album* and *Bryonia* the pollen grains are of two
sorts, but the eggs are all alike, so that male and female offspring
are formed in about equal numbers. The sex-determining genes
are seemingly lodged in the X-chromosomes, which also usually
bear other genes so that certain characters may be sex-linked.

Incompatibility in Flowering Plants (p. 449) is likewise geneti-
cally controlled. In the cultivated races of the Sweet Cherry
(*Prunus avium*) the pollen tube in self-pollinated plants always fails
to reach the ovary, and cross-pollination between two incompatible
races has a like result. Incompatibility depends on the presence of
identical genes in the haploid nuclei of the pollen and the diploid

ones of the style. When the parent is pollinated with pollen from the offspring of a compatible cross, only half the pollen grows normally, since the rest because of segregation contains the same genes as the parent. Several genes (multiple allelomorphs, cf. below) are involved, identical ones inducing production of substances in the style comparable to antibodies. Other hermaphrodite flowers show even more complex relations. Heterothallism in Fungi probably depends upon similar factors, and particularly complex instances occur among Basidiomycetes (p. 335).

Although the effects of genes can often be studied independently, the genes being treated as distinct hereditary units, each probably influences several characters and interacts with others in the same gene-complex. Complementary genes are illustrated by the hybrids with coloured flowers resulting from a cross between two white-flowered Sweet Peas (p. 596). In the second generation the ratio of coloured to white is 9 : 7, since both dominants must be present (cf. Fig. 413) to produce colour. Numerous other instances of paired characters giving such unusual ratios are explicable on the basis of gene-combination. The phenotype thus evidently depends on the whole gene-complex, as well as on the external environment. Although sometimes due to the latter, continuous variations are probably mostly caused by systems of genes, individually similar and slight in their effects and supplementary to one another (polygenic systems).

A gene may occur in more than two phases, as in those determining incompatibility in flowers and in certain Basidiomycetes. All such *multiple allelomorphs* are due to gene-mutation, being modifications of the same general character; only one phase is present at the particular locus on each homologous chromosome.

There is evidence that the determinants for a character are sometimes lodged within the cytoplasm (*plasmagenes*). Thus, certain characteristics of the cross between *Epilobium hirsutum* and *E. luteum* are determined by the female parent, although the chromosome-complement of the hybrid must be the same, no matter whether the one or the other furnishes the pollen. Similarly, the capsules obtained by crossing *Funaria hygrometrica* with *F. mediterranea* vary in shape according to the species serving as the female parent, and diploid gametophytes propagated vegetatively from the respective sporogonia differ with respect to shape of leaf. Other characters of these mosses are, however, transmitted in the usual way. The instances given must be due to *cytoplasmic inheritance*. In analogous examples in *Primula* and *Oenothera*, in which yellow-coloured leaves appear only when one parent acts as female, inheritance probably takes place through the plastids.

Changes in the chromosome-complement are not only those brought about during normal meiosis. Since the nuclei of Flowering Plants ordinarily contain pairs of homologous chromosomes, the diploid number is usually some multiple of two, even though the haploid number may be odd. When two species or distinct varieties with the same chromosome-number are crossed, the nuclei of the diploid hybrid contain two sets of chromosomes which, in part at least, are dissimilar. Pairing at meiosis will therefore be impossible or incomplete so that there is no balanced separation of chromosomes. Such hybrids are usually in great part sterile, although they can sometimes be propagated vegetatively.

This was so with the hybrid (*Primula kewensis*) obtained by crossing *P. floribunda* and *P. verticillata*. Vegetatively propagated plants, however, bore a number of flowering branches producing viable seed. The resulting plants proved to be tetraploid and must have arisen through fusion of diploid gametes, resulting from failure of chromosome-separation at meiosis. The tetraploid nuclei have four sets of chromosomes, two unlike the other two, so that normal pairing is possible. Such tetraploid plants are called *allotetraploids* and further examples are furnished by *Galeopsis tetrahit*, derived from the cross between *G. pubescens* and *G. speciosa*, and the hybrid known as *Raphano-Brassica*, produced by crossing Radish and Cabbage.

Such replication of chromosomes is an instance of *polyploidy*, which is by no means confined to the offspring of hybrids. Tetraploids, for example, may arise through chromosome-doubling in vegetative cells owing to non-separation of the daughter-chromosomes in mitosis. This condition is common in plants and can be induced by appropriate treatment with colchicine which suppresses spindle-formation, or by exposure to temperature-extremes. The shoots arising from the stump of a Tomato-plant that has been repeatedly cut back are often tetraploid, and, propagated as cuttings, afford tetraploid plants. Such *autotetraploids* resemble the parent, though usually somewhat larger and often appreciably less fertile.

If meiosis is suppressed in one parent, triploid plants may arise by fusion of a diploid with a haploid gamete, but triploid individuals can also be produced by crossing a tetraploid and a diploid plant. Further chromosome-doubling gives hexaploids from triploids, octoploids from tetraploids, etc. In diverse genera (*Rosa*, *Rumex*, *Primula*) the diploid chromosome-numbers of the various species are multiples of a basic number (see p. 602), which suggests that these species have originated in association with polyploidy. In *Biscutella lævigata*, however, plants with 2, 3, 4, 5, and 6 sets of chromosomes are sufficiently alike to be grouped in one species. Certain genera (e.g. *Carex*, *Iris*) exhibit a very wide range in

39

chromosome-numbers. The rare haploid sporophytes found among Flowering Plants are usually smaller than the diploid individuals and markedly infertile.

CHROMOSOME-NUMBERS OF CERTAIN GENERA.[1]

Rosa spp. 14 (*R. indica,* diploid); 21 (*R. provincialis,* triploid); 28 (*R. gallica,* tetraploid); 35 (*R. canina,* pentaploid); 42 (*R. Moyesii,* hexaploid); 56 (*R. hilliana,* octoploid).

Iris spp. (Haploid numbers), 8, 9, 10, 11, 12, 13, 14, 15, 16, 17, 18, 19, 20, 21, 22, 23, 24, 36, 41–42, 42, 43–44, 54–56.

Primula spp. 16 (*e.g.* Sections *Stenocalyx* and *Souliei*); 18 (*Verticillatæ, Malacoides*); 20 and 22 (most frequent); 24 (*Septemlobæ* and *Bullatæ*); 36, 40, 44, 54, 72, 126.

Fragaria spp. 14 (*F. vesca,* diploid); 42 (*F. elatior,* hexaploid); 56 (*F. virginiana,* octoploid); 56 also in *F. chilænsis* and the Garden Strawberry.

Prunus spp. 16 (*P. persica, P. avium*); 32 (*P. cerasus, P. spinosa*); 48 (*P. domestica, P. malaheb*).

The considerable degree of infertility in autopolyploids is due to each of the homologous chromosomes, now three or more, tending to pair with any of its fellows and often to pair in part with one, in part with another (Fig. 415*, C). This leads to irregularities in segregation at meiosis. There are usually fewer chiasmata, and these may arise between more than two homologous chromosomes affording *multivalents,* while if one of the aggregate fails to form chiasmata with any of the others, it remains as a univalent at metaphase. Thus, in a triploid there may be trivalents, bivalents and univalents, in a tetraploid tetravalents as well. Allopolyploids, on the other hand, commonly exhibit normal segregation. The univalents of autopolyploids are frequently lost during meiosis or may become incorporated without division in a daughter-nucleus of the first division.

This is one mode of origin of *polysomics,* in which one or more chromosomes of the complement may be more frequent than the others. Polysomics have been extensively studied in the Tomato and in *Datura.* In the latter many different kinds have been obtained experimentally, corresponding to each of the 12 chromosomes of the haploid set. The presence of one chromosome three (or more) times, instead of twice, generally affects specific regions of the plant. Thus, when a certain chromosome occurs three times (trisomic) in an otherwise diploid *Datura,* the fruits are flattened as compared with those of the normal diploid, while when present four times (tetrasomic) the flattening is even more marked. Polysomics are usually less vigorous than their diploid relatives.

[1] For further data of the same kind, see *C. D. Darlington* and *E. K. Janaki Ammal,* Chromosome Atlas of Cultivated Plants. Allen & Unwin, 1945 (397 pp.).

Another way, in which the chromosome-complex can be altered, is by breakage of entire chromosomes, the fragments often joining to form new combinations with differing arrangements of genes. Such changes are readily brought about by exposure to X-rays, but, although they certainly occur also in nature, it is not known how frequent they are. Fragments of chromosomes, devoid of the centromere, disintegrate unless they join on to the broken ends of other chromosomes containing a centromere. In this way one or more *translocations* from one chromosome to another may occur, and these are often reciprocal, thus affording new linkage groups. It is probable that extensive changes of this kind have led to the unusual condition found in some (hybrid) species of *Oenothera* (incl. *O. lamarckiana*) and certain other Flowering Plants. In the *Oenotheras* most or all of the chromosomes are not present as homologous pairs, although part of each is duplicated in another chromosome. At metaphase of meiosis in *O. muricata* a single multivalent, with fourteen chromosomes arranged in a ring is produced, while in *O. lamarckiana* there is one bivalent and a ring of twelve chromosomes.

The material nature of the genes is still incompletely established, nor is their mode of action clear, although it seems probable that they influence enzymes concerned in protein-synthesis. During the resting stage the chromosomes contain only scanty amounts of nucleic acids. Their conspicuous staining properties during nuclear division are due to their becoming coated with the highly polymerised desoxyribose nucleic acids which are found only here, in the cells of Bacteria, and seemingly in certain of the larger viruses. These substances have long thread-like molecules, with a very high molecular weight, and their presence seems to be essential for the reproduction of the genes. The nucleotides, from which nucleic acids are formed, consist of phosphate, the pentose sugar ribose, and a purine- or pyrimidine-base. At telophase, when the condensed chromosomes uncoil, the acid is thought to break down into the much simpler ribose nucleic acids, most of which are either stored in the nucleolus or pass into the cytoplasm. The amount of ribose nucleic acids in the cytoplasm of a cell appears to be related to its capacity to effect protein-synthesis, so that the latter process may well be influenced by the genes, each of which would determine the formation of specific proteins through the agency of the ribose nucleic acid, just as its own reproduction is apparently determined by its association with desoxyribose nucleic acid. It is thus possible that the cytoplasm provides the raw materials for the operations of the genes, which in their turn govern the protein-synthesis within the cell and thus determine the characteristics of the organism.

It has long been familiar to gardeners that shoots, which show a mingling of the characters of scion and stock, are sometimes produced as a result of grafting (p. 252), and for some time these were thought to be of a hybrid character. The intermediate nature of these so-called *graft-hybrids* or *chimæras* is a result of the fact that both scion and stock contribute to their development, the tissues of the one commonly forming a skin over those of the other. When this is so, the product is called a periclinal chimæra. The character of the seeds, and of the resulting offspring, is determined by the plant responsible for the formation of the subepidermal layer from which the archesporial tissue (pp. 437, 445) arises. This explains the fact that the seeds of graft-hybrids always breed true to the characters of either the scion or the stock. The commonest example of such a chimæra is that known as *Cytisus adami*, which is due to the grafting of the Purple Broom (*Cytisus purpureus*) on the Laburnum (*Laburnum anagyroides*). In other chimæras the tissues are not distributed in this regular manner. The mode of origin of many chimæras (*e.g.* zonal *Pelargonium*) is uncertain.[1]

The *theory of evolution* interprets the resemblances between the members of a genus or family (cf. pp. 277, 611) as the necessary consequence of their origin from a common ancestor or from closely related forms. The previous discussion has shown how new types can arise as an outcome of mutation, hybridisation, etc. Since these show a great resemblance to their known parents, it is reasonable to regard the many features in common, between the species of a genus or between the genera of a family, as indications of a natural affinity between them. This is strikingly portrayed in families with marked physiognomic characteristics, as, for example, the succulent Crassulaceæ and Cactaceæ, the essentially aquatic Potamogetonaceæ and the completely parasitic Orobanchaceæ.

What has already been said, then, with regard to the distribution of species (p. 570) should also apply in a general way to genera and families, if these really comprise groups of forms with natural affinities. In many, indeed, the same principles are applicable; for example, the genus *Commidendron* (a member of the Compositæ), with three species, is restricted to St. Helena, and whole families are sometimes largely confined to definite areas, as the Epacridaceæ (which are closely allied to the Ericaceæ) to Australia and Tasmania.

Geological research has shown that oceans and continents have undergone manifold changes in area and level, even during the period of existence of many living species. These secular changes

----

[1] For further details, see W. Neilson Jones, *Plant Chimæras and Graft Hybrids*. Methuen & Co., 1934 (136 pp).

probably afford the clue to the *discontinuous distribution* of many species and families. Certain groups, now represented only in widely separated areas over the earth's surface (*e.g.* the Cycads, Fig. 416), are known to be ancient, and may well have attained their wide distribution before the present barriers were as pronounced or had even become established. A similar instance is furnished by the occurrence of the same arctic species (p. 575) on the tops of many high mountains, although the present-day climate of the plains offers an insurmountable barrier to their dispersal from one chain to the other.

The conception of evolution regards the organic world, as we find it to-day, as consisting not of a number of immutable forms, but as presenting one phase in an ever-changing series. The organisms of the present are the offspring of those of the past, and will themselves, in turn, give rise to the organisms of the future. Those animals or plants which have become extinct must be supposed to have failed to "make good" in the competitive struggle. From the fossil records it is known that whole floras and faunas have thus perished, leaving no living representatives or only much modified descendants (cf. pp. 368A, 385, 388, 402–407). Such disappearance may well be an outcome of the secular, but none the less profound, changes that have marked the history of the earth's surface since life first appeared. Organisms, unsuited to the new conditions, would inevitably perish as a result of being handicapped in competition against, either their more adaptable contemporaries, or new forms which were better equipped to withstand the changed environment.

It is probable that all forms of life have developed from relatively simple undifferentiated unicellular organisms, many of whose descendants, through the ages, have gradually acquired an increasing complexity of structure in relation to progressive division of labour. On this hypothesis, if our knowledge of all the extinct plants of former eras were complete, we could reconstruct the genealogical history (*phylogeny*) of the present-day forms. Those of the past would furnish the links connecting genus with genus, and family with family, till all were connected up to the primitive simple organisms from which they sprang when life first developed. The fact that many fossil plants and animals do combine characters, that now serve to distinguish separate groups, is one of the strongest pieces of evidence for such a conception. Moreover, the geographical distribution of living plants and animals, showing, as already noted, restriction of similar species to definite areas, is most readily explained as due to their origin, in that area, from common or closely related parents. The important rôle of hybridisation in

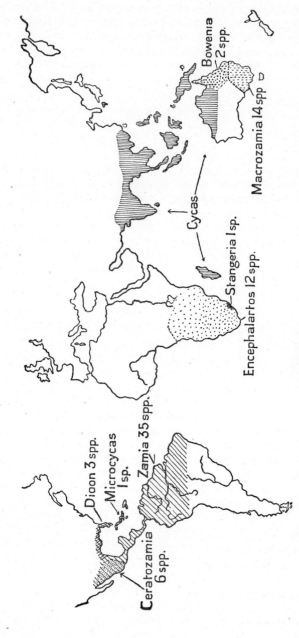

FIG. 416. Map of world showing present-day distribution of the genera of Cycadales.

producing new species (*speciation*), however, shows that the concept of a genealogical tree is too simple. It is also clear that forms resembling one another closely may have arisen from altogether distinct ancestors.

The features characteristic of the various members of a genus or family are often fully apparent only in the adult state, whilst the earlier the stage of development of an organism, the more difficult does the determination of its identity become. The history of the individual may be regarded as, to a very limited extent, recapitulating the history of the race; in this connection it may be noted that the initial stage in the life-cycle of most individuals is a single cell. Such an interpretation also explains the frequent occurrence of rudimentary structures (*e.g.* the gill-slits in the embryo of the Chick, or the pinnate leaves in the seedling stages of species of *Acacia* possessing phyllodes, Fig. 417), which may perform no function, or are even completely lost in the adult. Even amongst living organisms a graduated series, as has been seen in Chapters XXV to XXXVIII, can be recognised. The simplest members of this series are doubtless relics, though almost certainly modified, of the earliest flora, which have found a place in the economy of nature even under existing conditions.

The highest efficiency is only attained by great specialisation which proportionately diminishes the capacity for adaptation to a new environment. But the world of living things is a world of never-ceasing change, and hence the past history of the organic universe is the history of extinction of specialised races and individuals. The future of a group is thus seen to be dependent upon its less specialised, and thus at the moment less successful, members. But as in time, so too in space, the spread of a species may be handicapped by its lack of plasticity.

The brief review of the groups which we have given is sufficient to indicate that the extinct Clubmosses and Horsetails, in the era of their success, were more specialised and more complex than their present descendants, which play so subordinate a rôle, and probably owe their survival to features which characterised the less successful members of these groups in the past. Such considerations lead one to suspect that the subordinate groups and individuals of any one age are the most likely starting-points for the dominant vegetation of the next, and so we can understand why the fossil record presents us with abundant examples of clearly defined groups (*i.e.* of the prevalent successful forms) and comparatively few representatives of groups "in the making." Indeed, the fossil plants of past ages and the living organisms of to-day combine to emphasise the rarity of the "missing link" which,

like the thinker in advance of his age, is not sufficiently in harmony
with the environment to command success, but yet marks the

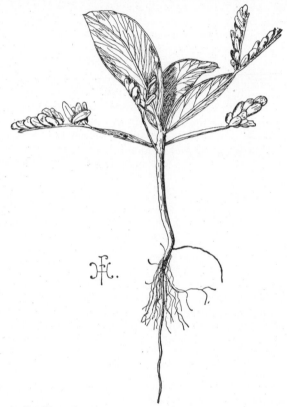

FIG. 417. Seedling of an *Acacia*, showing the gradual differentiation of
phyllodes, and suppression of the laminæ, in leaves of successive ages.

beginnings of the facies of the future.   Progress in the reconstruction of the genealogical tree of the Vegetable Kingdom is therefore
slow, and many groups remain in striking isolation.

[Important reference-works on heredity and evolution are: C. Darwin,
The Origin of Species, J. Murray, London, 1901 (703 pp.); W. Bateson,
Mendel's Principles of Heredity, Cambridge Univ. Press, 1913 (413 pp.); M. B.
Crane and W. J. C. Lawrence, *The Genetics of Garden Plants*, Macmillan & Co.,
4th edit., 1952 (299 pp.); R. C. Punnett, *Mendelism*, Macmillan & Co., 6th edit.,
1922 (219 pp.); C. D. Darlington, *Chromosomes and Plant Breeding*, Macmillan
& Co., 1932 (112 pp.); J. B. S. Haldane, *Causes of Evolution*, Longmans, Green
& Co., 1932 (235 pp.); C. D. Darlington and K. Mather, *The Elements of
Genetics*, Allen & Unwin, 1949 (446 pp.).   For a general introduction to the
subject, see also W. George, *Elementary Genetics*, Macmillan & Co., 1951
(171 pp.).]

CHAPTER XLIX

CLASSIFICATION OF BRITISH FLOWERING PLANTS

CLASSIFICATION of plants [1] is necessary in order to provide a general plan of the immense diversity of forms. Moreover, since plants are classed on the basis of all their characteristics, classification aims at placing similar plants near together and dissimilar ones more or less far apart, so that the more perfect it becomes, the more completely does it afford an expression of the relationships between the different forms. Any classification is, however, necessarily arbitrary because it cannot indicate cross-connections and because it presents in two dimensions only what is really a three-dimensional complex. The following epitome of the main groups of the Vegetable Kingdom includes those already described in Chapters XXV to XXXVIII, but also adds some others less familiar in order to give a more complete picture of the range of plant-form involved.

1. Thallophyta.

    Algæ.
        (a) Cyanophyceæ or Myxophyceæ (Blue-green Algæ).
        (b) Chlorophyceæ (Green Algæ).
        (c) Xanthophyceæ or Heterokontæ (Yellow-green Algæ).
        (d) Chrysophyceæ (Orange-yellow Algæ, include many motile species).
        (e) Bacillariophyceæ (Diatoms).
        (f) Dinophyceæ or Peridinieæ (mainly motile organisms of fresh or salt water).
        (g) Phæophyceæ (Brown Algæ).
        (h) Rhodophyceæ (Red Algæ).
    Charophyta (Stoneworts), sometimes included in Chlorophyceæ.
    Myxomycetes (Slime Fungi).

---

[1] Valuable reference-books are: J. C. Willis, *A Dictionary of Flowering Plants and Ferns*, Cambridge Univ. Press, 6th edit., 1931 (752 pp.); J. Lindley and T. Moore, *The Treasury of Botany*, 2 vols., London, 1884, which contains miscellaneous information about the higher plants; A. B. Rendle, *The Classification of Flowering Plants*, 2 vols., Cambridge Univ. Press, 1925; J. Hutchinson, *The Families of Flowering Plants*, 2 vols., Macmillan & Co., 1926–34; A. S. Hitchcock, *Methods of Descriptive Systematic Botany*, T. Wiley, New York, 1925 (216 pp.). Floras are listed on p. 578.

Bacteria.

Fungi.

(*a*) Phycomycetes {Zygomycetes (incl. *Mucor*). Oomycetes (incl. *Pythium*).

(*b*) Basidiomycetes.

    (1) Uredineæ (Rust Fungi).

    (2) Ustilagineæ (Smuts and Bunt).

    (3) Eubasidii {Hymenomycetes (Toadstools and Mushrooms). Gasteromycetes (Puff-balls, Stinkhorn, etc.).

(*c*) Ascomycetes {Plectomycetes (incl. *Eurotium*). Discomycetes (incl. *Peziza*, etc.). Pyrenomycetes (*Claviceps*, etc.).

(*d*) Lichenes (Fungi symbiotic with Algæ).

2. Archegoniatæ.

A. Bryophyta.

    (*a*) Hepaticæ (Liverworts).

        (1) Marchantiales (incl. *Fegatella*, *Marchantia*, etc.).

        (2) Jungermanniales (incl. *Cephalozia*, *Pellia*, etc.).

        (3) Anthocerotales.

    (*b*) Musci (Mosses).

        (1) Sphagnales (Bog-mosses).

        (2) Andreæales.

        (3) Bryales (incl. most of the Mosses).

B. Pteridophyta.

    Filicales (Ferns).

    Psilophytales (Fossil), see p. 368A.

    Psilotales (*Psilotum* and *Tmesipteris*).

    Sphenophyllales (Fossil), see p. 407.

    Equisetales (Horsetail "Ferns" and Fossil Calamites).

    Lycopodiales (incl. *Lycopodium*, *Selaginella*, *Lepidodendron* (Fossil), and *Isoetes*).

3. Spermaphyta.

    1. Pteridospermæ (*Lyginopteris*, Fossil only).

    2. Gymnospermæ.

        Cycadales.

        Bennettitales (Fossil only).

        Cordaitales (Fossil only), see p. 407.

        Ginkgoales (Maidenhair Tree, *Ginkgo*).

        Coniferales (*Pinus*, *Taxus*, etc.).

        Gnetales.

    3. Angiospermæ.

        Monocotyledones (incl. Liliaceæ, Gramineæ, etc.).

        Dicotyledones.

            (*a*) Archichlamydeæ or Polypetalæ (Ranunculaceæ, Leguminosæ, etc.).

            (*b*) Sympetalæ (Primulaceæ, Scrophulariaceæ, etc., an artificial assemblage of the more specialised families).

The rest of this chapter is devoted to a very brief summary of some of the salient characteristics of the families of Angiosperms most commonly represented in the British flora. In the taxonomy of Flowering Plants, as in that of other classes (p. 277), the constituent members are placed in various aggregates resembling one another in an increasingly greater number of features.

Thus, certain plants are classed together as *species*, such as the different strains of *Capsella bursa-pastoris* (Fig. 3) or the different habitat-forms of *Gnaphalium uliginosum* (Fig. 407). The individuals differ only in few or less important details, such as size, shape of leaves, presence or absence of hairs, time of flowering, etc. Within the species are included *varieties* which differ in a few heritable characters and *ecads* or *forms* which show non-heritable differences imposed by habitat-conditions.

Different species are grouped together in a wider aggregate, the *genus*, as, for example, the diverse species of *Ranunculus*; all the species of such a genus resemble one another in certain important characters, but differ in more numerous and more significant respects than the individuals of the same species. For instance, in *Ranunculus* all the species agree in having flowers with a calyx and corolla, nectary-bearing petals, numerous stamens, a fruit composed of a collection of achenes, etc. The individual species, on the other hand, differ in habit, in the shape and degree of lobing of the leaves, the size and colour of the petals, the form of the peduncle, and the character of the pericarp, as well as in many other smaller points. *Ranunculus*, together with other genera such as *Clematis, Anemone, Caltha, Helleborus, Aquilegia, Aconitum, Delphinium*, etc., are comprised in the *family* Ranunculaceæ, all of them being distinguished by possessing leaves with sheathing bases, a hypogynous flower, numerous stamens, an apocarpous ovary, and fruits usually consisting of achenes or follicles. It is a convention justified by experience that the characters of the reproductive organs are used to distinguish genera and aggregates of higher order, whilst characters of the vegetative organs serve more particularly to identify species. Related families are grouped together into *cohorts*. Thus Ranunculaceæ, Nymphæaceæ, Berberidaceæ, etc., belong to the cohort Ranales.

All the species of a given genus are in scientific usage designated by a common Latin name, all the Buttercups being species of the genus *Ranunculus*. The species are distinguished by a second Latin word placed after that denoting the genus; thus, the Meadow Buttercup is known as *Ranunculus acris*, whilst the Field Buttercup is *Ranunculus arvensis*. The letter L (for Linnæus) or other abbreviation following a Latin binomial indicates the botanist by whom the species was first properly described.

In describing the following families we shall frequently employ a *floral formula* to indicate the usual number of parts in the successive whorls. The number of members in each is represented by a numeral and, where there is more than one whorl of the same kind, the numbers for each whorl are joined by a + sign. The calyx is represented by K, the corolla by C, a perianth by P, the stamens by A, and the ovary by G. The joining together of members of a whorl is indicated by putting the corresponding numeral in brackets, whilst a line above or below the numeral representing the ovary marks the inferior or superior position of the latter. Apart from this, the following abbreviations are employed: *alt.*, alternate; *anem.*, anemophilous; *apocarp.*, apocarpous; C, corolla; *cpd.*, compound; *cpl.*, carpel; *end.*, endosperm present; *end. O*, endosperm absent; *entom.*, entomophilous; *epig.*, epigynous; *exstip.*, exstipulate; *flr.*, flower; *hypog.*, hypogynous; *inf.*, inferior; *infl.*, inflorescence; *irreg.*, irregular; K, calyx; *opp.*, opposite; *ov.*, ovary; *perig.*, perigynous; *plac.*, placenta; *protandr.*, protandrous; *protog.*, protogynous; *reg.*, regular; *sp.*, species; *sta.*, stamen; *stip.*, stipulate; *sup.*, superior; *syncarp.*, syncarpous; *unisex.*, unisexual; ♂, male; ♀, female; ☿, hermaphrodite; ∞, numerous.

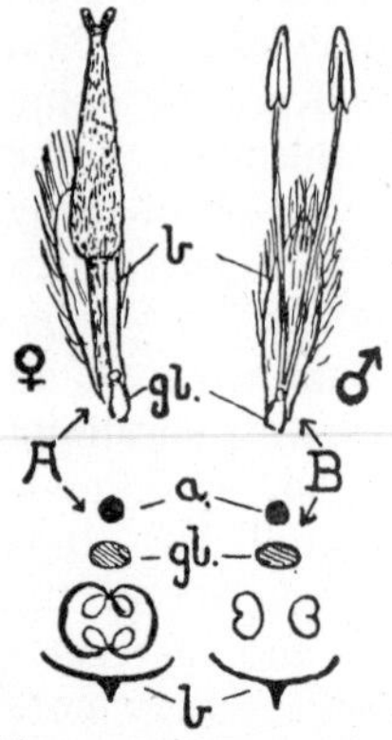

A. DICOTYLEDONS

(*a*) ARCHICHLAMYDEÆ (Families 1–17)
Perianth, when present, usually with free parts.

1. SALICACEÆ (SALICALES)

FIG. 418. Structure of flowers of *Salix caprea* (enlarged). The ♂ and ♀ flowers above and the corresponding floral diagrams below. *a*, axis of catkin; *b*, bracts; *gl.*, honey-glands.

Trees and shrubs with alt. stip. leaves, the stipules often caducous. Infl. a catkin. Flrs. diœcious, unisex., hypog., naked. ♂ flrs. (Fig. 418, ♂) with 2–∞ sta., anthers often brightly coloured. ♀ flrs. (Fig. 418, ♀), ov. sup., bicarpellary, unilocular, with two parietal placs. bearing ∞ ovules; stigma bilobed. Small nectary (Fig. 418, *gl.*) or its equivalent in both flrs. Fruit a capsule, seeds bearing tufts of hairs, end. O. Entom. or anem.

The British genera are:—*Salix* (Willow, Fig. 418), with 2–5 sta. in the ♂ flrs., and a one- or two-toothed nectary, entom.; *Populus* (Poplar), with ∞ sta. and a cup-shaped structure analogous to the nectary of *Salix*, anem.

2, 3. BETULACEÆ AND FAGACEÆ (FAGALES)

Trees and shrubs, with almost naked flrs., the ♂ in definite catkins. The Betulaceæ (Fig. 419, C–F) have partial infl. which are reduced dichasial cymes subtended by an involucre of fused bracts; the ♀ flrs. of 2 cpls., ov. biloc. inf., with one pendulous ovule in each loc., ♂ with 2–10 sta. (Fig. 419, F). Chief genera: *Corylus* (Hazel, Fig. 314); *Betula* (Birch, Fig. 419, E); *Carpinus* (Hornbeam, Fig. 419, C and D); and *Alnus* (Alder, Fig. 419, F).

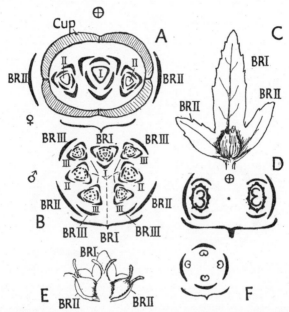

FIG. 419. Betulaceæ and Fagaceæ. A, Floral diagram of female, and B, Floral diagram of male partial inflorescence of *Castanea vulgaris*. Both are reduced dichasia, the successive flowers being numbered in order of development: I, II, III. C, Female flowers and subtending bracts of *Carpinus betulus*, in fruiting stage. D, Floral diagram of same. E, Group of three female flowers of *Betula*. F, Floral diagram of male flower of *Alnus*. BR. I . . . BR. III, bracts of successive flowers; BR. II is bract of the second flower and bracteole of the first.

The Fagaceæ (Fig. 419, A and B) have still more reduced dichasial infl., the ♀ flrs. of 3 cpls. being contained in a cupule (p. 474); ov. triloc. (p. 477) inf., with 2 ovules in each loc. Fruit a one-seeded nut. Chief genera: *Quercus* (Oak, Fig. 362), with cup-like cupule; *Fagus* (Beech) and *Castanea* (Sweet Chestnut), both with prickly cupules.

4. URTICACEÆ (URTICALES)

Herbs with alt. or opp. stip. leaves, often with stinging hairs (p. 160). Flrs. unisex. (Fig. 420); P inconspicuous, of 4–5 members; sta. 4–5, opp. P; ov. bicarp., uniloc., 1 orthotropous ovule; anem. Fruit an achene.

British genera: *Urtica* (Stinging Nettle, Fig. 420, A and B); *Parietaria* (Pellitory, Fig. 420, C). *Humulus* (Hop, Fig. 10) belongs to the allied Moraceæ, which also include Fig and Mulberry.

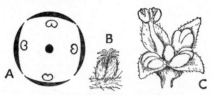

FIG. 420. Urticaceæ. A, Floral diagram of male flower, and B, side-view of female flower of *Urtica*. C, Male flower of *Parietaria*, showing stamens opposite perianth segments.

5. POLYGONACEÆ (POLYGONALES)

Herbs, with alt. leaves with ochrea (Fig. 74, E). Infl. usually spike-like. Flrs. (Fig. 421) inconspicuous; P 3 + 3 in *Rumex* (Dock, Fig. 421, A), 5 in

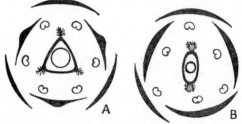

FIG. 421. Polygonaceæ. Floral diagrams of *Rumex* (A) and *Polygonum* (B).

Polygonum (Knotweed, Fig. 421, B), 2 + 2 in *Oxyria*; A 5–8; G (3–2), ov. sup., uniloc., one basal orthotropous ovule. Fruit a trigonous or biconvex achene, P persistent.

To this family belong *Rheum* (Rhubarb) and *Fagopyrum* (Buckwheat).

6. CHENOPODIACEÆ (CENTROSPERMÆ)

Herbs with exstip. leaves and small flrs., unisex. or ☿, often halophytes (p. 566). P 3–5; sta. usually 3–5; G 2, ov. uniloc. with one campylotropous ovule. Fruit an achene.

British genera: *Atriplex* (flrs. unisex.); *Beta* (Beetroot, ov. half-inf.); *Chenopodium* (Goosefoot); *Halimione*; *Salicornia* (succulent halophytes, Fig. 400, with embedded ☿ flrs., A 1–2); *Salsola* (p. 510, solitary axillary flrs.); *Suæda*.

7. CARYOPHYLLACEÆ (CENTROSPERMÆ)

Annual or perennial herbs with opp., often exstip., entire leaves and swollen nodes, mostly glabrous. Infl. mostly a dichasial cyme (Fig. 290, H). Flrs. reg., mostly ☿ (sometimes unisex. in *Lychnis*), hypog., usually with K5 C5 A5 + 5 G(3 to 5) (Fig. 422, C). K poly- or gamosepalous; petals free, often divided (Fig. 422, A, B) or clawed, sometimes with a corona (*Lychnis*), or absent; sta. in 2 whorls, mostly 10, sometimes 8, often of two lengths; ov. sup. syncarp., of 2–5 cpls., when 5 cpls. either opp. the petals or sepals, with a free central plac., usually bearing ∞ ovules (Fig. 422, E). Stigma with as many lobes as there are cpls. Honey formed at base of sta. (Fig. 315, C). Fruit usually a capsule opening by apical teeth (Fig. 333, *f*), an achene in *Scleranthus*; seeds end. Mostly entom., commonly protandr. Non-poisonous.

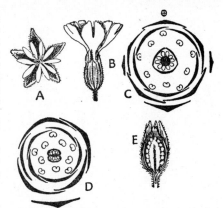

The family is subdivided into:

(i) *Alsineæ*:—Calyx polysepalous; flrs. open and shallow (Fig. 422, A). The British genera are: *Honkenya*, with *H. peploides*, a maritime succulent; *Cerastium* (Mouse-ear Chickweed), petals notched, leaves hairy; *Sagina* (Pearlwort), some sp. apetalous and self-pollinated; *Scleranthus*, with stipules, flrs. apetalous and self-pollinated, with only 1 ovule, a common weed of corn-

Fig. 422. Caryophyllaceæ. A, Flower of *Stellaria media* (Chickweed), showing open type. B, Flower of *Lychnis*, showing tubular type. C, Floral diagram of *Silene*. D, Floral diagram of *Dianthus*. E, Longitudinal section of fruit of *Lychnis*, showing free central placentation.

fields; *Spergula* (Field Spurrey), a weed with stip. and dwarf-shoots (Fig. 69); *Spergularia*, maritime, with stip. leaves; *Stellaria* (Stitchwort), petals deeply cleft (Fig. 422, A).

(ii) *Sileneæ*:—Calyx gamosepalous; petals clawed; tubular flrs. (Fig. 422, B). The chief British genera are: *Agrostemma* (Corncockle), a weed of corn-fields; *Dianthus* (Pink), with only 2 styles (Fig. 422, D); *Lychnis* (Campion, Fig. 422, B), with a well-marked corona (p. 435); *Silene* (Bladder Campion), often with an inflated K (Fig. 422, C).

8. RANUNCULACEÆ (RANALES)

Mostly perennial herbs with alt. (except *Clematis*), occasionally stip. leaves, often deeply palmately lobed and having sheathing bases; stem a root-stock or rhizome with fibrous roots and often bearing radical leaves. Infl. usually cymose, but sometimes a raceme (*Delphinium, Aconitum*) or a single terminal flr. (*Anemone*). Flrs. mostly reg., ☿, hypog., all parts free, commonly with A ∞ G ∞ (Fig. 423). Perianth either consists of K and C (*Ranunculus*, Fig. 293, A) or of one or more petaloid whorls; sta. ∞ , often extrorse, mostly spiral; ov. apocarp., sup. Nectaries of various shapes, between sta. and perianth. Fruit a collection of achenes or follicles (capsule in *Nigella*, berry in *Actæa*); seeds end. Mostly entom. and often protandr. An acrid juice (sometimes poisonous) often present.

The family is subdivided into:

(i) *Anemoneæ* (with achenes): The chief British genera are: *Anemone*, involucre of 3 bracteoles, achenes often with aborted ovules; *Clematis*, a woody climber with opp. leaves, pollen-flrs., and feathery styles (Fig. 337, F); *Ranunculus* (Fig. 423), incl. yellow-flowered sp. and the white-flowered Water Buttercups (Fig. 386), with definite stipules; *Thalictrum* (Meadow-rue), with stip. leaves, a small deciduous perianth, and with pollen-flowers or anem.

(ii) *Helleboreæ* (with follicles):—The chief British genera are: *Aconitum* (Monkshood), with irreg. flrs. and reduced

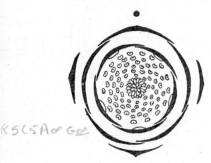

K5C5A∞G∞

FIG. 423. Floral diagram of
Ranunculus.

petals, two of which form nectaries beneath the hood (Fig. 324); *Actæa* (Baneberry), with a berry of 1 cpl.; *Aquilegia* (Columbine), with 2 perianth-whorls, each of the inner members being produced into a spur; *Caltha* (Marsh Marigold), nectar at base of cpls.; *Delphinium* (Larkspur), irreg. flr. having a single spur into which two nectary-bearing processes from the petals project (p. 453); *Eranthis* (Winter Aconite) (Fig. 296); *Helleborus* (Christmas Rose), with a persistent perianth-whorl, often green, and trumpet-shaped nectaries (Fig. 315, D); *Trollius* (Globe-flower), with perianth completely covering flr. which is usually self-pollinated.

Belonging to the same cohort Ranales are two other British families. The NYMPHÆACEÆ are aquatic perennials, with thick rhizomes and floating leaves (Fig. 379), K 4–5, C and A ∞ and spiral, G 10–20, fruit a capsule with projecting parietal plac. and ∞ ovules. British genera: *Nuphar* (Yellow Water Lily); *Nymphæa* (White Water Lily).

The BERBERIDACEÆ have only one British representative (*Berberis vulgaris*), and are mostly shrubs with usually trimerous (p. 266) flrs. (dimerous in the cultivated *Epimedium*); sta. dehiscing by valves; ov. of 1 cpl. with 1 ovule; fruit a berry.

9. CRUCIFERÆ (RHŒADALES)

Annual or perennial herbs with alt. exstip. leaves, often bearing branched hairs; leaves simple or more or less pinnately lobed (Fig. 3), often radical; roots occasionally tuberous. Infl. a raceme *without bracts*, often corymbose at first. Flrs. usually white or yellow, reg., ⚥, hypog., all parts except cpls. free, usually with K2 + 2 C4 A2 + 4 G(2) (Fig. 424). Calyx of 2 outer median and 2 inner lateral sepals, often upright; petals often clawed and alternating with the 4 sepals; sta. 2 short and 4 long (tetradynamous) or rarely 4 or 2 (Fig. 424, F, G); ov. syncarp., bicarp., with a septum and 2 parietal placs., sup. (D). Stigma usually bilobed (B). Nectaries at base of 2 short sta. (A), the nectar collecting in pouches formed by the lateral sepals (Fig. 317). Fruit a siliqua (Fig. 333, *d*) or silicula (Fig. 4, B); seeds end. O., with a curved embryo. Mostly entom. and protandr. Non-poisonous.

Important British genera with siliquas are: *Alliaria* (Hedge Mustard); *Arabis*; *Barbarea*, occasionally with bracts to infl.; *Brassica* (Cabbage, Cauliflower, Kohlrabi, Turnip, Brussels Sprouts); *Cardamine* (Milkmaid), often with explosive fruits (p. 480); *Cheiranthus* (Wallflower, Fig. 424, A–D); *Dentaria* (Coral-root), with bulbils (p. 234); *Matthiola* (Stock); *Nasturtium* (Water-cress); *Sinapis* (Charlock, Wild Mustard).

Genera with siliculas include: *Capsella*; *Cochlearia* (Scurvy Grass, Horseradish); *Erophila* (Whitlow-grass); *Iberis* (Candytuft) (Fig. 316); *Lepidium*

(Cress, Fig. 424, F); *Subularia* (Awlwort), a submerged aquatic with cylindrical leaves.

Genera with indehiscent fruits are: *Cakile* (Sea Rocket), with lomentum; *Crambe* (Sea-kale), maritime, with fleshy leaves and a spherical fruit; *Isatis* (Woad), employed in dyeing; *Raphanus* (Radish), with a lomentum; *Coronopus* (Wart-cress), a common weed with two-seeded fruits.

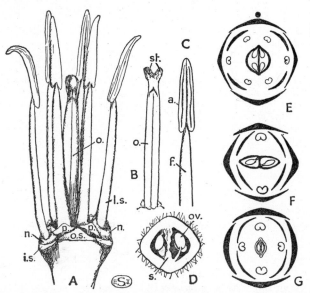

FIG. 424. Cruciferæ. A, Flower of *Cheiranthus* with sepals and petals removed. *l.s.*, lateral stamens; *n.*, nectary; *o.*, ovary; *o.s.* and *i.s.*, scars of outer and inner sepals; *p.*, petal scars. B, Ovary (*o.*) bearing two stigmas (*st.*). C, A single stamen showing filament (*f.*) and anther (*a.*) dehiscing. D, Transverse section of ovary showing ovules (*Ov.*) and septum (*s.*). E, Floral diagram of *Cheiranthus*. F, Floral diagram of *Lepidium virginianum*. G, Floral diagram of *Cardamine hirsuta*.

10. PAPAVERACEÆ (RHŒADALES)

Mostly herbs with alt. leaves and latex (p. 94). Flrs. reg., K2 caducous, C2+2, A∞, G($\underline{2-\infty}$), ov. syncarp. uniloc. with parietal plac. and ∞ ovules. Fruit a capsule (Fig. 333, *h*).

The British genera are: *Chelidonium* (Greater Celandine) and *Glaucium* (Horned Poppy), with yellow latex, pod-like fruits of 2 cpls., the latter with a septum as in Cruciferæ; *Meconopsis* (Welsh Poppy), with 5–6 cpls., and *Papaver* (Poppy), with 4–20 cpls., have capsular fruits (Fig. 333, *h*).

The closely allied FUMARIACEÆ are devoid of latex and have irreg. flrs. with K2, C4, A of two tripartite stamens, G($\underline{2}$). Fruit one-seeded.

11. ROSACEÆ (ROSALES)

Perennial herbs (*Alchemilla arvensis* is an annual), shrubs, or trees, with alt., often stip. leaves which are simple or compound. Infl. cymose or racemose. Flrs. reg., mostly ⚥, hypog. or epig. or most commonly perig., all parts generally

40

free, usually with K5 C5 A5 + 5 + 5 + . . . (few in certain genera), G∞. Calyx occasionally with an epicalyx (Fig. 297, D); ov. usually apocarp. and sup. (syncarp. and inf. in *Malus*). Receptacle more or less hollowed out (Fig. 292, B, C). Honey formed on receptacle between sta. and cpls. Fruit various, a drupe or an aggregate of drupes or achenes; false fruits (Fig. 336, C–E) in certain genera. Mostly entom. and often protandr.

The following subdivisions of the family are British:—

(i) *Spiræoideæ*:—Relatively few whorled follicles borne on a small central protuberance of the but slightly concave receptacle. Many sp. of *Spiræa* are cultivated shrubs.

(ii) *Pomoideæ*:—Shrubs or trees, with an inf. syncarp. ov.; generally a false fruit. British genera are: *Cratægus* (Hawthorn); *Malus* (Apple, Fig. 292, A; 336, E, *Pyrus* (Pear), *Mespilus* (Medlar); and *Sorbus* (Mountain Ash).

(iii) *Rosoideæ*:—Shrubs and herbs, with apocarp., perig. flrs. and a more or less deeply hollowed receptacle (Fig. 292, B and C). The most important genera are: *Agrimonia* (Agrimony), with cup-shaped receptacle bearing hooks (Fig. 339, A), ov. of 1 or 2 cpls.; *Alchemilla* (Lady's Mantle), apetalous tetra-merous flrs., with cup-shaped receptacle, few cpls., Fly-pollinated; *Fragaria* (Strawberry), with epicalyx; *Geum*, with epicalyx (Fig. 297, D) and fruit of hooked schenes (Fig. 339, D); *Potentilla* (Cinquefoil, Tormentil, Fig. 426, C); *Poterium* (Salad Burnet), apetalous unisex. tetramerous flrs. with branched stigmas, fruit of 1–3 achenes, anem.; *Rosa* (Fig. 336, C); *Rubus* (Blackberry, Raspberry), fruit of a number of drupes (Fig. 335, G and H); *Filipendula* (Meadow-sweet).

(iv) *Prunoideæ*:—Trees, with a single cpl. in a concave receptacle; fruit a drupe (Fig. 335, E and F); *Prunus* (Almond, Apricot, Cherry, Plum, Sloe).

12. SAXIFRAGACEÆ (ROSALES)

Herbs or shrubs, with perig. or epig. flrs., K5 C5 A5 or 5 + 5, G2 (Fig. 425, A–C); ov. uniloc. with parietal plac. or bilocular with axile plac., loculi often separate above; often markedly protandr. Fruit a capsule or berry.

The British genera are: *Chrysosplenium* (Golden Saxifrage), apetalous marsh-plants; *Parnassia* (Grass of Parnassus), with 5 sta., branched staminodes and 3–4 cpls.; *Ribes* (Currant, Gooseberry), fruit a berry (Fig. 335, A, B, and Fig. 425, B); *Saxifraga* (Fig. 425, A and C), leaves often with chalk-glands (p. 197; Fig. 117, C), fruit a capsule, many alpines.

13. CRASSULACEÆ (ROSALES)

Mostly succulent herbs, with alt. leaves and usually cymose infl.; K4–12 C4–12 A8–24 G usually 5, apocarp. (Fig. 425, D). Fruit a collection of follicles.

The chief British genera are: *Umbilicus* (Wall Pennywort), C gamopetalous, with a corm; *Sedum* (Stonecrop, Fig. 357, A, C; 425, D).

14. LEGUMINOSÆ (ROSALES)

Annual or perennial herbs, shrubs, or trees, with alt. stip. leaves, usually cpd. and pinnate, leaflets entire, frequently modified into tendrils; roots with root-nodules (p. 219 and Fig. 133). Infl. racemose. Flrs. irreg., ☿, slightly perig., usually with K(5) C5 A(5 + 5) G1 (Fig. 426, A). K more or less gamo-sepalous, frequently two-lipped (Fig. 320, A), odd sepal anterior (Fig. 426, A, B);

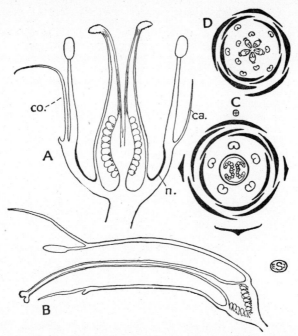

FIG. 425. Saxifragaceæ and Crassulaceæ. A, Longitudinal section of flower of *Saxifraga cordifolia*, showing perigyny. B, Ditto of *Ribes aureum*. C, Floral diagram of *Saxifraga*. D, Floral diagram of *Sedum*. *ca.*, calyx; *co.*, corolla; *n.*, nectary.

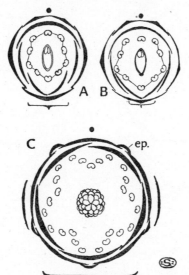

FIG. 426. A–B, Leguminosæ. C, Rosaceæ. A, Floral diagram of *Genista anglica*, B, of *Lathyrus odoratus*. C, Floral diagram of *Potentilla reptans*. *ep.*, epicalyx.

C papilionaceous (cf. p. 456); sta. joined by their filaments to form a tube (Fig. 426, A), or the posterior one free (Fig. 426, B); ov. usually pod-like, enclosed in sta.-tube, with ovules parietal on ventral suture. Fruit a legume (Fig. 333, *c*). All entom., visited mainly by Bees.

The commoner British genera which all belong to the subdivision *Papilionaceæ* are: *Anthyllis* (Kidney-vetch), with inflated hairy calyx; *Sarothamnus* (Broom), all sta. joined, pollen flrs. (Fig. 320, A, B); *Genista* (Needle Furze), all 10 sta. joined, pollen-flrs. (Fig. 426, A); *Lathyrus* (Sweet-pea) (Fig. 320, C–E; 426, B); *Lotus* (Bird's-foot Trefoil) (Fig. 321), with piston-mechanism; *Medicago* (Medick), with spirally coiled legumes, frequently provided with hooks for animal-distribution, often indehiscent; *Melilotus* (Melilot), with keel-petals free from one another; *Ononis* (Rest-harrow), all 10 sta. joined; *Trifolium* (Clover), with flrs. in racemose heads (Fig. 319) and trifoliate leaves; *Ulex* (Furze or Gorse); *Vicia* (Vetch).

In the following genera the fruit is a lomentum which breaks up at maturity into one-seeded parts: *Hippocrepis* (Horseshoe-vetch); *Onobrychis* (Sainfoin); *Ornithopus* (Bird's-foot).

Amongst foreign representatives are: *Phaseolus* (Runner Bean); *Pisum* (Pea); *Vicia faba* (Broad Bean). Others, although possessed of papilionaceous flrs., have 10 free sta., e.g. *Cercis* (Judas tree), whilst still others have reg. flrs. which are densely grouped and have fewer sta. (*Mimosa*) or have ∞ conspicuous sta. (*Acacia*).

15. GERANIACEÆ (GERANIALES)

Herbs, often with aromatic foliage, leaves alt. Infl. cymose. Flrs. (Fig. 427, A) reg., K5 C5 A5 + 5 G(5), outer sta. opp. petals, usually one ovule in each loculus. Fruits schizocarpic (Fig. 334, B).

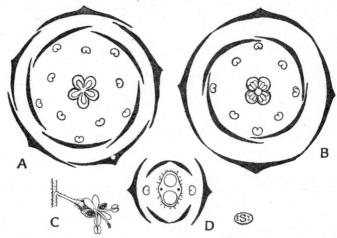

FIG. 427. Geraniaceæ and Onagraceæ. A, Floral diagram of *Geranium*. B, Floral diagram of *Epilobium*. C, Flower of *Circæa*. D, Floral diagram of same.

The chief British genera are: *Erodium* (Stork's Bill), with 5 sta. and 5 staminodes (p. 437); *Geranium* (Fig. 427, A), with 10 sta. The exotic *Pelar-*

gonium (Garden Geranium) has a slightly zygomorphic flr., with a spur concealed by fusion with the peduncle.

In the allied LINACEÆ (*Linum*, Flax), each cpl. contains two ovules, and there are 10 loculi in the ov., each with one ovule (p. 442).

16. ONAGRACEÆ (MYRTIFLORÆ)

Annual or perennial herbs, with opp. or alt. leaves. Infl. usually racemose. Flrs. dimerous (Fig. 427, C, D), or tetramerous (Fig. 311 and 427, B), ov. of 2–4 cpls., inf., 2–4 loculi with axile plac. and usually ∞ ovules, protandr. Fruit usually a capsule.

The common British genera are: *Circæa* (Enchanter's Nightshade, Fig. 427, C and D), with dimerous flrs. and hooked indehiscent fruit (Fig. 339, B); *Epilobium* (Willow-herb) and *Oenothera* (Evening Primrose) have tetramerous flrs. with 8 sta. (Fig. 311).

17. UMBELLIFERÆ (UMBELLIFLORÆ)

Mostly perennial herbs, with large, alt., exstip., usually cpd. leaves having big sheathing bases (Fig. 74, C); stem hollow and often ribbed (Fig. 87, A); tap-root generally prominent. Infl. usually a cpd. umbel, frequently with enlargement of the petals of the outermost flrs. Flrs. small, usually white or yellow, reg., ☿, epig., all parts except cpls. free, almost invariably with K5 C5 A5 G ($\bar{2}$) (Fig. 428, A, B). K very small, inconspicuous; petals often distant from one another; sta. 5, introrse; ov. inf., biloc., with 1 ovule in each compartment; stigma bilobed. Nectary as a disc on top of ov. (Fig. 428, B). Fruit a schizocarp (Fig. 334, A; 428, C, D); seeds end. Mostly protandr. and visited by Flies and Beetles. All parts of the plant usually contain aromatic oils, often of commercial value (*e.g.* Angelica, Aniseed, Caraway, etc.; cf. p. 90).

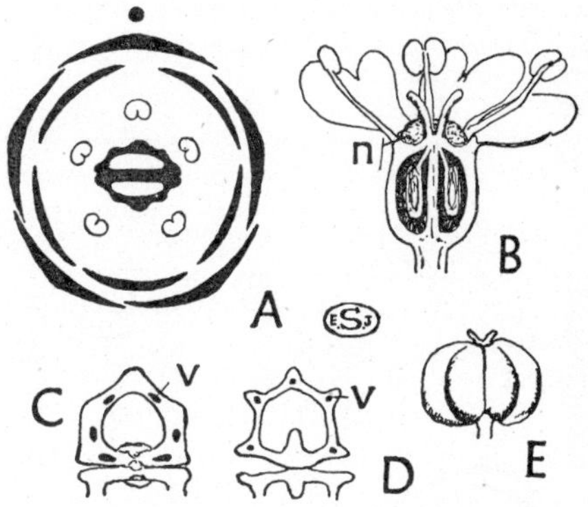

FIG. 428. Umbelliferæ. A, Floral diagram of *Heracleum*. B, Longitudinal section of flower of *Aethusa* (after Le Maout). C and D, Transverse sections of fruits of *Fœniculum* and *Conium*. E, Fruit of *Hydrocotyle*. *n.*, Nectary. *v*, Oil ducts.

The following are some of the commoner British genera: *Aegopodium* (Bishop's-weed); *Anthriscus* (Beaked Parsley), a spring hedge-plant; *Bupleurum*, with simple entire leaves; *Carum* (Caraway, Parsley); *Conopodium* (Pig-nut), with a tuberous root-stock, common in woods and meadows; *Crithmum* (Rock-samphire), found on rocky coasts, with fleshy leaves; *Daucus* (Carrot), with a tuberous root and spiny fruits; *Eryngium* (Sea-holly), a sand-dune plant, with palmately lobed spinous leaves and cymose capitula of blue flrs.; *Fœniculum* (Fennel), used in flavouring; *Heracleum* (Hogweed), common hedge-plant (Fig. 428, A, B); *Hydrocotyle* (Marsh Pennywort), with peltate leaves (Fig. 428, E); *Oenanthe* (Water Dropwort), marsh- or water-plants;

Peucedanum (Parsnip), with a tuberous root, the wild form characteristic of chalk-pastures; *Sanicula* (Wood Sanicle), with flrs. in cymose umbels, simple palmately lobed leaves, and fruits with hooked spines; *Scandix* (Shepherd's Needle), a common weed of cultivated ground, with much elongated fruits.

The following are very poisonous: Fool's Parsley (*Aethusa*), a garden-weed; Wild Celery (*Apium*), the form used commercially having been rendered harmless under cultivation; Water Hemlock (*Cicuta*), a marsh-plant; Hemlock (*Conium*).

The ARALIACEÆ (including the Ivy, *Hedera*), and the CORNACEÆ (including Dogwood, *Cornus*) belong to the same Cohort Umbelliflorae.

(b) SYMPETALÆ (Families 18–32)

Parts of C fused, sta. generally few and epipetalous.

18. ERICACEÆ (ERICALES)

Small shrubs or trees, with alt. small evergreen leaves (Fig. 373), xeromorphic in habit. Infl. usually racemose. Flrs. (Fig. 299, B) usually with K4–5 C(4–5) A 4+4 or 5+5 G($\underline{4-5}$); outer sta. opp. petals; sta. with dehiscence by terminal slits or pores and often with appendages (Fig. 301, E), pollen in tetrads (p. 438); ovules usually several in each loculus, sometimes one; nectary round base of ovary. Fruit capsular or a berry.

The common British genera are: *Calluna* (Ling, Heather), with a deeply cleft 4–partite C and a loculicidal capsule; *Erica* (Heath, Fig. 373), with urn-shaped C (Fig. 299, B) and septicidal capsule; *Pyrola* (Wintergreen), evergreen, humus-loving plants, with one whorl of 5 sta.; *Oxycoccus* (Cranberry) and *Vaccinium* (Bilberry, Whortleberry, Cowberry), fruit a berry. *Rhododendron* and *Azalea* are members of this family.

19. PRIMULACEÆ (PRIMULALES)

Annual or perennial herbs, with generally simple, alt., exstip. leaves, often radical. Infl. a raceme or umbel, or with solitary flrs. Flrs. reg., ⚥, hypog., pentamerous, usually with K(5) C(5) A5 G($\underline{5}$) (Fig. 429). Corolla-tube often long, but very short in *Anagallis* and *Lysimachia*; sta. opp. the petals and epipetalous; ov. sup. (half-inferior in *Samolus*), uniloc., with free central plac. bearing ∞ ovules (Fig. 318); stigma capitate (p. 441). Nectar often formed at base of ovary. Fruit a capsule opening by teeth or lid; seeds end. Mostly entom., occasionally showing heterostyly (p. 455).

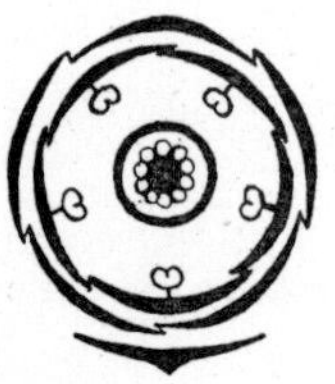

The British genera are: *Anagallis* (Scarlet Pimpernel) and *Centunculus*, a rare plant found in inundated places,

FIG. 429. Floral diagram of Primulaceæ (*Primula*).

have capsules dehiscing by a lid; *Glaux* (Sea Milkwort), a succulent maritime plant, apetalous, self-pollinated; *Hottonia* (Water-Violet), heterostylic; *Lysimachia* (Creeping Jenny, Yellow Pimpernel, Loosestrife), some sp. heterostylic, some with staminodes alt. with the sta.; *Primula* (Cowslip, Oxlip, Primrose) (Fig. 318) with heterostylic flrs.; *Samolus* (Brookweed), a marsh-plant, with staminodes alt. with the sta. and bracts borne half-way up the peduncles; *Trientalis* (Wintergreen), northern plant with more than five petals.

20. GENTIANACEÆ (CONTORTÆ)

Herbs, usually with opp. entire exstip. leaves. Infl. often a dichasial cyme. Flrs. usually K(4–5) C(4–5) A4–5 G(2); petals twisted (Fig. 300, A, C); ov. uniloc. with parietal plac. and ∞ ovules. Fruit a capsule.

The common British genera are: *Blackstonia* (Yellow Centaury), C and A 6–8, leaves connate; *Centaurium* (Centaury), with 5 sta., both genera with inwardly projecting placentæ; *Gentiana* (Gentian, Fellwort), with 4- or 5-merous flrs., placentæ not projecting; *Menyanthes* (Bog bean), marsh-plant with trifoliate alt. leaves and petals bearing ∞ fleshy white protuberances.

21. CONVOLVULACEÆ (TUBIFLORÆ)

Climbing herbs with alt. exstip. leaves, frequently with a watery latex. Flrs. reg., K5 C(5) A5 G(2); C often trumpet-shaped (Fig. 299, C); ov. with axile placentæ and 2 ovules in each loculus. Fruit a capsule.

British genera: *Calystegia* (Convolvulus) and *Cuscuta* (Dodder, p. 214; Fig. 130).

22. SCROPHULARIACEÆ (TUBIFLORÆ)

Annual or perennial herbs, with alt. or opp., exstip., often hairy leaves. Infl. racemose or cymose. Flrs. usually irreg., ☿, hypog., generally with K(5) C(5) A4 G(2) (Fig. 430, C). K gamosepalous, mostly irreg.; C various; sta.

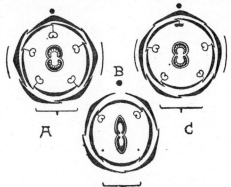

FIG. 430. Floral diagrams of Scrophulariaceæ. A, *Verbascum.* B, *Veronica.* C, *Scrophularia.*

usually 4, didynamous; ov. sup., bicarp., biloc., with swollen axile placs. bearing ∞ ovules (Fig. 323, D); stigma bilobed (Fig. 171, A). Nectar formed in a disc beneath the ov. Fruit a capsule; seeds end. All entom., mostly protandr. Many poisonous.

The principal British genera are: *Antirrhinum* (Snapdragon) (Fig. 323), with a closed corolla; *Digitalis* (Foxglove), with alt. leaves and irreg. tubular corolla (Fig. 299, E), poisonous; *Lathræa* (Toothwort, p. 215, Fig. 131); *Linaria* (Toadflax), with a closed corolla and a spur (p. 460); *Mimulus* (Musk), a river-side plant, with stigma sensitive to touch (p. 266); *Scrophularia* (Fig-wort), with opp. leaves and square stems and posterior staminode (Fig. 310 and 430, C), partial infl. a dichasial cyme; *Verbascum* (Mullein), with 5 sta. with very hairy filaments, and almost reg. flrs. (Fig. 430, A); *Veronica* (Speedwell), with almost reg. flrs. having K4 C4 (posterior petal larger than the others) A2 G(2) (Fig. 430, B).

The following are all meadow-plants and semi-parasites (p. 530); Red Eye-bright (*Odontites*), Fig. 372; Eye-bright (*Euphrasia*); Cow-wheat (*Melampyrum*); Red Rattles or Louseworts (*Pedicularis*); Yellow Rattle (*Rhinanthus*).

23. SOLANACEÆ (TUBIFLORÆ)

Mostly herbs with alt., sometimes cpd. leaves, and internal phloem. Infl. cymose, with frequent fusion of bract with axis resulting in displacement (Fig. 431, D and E). Flrs. (Fig. 431, A, B) often reg., with K(5) C(5) A5 G(2),

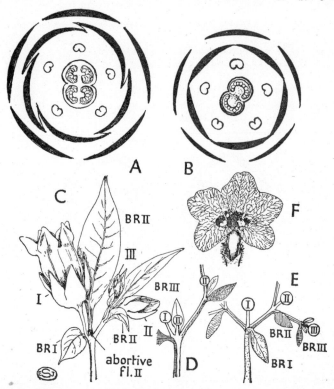

FIG. 431. Solanaceæ. Floral diagrams of *Datura* (A) and *Solanum* (B). C, Part of inflorescence of Deadly Nightshade (*Atropa belladonna*) to show mode of branching, represented by a diagram in D. E, Diagram of inflorescence of *Datura stramonium*. F, Single flower of Henbane (*Hyoscyamus niger*) to show zygomorphic corolla.

usually protog.; ov. biloc., axile plac., septum usually oblique to median plane (Fig. 431, B). Fruit usually a berry (Fig. 335, C, D). Many are poisonous.

The principal British genera are: *Atropa* (Deadly Nightshade, Fig. 431, C), with bell-shaped C and sta. dehiscing by slits; *Hyoscyamus* (Henbane, Fig. 431,

F), fruit a capsule opening by a lid; *Solanum* (Bittersweet, Woody Nightshade, Fig. 431, B), sta. with porous dehiscence.

Exotic sp. of *Solanum* include the Potato (*S. tuberosum*) and the Tomato (*S. lycopersicum*), the cultivated varieties of which often possess more than 2 cpls. *Datura stramonium* (Thornapple) (Fig. 49 and 431, A) is an important medicinal plant, with lobed plac.

24. LABIATÆ (TUBIFLORÆ)

Annual or perennial herbs, with opp., exstip., often hairy and glandular leaves; square hollow stems (Fig. 70, C and 87, B), swollen at the nodes. Infl. primarily racemose, but axillary flr.-clusters are dichasia (cf. p. 428). Flrs. irreg., ⚥ (occasionally unisex.), hypog., usually with K(5) C(5) A4 G(2) (Fig. 432). K persistent, generally with 5 prominent teeth, often slightly irreg. (Fig. 297, C); C bilabiate (Fig. 299, D); sta. usually didynamous, beneath upper lip of corolla; ov. quadriloc., each loculus with 1 ovule; stigma bilobed. Nectar produced by a disc at base of ov., or restricted to its anterior side. Fruit schizocarpic of 4 achenes (Fig. 334, D); seeds end. All entom. and mostly protandr. Leaves often forming aromatic oils (*e.g.* Lavender, Rosemary, Marjoram; cf. pp. 90, 161).

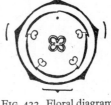

FIG. 432. Floral diagram of Labiatæ (*Lamium*).

British genera with 4 sta. of almost equal length are: *Mentha* (Mint); *Origanum* (Marjoram), a characteristic plant of chalk; and *Thymus* (*Thyme*). All three have only slightly irreg. C.

British genera which have 2 long and 2 short sta. are: *Ajuga* (Bugle), with a small upper lip; *Galeobdolon* (Yellow Deadnettle); *Galeopsis* (Hempnettle); *Lamium* (Deadnettle); *Glechoma* (Ground Ivy, Fig. 7) and *Nepeta* (Cat-mint), with the two upper sta. longer; *Prunella* (Self-heal); *Scutellaria* (Skull-cap), with two-lipped K, the upper lip pouch-like; *Stachys* (Woundwort); *Teucrium* (Wood Sage), with minute upper lip. The following have a specialised androecium: *Lycopus* (Gipsy-wort), with 2 perfect and 2 imperfect sta.; *Salvia* (Sage), with 2 fertile sta. only (Fig. 322).

25. BORAGINACEÆ (TUBIFLORÆ)

Annual or perennial herbs with bristly hairs. Infl. cymose, often coiled in the younger parts. Flrs. (Fig. 433, A) usually reg., K(5) C(5) A5 G(2). K persistent around fruit, which is schizocarpic of 4 achenes (Fig. 433, D), as in Labiatæ.

The common British genera are: *Anchusa* (Fig. 433, A); *Borago* (Borage), with projecting sta.; *Lithospermum* (Gromwell), with very hard whitish fruits; *Myosotis* (Forget-me-not); *Symphytum* (Comfrey), with bell-shaped C. All these have small scales in the throat of the C. *Echium* (Viper's Bugloss), with irreg. C and projecting sta., lacks such scales. The flrs. of *Pulmonaria* are heterostylic. To this family belongs the garden Heliotrope.

26. LENTIBULARIACEÆ (TUBIFLORÆ)

Insectivorous marsh or aquatic herbs, leaves alt. Infl. racemose or solitary. Flrs. irreg. (Fig. 433, B, C), K(3); C (5), 2-lipped; A2, anthers unilocular; G(2), ov. uniloc. with free central plac. (Fig. 433, B). Fruit a capsule. end. O.

The British genera are: *Pinguicula* (Butterwort) (Fig. 135); *Utricularia* (Bladderwort) (Fig. 137).

27. PLANTAGINACEÆ (PLANTAGINALES)

Herbs with radical rosettes. Infl. a spike (Fig. 313). Flrs. reg., anem., K(4) C(4) A4 G($\underline{2}$); C chaffy; sta. with long filaments attached at middle of anther; ov. with 2–4 loculi, axile plac. Fruit a capsule dehiscing by a lid (Fig. 333, g).

The British genera are: *Plantago* (Plantain), with ⚥ flrs.; *Littorella* (Shore-weed), aquatic, with unisex. flrs.

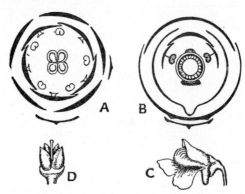

FIG. 433. Boraginaceæ and Lentibulariaceæ. A, Floral diagram of *Anchusa*. B, Floral diagram of *Utricularia*. C, Single flower of *Utricularia*. D, Fruit of *Myosotis*.

28. RUBIACEÆ (RUBIALES)

A family represented in Britain only by one tribe whose characters are: Herbs, with opp. leaves and stips. simulating whorls (4–10 at a node) (cf. p. 128). Infl. cymose. Flrs. (Fig. 434, A and H), reg., K(0–6) C(4–5) A4–5 G($\overline{2}$); ov. biloc., with 1 ovule in each loculus. Fruit generally schizocarpic.

The British genera are: *Asperula* (Woodruff, Fig. 434, A), woodland herb; *Galium* (Bedstraw, Cleavers, Fig. 8), with white or yellow flrs.; *Rubia* (Madder, Fig. 434, H), hedge-plant with leathery leaves, greenish flrs. and fleshy fruit. All these have only a vestigial K. *Sherardia* (Field Madder), with mauve flrs., has a well-defined K.

29. CAPRIFOLIACEÆ (RUBIALES)

Shrubs and herbs, usually with opp. stip. or exstip. leaves. Infl. usually a corymbose cyme. Flrs. (Fig. 434, B–G) reg. or irreg., K(5) C(5) A5 G($\overline{2-5}$), ov. with 1 ovule in each loculus, often uniloc. by abortion (Fig. 434, D). Fruit usually a berry or drupe.

The common British genera are: *Adoxa* (Moschatel), small woodland herb with alternate leaves and greenish flrs. in 5-flowered heads; *Lonicera* (Honey-suckle), with irreg. flrs. (Fig. 327 and Fig. 434, B); *Sambucus* (Elder), leaves pinnate, stip., stamens extrorse (Fig. 434, F); *Viburnum* (Guelder Rose, Wayfaring tree, Fig. 434, D and G), with simple leaves (Fig. 75, A) and drupes. The cultivated shrub *Diervilla* has capsular fruits. The Snowball Tree (*Symphori-carpus*) has white fruits with two fertile and two abortive loculi (Fig. 434, E).

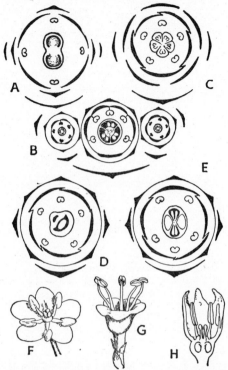

FIG. 434. Rubiaceæ and Caprifoliaceæ. A, Floral diagram of *Asperula*. B, Diagram of partial inflorescence of *Lonicera*. C, Floral diagram of *Leycesteria*. D, The same of *Viburnum opulus*. E, The same of *Symphoricarpus*. F, Flower of *Sambucus*, showing extrorse, and G, of *Viburnum opulus*, showing introrse stamens. H, Longitudinal section of flower of *Rubia peregrina*.

30. COMPOSITÆ (CAMPANULATÆ)

Annual or perennial herbs, with usually alt., exstip. leaves, often hairy. Infl. a capitulum, with an involucre of bracts, composed either of disc- and ray-florets (Fig. 312, A), or of ligulate florets only (Fig. 435, A), or of tubular ones only. Flrs. rarely with bracts, frequently yellow, reg. or irreg., ⚥ or unisex., epig., usually with Ko C(5) A(5) G(2̄) (Fig. 435, C). K usually absent or represented by a pappus (p. 433); petals joined to form a tube or a ligulate structure (Fig. 297, E and 435, A); sta. syngenesious, introrse; ov. uniloc., with 1 basal ovule; stigma bilobed. Nectary ring-shaped round base of style. Fruit an achene, with pericarp and testa joined (p. 474), surmounted by the pappus. Mostly entom. and protandr. (cf. p. 462). A considerable number are common weeds.

The family is subdivided into:—

(i) *Tubuliflorae*:—Disc-florets tubular; no latex. The chief British genera are: *Achillea* (Milfoil), with few-flowered capitula densely aggregated into corymbs, no pappus; *Anthemis* (Mayweed), cornfield-weeds, with bracts to individual flrs.; *Aster* (Michaelmas Daisy), the British sp. maritime with fleshy leaves; *Bellis* (Daisy), no pappus; *Bidens* (Burr Marigold), marsh-plant, with opp. leaves and barbed bristles replacing pappus (Fig. 339, C); *Chrysanthemum*

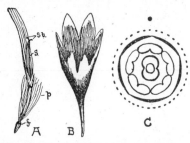

(Dog-daisy); *Erigeron* (Fleabane), a chalk-plant; *Inula* (Ploughman's Spikenard, Elecampane); *Matricaria* (Chamomile), cornfield-weeds; *Pulicaria* (Fleabane); *Senecio* (Groundsel, Ragwort); *Solidago* (Golden Rod); *Tussilago* (Coltsfoot), solitary capitulum appearing before the leaves, and having unisex. flrs. only (p. 449).

Fig. 435. A, Strap-shaped hermaphrodite floret of Dandelion (enlarged). *f*, ovary; *p*, pappus; *s*, stamen-tube; *st.*, stigma. B, Neuter floret of Cornflower (enlarged). C, Floral diagram of hermaphrodite floret of Compositæ.

The following genera of Tubulifloræ have only tubular flrs. in their capitula: *Antennaria*, with diœcious capitula; *Arctium* (Burdock), fruits with hooks on involucre (p. 483); *Artemisia* (Mugwort, Absinth, Wormwood), maritime or hedgeplants; *Carduus, Cirsium* (Thistles); *Centaurea* (Hardheads, Cornflower), with neuter outer flrs. (Fig. 435, B), irritable sta., and fringed bracts to involucre; *Eupatorium* (Hemp Agrimony), a marsh-plant with opp. leaves; *Filago* (Cudweed), with dense covering of white hairs; *Tanacetum* (Tansy), used medicinally.

(ii) *Ligulifloræ*:—All florets ligulate (Fig. 435, A); latex present. The more important British genera are: *Cichorium* (Chicory), with blue flrs.; *Hieracium* (Hawkweed) (p. 472); *Hypochœris* (Cat's-ear), with scaly bracts to individual flrs.; *Lactuca* (Lettuce); *Lapsana* (Nipplewort), common gardenweed, without a pappus; *Sonchus* (Sow-thistle); *Taraxacum* (Dandelion); *Tragopogon* (John-go-to-bed-at-noon, Salsify), with tuberous root, narrow grasslike leaves, and long bracts.

The following Compositæ are often cultivated: Artichoke and Cardoon (*Cynara*), young capitula of former used as a vegetable; *Dahlia*, with tuberous roots; Sunflower, Jerusalem Artichoke (*Helianthus*); *Scorzonera*, a vegetable with tuberous root.

31. CAMPANULACEÆ (CAMPANULATÆ)

Herbs with alt. exstip. leaves and usually possessing latex. Infl. racemose. Flrs. (Fig. 436, A, B, E) reg. or irreg., protandr., K5 C(5) A5 or (5) G($\overline{2-5}$); sta. sometimes syngenesious; ov. 2–5-locular, with axile plac. Nectary round base of style. Fruit a capsule (pp. 476, 480).

The commoner British genera are: *Campanula* (Harebell, Canterbury Bell, Fig. 299, A, and 436, A and B); *Jasione* (Sheep's Bit), infl. a cymose capitulum, sta. syngenesious, 2 cpl. (Fig. 436, E); *Lobelia*, flrs. irreg., sta. forming a tube, the commoner of the two British sp. a submerged aquatic; *Specularia* (Venus' Looking-glass), with pod-like capsule and shining elliptical seeds.

32. DIPSACEÆ (AGGREGATÆ)

Herbs with alt. or opp. exstip. leaves. Infl. a cymose capitulum. Flrs. (Fig. 436, C and D) slightly irreg., protandr., K5 C(5) A4 G($\overline{2}$); K with epicalyx; sta. free; ov. uniloc. with 1 pendulous ovule. Nectary at base of style. Fruit an achene.

The British genera are: *Dipsacus* (Teasel), with connate leaves and conical capitula, order of flowering from the middle upwards and downwards; *Scabiosa* (Scabious), often with deeply lobed leaves, K bristly (Fig. 436, C and D).

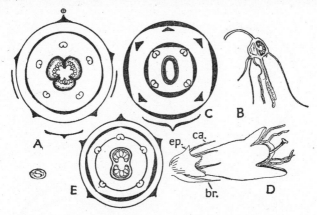

FIG. 436. Dipsaceæ and Campanulaceæ. A, Floral diagram, and B, Longitudinal section of flower of *Campanula*. C, Floral diagram, and D, Flower of *Scabiosa succisa*. E, Floral diagram of *Jasione*, showing joined anthers. *br.*, bract; *ca.*, calyx; *ep.*, epicalyx.

B. MONOCOTYLEDONS

33. LILIACEÆ (LILIIFLORÆ)

Perennial herbs, with underground rhizomes or bulbs, and sheathing lanceolate leaves, often radical. Infl. various, commonly a raceme. Flrs. reg., ⚥, hypog., generally with P3 + 3 A3 + 3 G(3) (Fig. 437, A). P generally petaloid, free or joined; sta. occasionally epipetalous; ov. triloc., with axile placs., usually bearing ∞ ovules. Nectar often formed in ovary-wall (p. 452). Fruit a berry or capsule; seeds end. Many early-flowering.

The chief British genera having berries are: *Asparagus*, with linear cladodes (Fig. 352); *Convallaria* (Lily of the Valley), and *Polygonatum* (Solomon's Seal), both woodland-plants with a gamopetalous perianth, the latter with leafy stems; *Paris* (Herb Paris), woodland calcicole, with an often tetramerous flr., and Fly-pollinated (p. 464); *Ruscus* (Butcher's Broom) (Fig. 353, B), flrs. unisex., the ♂ with 3 sta., the ♀ with a uniloc. ov.

The following British genera have capsules: *Allium* (Onion, Garlic), with a cymose umbel, flrs. often replaced by bulbils (p. 234); *Colchicum* (Meadow Saffron), with a corm and a very long corolla-tube, flrs. in autumn, fruits in spring when the leaves appear; *Lilium*, with anthers movable on tops of filaments; *Muscari* (Grape Hyacinth), with bell-shaped C; *Narthecium* (Bog Asphodel), marsh-plant with *Iris*-like leaves; *Ornithogalum* (Star of Bethlehem); *Scilla* (Wild Hyacinth); *Tulipa*.

To the Cohort Liliiflorae also belongs the family JUNCACEÆ. These are mostly perennial herbs, often with scale-leaves and photosynthetic stems (p. 506); flrs. inconspicuous, with P3 + 3 scaly, A3 + 3 G(3). Fruits capsular. The two British genera are: *Juncus* (Rush), with triloc. ov., axile plac. and ∞ ovules; *Luzula* (Woodrush), with uniloc. ov., parietal plac., and 3 ovules.

34. AMARYLLIDACEÆ (LILIIFLORÆ)

Perennial herbs, with bulbs (p. 233) and leaves like those of Liliaceæ. Infl. often a cymose umbel. Flrs. (Fig. 437, B), reg., generally with P3 +3 A3 +3

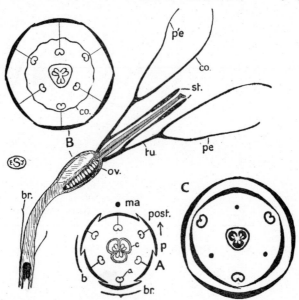

FIG. 437. A, Floral diagram of *Scilla* (Liliaceæ). *a.*, anther; *b.*, bracteole; *br.*, bract; *ma.*, inflorescence axis; *p.*, perianth. B, Floral diagram and longitudinal section of the flower of *Narcissus* (Amaryllidaceæ). *br.*, bract; *co.*, corona; *ov.*, ovary, showing loculus on one side and septum on the other; *pe.*, outer, and *p'e.*, inner perianth-segments; *st.*, stamen; *tu.*, tube; C, Floral diagram of *Crocus* (Iridaceæ).

G(3̄); P free or joined; sta. sometimes epipetalous; ov. triloc. with axile placs., bearing ∞ ovules. Fruit a capsule; seeds end. Chief difference from Liliaceæ lies in the epig. flr.

The British genera are: *Galanthus* (Snowdrop), flr. solitary; *Leucojum* (Snowflake); *Narcissus* (Daffodil), with long P-tube (Fig. 293, B, and Fig. 437, B).

35. IRIDACEÆ (LILIIFLORÆ)

Mostly perennial herbs, with rhizomes or corms and sword-shaped leaves arranged in two ranks and overlapping at the base. Infl. cymose. Flrs. (Fig. 437, C) ☿, similar to Liliaceæ, but with an inferior ov. and only 3 extrorse sta. belonging to the outer whorl. Fruit a capsule.

Of the British genera *Crocus* and *Sisyrinchium* (Blue-eyed Grass) have reg. flrs. In *Iris* the three styles are petaloid, a small ridge on the inner surface representing the stigmas; a sta. lies between each style and one of the outer petals, and biologically the flr. is comparable to three zygomorphic ones. *Gladiolus*, with one Brit. sp., and the commonly cultivated *Montbretia* have zygomorphic flrs. Most Iridaceæ are natives of S. Africa or Central America.

36. CYPERACEÆ (GLUMIFLORÆ)

Mostly perennial herbs with triangular aerial stems and Grass-like tristichous (p. 119) leaves, the leaf-base forming a closed sheath. Flrs. (Fig. 438) usually unisex. in spikes, P absent, or represented by bristles (Fig. 438, C), A usually 2–3, G(2–3), ov. uniloc. with 1 ovule, anem. Fruit an achene.

The common British genera are: *Carex* (Sedge), usually with ♂ and ♀ flrs.

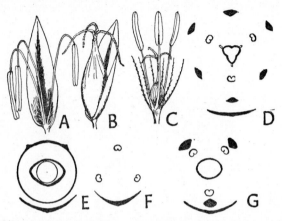

FIG. 438. Flowers and floral diagrams of Cyperaceæ. A, Male, and B, Female flowers of *Carex*. C, Flower, and D, Floral diagram of *Scirpus*. E and F, Floral diagrams of the female and male flowers of *Carex*. G, Floral diagram of *Eleocharis palustris*.

in separate spikes with conspicuous bracts, ♂ with 2–3 sta. (Fig. 438, A, F), ♀ with ov. of 2–3 cpls., surrounded by a protective sheath (Fig. 438, B, E); *Cladium*, characteristic of Norfolk fens; *Cyperus* (Galingale), with ☿ flrs. having a distinct P; *Eleocharis* (Club-rush, Fig. 438, G), cpls. 2–3, single terminal spikelet; *Eriophorum* (Cotton-grass), P bristles becoming long and silky in fruit; *Scirpus* (Bulrush), spikelets usually clustered and lateral, ☿ flrs. (Fig. 438, C and D).

37. GRAMINEÆ (GLUMIFLORÆ)

Annual or perennial herbs, with alt. distichous leaves having linear blades, long sheathing usually split bases, and ligules (p. 126 and Fig. 73, G); nodes swollen; stems commonly hollow and jointed; intercalary meristems above nodes (p. 258). Branching takes place freely from nodes (tillering), resulting in some sp. in tufted growth. Unit of infl. a *spikelet* (Fig. 439, A and B), *i.e.* a small group of 1–5 sessile flrs. borne on a very short axis, with a pair of bracts (*glumes*, Fig. 439, *l.g.* and *u.g.*) at the base, which more or less enclose the flrs.; spikelets arranged in cpd. inflrs. which are either cpd. spikes (e.g. *Triticum*) or cpd. racemes (e.g. *Avena*). Individual flrs. arising in axils of bracts (*flowering glumes*, Fig. 439, *f.g.*), the tips of which often form *awns* (Fig. 439, A, *a*); very low down on the peduncle each flr. bears a two-keeled bracteole (the *pale*, Fig. 439, *p*); the parts of the flr. till mature completely hidden between flowering glume and pale. Flrs. reg., ☿, hypog., generally with A3 G(2) (see Fig. 439, C). Between the sta. and the flowering glume two small green fleshy outgrowths, the *lodicules* (Fig. 439, *ld.*), perhaps representing members of a reduced perianth. Sta. with long filaments and large, loosely hinged anthers (Fig. 439, A). Ov. with 1 ovule; stigma usually two-lobed and feathery (Fig. 439, A). Fruit an achene with pericarp and testa fused (p. 474); seed end., with embryo at one side (Fig. 17, I). Anem., mostly protog.

The principal British genera are: *Agropyron* (Wheat- or Couch-grass), with spikelets compressed at right angles to main axis; *Agrostis* (Bent-grass), with

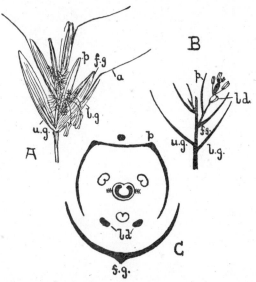

FIG. 439. Structure of spikelets and flowers of Grass (*Avena fatua*). A, Complete spikelet with parts spread out, containing three flowers, only one of which is open. B, Diagram of a spikelet with all parts of axis elongated. C, Floral diagram. *a*, awn; *f.g.*, flowering glume; *ld.*, lodicules; *l.g.*, lower glume; *p*, pale; *u.g.*, upper glume.

one-flowered spikelets; *Alopecurus* (Foxtail-grass), with a cylindrical compact infl.; *Anthoxanthum* (Sweet Vernal-grass), contains cumarin, flrs. with only 2 sta., lodicules absent; *Avena* (Oat), with long twisted awns (p. 483); *Brachypodium* (False Brome-grass), in woods, flrs. with 2 or 3 sta.; *Briza* (Quaking-grass), calcicole, with ovate spikelets; *Bromus* (Brome-grass), with prominent awns; *Cynosurus* (Dog's-tail grass), on heaths, lower spikelets consisting only of glumes, the latter with a comb-like edge; *Dactylis* (Cock's-foot Grass), with all flrs. to one side, characteristic of meadows; *Deschampsia* (Tussock-grass), heaths, with two-flowered spikelets; *Elymus* (Lyme-grass), on sand-dunes; *Festuca* (Fescue), with many-flowered spikelets; *Glyceria* (Manna-grass), aquatic; *Helictotrichon*; *Holcus* (Soft-grass), hairy leaves; *Hordeum* (Barley), very long rough awns; *Lolium* (Rye-grass), in meadows, infl. flat with spikelets in 2 rows; *Melica* (Melic-grass), in woods, with one- to two-flowered spikelets and a single anterior lodicule; *Molinia* (Moor-grass), spikelets often purplish; *Nardus* (Mat-grass), on moors; *Phalaris*; *Phleum* (Cat's-tail Grass, Timothy-grass), with toothed flowering glumes and cylindrical infl.; *Phragmites* (Reed), swamp-plant, sometimes 16 ft., lower flrs. in each spikelet ♂; *Poa* (Meadow-grass), leaf-tip boat-shaped; *Ammophila* (Marram-grass) (p. 562); *Spartina* (Cord-grass), on salt-marshes, with 2–3 very large stigmas.

Most Bamboos (*Bambusa*) have three lodicules and six stamens in two whorls. The Maize (*Zea*) has unisex. flrs. and the ♀ two fused stigmas.

Grasses are of great economic importance as cereals (see p. 75) and as fodder plants. The Sugar Cane (*Saccharum*), the Bamboos, and Esparto Grass are also important economically.

38. ORCHIDACEÆ (MICROSPERMÆ)

Perennial herbs, often with tuberous roots (p. 113), mostly with a mycorrhiza; leaves lanceolate or scaly, often radical. Infl. racemose, often a spike and frequently with coloured bracts. Flrs. irreg., ☿, epig., twisting through half a circle during their development (Fig. 326, B), generally with P3 +3 A1 G(3̄) (Fig. 440). P of 2 petaloid whorls, the posterior member (in mature flr. anterior in position) of the inner whorl enlarged to form the labellum (Fig. 326, A–C, *l*). Essential organs borne on a central column (Fig. 326, D, *c*) and generally consisting of 1 large sta. and a tricarp. ov. Sta. at top of column, with 2 prominent anther-lobes, each occupied by a pollinium (*p* in Fig. 326, D, see also p. 438) which is attached by a short stalk-like caudicle (*ca.*) to a pouch, the rostellum (*r*), above the stigmatic surfaces (*s*); 2 staminodes (*Std.*) often present on either side of the fertile sta.; ov. generally elongated and stalk-like (Fig. 326, B, *o*), uniloc., with 3 parietal placs. each bearing ∞ ovules; stigmatic surfaces 2, often more or less confluent. Labellum often prolonged into a spur (Fig. 326, B, *sp.*), at base of which the nectar is formed. Fruit a capsule with ∞ very minute seeds, end. O. Mostly entom. Many are found in woodlands, often on chalk-soils. All British sp. terrestrial.

FIG. 440. Floral diagram of Orchidaceæ (*Orchis mascula*). The parts are shown in the positions which they occupy before twisting.

The family is subdivided into *Monandræ* (with only one fertile sta.) and *Diandræ* (with 2 fertile sta.), the former being mainly represented in Britain.

The principal British genera of *Monandræ* are: *Aceras* (Man-Orchis), with 4 pronounced lobes to labellum, no spur, green flrs.; *Corallorhiza* (Coral-root), a saprophyte; *Epipactis* (Helleborine), greenish-purple flrs., Wasp-pollinated; *Platanthera* (Butterfly-Orchis), Moth-pollinated, with night-scented white flrs. and long spurs containing free nectar; *Listera* (Twayblade), with 2 prominent leaves and greenish flrs.; *Neottia* (Bird's-nest Orchid) (Fig. 132, p. 218); *Ophrys* (Bee-Orchis, Fly-Orchis), flrs. without a spur and resembling various insects; *Orchis* (Fig. 326); *Spiranthes* (Lady's Tresses), with a twisted spike and fragrant white flrs.

The only member of *Diandræ* in Britain is *Cypripedium* (Lady's Slipper), with a large pouch-like labellum, 2 fertile sta., a large staminode, and a three-lobed stigmatic surface.

39. ALISMACEÆ (HELOBIEÆ)

Aquatic herbs, leaves mostly with a petiolate lamina and frequently with prominent apical hydathodes, often with latex-cells. Infl. often with whorled flrs. Flrs. (Fig. 441, B–E) ☿ or unisex., usually with K3 C3 A3 +3 to ∞, G6–∞ ; ov. usually apocarp. Fruit an aggregate of achenes or follicles.

The chief British genera are: *Alisma* (Water Plantain), with A3 + 3 G∞, and achenes (Fig. 441, B and C); *Butomus* (Flowering Rush, sometimes placed

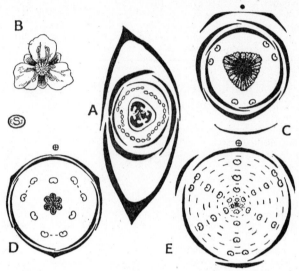

FIG. 441. A, Floral diagram of *Stratiotes* (Hydrocharitaceæ). B–E, Alismaceæ. B, Flower of *Alisma plantago*. C, Floral diagram of same. D, Floral diagram of *Butomus*. E, Floral diagram of male flower of *Sagittaria*. (After Salisbury.)

in a separate family), with A6 + 3 G6, and follicles (Fig. 441, D). These genera are ☿, but *Sagittaria* (Arrowhead, Fig. 387; Fig. 441, E) is unisex., with A∞ G∞ ; fruits are achenes.

The HYDROCHARITACEÆ (*Hydrocharis*, *Stratiotes*) (Fig. 441, A) are closely allied to the Alismaceæ and chiefly distinguished by having an inf. ov.

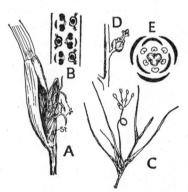

FIG. 442. A, Inflorescence and, B, Diagram of the male and female flowers of *Zostera*. C, *Ruppia*. D, Flower, and E, Floral diagram of *Triglochin palustre*.

40. POTAMOGETONACEÆ (HELOBIEÆ)

Mainly aquatics, with submerged and sometimes floating leaves having sheathing bases with scales on the inner surface.   Infl. usually a spike (Fig. 291). Flrs. ⚥ or unisex., P. absent or scale-like, A1–4 G1–4; cpls. often joined at the extreme base, each with 1 ovule; anem. or hydrophilous.   Fruit generally an achene.

The common British genera are: *Potamogeton* (Pondweed), A4 G4 (Fig. 291), achenes sessile; *Ruppia*, with stalked achenes (Fig. 442, C).   These two genera have ⚥ flrs., but *Zostera* (Eel-grass) has unisex. flrs. in the same infl. (Fig. 442, A and B).   *Triglochin* (Arrow-grass) belongs to a closely allied family Juncaginaceæ, marsh-plants with Rush-like leaves, P3+3 A3 G(6), syncarp., all or only 3 cpls. fertile.

APPENDIX

I. *The Compound Microscope* (Fig. 443).[1]—This consists essentially of a stand which has for its purpose the appropriate support and adjustment of the optical parts. The latter comprise two systems of lenses, known respectively as *ocular* (*Oc.*) and *objective* (*Ob.*), whilst accessory structures are constituted by a mirror (*M.*) for reflecting light, and a *condenser* (*Co.*) for concentrating light upon the object.

The stand consists of a heavy *foot* or base (*Fo.*), bearing a rigid upright *pillar* (*L.*). To the latter the remaining portions of the microscope are hinged in such a way that the whole can be employed either in a vertical or in an inclined position. The part actually hinged to the pillar is known as the *limb*, and to this the flat *stage* (*S.*) is attached, at right angles, at the lower end, and the *body tube* (*T.*) towards the upper end. The stage, which is usually square, is perforated by a central aperture through which the light from the mirror reaches the object. In transferring the microscope from place to place, it should always be carried by the non-movable parts.

The body tube is a hollow brass cylinder and is adapted to take the *ocular* or *eyepiece* (*Oc.*) at its upper, and the *objectives* (*Ob.*) at its lower, end. In order to secure rapid change of magnification, a *nosepiece* (*N.*), bearing two or three objectives, is screwed into the lower end of the body tube; by simply turning this a different objective can be brought to bear on the object. The distance between eyepiece and objective can be increased or decreased by pulling out or pushing in the draw-tube (*D.t.*), which is fitted into the upper end of the body tube; the body tube length for which most objectives are corrected is 170 mm. In order to focus the object clearly, the entire system of lenses can be moved nearer to, or farther from, the stage by means either of the coarse or fine adjustments. The *coarse adjustment* usually consists of two large milled heads (*C.*) on either side of the limb, and by turning either of these, which actuate a rack and pinion mechanism, a relatively large movement is brought about. The *fine adjustment* is generally operated by a milled head (*F.*), situated at the top or side of the limb, and by this means a very slight movement is effected, enabling greater accuracy of focussing to be attained.

Below the stage is fixed an adjustable aperture, the *diaphragm* (*D.*), by means of which the amount of light reaching the object on the stage can be regulated. If a condenser is present, it is placed between the diaphragm and the stage, and, in the best instruments, its distance below the stage is adjustable by means of another milled head (*H.*). The mirror (*M.*), which is concave on one surface and flat on the other, is either attached to the under side of the stage or (as in the type illustrated) forms part of the adjustable system bearing the condenser.

---

[1] See E. J. Spitta, *Microscopy*, J. Murray, 3rd edit., 1920 (537 pp.); J. Belling, *The Use of the Microscope*, McGraw·Hill Book Co., 1930 (315 pp.).

The objectives most commonly in use are $\frac{2}{3}$ in. and $\frac{1}{6}$ in.,[1] which designations imply that, when focussed upon the object, they are approximately two-thirds and one-sixth inch respectively from the latter. These distances are the focal lengths, and the smaller they are the greater is the magnifying capacity of the lens. As a consequence, the longer focus lens is often spoken of as the *low power*, and the short focus lens as the *high power*. The image formed by the

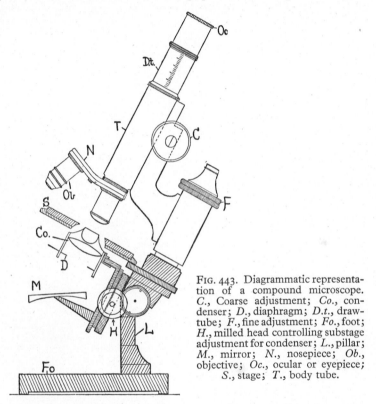

FIG. 443. Diagrammatic representation of a compound microscope. *C.*, Coarse adjustment; *Co.*, condenser; *D.*, diaphragm; *D.t.*, drawtube; *F.*, fine adjustment; *Fo.*, foot; *H.*, milled head controlling substage adjustment for condenser; *L.*, pillar; *M.*, mirror; *N.*, nosepiece; *Ob.*, objective; *Oc.*, ocular or eyepiece; *S.*, stage; *T.*, body tube.

objective is projected on to the eyepiece, where it becomes further magnified. The amount of magnification of the eyepiece is commonly indicated by a number engraved upon it.

The object to be examined, mounted on a glass-slip in water or some other appropriate fluid and covered with a cover-glass, is placed on the stage, and light is projected on to it from below by means of the mirror. If a condenser is present, the flat side of the mirror is employed, but if not, the concave side. To focus the object, *gradually* lower the tube by means of the coarse adjustment till the image becomes clear, and then turn the milled head to and fro until the image appears most distinct. Proceed in the same way when

---

[1] For the study of Bacteria and other minute organisms, higher powers are required, such as $\frac{1}{12}$-in. oil immersion objectives, in which a small drop of cedar oil between objective and cover-glass forms part of the optical system.

using the high power, but exercise the greatest care not to bring the objective in contact with the cover-glass, and *immediately* the image *begins* to appear use the fine adjustment only. The aperture of the diaphragm should be diminished till the maximum amount of detail is visible, whilst by adjusting the condenser the light reflected from the mirror can be accurately focussed upon the object.

In working with the microscope, it is best to accustom oneself to employ either eye. When drawing, view the object with the left, and sketch with the aid of the right, eye. As a first exercise in microscopic observation, it is well to examine the small air-bubbles almost invariably present in large numbers in a drop of water. Under the low power these appear as black dots or bright patches with broad dark margins; this dark border is due to refraction. Adjust the slide so that one of the smaller bubbles is in the centre of the field of view, and turn the nosepiece so as to view the bubble with the high-power lens. Using the fine adjustment, it will be noted that at a high focus the curved surface is seen and the outline appears shadowy, whilst at a lower focus only the circular equatorial portion (the *optical section*) is visible, and the outline becomes well defined.

II. *Measurement under the Microscope.*—This is accomplished by means of an eyepiece micrometer and a stage micrometer (both obtainable from the usual dealers in microscopic requisites). The stage micrometer is an ordinary slide on which is mounted a scale of one millimetre, divided into tenths and hundredths, and obtained by photographic reduction. The eyepiece micrometer fits into the ocular, and consists of a scale that is usually divided into a hundred equal parts. For each objective the value of a division of the eyepiece micrometer is determined in terms of the divisions of the stage micrometer (*i.e.* in hundredths of a millimetre). If subsequently any object is measured with the eyepiece scale, its actual size can be calculated. The size of microscopic objects is measured in μ ($=$ ·001 millimetre).

III. *Section-cutting.*—During this operation both razor and material should be kept moist with either water (for fresh material) or spirit (for preserved material). Hold the object between the thumb and first finger of the left hand, and arrange the tips of the remaining fingers so as to form a rest on which the razor blade can be glided backwards and forwards through the material. Note that the razor must be gently drawn through the object, and not pressed, as in ordinary cutting. The greatest care should be taken that the axis of the object is either at right angles (for transverse sections) or parallel to the razor blade (for longitudinal sections). For longitudinal sections only a very short length of the stem, etc., should be used. When very thin objects, such as leaves, are to be cut transversely, small rectangular pieces, including a vein, are embedded in a vertical incision made in a short length of Elder-pith, saturated with either water or spirit. Sections are then cut of the pith, as well as of the embedded object.

After cutting, transfer the sections to a slide, on which a drop of water or dilute glycerine has previously been placed, by means of a well-moistened brush, and reject all but the *two thinnest*. Complete sections are mostly quite unessential, whilst the small pieces will usually be the thinnest. Oblique sections, even if thin, are usually of little value. The razor should be carefully cleaned by wiping it from the back towards the edge.

IV. *Preserving and Staining.*—To preserve material for anatomical in-vestigation, ordinary methylated spirit will usually serve, provided there is at least four times the volume of liquid as of material. For showing nuclear structure, however, other fixatives are employed,[1] *e.g.* acetic alcohol, made by adding one part of glacial acetic acid to four parts of alcohol. After remaining in this for a few minutes up to several hours, according to the texture of the material, the latter is transferred to ordinary spirit.

For staining, the thinnest sections (cf. p. 638) should be placed in a few drops of safranin,[2] on a slide, for from five to fifteen minutes, more safranin being added at intervals to replace that lost by evaporation. The excess of the stain is now removed by washing the sections with spirit, and then a few drops of Kleinenberg's hæmatoxylin are allowed to act for half a minute. After this the sections are washed with spirit, and permanent preparations are made in the following way:—

The spirit is changed several times, finally using absolute alcohol. In this way dehydration (*i.e.* removal of water) is effected. To the alcohol a little clove oil is then added, and this mixture is in turn replaced by pure clove oil. The sections should now become transparent, and, if this fails to occur, they have not been sufficiently dehydrated. After two to three minutes the oil is poured off, and Canada balsam, dissolved in xylol, added. A cover-glass is then carefully let down on to the sections, and the slide placed on one side till the balsam sets. Throughout all these processes the greatest care should be taken that the sections are never without a covering of liquid.

If permanent preparations are not required, such stains as phloroglucin, aniline chloride, etc. (cf. Appendix V), can be employed to differentiate the tissues, and the sections are usually mounted in glycerine diluted with an equal volume of water. Preparations can also be mounted in glycerine jelly, such mounts being much more rapidly and easily prepared than those with Canada balsam, but they often perish after some years.

Liquid stains commonly employed are as follows:—

Aniline Blue.—Saturated solution in alcohol or water, with a trace of acetic acid.

Bismarck Brown.—Dissolve 2 grams in 100 c.c. of 70% alcohol. Stain for about 1½ minutes.

Eosin.—1% solution in either water or alcohol. Stain for 3 to 5 minutes.

Gentian Violet.—1% solution in water. Stain for from 10 to 15 minutes, transfer to alcohol, and quickly counterstain with Bismark brown.

Hæmatoxylin.—Best bought prepared ready for use.

Methylene Blue.—Saturated aqueous solution, greatly diluted for live staining.

Safranin.—1% solution in 50% alcohol.

Many others are in use (see the works cited below).

V. Reagents.—Details as to the mode of preparation of the principal reagents mentioned in this book are given in the following:—

Ammoniated Copper Oxide (Cuprammonia).—This reagent must be freshly prepared. Add ammonium chloride, and subsequently excess of sodium hydrate, to a solution of copper sulphate. The blue precipitate produced is

---

[1] See C. J. Chamberlain, *Methods in Plant Histology*, Univ. of Chicago Press, 5th edit., 1933 (416 pp.); H. J. Conn, *Biological Stains*, New York, 3rd edit., 1936 (276 pp.); A. B. Lee, *The Microtomist's Vademecum* (edited by G. J. B. Gatenby), J. A. Churchill, 10th edit., 1937 (784 pp.); G. J. B. Gatenby, *Biological Technique*, Churchill, 1937 (130 pp.), gives information on the theory of staining and other technical methods.

[2] Or methyl blue can be used, the sections being left in this for about half a minute.

filtered and washed thoroughly, and then dissolved in a small quantity of strong ammonia.

Aniline Sulphate.—Dissolve 0·1 gram in 10 c.c. of water and add a drop of sulphuric acid. The chloride is often used instead of the sulphate.

Chlor-zinc-iodide.—Dissolve an excess of zinc in pure hydrochloric acid and evaporate to the consistency of strong sulphuric acid; as much potassium iodide is added to the solution as it will dissolve and then as much iodine. In applying the test use sections mounted in water. The solution loses its properties after some weeks.

Eau de Javelle (mainly potassium hypochlorite).—Mix 20 parts of chloride of lime with 100 parts of water. Allow to stand, and then add a solution of 15 parts of caustic potash in 100 parts of water. Filter after some hours and use the filtrate.

Fehling's Solution (an alkaline solution of cupric oxide) (after Haas).—This is best obtained by mixing equal quantities of a solution containing 69·28 grams of pure crystallised copper sulphate in 1 litre, and of a solution containing 350 grams of Rochelle salt (sodium potassium tartrate) and 100 grams of sodium hydrate in 1 litre. The resulting solution is of a clear dark blue colour. Ten cubic centimetres of this solution are reduced by 0·05 gram of glucose.

Iodine Solution.—This is made by dissolving crystals of iodine in a strong solution of potassium iodide. For use this is diluted to a light brown colour. Tincture of iodine is a solution in alcohol.

Light Green.—This can be dissolved in water, alcohol, or clove oil. To make an alcoholic solution 1 gram is dissolved in 100 c.c. of alcohol.

Millon's Reagent.—This is a mixture of mercuric nitrate and nitrite. It can be prepared by dissolving 15 grams of mercury in 30 grams of cold nitric acid (sp. gr. 1·42), which operation should be performed in a fume cupboard. Dilute with twice the volume of distilled water, and filter after two hours. This reagent can also be bought ready made from the usual dealers in chemicals.

Phenylhydrazine Hydrochloride (after Mangham).—Prepare separate solutions, in ten times their weight of glycerine, of phenylhydrazine hydrochloride and sodium acetate respectively. Place the material to be investigated in equal drops of these two solutions, thoroughly mixed, and, after covering with a cover-glass, heat for one to several hours in an oven.

Phloroglucin.—Prepare a saturated solution in alcohol. Treat material with this for a short time, and then mount in strong hydrochloric acid.

Pyrogallate of Potash.—This is obtained by dissolving pyrogallic acid in water and adding an excess of caustic potash (which should not be done until immediately before the experiment is started). This solution absorbs oxygen very energetically, as a result of which it takes on a brown colour.

Scharlach Red.—Prepare a saturated solution in a mixture of 70 parts absolute alcohol and 30 parts water by volume. Filter and keep well stoppered.

Sulphuric Acid.—For cellulose tests it is usual to employ the concentrated acid. *Great care must be exercised in its use,* and strong ammonia should be at hand to neutralise any drops that may be spilled.

VI. *Artificial Sea-water.*—For this purpose Tidman's sea-salt, dissolved in distilled water in appropriate concentrations, can be employed; or a solution can be made according to the following formula given by Osterhout:—

> 1000 parts sodium chloride (gram-molecular solution).
>   78 ,,   magnesium chloride (gram-molecular solution).
>   38 ,,   magnesium sulphate (gram-molecular solution).
>   22 ,,   potassium chloride (gram-molecular solution).
>   10 ,,   calcium chloride (gram-molecular solution).

This solution has an osmotic potential of about 22·4 atmospheres; when diluted with an equal volume of distilled water, the osmotic potential is halved, when diluted with twice its bulk of distilled water the osmotic potential is one-third of that of the undiluted solution, and so on.

For the following data, which refer to strengths of Tidman's sea-salt, we are indebted to Prof. F. M. Haines:—

Concentration of solution in grams per 100 c.c.	Osmotic potential in atmospheres.	Concentration of solution in grams per 100 c.c.	Osmotic potential in atmospheres.
0·01	0·08	0·7	5·6
0·02	0·16	0·8	6·4
0·03	0·24	0·9	7·15
0·04	0·32	1·0	7·95
0·05	0·40	1·1	8·7
0·06	0·48	1·2	9·6
0·07	0·56	1·3	10·3
0·08	0·64	1·4	11·1
0·09	0·72	1·5	11·9
0·1	0·8	1·6	12·7
0·2	1·6	1·7	13·5
0·3	2·4	1·8	14·3
0·4	3·2	1·9	15·1
0·5	4·0	2·0	15·9
0·6	4·8		

The osmotic potential for concentrations between those given in this table are proportional to the values between which the particular concentration lies.

VII. *Artificial Semi-permeable Membranes.*—The membranous precipitate of copper ferrocyanide can be deposited in celloidin or in the wall of a small pot of unglazed porous porcelain. The latter is thoroughly washed so that it is impregnated with water. It is then nearly filled with a dilute solution of copper sulphate (2·5 grams per litre) and stood in a solution of potassium ferrocyanide (2·1 grams per litre), where it is left for some time. Ultimately it is thoroughly washed and soaked in water. It is best to prepare several pots in this way, as some are sure to be faulty. To overcome this difficulty, the copper ferro-cyanide precipitate can be deposited in a film of gelatine, formed over one end of a piece of glass tubing by dipping it in 20 per cent. gelatine to which a little potassium bichromate has been added; the latter has the effect of rendering the gelatine insoluble, if it is allowed to set in the light. After this the tubing is filled with the copper sulphate and the closed end allowed to dip into the potassium ferrocyanide solution until the gelatine has acquired the brown colour of the precipitate.

The membrane of celloidin can be obtained by pouring a solution of the latter on a clean mercury surface contained in a Petri dish and allowing the solvent to evaporate away. The membrane which remains is then fitted over the open end of a thistle funnel, the overlapping portion being tied securely round the flange of the bulb. In drying, the membrane contracts slightly and becomes stretched taut. A very strong combination is obtained if two membranes of this kind are fitted over one another.

A piece of pig's bladder, which should be thoroughly dried before use, stretched over the end of a thistle funnel, is often quite effective as a semi-permeable membrane.

VIII. *Analysis of Ash.*—The presence of a few of the elements can be detected very simply.   Thus, if a clean platinum-wire be moistened with hydrochloric acid, dipped into the ash, and held in the non-luminous flame of a Bunsen burner, the yellow colour indicates the presence of sodium.   If the flame is viewed through a piece of blue cobalt-glass, the violet colouration due to potassium is recognisable.   If the ash is boiled with water, the filtrate, after being acidified with hydrochloric acid, gives a white precipitate with barium chloride, thus indicating the presence of sulphur in the form of sulphates.   A portion of the filtrate treated with an equal amount of dilute nitric acid, followed by an excess of ammonium molybdate solution, gives on boiling a yellow precipitate due to the presence of phosphates.

IX. *Details of Water- and Sand-cultures.*—In place of water-cultures, sand-cultures may be prepared in the following way: A quantity of silver sand is strongly heated for some time and allowed to cool again.   After this, boiling water is allowed to drain through it several times in succession.   The sand is then placed in small pots which are watered daily with the different kinds of culture-solutions.   For such experiments it is advisable to employ plants which readily grow in a sandy soil, such as Poppy or Cress.

If water-cultures are continued for some time, it is advisable to renew the culture-solution every few weeks.   Should the roots begin to show a growth of Moulds or Bacteria, the latter should be carefully removed with a fine brush; to prevent a growth of this kind on the under sides of the corks, the latter should be charred.   Large jars should be used for the experiments, whilst as regards plants Maize, Wheat, Sunflower, etc., give good results.

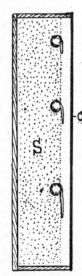

For solution without nitrogen, see p. 207.   To make up one lacking sulphur, substitute magnesium nitrate for magnesium sulphate and calcium nitrate for calcium sulphate.   To eliminate phosphorus, use ferric sulphate instead of ferric phosphate.   For the solution without calcium, employ magnesium nitrate in place of calcium sulphate, and for the one without potassium, substitute sodium for the potassium salt.

X. *Method of obtaining Seedlings with Straight Radicles and Plumules* (Fig. 444).—A flat seed-box is filled with moist sand, in the surface of which are embedded rows of soaked seeds parallel to the long sides of the box.   The seeds must be so placed that their radicles are all directed towards the same side and lie parallel to one another; about 2 inches should be left between the successive rows (Fig. 444).   The box is covered, either with a sheet of cardboard or a piece of wood which is merely tied on, so as to be readily removed.   The whole is then stood on one of its edges or suspended, vertically, with all the radicles pointing downwards.   A very considerable proportion of the seeds will be found to develop straight radicles and plumules (Fig. 444).

FIG. 444. Section of box to show method of growing seedlings with straight plumules and radicles. *S*, sand; *C*, cover of box.

XI. *Method of marking Radicles or Plumules with Indian Ink.*—The marking may be most conveniently carried out by using a piece of cotton, stretched on a short piece of bent fish-bone or other flexible material like an archer's bow. The radicle or plumule is laid along the edge of a scale and the marks are made by the stretched cotton which is moistened with Indian ink.

XII. *Attachment of Rubber Tubing in an Air-tight Manner.*—The internal diameter of the tubing should be somewhat smaller than the diameter of the object to which it is to be attached. Moistening with water will make it easier to slip the tubing over the object. To ensure an air-tight connection, thin copper wire may be firmly twisted around the points of junction.

XIII. *Method of filling a Narrow Tube with Liquid* (Fig. 445, A).—A fine glass-tube is attached to a small funnel and inserted into the tube to be filled, so as to reach to its base. The liquid is then poured into the funnel and, as the wider tube fills, the narrower one is withdrawn.

XIV. *Method of passing a Branch through a Hole in a Rubber Cork* (after Osterhout, Fig. 445, B).—A cork-borer, wide enough to take the branch, is passed through the hole in the cork, in the opposite direction to that in which it is desired to insert the branch. The latter is pushed some little way into the borer (Fig. 445, B), which is then slowly withdrawn, thus leaving the branch in the cork.

XV. *Graduation of Scale in Apparatus shown in Fig. 154.*—The apparatus is laid down horizontally, with the pointer at the base of the scale, and a centimetre scale is placed vertically (*i.e.* parallel to the support) against the end of the short arm of the lever. This latter is then moved through successive intervals and the corresponding positions of the pointer on the arc (*a*) marked off.

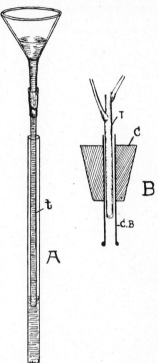

FIG. 445. A, Method of filling a narrow tube with liquid. *t*, glass-tube filled with water and attached to funnel. B, Method of passing a branch through a hole in a rubber cork (after Osterhout). *C*, cork; *C.B.*, cork-borer; *T*, shoot.

XVI. *Method of covering Leaves with Stencil-plates.*—The stencil-plate is placed on the upper side of the leaf, whilst a piece of cardboard of equal size and perforated by a number of small holes is fixed in a corresponding position on the lower surface. The two structures can be kept in position by fastening them with spiral paper-clips.

XVII. *Gelatine-washers.*—A short length of glass tubing, about $\frac{3}{4}$ in. internal diameter and corked at one end, is filled with a solution of gelatine in hot water. After cooling the cylinder of gelatine is removed and cut into $\frac{1}{4}$ in. discs into which holes of the required size are made with a cork-borer.

INDEX

*The principal references are printed in heavier type. Illustrations are indicated by an * after the paginal reference.*

Abies, 409, 417, 418.
Abietineæ, 409, 410, 414, 418.
Abscission, layer 192.
Absinth (*Artemisia*), 628.
Absorption of, carbon dioxide, 164, **209,** 543; light, 209, 210 *; mineral salts, 49, **206** *et seq.,* 496 *et seq.;* organic material, 218, 221, 222, 315; oxygen, **236** *et seq.,* 543; water, by cells, 44 *et seq.;* by roots, 6, 100, **108,** 109, **193,** 493; by seeds, 21, 26, 34.
Acacia, 70, 125, 507, 607, 608,* 620; *A. catechu,* 70; *A. lophantha,* 269 *; *A. senegal,* 70.
Acacia, False, see *Robinia pseudacacia.*
Accessory buds, 115, 264.
Acer, 181; *A. campestris,* 61, 181, 515, 517, 527; *A. pseudoplatanus,* 122,* 126, 130, 151, 168, 175, 180,* 181, 442, 480, 481 *; *A. saccharinum,* 77, 177; *A. striatum,* 186.
Aceras, 633.
Acetaldehyde, 241A.
Achene, 474, 475.*
Achillea, 226,* 627; *A. millefolium,* 529; *A. ptarmica,* 538.
Achlya, 316.
Aconite, Winter, see *Eranthis.*
Aconitine, 89, 90.
Aconitum, 441, 460, 461,* 475,* 616; *A. napellus,* 89.
Acorn (*Quercus*), 27, 474, 477.
Acorus calamus, stem, 141,* 142.
Acquired characters, inheritance of, 584.
Actæa, 616.
Acuminate, 125.
Acute, 125.
Adaptation, 486, 500, 511, **521, 528, 544, 551,** 552, **584,** 607.
Adiantum, 371, 374.
Adoxa, 36, 151, 152,* 520, 626; *A. moschatellina,* 516, 577.
Adsorption, 48, **50,** 84.
Adventitious roots, 31, **108,** 369, 383, 550; shoots, **119,** 226, 251.
Aecidium, 329,* 330.*
Aegopodium, 145,* 621; *A. podagraria,* 167.*
Aerating system, 165, **237;** of aquatics, 544, 545,* 550; of marsh-plants, 540.
Aerenchyma, **540,** 566, 567.*
Aerial roots, **111, 112.***
Aerobic respiration, 241 *et seq.*

Aesculus, 82, 117,* 118, 130 *et seq.,* 159, 428; fruit, 477; stem-structure, 173 *et seq.**
Aethusa, 621,* 622.
African rubber (*Landolphia*), 97.
After-ripening, 20.
Agar-agar, 298, 347.
Agave, 67.
Aggregatæ, 628.
Agrimony (*Agrimonia*), 482,* 483, 618.
Agropyron, 632; *A. junceiforme,* 558.
Agrostemma, 34, 165, 471, 615.
Agrostis, 526, 564, 632.
Air-canals, 388, 540, **545.**
Air-content of soil, **489,** 492.
Air-spaces, see Intercellular spaces.
Aira, see *Deschampsia.*
Ajuga, 518, 520, 625.
Alanine, 213B.
Albumins, 82.
Alchemilla, 132, 472, 618; *A. alpina,* 528; *A. arvensis,* 617.
Alcohol, 241, 340, 348.
Alcoholic fermentation, **241** *et seq.,* 340, 341.
Alder, see *Alnus ;* — Buckthorn, see *Frangula alnus.*
Aleurites, 80.
Aleurone grains, 81.*
Algæ, 42, 59, **271** *et seq.,* 335, 542, 567, 597, 609; of Lichens, 281, 341, 342.
Alginic acid, 298.
Alisma, 432, 472,* 634*; *A. plantago* 154, 538, 539.
Alismaceæ, 633, 634.*
Alkaloids, 87, **89,** 337.
Allelomorphs, **588,** 589, 594, 595, 598.
Alliaria, 616; *A. petiolata,* 527.
Allium, 234, 428, 435, 437,* 629; *A. cepa,* 12, 77, 153,* 169; seed and germination of, 32 *et seq.*;* *A. ursinum,* 235,* 516, 520.
Allopolyploids, 601, 602.
Almond, see *Prunus amygdalus.*
Alnus, 62, 220, 524, 555, 572, 613.
Alopecurus, 632; *A. pratensis,* 529.
Alpine pasture, 528; -plants, 91, 502, 528, 575, 599.
Alsineæ, 615.
Alternate leaves, 119.
Alternation of generations, 368, 384, 385; in Algæ, 314.
Althæa, 151, 439.*

645

42

/ young anther

Place on slide in 1 drop of
aceto-carmine heat for 2 minutes
over very low bunsen (or cas) adding
more a/carmine if necessary, (no boil)
agitate with every needle, remove
from bunsen cover ▱ and tap with
needle to squeak anther examine
If not stained add in